8895 4-

Lab open

Mon ⎤
Tues ⎬ aft
Thurs ⎦

Wed ⎤ nite
Fri ⎦

VERTEBRATE EMBRYOLOGY

VERTEBRATE

EMBRYOLOGY

The Dynamics of Development

Roberts Rugh

College of Physicians & Surgeons
of Columbia University

HARCOURT, BRACE & WORLD, INC.

NEW YORK / CHICAGO / BURLINGAME

LIBRARY OF CONGRESS CATALOG CARD NUMBER: 64-12975

PRINTED IN THE UNITED STATES OF AMERICA

COVER PHOTOGRAPHS   Polar body formation in human egg:
back, first polar body; *front,* first and second polar bodies.
TITLE PAGE PHOTOGRAPH   Late human morula.
(All from L. B. Shettles, *Ovum Humanum,* Hafner, New York, 1960.)

Preface

The purpose of this text is to emphasize the dynamic nature of embryonic development by presenting the normal sequence of events that transform an apparently structureless egg into an individual having all the structures and functions characteristic of a vertebrate organism. The intensely interesting dynamic processes of normal development must be understood fully by the student before he can competently analyze results of experimentation and thus profit by the experimental approach to embryology.

Since development depends on the union of cells specialized for reproduction, each section begins with a description of the reproductive systems and then proceeds from the maturation of the sperm and egg cells through fertilization and on to birth. The arrangement of the text into complete and separate developmental histories—of the frog, chick, mouse, pig, and human—gives the student a clear-cut picture of each organism as it forms. Consequently, he can easily recognize similarities and variations in development. As each section is a discrete unit, the instructor can omit any one without destroying continuity. The mouse is included because its early embryo provides much information not readily available from the pig or human. Furthermore, the mouse is becoming the most extensively used laboratory animal, and the study of its embryo in the living state is possible in any laboratory.

Rather than burden the student with the many theories explaining each phenomenon of embryonic development, the author presents only the most widely accepted interpretation. To this end, he has drawn widely from diligent predecessors in the field, particularly Arey, Lillie, McEwen, and Patten, acknowledging with gratitude their contributions and those of the many others who have aided and encouraged this work. He has been especially fortunate in having had access to the library of the Marine Biological Laboratory, Woods Hole, Massachusetts.

December, 1963   ROBERTS RUGH

Contents

VERTEBRATE EMBRYOLOGY

Introduction

1

More than any other biological discipline, the science of the embryo is a study of constant change. Although embryos at the same period of development may be compared, and the continuous changes are predictable, regulated, and directed toward specific goals, at no two successive moments in its development can any one embryo be considered the same. The alterations in the developing embryo are not mere shiftings of parts or positions. They constitute a synthesis from an apparently simple single-celled zygote with unrealized potentialities to a complex multicellular organism with such functioning structures as cells, tissues, and organs. This change from ~~apparent simplicity~~ to obvious complexity is sometimes called *differentiation*—and it is probably the single underlying characteristic of embryonic development. At every stage the embryo's energies are directed toward its transformation into a fully independent organism, able to ingest, digest, respire, react, and reproduce itself.

The period of embryonic development may last for days, as with the chick or mouse, or for years, as with the elephant (see Chapter 5). Any particular stage may be identified by the time since fertilization of the egg (as 24-hour or 10-day embryo), by the presence of certain structures (as 5-somite embryo), or by size (as 16-mm. embryo). Some forms pass through a larval stage in water before reaching developmental maturity, and others develop within a shell or a uterus. During late intrauterine life a mammalian embryo is known as a *fetus*. In every species, however, the organism is legitimate subject matter for embryology until it becomes in all respects functionally independent.

To understand the process that transforms a fertilized egg into a frog, chick, mouse, pig, or human, one should first be acquainted with the final stage of development (anatomy), the functional changes occurring throughout development (physiology), the chemical foundations of development (biochemistry), the varieties of tissues appearing during development (microscopic anatomy or histology), and the limitations as well as the possibilities in development (genetics). One cannot simply dissect an embryo or subject it to environmental (experimental) variables and know how development proceeds. Relying on purely descriptive embryology is like isolating a single frame of a moving picture, dissociating it from what goes before or what goes after. For instance, one can hardly comprehend the early formation of the brain if he does not first know the structure of the fully developed brain. Moreover, the structure of the brain is so closely related to its functions that it is meaningless to separate form and functions. Again, although there are basic similarities in the brains of various animals, there are also differences of genetic origin that distinguish the various species during development. Therefore, to study the embryo purely as a structure, or a functional unit, or an expression of genetic influences is to miss its major contribution to biology, namely, the *dynamic equilibrium of the developmental process.*

If one reduces matters to their simplest common denominator, he considers in anatomy the cell nucleus, in physiology the enzyme, and in embryology the *gene.* The gene is a single, complex molecule of high molecular weight and great stability, capable of influencing the chemicals of its environment to react along certain rather limited lines. Although the eggs of a turtle and a bird may appear identical, the respective genetic potentialities invariably develop one into a turtle and the other into a bird. One can bring together in a single finger bowl of sea water the fertilized eggs of sea urchins, starfishes, worms, mollusks, and fishes; yet each egg will proceed along its predestined path of development to become an integrated group of cells recognizable as a species, uncontaminated by the proximity of the other developing embryos. And each representative of a species will possess individual characteristics, depending upon its genetic constitution.

Despite this diversity of development due to genetic differences, which is ultimately expressed in differences between adult organisms, there are common trends in development that make it easy to confuse the early embryos of the chick, mouse, pig, and human. Comparative embryology emphasizes these similarities, and certain arguments in support of the *theory of evolution* are based upon them. Around 1830 von Baer pointed out that different species resemble each other more in the early stages of development than in the later stages. This led Haeckel, in 1867, to offer a *theory of recapitulation,* which suggested that the development of any organism recapitulated or repeated its ancestral development. This theory evoked all sorts of misinterpretations, the most erroneous being that, if man was derived from anthropoid stock, for instance, he must pass through a monkey stage in his embryonic development. The chief speculation was that the similarities in the early development of higher animals of different species, no matter how diverse they are as adults, demonstrated common ancestry.

Biology would be greatly simplified if proof existed that there is essentially one kind of protoplasm and that all animals and plants are related somewhere far back in their origins. It is easy to argue the interrelationships of the human races because calculations involving only 32 past generations (or about 10 centuries) account for more ancestors of a single individual than have ever existed at one time. And 10 centuries are hardly significant in biological time. Other species may have been related and become divergent in the same environment owing to mutations.

There is another possible explanation of the similarities in early embryonic development. According to Darwin, *natural selection* (or elimination by nature) leaves those individuals that, by reason of genetic constitution and/or adaptation to the environment, are favored to survive. Thus nature sorts out of the wide range of possibilities those that are suited to nature, and thus the great variety of genotypes provides the soundest basis for species survival. Natural selection brings about a degree of conformity in all organisms, since those that do not meet nature's requirements are eliminated.

The embryo is extremely sensitive to its surroundings. Whether it develops in sea water or in fresh water, in a shell or in the uterus, it is subjected to the normal vicissitudes of its environment, and its survival is challenged to a much greater degree than the survival of the independent organism into which it develops. To reach its goal, the embryo must endure variations in temperature, moisture, salinity, oxygen concentration, and nutrition, and despite the adaptive and protective mechanisms it devises, extremes in any of these conditions are often fatal. Of some 100,000,000 eggs laid by an oyster in one season, only 3 to 4% survive to the adult stage. The human female matures over 400 ova, and the human male billions of spermatozoa, during a reproductive life span, but rarely do even 15 or 20 develop into new individuals. Fortunately excessive egg and sperm production outweighs the terrible waste.

Darwin's theory of natural selection may therefore apply to the fertilized egg and every succeeding stage in development. If so, conformity should increase with each generation, to the limits of genetic potentialities, and those that conform and survive should produce the next generation. In the extreme of natural selection one species alone should survive.

If natural selection is involved, how then have some 250,000 different species of animals developed and survived? In the first place, environments alter, and during the long history of living matter on earth nature has changed tremendously. Secondly, although most organisms have regulatory powers, they also possess rather remarkable tolerances to variations in environmental conditions. Embryos can develop between 4 and 37°C., although embryos of certain species readily die at either of these limits; this range of temperature tolerance is not wide in comparison to the range available on earth, −270 to 5000°C., and when life first developed, the environmental temperature range may have been quite different. Moisture and salinity, too, have likely changed. Some theorize that a common aquatic ancestry is probable since all embryos develop in moisture. The similarity of the types and relative concentrations of salts in blood and other body fluids to those in the sea also suggests a common aquatic origin. Oxygen is essential to life, but organisms have even developed ways to adjust to limited variations in its concentration. The ranges of all these variables have shifted during the ages past, and further shifting in future centuries should result in "naturally selected" embryos and adults that differ from those of the present.

Despite the inverted argument that similarities in embryonic development are the final proof of the theory of evolution, which is based primarily upon comparative morphology of adult organisms, embryonic evidence only corroborates, circumstantiates, or supplements evolutionary theory; it is not convincing in itself. Similarity among embryos does not prove kinship; it may be simply the consequence of natural selection of those adults "fit to survive." Conversely, the apparent evolutionary relationship of adult forms may be the outcome of natural selection among embryos. Nevertheless, the theory of evolution is valuable in affording the student a proper perspective on the basic similarities and differences among the various embryos.

In summary, then, the student of embryology must first analyze the developmental processes that are similar and then proceed to those that differ because of differences in genes. Since the latter result in species differences, here the fundamentals of embryology must give way to specifics, and the various embryos must be distinguished and studied separately.

This text concentrates on five vertebrate forms—the frog, chick, mouse, pig, and human—devoting a chapter to each one. The student is therefore able to trace the history of each embryo and to compare the origins, changes, and ultimate dispositions of its major structures with those of equivalent structures in other embryos. As he becomes familiar with the marked similarities in embryonic development (Fig. 1.1), he can better recognize and understand the processes that produce variations.

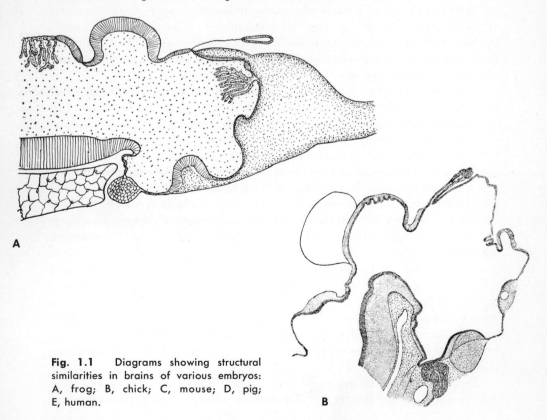

A

B

Fig. 1.1 Diagrams showing structural similarities in brains of various embryos: A, frog; B, chick; C, mouse; D, pig; E, human.

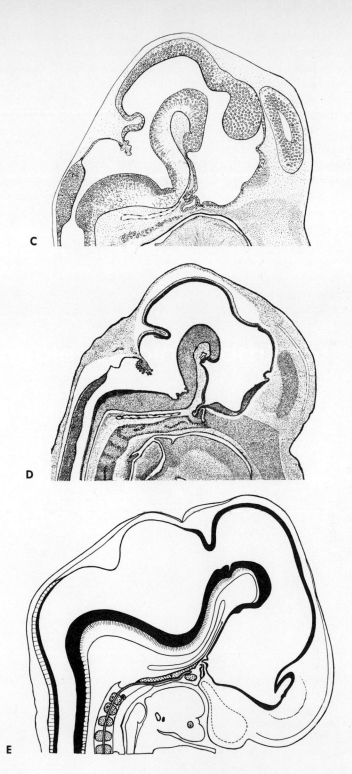

C

D

E

A Survey

of Embryonic Development

2

■ Introduction

There are certain basic stages through which all embryos, whatever their origins, must pass before they digress in the direction of species differentiation. One should keep these patterns in mind while observing the unfolding development in any particular species. The following discussion may be considered a table of contents of the major developmental processes, a skeletal outline of what we shall study in considerable detail with frog, chick, mouse, pig, and human embryos.

■ Maturation

With a very few exceptions among the lower invertebrates, all multicellular animals reproduce by the union of two unlike *germ* cells (*gametes*), one (the *spermatozoon*) being derived from the male and the other (the *ovum*, or egg) from the female. Each is structurally and functionally unlike any other cell of the body, and each must undergo certain changes before it unites with the other to produce a new generation. The major processes involved in these changes are (1) cell proliferation (*mitosis*), in which the primitive germ cells repeatedly divide into like cells; (2) cell growth, in which there is a cessation of mitosis in favor of the acquisition of protoplasm; and (3) cell maturation (*meiosis*), which comprises two final divisions, one of which reduces the number of *chromosomes* in the nucleus. Mitosis consists of the following stages: *interphase*, a so-called rest period between divisions; *prophase*, during which chromosomes appear and a *mitotic spindle* forms; *metaphase*, during which the chromosomes line up at the center of the spindle; *anaphase*, during which each chromosome splits into two *chromatids*, which move to opposite poles of the spindle and become chromosomes; and *telophase*, during which the chromosomes at each pole form a new nucleus and the cytoplasm divides to produce two new cells, identical to the parent cell. Meiosis consists of one

9

Meiosis —

one division in which homologous chromosomes pair and separate and another in which each chromosome splits into two chromatids, as in mitosis, with the result that the new cells contain only half the chromosomes of the parent cell.

Each of the two cells joining to produce another generation must represent only half of the necessary genetic potentials of the new generation; else with each succeeding generation there would be a doubling of these potentials, and cells would become progressively larger. Thus the prime element in the maturation process is the reduction to half (*haploid*) of the chromosomal complex, the bearer of the genes. When the sperm fertilizes the ovum, there is restoration of the normal (*diploid*) number of chromosomes and associated genes. However, maturation involves more than mere reduction of the chromosomes, and the maturations of the ovum and the sperm are in themselves quite different. In the maturation of the ovum, *yolk* (*deutoplasm*) and *cytoplasm* accumulate around one nucleus, greatly enlarging its cell, and the other nuclei resulting from divisions are destroyed. In the maturation of the sperm, no yolk or cytoplasm accumulates, the resultant cells are equal in size, and all survive.

During maturation the ovum and the sperm are prepared to complement each other and initiate a process resulting in the ultimate formation of a new individual similar to those from which they were derived. The definition of a species is related to the fertilizability of the ova by sperm produced by its individuals, implying maximum compatibility. However, ova may sometimes be fertilized by foreign sperm, and the offspring may represent a cross between the two species, or one genetic line may completely dominate the other. Generally a cross, such as the mule produced from the horse and ass, is infertile. In any species the sperm is recognizably distinct from the ovum, structurally and functionally; in fact, the ova of various species, as well as the sperm, are more alike than are the male and female germ cells of the same species. This distinction does not make ovum and sperm incompatible; rather they are mutually necessary for the survival of both themselves and the descendant line to which they give rise.

At one time scientists believed that each ovum contained a definite system and that the sperm merely activated its development or, conversely, that each sperm head contained a miniature of the future organism, which penetrated the ovum and grew upon the nutriment therein until it was large enough to survive by itself. These views were discarded when powerful microscopes revealed no evidence of any preformed individual in the ovum or sperm. The current opinion, supported by genetic studies, rejects the theory of *preformation* but holds that the genes in the ovum nucleus and the sperm nucleus predetermine in the minutest detail what kind of individual will develop. Fertilization is therefore not merely a stimulus producing a particular response but a union of potentialities that together transform through regulated processes into an independent organism.

The chromosome number for any species is quite standard and can be taken as one of the identifying features of that species. However, there may be a number difference between adult males and females, owing to the absence or presence of a sex-specific chromosome. If the total number of chromosomes in *somatic* (body) cells differs for male and female, the sex with the uneven number will, of necessity, produce two types of germ cells, since an uneven number cannot be divided into equal parts. For many years it was believed that man's somatic cells contained 48 chromosomes (diploid set); then it was believed that the 48th chromosome in the male was a bit smaller than its counterpart in the female; then it was believed that the 48th chromosome was absent in the male, leaving the male 47 chromosomes while the female had 48. Now the theory is that the diploid chromosome number for the human is 46, with 22 pairs of autosomes and an XX set of sex chromosomes in the female and 22 pairs of autosomes and an XY set of sex chromosomes in the male. Thus sex is determined by the zygotic combination of chromosomes. In other words, the initial influence in sex differentiation is the chromosome make-up of the fertilized ovum (*zygote*). The fact that sex ratios are generally close to 50/50 is supporting evidence for this conclusion, and the slight disparity in the human (106 males to 100 females) is possibly explained in Chapter 8. Whether environment (external or internal) has any influence on the ultimate outcome or not, the initial direction of sex development is predetermined by the particular combination of gametes.

Oögenesis

The term *oögenesis* refers to the process by which mature ova are produced. During embryonic development primordial germ cells originating in some other region migrate to the *genital ridge*, a longitudinal mesodermal thickening on each side of the body that develops into the ovary and that is closely associated with the kidney primordium. Some or all of these cells become ova. Presumptive ova also arise by proliferation of the germinal epithelium that encloses the ovary. By the time of metamorphosis, hatching, or birth the young ovaries contain most, if not all, of the cells that will give rise to ova during the entire life span. Throughout the reproductive period there is a continuous flow of ova being prepared for the sperm. However, many of the cells originally destined to form ova become nurse (*follicle*) cells or fall by the wayside. It has been estimated, for instance, that at birth the human ovary contains over 300,000 possible ova; by puberty the number declines to 15,000; and during the reproductive life of the individual only about 400 reach maturity. The ova receive their nourishment from the surrounding follicle cells, each of which might have become an ovum.

The primordial germ cell cannot be distinguished from a somatic cell. However, a cell destined to become an ovum undergoes frequent division and then, for reasons as yet undetermined, stops dividing and begins to grow. Such a cell is known as an *oögonium*. As soon as it reaches its maximum growth, it is termed a *primary oöcyte*. Growth involves principally the accumulation of yolk, with possibly the synthesis of some protoplasm. The enlargement occurs through diffusion from the follicle cells.

The primary oöcyte undergoes two successive divisions resulting in unequal distribution of the cytoplasm and yolk. These divisions are not mitotic because the final cells are not exactly equal with respect to the chromosomes (a requisite of mitosis). Actually there is nuclear division, with the discarding of one-half of the nucleus into a minimal mass of cytoplasm, which forms, in the first division, the *first polar body*. The remaining cell, the *secondary oöcyte*, continues to grow, becoming larger and larger without a corresponding enlargement of its nuclear substance. The second division, which produces the *second polar body*, generally does not occur until the egg cortex has been invaded by a single spermatozoon in the process of fertilization, although it may be completed in some species without fertilization. Thus from one oögonium arise one mature ovum and its discarded nuclei. The first polar body usually undergoes a division of its own, so that there are three polar bodies—each having the same kind of nucleus as the ovum, but without attendant cytoplasm and yolk. The three nuclei figuratively sacrifice their life substance (cytoplasm) to the fourth.

The most important change occurring during maturation is the exact distribution of the chromosomal material to the daughter nuclei. This phenomenon can be explained best in terms of a single pair of *allelomorphic* chromosomes, if it is remembered that the same process applies to each other pair independently. The pair of chromosomes may be chosen with regard to a specific pair of genes they carry, as follows:

Certain types of mental subnormality, due to faulty development of parts of the brain, may be inherited as recessive characteristics. In other words, an individual may carry the gene for such a trait but have it covered by the simultaneous presence of the normal gene. Such an individual has perfectly normal intelligence. If "N" represents the normal gene and "n" the subnormal gene, and if (for the sake of clarity) all of the many other genes on the two chromosomes are disregarded, an oögonium with its full set of chromosomes (diploid) is indicated by the heterozygous condition of "Nn." When this cell undergoes simple mitosis, each resultant cell must have "Nn," because mitosis produces like cells. Before division, therefore, there must be a doubling of the genes "Nn" so that one-half of the doubled amount will go to each resultant cell. In some species this doubling occurs before the first maturation division, which results in the secondary oöcyte. Thus the secondary oöcyte is identical with its predecessor except that one-half the nucleus has been discarded. In this case, the nucleus of the secondary oöcyte and the nucleus of the polar body each contain "Nn." The succeeding division *must* be different, for "N" must be separated from "n." Otherwise, the ovum will not be haploid, and the resultant zygote will have an accumulation of chromosomes (and genes). Since the first division is equal with respect to the chromosomes, as it is in mitosis, it is called *equational division*. The second, which results in a reduction in chromosomes by a separation of members of pairs, is called *reductional division*. In the maturation of germ cells (ova or sperm) both divisions, which together constitute meiosis, must occur before the gamete is ripe.

In some species the two divisions are reversed in order, the first being reductional and the second equational. The first division separates "N" from "n" so that each cell has half the somatic number of chromosomes and either "N" or "n," but never both. Then "N" grows and divides into "N" plus "N," and "n" grows and divides into "n" plus "n." Consequently, the resultant ovum receives either "N" or "n," but never both "N" and "n." The original "Nn" combination develops into "NNnn," with each gene going to a separate nucleus. One remains as the nucleus of the ovum, and the other three are discarded in the polar bodies. Regardless of the order in which the divisions occur, therefore, a haploid nucleus results.

These are the fundamental changes taking place in egg maturation, for all pairs of chromosomes and their associated genes. With its genetic constitution now reduced to half that of the oögonium, the ovum is ready to receive a similar contribution from the sperm, which will be either "N" or "n," but never both. Thus, the diploid allelomorphic condition will be restored.

Spermatogenesis

The sex cells of the male probably arise elsewhere but migrate to the genital ridge and there develop into the threadlike, continuous *seminiferous tubules* of the *testes*. These tubules are full of dividing cells until just before sexual maturity, when they acquire a central *lumen* (cavity) into which the tails of mature spermatozoa are suspended.

A section of a mature seminiferous tubule shows an outer coating of connective tissue and inner layers of germ cells in various stages of maturation. The *Sertoli cells*, permanent sustaining cells in contact with the connective tissue wall, or *basement membrane*, act as nurse cells by means of which the maturing sex cells acquire nutrition. Their inner ends are generally filled with the heads of developing spermatozoa.

The primitive germ cells of the testes divide frequently by ordinary mitosis to become eventually *spermatogonia*. Although these are morphologically still quite typical spherical cells, they are destined to be spermatozoa. Each spermatogonium stops dividing (as does an oögonium) and enlarges into a *primary spermatocyte*, which often shows distinct chromosomal configurations. A division without growth then gives rise to two *secondary spermatocytes*, invariably smaller than the parent cell from which they came. Another nuclear and cytoplasmic division follows, resulting in two *spermatids*. Each original spermatogonium thus produces four equal-sized spermatids. (In this last respect spermatogenesis and oögenesis are quite different.) Finally there is a metamorphosis, a complex transformation without division, into the spermatozoon. With each stage in its development, the male germ cell appears to move inward toward the lumen of the seminiferous tubule.

Between the primary spermatocyte and the secondary spermatocyte stages, there must be either a reduction of chromatin material (reductional division) or an equal cellular division. The next division, into spermatids, completes the maturation process, being either reductional or equational depending upon the nature of the earlier division. These two divisions, the only ones occurring during the transition from spermatogonium to spermatozoon, parallel the two maturation divisions of the ovum.

The mature spermatozoon is almost completely devoid of protoplasm. It consists of a compact nucleus, which fills the head, a middle piece, and a flagellum-like tail. Its life is limited by its lack of nutrition and its intense activity. Its motility and penetrating powers are functional in the fertilization process. In contrast with the ovum, the spermatozoon is small and motile; it is produced in great numbers; it has no protective coating or sheath, no yolk, and little cytoplasm; it retains its *centrosome* as an aid in fertilization and early cleavage; it has an *acrosome* (*perforatorium*) and a condensed nucleus, with no evidence of a *nucleolus* (*plasmosome*); and it is suspected, in many vertebrates, to consist of two types with respect to sex predetermination. Table 2.1 compares the spermatozoon and the ovum.

▪ Fertilization

The phenomenon of *fertilization* involves two distinguishable processes. The first in point of time is the *activation* of the ovum. In most instances this activation can be accomplished only by a mature spermatozoon of the same species,

Table 2.1   Comparison of mature spermatozoon and ovum

	SPERMATOZOON	OVUM
origin	secondary spermatocyte—two	primary oöcyte—one ovum plus three polar bodies
nutrition in gonad	Sertoli cells	follicle cells
maturation	completed within the testis	incomplete in ovary; generally completed after fertilization
production	many, continuous	few, periodic (except oyster, etc.)
size	small	variable, large
shape	elongate, tadpole-like	usually spheroid
protection	none	secondary and tertiary membranes
motility	active (except in nematodes and arthropods)	inactive (except in nematodes and arthropods)
motile organs	flagellum (tail)	none
cytoplasm	small amount	large amount
yolk (deutoplasm)	none	variable, generally much
mitochondria	from spiral coil of middle piece	diffuse
Golgi apparatus	forms acrosome	diffuse
plasma membrane	present	present
nucleus	compact	vesicular
nucleolus	indistinguishable	present
nuclear membrane	present	present

although some ova may be activated by mature sperm of other species or by other natural or artificial means (*parthenogenesis*). The outer layer of the ovum, or the *cortex*, is usually sensitive to a particular kind of stimulus that sets in motion certain operations that continue indefinitely, or as long as the ovum, embryo, or individual that develops survives. The second fertilization process is *syngamy*, the fusion (union) of the sperm and egg *pronuclei*, with consequent union of their haploid sets of chromosomes. This fusion restores the full or diploid number of chromosomes found typically in all cells of the adult organism. When activation occurs without a spermatozoon, only the haploid set of egg chromosomes is available, so that further development is rare and often difficult; nevertheless, it proceeds naturally in some forms, such as the honey bee, in which the haploid bees are male drones.

In normal fertilization, the two processes, activation and syngamy, start a chain reaction that ultimately results in an organism similar to that which originally produced the ovum or the spermatozoon. A listing in sequence of the usual changes accompanying fertilization follows:

1. The sperm head contacts the egg cortex, and *cytolysis* (dissolution) of the cortex begins at the point of contact (activation).

2. The *vitelline (fertilization) membrane* is elevated.

3. The sperm head, containing the nucleus, enters the egg cytoplasm and causes local *gelation*.

4. Any suspended steps in egg maturation are completed, the spermatozoon generally waiting at the periphery.

5. The spermatozoon invades the ovum, creating a pathway in pigmented eggs known as the *penetration path*.

6. The sperm nucleus (head) reverses its original position so that the trailing centrosome (in the middle piece) precedes the nuclear material. This reversal requires a 180° rotation of the sperm head.

7. The two pronuclei (male and female) fuse or approximate (syngamy) to form the zygote, and the diploid number of chromosomes is restored.

8. The male centrosome divides and gives rise to the *mitotic spindle* for the first cleavage. There is equal division of the chromosomes even though those from each pronucleus may not actually mingle before the first division.

▪ Cleavage

As a rule the mature egg possesses a disproportionate ratio of yolk to cytoplasm, especially in comparison with the nuclear/cytoplasmic ratios of any cells in the adult organism. The yolk accumulation is a source of nutrition during the long process of development. The normal ratio of yolk to cytoplasm is eventually re-established by a succession of divisions into smaller and smaller units (cells), with a synthesis (constructive formation) of nuclear material prior to each division. There is no synthesis of yolk at this stage—only of nuclear material. This nuclear synthesis and cell division is known as _cleavage._ It varies in details in different forms owing to the amount and distribution of yolk and to genetic influences. The nuclear aspect of a cleavage is essentially like that of any other mitosis. However, there is no appreciable and concomitant increase in the amount of cytoplasm as there is in usual mitotic changes.

■ Blastulation

As cleavage proceeds, smaller and smaller cells (_blastomeres_) form, and as cell size diminishes, cleavage accelerates. Obviously, a mass of more or less spherical cells cannot have completely contiguous surfaces, even as would be impossible in a group of grapes or marbles. Soon, therefore, the cluster of cleaving cells acquires a cavity, known as the _blastocoel._ The blastocoel is centrally located in early embryos with little yolk (for example, the mammal) and peripherally placed in those with abundant yolk (for example, the chicken). The cavity is generally filled with a secretion derived from the surrounding cells. When the blastocoel appears, the embryo becomes a _blastula,_ although cleavage continues unabated.

■ Gastrulation

The _gastrula_ phase is probably the first of the very critical stages in embryonic development and possibly the most critical with respect both to normal development and to survival. It is that stage at which the single-layered ball of cells becomes folded in such a way as to form two and then three layers of cells. These layers are identified by their positions, the outermost being the _ectoderm,_ the innermost the _endoderm,_ and the intermediate the _mesoderm._ They are called _germ layers_ because in them reside the basic materials for the major organs and tissues. These layers are of great topographical potential. During the layering, due to infolding, ingrowing, or a combination of the two, their constituent cells acquire characteristics that cause them to develop along different lines. Cells transplanted from one layer to another before such _differentiation_ begins adapt themselves to a new direction of development. Those remaining in their original positions, however, follow established, distinct patterns. In general, the ectoderm gives rise to the skin, special sense organs, and nervous tissues; the endoderm gives rise to the lining of the digestive tract and its derivatives; and the mesoderm gives rise to the muscles, connective tissue, skeleton, etc. The first indication of a division of labor thus occurs with gastrulation. If the embryo succeeds in achieving a three-layered (_triploblastic_) state, its chances for survival are good under unaltered environmental conditions.

Concurrently with the inward flow of cells during gastrulation, a new cavity, known as the *archenteron* or *gastrocoel*, forms. It is separate from the blastocoel and is the forerunner of the gut and its derivatives.

■ Organogenesis

The formation of the organ systems of the embryo begins almost immediately upon completion of the gastrula. In fact, experimental evidence indicates that even certain areas of the blastula are predestined to give rise to specific organs. The spatial relations among the cells of such areas, not the elements within the cells, direct the course of development. Thus influences that organize the embryo are apparent at a very early stage in its *ontogeny*. In some embryos certain organs are temporary, functioning only during embryonic or larval life and being replaced by more complicated structures that function at later stages or in the adult. In most forms, however, there is a gradual realization of the organ systems necessary to the adult, all properly integrated into the organism as a whole.

A generalized picture applicable to most vertebrates is possible even at this relatively late stage in development. The dynamic changes occurring in a typical vertebrate embryo during early organogenesis may be outlined as follows:

The outermost layer (ectoderm) folds inward to form pockets at either end representing the mouth and the anus. Between these, and on the uppermost (*dorsal*) side, it forms a groove, then two folds, and finally a closed tube, which together represent the brain and spinal cord, the tube remaining as the brain ventricles and the spinal canal. Cells migrate out from this axial central nervous system to give rise to the peripheral nervous system, which spreads throughout the body, joining ectodermally derived sense organs in the outer skin. Thus, although the nervous system is derived from the ectoderm, it ultimately penetrates every part of the body.

The innermost layer (endoderm), usually the second layer to be formed, gives rise to the lining membranes of the entire alimentary tract and its derivatives, such as the thyroid, lungs, liver, stomach, pancreas, intestines, and bladder.

The intermediate layer (mesoderm), last to appear and to differentiate, forms the bulk of the body—the muscles, cartilage, and bone—and such organs as the gonads, kidneys, adrenals, and heart. The primitive embryonic mesoderm, before it differentiates toward its potential end products, is known as *mesenchyme*. Mesenchymal differentiations into various cell types may be summarized as follows: the primitive mesenchymal cells develop into the endothelial lining of all blood vessels and into *lipoblasts, macrophages, hemocytoblasts, myoblasts, fibroblasts, chondroblasts,* and *osteoblasts;* lipoblasts become fat cells; macrophages give rise to phagocytes; hemocytoblasts give rise to blood elements such as erythrocytes, monocytes, platelets, and leucocytes; myoblasts give rise to muscle (cardiac, smooth, and striated); fibroblasts become fibrous connective tissue; chondroblasts become cartilage; and osteoblasts become bone.

By the time the primary germ layers are clearly defined, all vertebrates have acquired a transient axial skeleton, the *notochord*. This is structurally much like cartilage and extends almost the full length of the anterior-posterior axis of the embryo directly beneath the developing central nervous system. It persists as the centra of the vertebrae.

The anterior end of most vertebrate embryos appears to differentiate earlier or at a faster rate than the more posterior structures. Whether this *cephalization* is due to evolutionary survival factors, to metabolic differences within an axiate embryo, or to teleological factors requiring the prior organization of a controlling nervous system has not been resolved. Whatever its cause, the apparent imbalance is maintained until quite late in ontogeny.

This chapter is intended to provide the student with a comprehensive view of what is to follow. It is based upon years of study and acquaintance with a very large number of embryos of a great variety of forms and represents an attempt to call attention to a core of similarity among all of them.

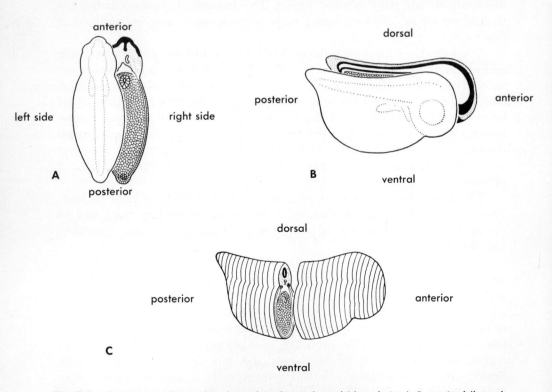

Fig. 2.1   Sections used in embryological study: A, frontal (dorsal view); B, sagittal (lateral view); C, transverse (lateral view).

Only after the student has read about and studied by himself the major vertebrates presented in this book will he fully comprehend the complexities of a development built upon a simple basic pattern. He is now ready to investigate the embryology of the frog, the chick, the mouse, the pig, and the human, with emphasis on both their fundamental similarities (as outlined in this chapter) and their fundamental differences, remembering at all times that he is viewing at isolated moments a never-ending and dynamic process leading toward a more complex, more integrated, and more independent and self-sufficient organism.

In the study of any embryo, complete organisms taken at various stages of development are necessary to show the changes in external features with embryonic growth. In addition, three types of sections are required for a thorough knowledge of embryology (Fig. 2.1). A frontal section divides the specimen into ventral and dorsal portions; a sagittal section divides the specimen into left and right portions; and a transverse section divides the specimen into anterior and posterior portions. The word longitudinal describes a lengthwise section not yet identifiable as frontal, sagittal, or transverse. Throughout the text the figure captions indicate the types of sections shown.

THE FROG:

An Aquatic Vertebrate

Introduction

The mature male of the common leopard frog species (*Rana pipiens*) measures 60 to 110 mm. from snout to *anus*. It can usually be distinguished from the female by its smaller, streamlined body (the female having a flabby, distended abdomen), darkened thumb pad, low guttural croaking, and the absence of peritoneal cilia (Fig. 3.1). Some frog species also exhibit color variations between the sexes. *Rana pipiens* becomes sexually mature when it attains a body length of 60 mm. and from then on it breeds once each year. The breeding season is determined by the temperature and other environmental conditions, being as early as March in the far South and as late as May or June in the far North. Germ cell formation occupies the long interval between breeding seasons.

Reproductive Systems

Male

The paired *testes* are small, ovoid organs closely associated structurally and functionally with the *mesonephric* kidneys. A mesentery, the *mesorchium*, attaches each testis to its related kidney (Fig. 3.2), and *vasa efferentia* pass from the *seminiferous tubules* of each testis between the membranes of the mesorchium into *Bowman's capsules* in the kidney. Thus the sperm-conducting tubules send their products into the anterior uriniferous tubules of the kidney, where the sperm and urine are mixed (Fig. 3.3). The *mesonephric* (*Wolffian*) *duct* serves as both the *vas deferens* and the *ureter*, so that it is truly urogenital. A glandular enlargement of the posterior end of this duct forms the *seminal vesicle*.

Spermatogenesis is a continuous process, although there is a preponderance of certain cell types at certain seasons. From fall until spring the seminiferous tubules contain approximately equal numbers of all stages from *spermatogonium* to *spermatozoon* (Fig. 3.4A); just before breeding the pro-

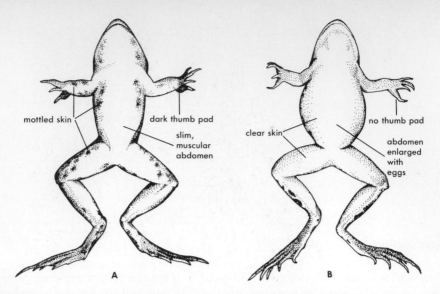

Fig. 3.1 Ventral views of adult frogs (*Rana pipiens*): A, male; B, female.

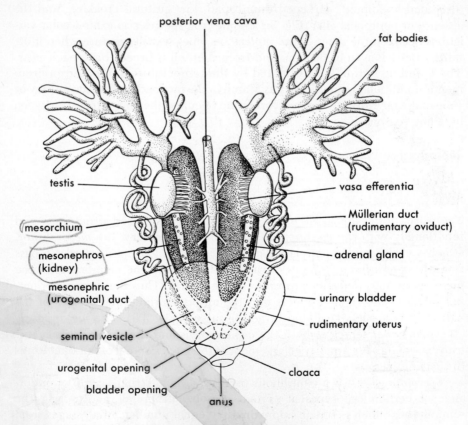

Fig. 3.2 Ventral view of urogenital system of adult male frog.

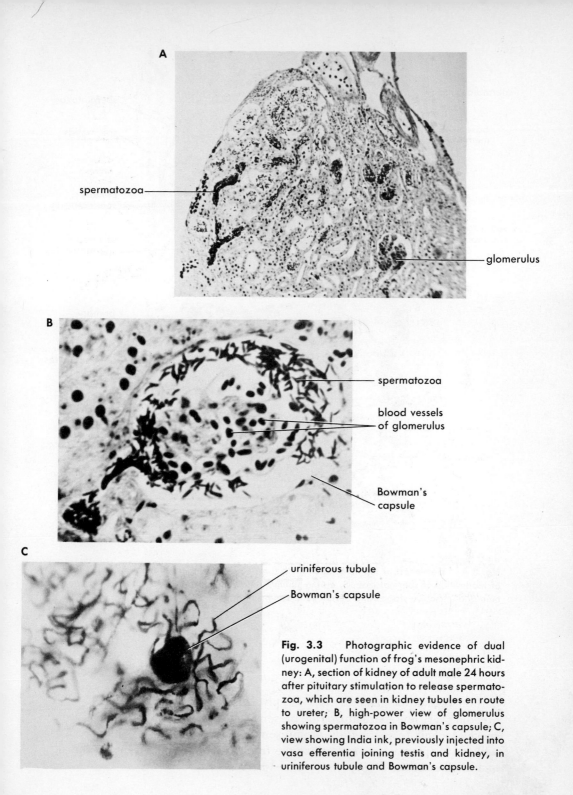

Fig. 3.3 Photographic evidence of dual (urogenital) function of frog's mesonephric kidney: A, section of kidney of adult male 24 hours after pituitary stimulation to release spermatozoa, which are seen in kidney tubules en route to ureter; B, high-power view of glomerulus showing spermatozoa in Bowman's capsule; C, view showing India ink, previously injected into vasa efferentia joining testis and kidney, in uriferous tubule and Bowman's capsule.

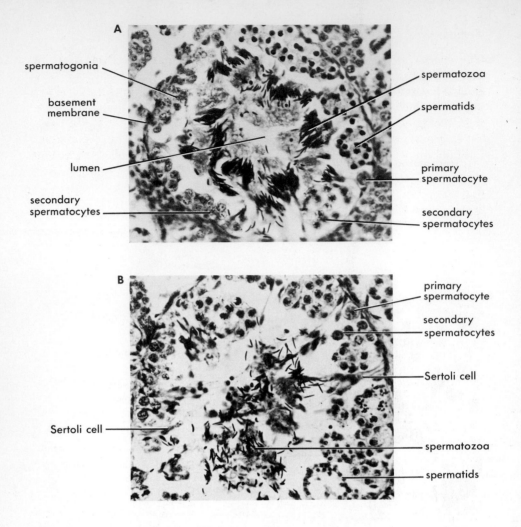

Fig. 3.4 Seminiferous tubule of adult male frog: A, during hibernation, showing all stages of maturation of spermatozoa; B, during summer, showing spermatozoa all liberated into lumen and immature stages and Sertoli cells around periphery.

portion of mature gametes rises sharply (Fig. 3.4B); and immediately after breeding very few spermatozoa are present, but all the preliminary stages, from spermatogonia to *spermatids,* are present in abundance. The male produces millions of spermatozoa to fertilize the few thousand eggs laid by the female in a single season.

Female

The *ovaries* are paired, multilobed organs, each enclosed in a thin layer of connective tissue, the *theca externa,* and attached to the dorsal body wall by a double-layered mesentery, the *mesovarium* (Fig. 3.5). At all times they contain *oögonia,* which are suspended from the walls of the hollow ovarian sacs awaiting development into either *primary oöcytes* or *follicle* (nurse) *cells* (Fig. 3.6).

Oögenesis begins immediately after the breeding season and continues until fall, by which time each of the eggs to be ovulated the following year is

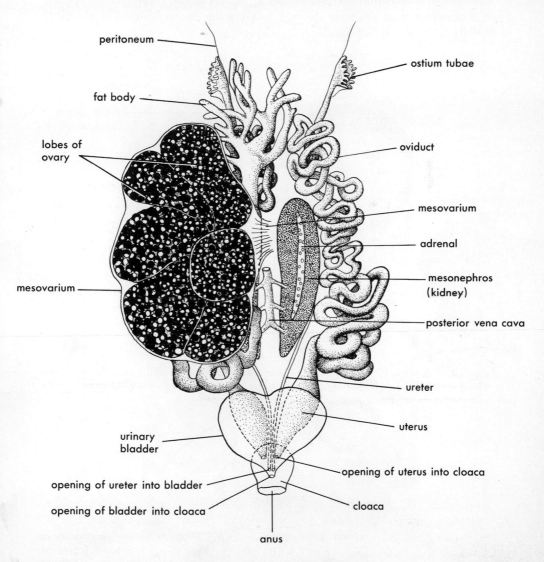

Fig. 3.5   Ventral view of urogenital system of adult female frog.

in the metaphase of the *first maturation division*—that is, the primary oöcyte (Fig. 3.7) has not yet discarded its *first polar body*. At *ovulation* (Fig. 3.8) the oöcytes are released from the ovarian surface over a period of a few hours. They fall into the peritoneal cavity, where cilia propel them anteriorly toward the flared end, or *ostium tubae*, of the adjacent *oviduct*. The paired oviducts are heavily coiled and characterized by a highly secretory lining, which deposits several layers of albumen on the oöcytes in transit. Each oöcyte completes the first maturation division in the upper part of the oviduct, extruding the first polar body into the space beneath the *vitelline membrane*. The *second maturation division* begins at once, but the chromosomes remain in metaphase from the time the egg reaches the uterus (some 4 hours after ovulation) until it is fertilized.

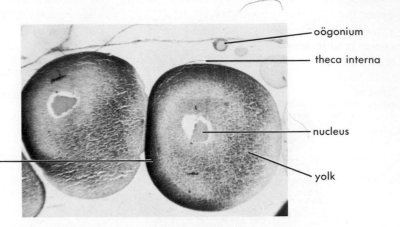

oögonium

theca interna

nucleus

pigmented animal hemisphere

yolk

Fig. 3.6 Section of ovary of recently metamorphosed frog, showing no primary oöcytes.

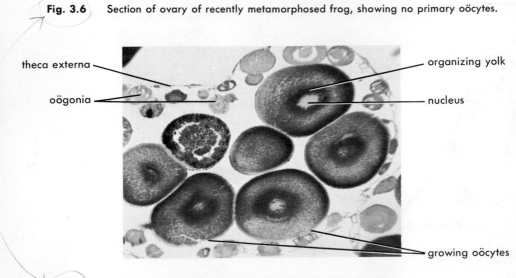

theca externa

organizing yolk

oögonia

nucleus

growing oöcytes

Fig. 3.7 Section of ovary of mature frog, showing two primary oöcytes.

■ Fertilization

Some 2000 to 3000 eggs are laid at one mating, invariably in water. As the eggs emerge from the *cloaca* of the female during *amplexus* (Fig. 3.9), which may last for several days, the male sheds clouds of sperm into the water. Fertilization therefore occurs outside the body.

Although thousands of active spermatozoa surround each egg as it is deposited in the water, generally only one succeeds in fertilizing it. At this time the egg is undergoing its second maturation division. The spermatozoon first activates or stimulates the egg surface to begin the drastic physical transformations necessary for successful fertilization. The dormant vitelline membrane elevates to become the *fertilization membrane*, creating a space around the egg known as the *perivitelline space*. In addition, the jelly deposited about the egg during its transport through the oviduct swells substantially to provide a mechanical covering that affords protection against abrasions and bacteria and, being flavorless, also against predatory aquatic animals (Fig. 3.10).

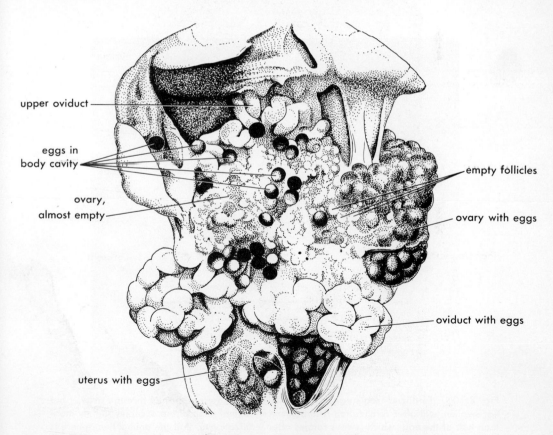

Fig. 3.8   Body cavity of adult female frog (*Rana pipiens*) at height of ovulation.

Fig. 3.9 Normal amplexus in toad (*Bufo Fowleri*).

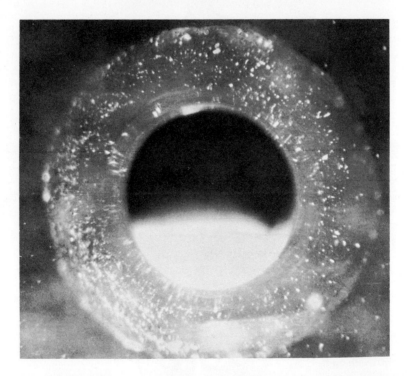

Fig. 3.10 Fertilized frog's egg, showing jelly added during journey through oviduct but not swollen until after fertilization. The pigmented animal hemisphere occupies slightly more than half of the egg, which always rotates after fertilization so that the animal hemisphere is uppermost.

Fertilization involves, in addition to activation and syngamy, the determination of embryonic axes. The effective spermatozoon enters the egg in the upper, dark *animal hemisphere* (Fig. 3.11A), where the egg *nucleus* (*germinal vesicle*) is located, drawing some surface pigment in with it. The result is a slight migration of pigment from other areas toward the point of penetration. The region opposite the entrance point and bordering the *vegetal hemisphere* exhibits greatest pigment recession, as indicated by an area of diluted pigment, the *gray crescent* (Figs. 3.11B, 3.12), rather than a sharp line between the two hemispheres.

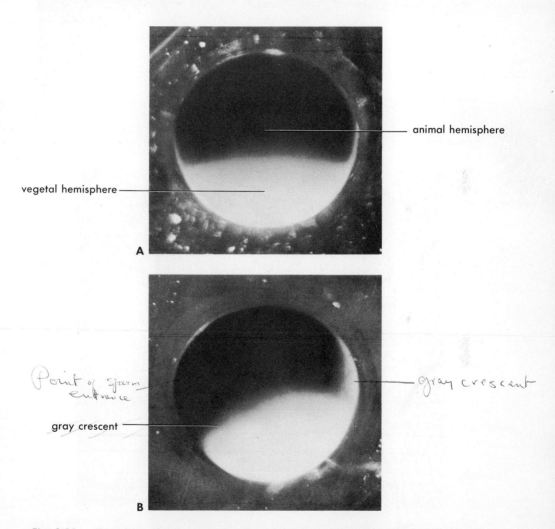

Fig. 3.11 Formation of gray crescent in frog's egg: A, immediately after fertilization egg is divided into distinct animal and vegetal hemispheres, associated with pigment and yolk; B, slight migration of surface pigment toward point of sperm entrance (at right) causes pigment to recede from opposite side, leaving gray crescent.

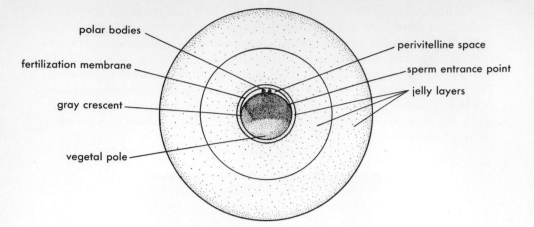

polar bodies

fertilization membrane

gray crescent

vegetal pole

perivitelline space

sperm entrance point

jelly layers

Fig. 3.12   Diagram of fertilized frog's egg.

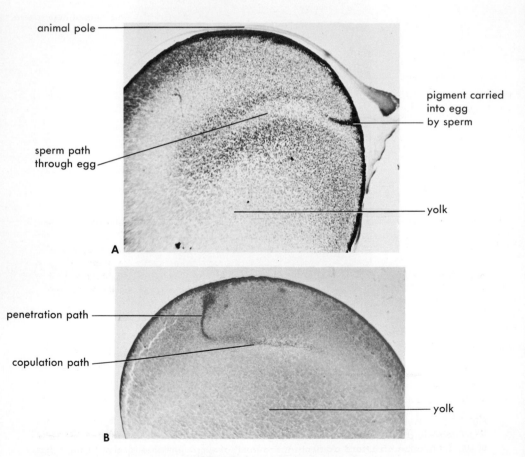

animal pole

sperm path
through egg

pigment carried
into egg
by sperm

yolk

A

penetration path

copulation path

yolk

B

Fig. 3.13   Sperm penetration and copulation paths in frog's egg.

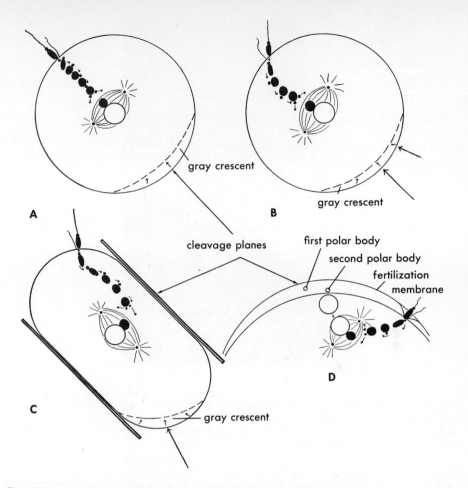

Fig. 3.14 Fertilization of frog's egg: A, sperm penetration and copulation paths in same direction, forming straight line, so that first cleavage bisects gray crescent; B, copulation path veering away from penetration path, so that first cleavage does not bisect gray crescent; C, compression reorienting egg protoplasm, so that cleavage spindle lies in plane of longest protoplasmic axis, regardless of sperm activity; D, lateral view showing slight movement of egg nucleus toward sperm nucleus, after egg nucleus has given off second polar body. (From R. Rugh, *The Frog*, McGraw-Hill, New York, 1951.)

The *sperm entrance path,* or the *penetration path,* can be identified by a cone of pigment pointing inward (Figs. 3.13A, 3.14A). After entrance, the sperm head may veer toward the egg nucleus so that the path changes. The second portion of the path, resulting in approximation of the male and female pronuclei, is known as the *copulation path* (Figs. 3.13B, 3.14B). It is the penetration path, however, that determines the axes of the future embryo (Fig. 3.14 C,D). A plane including the penetration point and any two points on the original egg axis (animal to vegetal pole, through the center of the egg)

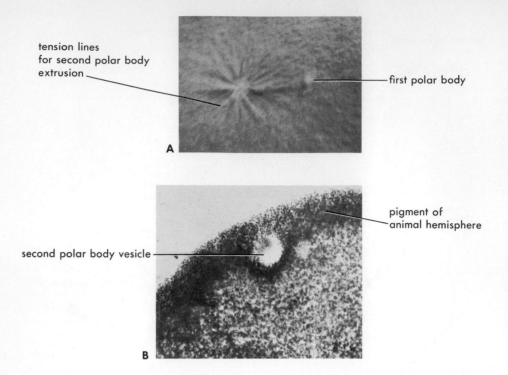

tension lines
for second polar body
extrusion

first polar body

A

second polar body vesicle

pigment of
animal hemisphere

B

Fig. 3.15   Polar body formation in frog's egg: A, first polar body and beginning of second polar body 20 minutes after fertilization; B, formation of second polar body vesicle; C, both polar bodies and second polar body pit; D, egg surface after polar body elimination, showing some depigmentation.

identifies the major embryonic axis for the particular embryo. Since the sperm entrance point, which represents the future anterior of the embryo, is opposite the gray crescent, the latter represents the future posterior of the embryo.

The introduction of the spermatozoon causes the egg to complete its second maturation division and eliminate the second polar body, a process normally requiring about 20 minutes (Figs. 3.15, 3.16). This reaction brings the egg nucleus so close to the surface that it could be plucked out with a sharp needle, leaving the sperm nucleus to effect development of an *andro-genetic* egg. Normally, however, the sperm nucleus joins the egg nucleus to restore the proper (diploid) number of chromosomes for the adult amphibian cells (Fig. 3.17).

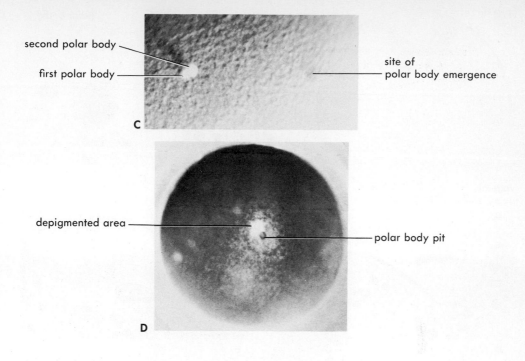

second polar body

first polar body

site of
polar body emergence

C

depigmented area

polar body pit

D

Fig. 3.15 (continued)

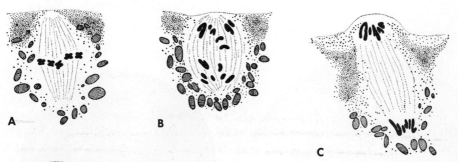

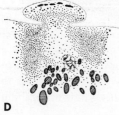

Fig. 3.16 Diagram of polar body emergence in frog's (*Rana pipiens*) egg: A, division spindle at time of fertilization; B, anaphase of maturation division, at which stage spindle can be seen from exterior of egg as black dot; C, early telophase; D, polar body just forming. (From R. Rugh, *The Frog*, McGraw-Hill, New York, 1951. Reproduced from Porter.)

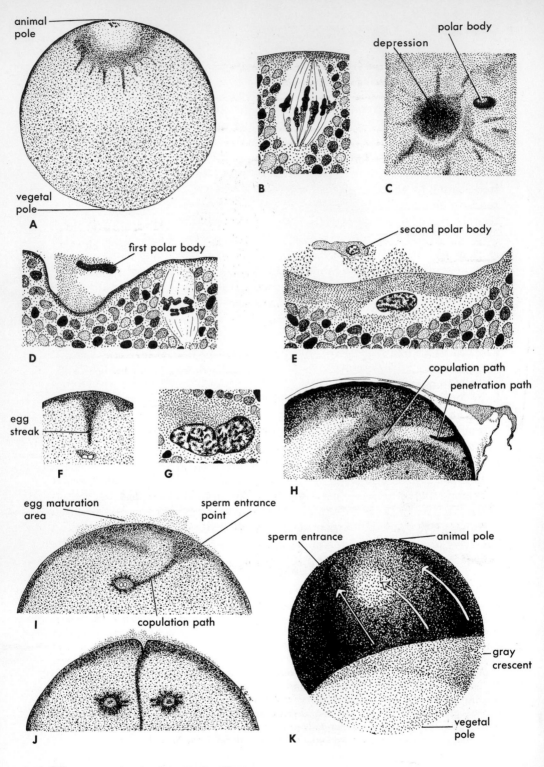

animal pole

vegetal pole

A

B

depression

polar body

C

first polar body

D

second polar body

E

egg streak

F

G

copulation path

penetration path

H

egg maturation area

sperm entrance point

copulation path

I

J

sperm entrance

animal pole

gray crescent

vegetal pole

K

■ Cleavage

Whereas the penetration path determines the embryonic axes, the copulation path establishes the first cleavage plane. When the penetration and copulation paths are in the same plane, the *cleavage furrow* bisects the gray crescent. Although environmental pressures may alter internal conditions, there is a natural tendency toward the coinciding of the gravitational plane, the sperm entrance point, the penetration path, the median plane of the egg, the median plane of the embryo, and the plane of the first cleavage.

Several so-called "laws" have been derived, largely from observations on free-floating fertilized egg cells. According to Pfluger, the first mitotic spindle tends to elongate in the direction of the least resistance; this behavior may characterize all free-floating cells. Balfour stated that the rate of cleavage varies inversely with the amount of yolk present, since yolk is a natural impediment to cleavage. Sachs stated that cells tend to divide into equal parts and that each new plane of division tends to bisect the previous plane at right angles. Finally, Hertwig asserted that the nucleus and its spindle are generally found in the center of the protoplasmic mass and that the axis of any division occurs at right angles to the protoplasmic mass. When contiguous cells develop, these laws do not always hold.

The frog's egg is *telolecithal;* that is, a large amount of yolk is concentrated at one pole, while cytoplasm and the nucleus are at the other pole. Although cleavage is total (*holoblastic*), it is somewhat impeded, owing to the large amount of yolk, and appears at first to be only partial (*meroblastic*). It starts at the dorsal animal hemisphere and eventually encircles and cuts through the yolk (Fig. 3.18). However, before the first cleavage is complete, the second one begins, at right angles to the first, so that the nature of the earlier cleavage is not obvious for some time. Forces within the egg initiate the cleavage process, although an observer of the first cleavage gets the impression of active infurrowing from without. The first cleavage begins about 2½ hours after fertilization, the second an hour later, the third half an hour later, the fourth 20 minutes later, and so forth, each successive division occurring after a shorter interval. The cleavage rate depends largely upon the environmental temperature, since frogs are *poikilothermic* (cold-blooded). The

Fig. 3.17   Fertilization phenomena in frog's (*Rana pipiens*) egg: A, shortly before ovulation nucleus has broken down and chromosomes have migrated toward apex of animal pole preparatory to formation of first maturation spindle; B, first polar spindle, with chromosomes in tetrad condition separating into respective dyads; C, after first maturation division (polar view); D, spindle of second maturation division (lateral view), with first polar body present in slight depression at animal pole; E, after fertilization, with second polar body present in depression of animal pole and female pronucleus reorganized; F, meeting of two pronuclei; G, two pronuclei in contact (high power); H, sperm penetration and copulation paths; I, sperm penetration and copulation paths and meeting of pronuclei; J, first cleavage furrow and daughter nuclei; K, egg just before first cleavage, with arrows indicating direction of pigment migration resulting in formation of gray crescent. (From O. E. Nelsen, *Comparative Embryology of the Vertebrates*, McGraw-Hill, New York, 1953. I, J from Hertwig.)

Table 3.1   Schedule of normal development*

| | TIME AFTER MATING† | |
STAGE	AT 18°C.	AT 25°C.
fertilization	0	0
gray crescent	1	½–1
rotation	1½	1
two cells	3½	2½
four cells	4½	3½
eight cells	5	4
blastula	18	12
gastrula	34	20
yolk plug	42	32
neural plate	50	40
neural folds	62	48
ciliary movement	67	52
neural tube	72	56
tail bud	84	66
muscular movement	96	76
heartbeat	5 days	4 days
gill circulation	6 days	5 days
tail fin circulation	8 days	6½ days
internal gills, operculum	9 days	7½ days
operculum complete	12 days	10 days
metamorphosis	3 months	2½ months

* From R. Rugh, *Experimental Embryology*, 3rd ed., Burgess, Minneapolis, 1962.
† In hours unless otherwise noted.

time between fertilization and first cleavage may vary from 2 to 12 hours without affecting future development. The resulting sections of the egg are the *blastomeres*. The first two cleavages produce blastomeres approximately equal in size. With the third cleavage, at right angles to both the first and second, there appear animal pole *micromeres* (small blastomeres), as compared with the vegetal pole *macromeres* (large, yolk-laden blastomeres). As the cleavages become more frequent, the blastomeres become smaller and smaller and may soon be recognized as cells. Table 3.1 is a schedule of development at two different temperatures.

■ Blastulation

Blastulation occurs when a cavity, the *blastocoel* (Figs. 3.18I–L, 3.19), appears among the increasing numbers of blastomeres. Its presence identifies the embryo as a *blastula*. The blastocoel develops at about the 32-cell stage and is responsible for a slight increase in total volume, although it causes no increase in mass. Because of the abundant vegetal hemisphere yolk, the blastocoel is in an eccentric position, lying just beneath the dorsal animal pole.

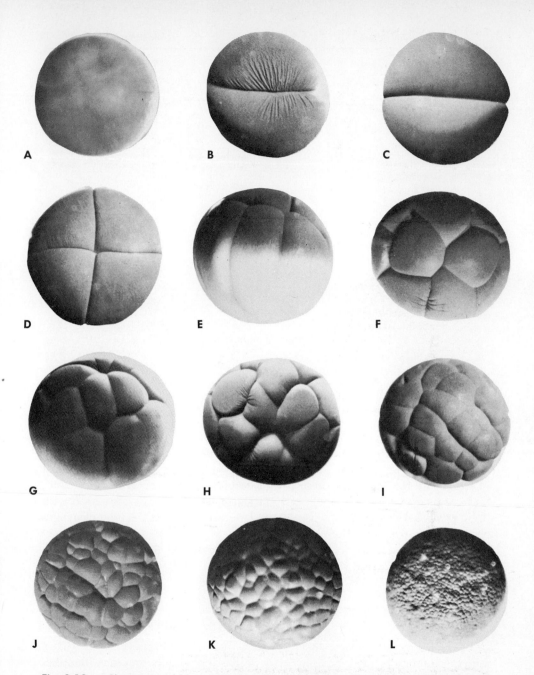

Fig. 3.18 Cleavage and blastulation in frog's egg: A, first indication of superficial cleavage; B, tension lines at surface, indicating formation of inner mitotic spindle; C, first cleavage complete; D, second cleavage complete; E, 8-cell stage, showing both animal and vegetal hemispheres; F, G, smaller blastomeres produced by continuing cleavages; H, beyond 64-cell stage; I, early blastula (animal hemisphere view); J, later blastula; K, L, true late blastula stage, with vesicular bastocoel just beneath animal pole.

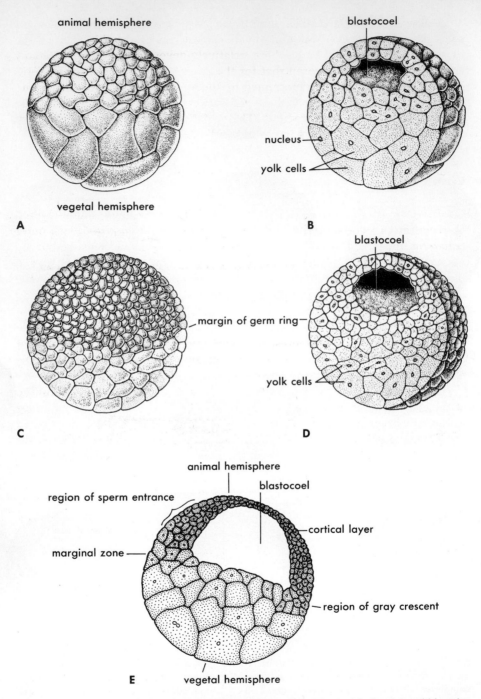

animal hemisphere

vegetal hemisphere

A

blastocoel

nucleus

yolk cells

B

C

blastocoel

margin of germ ring

yolk cells

D

animal hemisphere

region of sperm entrance

blastocoel

cortical layer

marginal zone

region of gray crescent

E

vegetal hemisphere

Fig. 3.19   Diagram of blastulation in frog's egg: A, cleaving egg; B, hemisected blastula; C, late blastula; D, hemisected late blastula; E, sagittal section. (From R. Rugh, *The Frog*, McGraw-Hill, New York, 1951. A, B, C, D adapted from Huettner.)

Following the 32-cell stage, there is no longer any synchrony in cleavage, since there is such great variation in yolk content among the cells. The dorsalmost cells of the animal hemisphere, relatively devoid of yolk, divide rapidly and soon form a multilayered roof for the blastocoel. In sections the depths of these cell layers can be determined by the amount of pigment carried into them from the animal hemisphere. Laterally the thickest layer marks the region opposite the gray crescent. The variations in thickness of cell layers anticipate the next and most important early step in embryogenesis.

■ Gastrulation

Gastrulation is the process that transforms an essentially single-layered blastula into a two-layered and finally a three-layered *gastrula*, with outer *ectoderm*, inner *endoderm*, and intermediate *mesoderm*. As cleavage continues, an involution (inturning) of the egg surface begins at the margin between the animal and vegetal hemispheres. This inturning creates a new cavity, the *archenteron* or *gastrocoel* (primitive gut), lined with endoderm and projecting inward. The endoderm is not a new layer of cells but, rather, cells that were a short time previously on the outside of the blastula and were later folded inside at the region of the gray crescent. The fold is called the *dorsal lip of the blastopore*, an unfortunate designation, since it does not open into the blastocoel but instead into the newly forming archenteron.

Gastrulation involves, first, a thinning of the layers of cells at the position of the gray crescent; cells deep within the multilayered blastular margin move toward the other side of the blastocoel. Involution begins in the gray crescent region (Fig. 3.20) and is naturally easier with fewer layers of cells. Those cells that first involute constitute the initial evidence of the dorsal lip of the

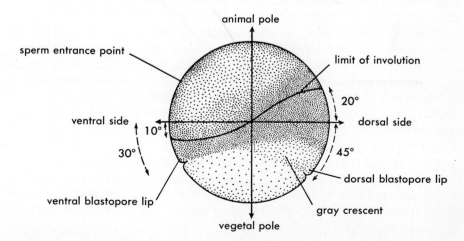

Fig. 3.20 Surface changes in frog's egg during gastrulation. (From R. Rugh, *The Frog*, McGraw-Hill, New York, 1951. Adapted from Pasteels.)

blastopore. Second, the margin of the animal hemisphere cells (which contain pigment) begins an *epiboly* or extension down over the vegetal hemisphere (Fig. 3.21); the diameter of the marginal zone becomes progressively smaller as it passes below the equator much in the manner of a constricting rubber ring. As the cells of the animal hemisphere are more rigid than those of the vegetal hemisphere, pressure is exerted on the latter, causing them to arch upward toward the blastocoel. Third, a few cells actually inturn at the lateral margins of the gray crescent to create lateral extensions of the infolding along the marginal zone. During this process the animal hemisphere continues its epiboly so that the lips of the infolding (blastopore) cells enclose the vegetal hemisphere. In other words, the cells at the point of initial involution move inward, drawing after them contiguous sheets of outside cells, which simultaneously roll over the vegetal hemisphere (Fig. 3.22). The lip of the blastopore eventually encircles the marginal zone, which becomes more and more constricted until only a small amount of vegetal hemisphere, the *yolk plug,* is visible (Figs. 3.21, 3.23).

Inside the embryo (Fig. 3.24) the inturning cells are largely endoderm, but proliferating from them into the region between endoderm and ectoderm are loose, active cells that organize into the mesoderm, or third germ layer. The mesoderm forms at almost the same time as the endoderm. The dorsal roof of the archenteron can be identified by persistent pigment in its constituent cells, derived from their original location in the outer animal hemisphere. Between the roof of the archenteron and the dorsal ectoderm appears a transient embryonic structure known as the *notochord.* It develops from *mesenchyme* (embryonic mesoderm), but whether it is of ectodermal or endodermal origin is not certain. During gastrulation the embryonic axes naturally change, and the embryo loses its spherical shape in favor of elongation and bilaterality, associated with notochord and mesoderm formation. The archenteron is the first elongating influence, forming an anteroposterior axis.

Gastrulation is possibly the most critical and the least understood process in embryonic development. Cells of the blastula seem predestined to either move inward or stay outside and consequently to develop into specific organs or tissues owing entirely to their positional relations to the blastula as a whole. Their predictable behavior has given rise to *fate maps* (Figs. 3.25, 3.26), which show the regions of the blastula producing the various organs and tissues. However, blastula cells may be transposed so that those ordinarily becoming skin of the forelimb, for example, develop rather into lining of the gut or muscle of the tail. The discovery that early areas can be thus rearranged without upsetting the topography of the embryo has led to the postulation of *organismic influences.* This means simply that there must exist a force or forces that integrate the various cellular parts of the developing embryo. Because the dorsal lip of the blastopore is so sensitive to disruption, leading to abnormalities of development, it has been considered by some the dominating center of development and has accordingly been given the name of the

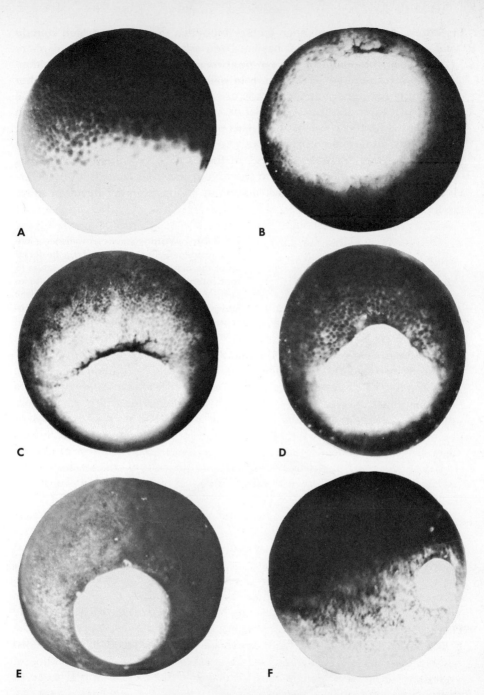

Fig. 3.21 Gastrulation in frog's egg: A, late blastula; B, first inturning of ectoderm; C, epibolic movement of animal hemisphere pigment toward forming dorsal blastopore lip; D, constriction of yolk plug, with most active involution at dorsal blastopore lip; E, F, continuing constriction of yolk plug by involution of confluent blastopore lips.

organizer. Yet numerous other factors influence development, and exactly
what or where the organizer is has not been established.

Once cells have moved to new positional relations in the gastrula, they
are irrevocably altered by the process called *differentiation*. Although the
alteration is not apparent, if the cells are transposed at this stage they will
retain their earlier destinies. Gastrulation is obviously a process of directional
movement (Figs. 3.22, 3.27), and if this movement of cells is interrupted in
any way, an abnormal embryo is likely to result. The movement is directed
by internal forces, or forces inherent in the early embryo, its cells, and cell
coatings. However, these forces are sensitive to external factors, so that "survival of the fittest" applies to gastrulation as well as to other developmental
processes.

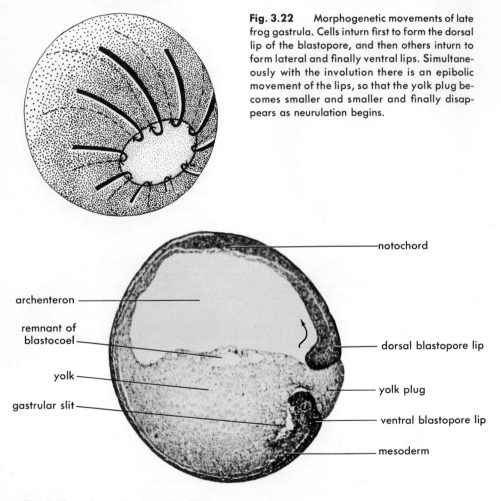

Fig. 3.22 Morphogenetic movements of late
frog gastrula. Cells inturn first to form the dorsal
lip of the blastopore, and then others inturn to
form lateral and finally ventral lips. Simultaneously with the involution there is an epibolic
movement of the lips, so that the yolk plug becomes smaller and smaller and finally disappears as neurulation begins.

notochord

archenteron

remnant of
blastocoel

yolk

gastrular slit

dorsal blastopore lip

yolk plug

ventral blastopore lip

mesoderm

Fig. 3.23 Sagittal section of yolk plug stage in frog,
showing movement over blastopore lips.

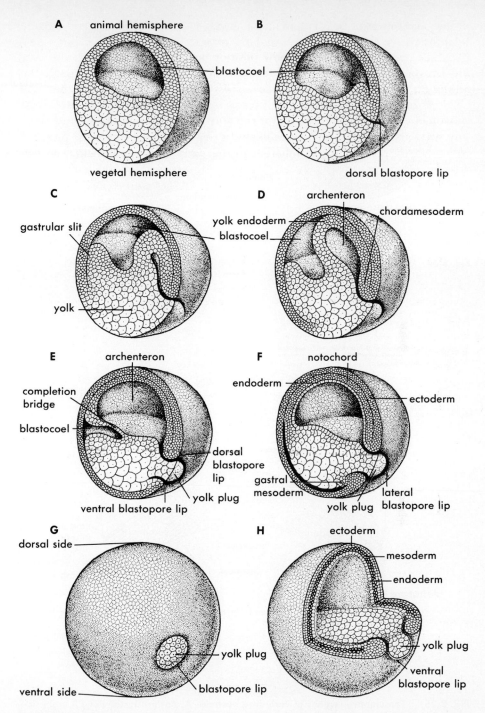

Fig. 3.24 Blastula to gastrula stages in frog. (From R. Rugh, *The Frog,* McGraw-Hill, New York, 1951. Adapted from Huettner.)

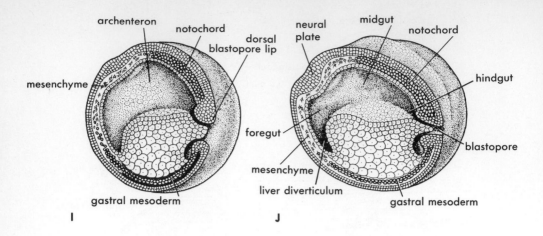

Fig. 3.24 (continued)

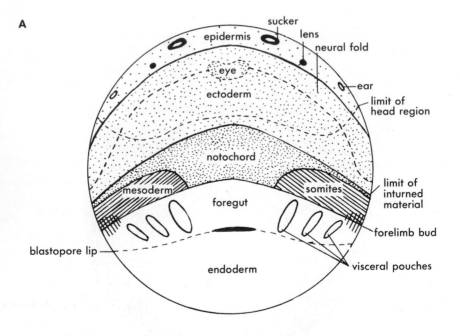

Fig. 3.25 Presumptive regions of early frog gastrula: A, posterodorsal view; B, right side view. (From R. Rugh, *Experimental Embryology*, 3rd ed., Burgess, Minneapolis, 1962. Adapted from Vogt.)

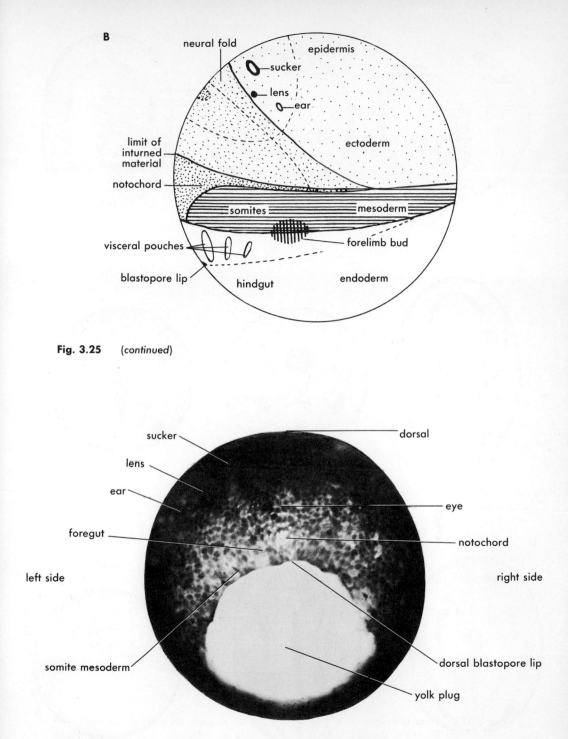

B

neural fold

epidermis

sucker

lens

ear

ectoderm

limit of
inturned
material

notochord

somites

mesoderm

visceral pouches

forelimb bud

blastopore lip

hindgut

endoderm

Fig. 3.25 (*continued*)

sucker

dorsal

lens

ear

eye

foregut

notochord

left side

right side

somite mesoderm

dorsal blastopore lip

yolk plug

Fig. 3.26 Organ primordia in frog gastrula. (Adapted from Vogt.)

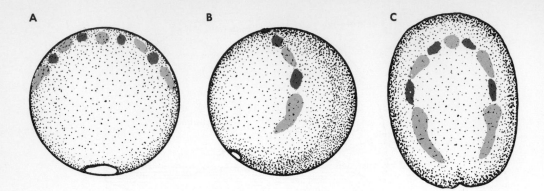

A   B   C

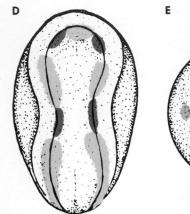   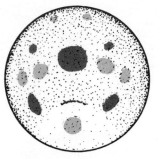   

D   E   F

G   H   I

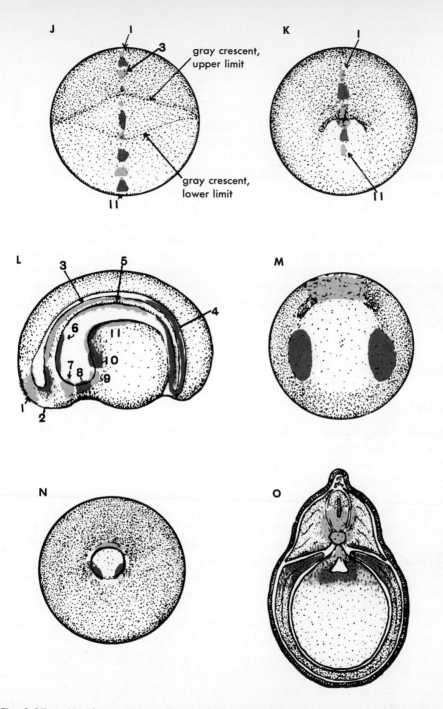

Fig. 3.27   Morphogenetic movements during gastrulation and neurulation in frog's egg, as indicated by spots of dye applied to egg at early stage. The dark gray patches are neutral red, and the light gray patches, nile blue sulfate. (Adapted from Vogt and Goettler.)

■ Neurulation

The nervous system arises from the ectoderm and eventually permeates every part of the body. Almost simultaneously with the formation of the anteroposterior axis, a dorsal thickening known as the *neural (medullary) plate*, the precursor of the central nervous system, appears (Figs. 3.28A,B, 3.29A). It extends from the dorsal lip of the blastopore anteriorly and comprises the dorsal axis of the embryo. A depression appears lengthwise in the dorsal thickening, and its sides fold toward each other to enclose a longitudinal groove, the *neural groove* (Figs. 3.28C,D, 3.29B,C). As soon as this early indication of the central nervous system is evident, the embryo may be called a *neurula* (Fig. 3.30). The *neural folds* or *ridges* close over the neural groove, first near the mid-body and then outward toward the ends. At its anterior end the *neural tube* (Figs. 3.28E, 3.29D) (which encloses the *neurocoel*) is open as the *anterior neuropore*, and at the posterior end, as the blastopore. As the blastopore becomes more and more constricted, the neural tube connects briefly with the posterior archenteron to form the *neurenteric canal*. The anterior neuropore (which marks the approximate position of the ultimate epiphysis) is the last vestige of open neural tube.

■ Organogenesis

Early embryo

Superficial examination reveals considerable development of the early embryo, as it forms anteroposterior, dorsoventral, and right-left axes while it elongates and acquires protuberances indicating inner changes toward organogenesis. On the forming head the anterior limits of the neural folds merge as a transverse neural fold, the *sense plate*. (This structure contains material eventually to form the fifth and seventh cranial ganglia, the mandibular arches, the lenses of the eyes, the olfactory placodes, and the oral suckers, most of which include some inner mesoderm.) The *stomodeum* (mouth cleft) forms in the mid-line and is lined with ectoderm. A pocket of this stomodeal ectoderm extends upward from the mouth toward the brain to form the *hypophysis*. Paired protuberances dorsolateral to the stomodeum are the *optic vesicles*, the beginnings of the eyes.

Vertical thickenings (which eventually give rise to the visceral arches) appear on the sides of the head behind the eyes. Posterior to the limits of these *gill plates*, and slightly dorsal, are paired *pronephric* (head kidney) protuberances. Still farther posteriorly, evidences of *myotomes*, or muscle segments, exist as V-shaped mesodermal masses, with the vertex of the V pointed forward.

Internally the gut is an endoderm-lined tube extending from one end of the embryo to the other; the neurocoel is a longitudinal cavity enclosed by neural (ectodermal) tissue; and the *coelomic spaces*, splits within the mesoderm, extend anteroposteriorly. Owing to these new cavities, the embryo

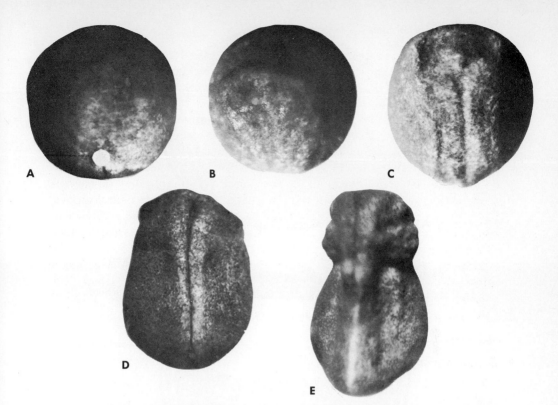

Fig. 3.28   Neurulation in frog: A, B, formation of neural plate; C, formation of neural folds; D, closure of neural folds; E, closure of neural folds into neutral tube complete, and head distinct.

enlarges, even though it takes in no outside food. The still-abundant yolk is so close to the gut endoderm that it may be digested by direct action, but shortly blood vessels develop to transfer the digested food materials to more distant regions of the embryo.

Neurula to late tail bud stage

In the frog, as in most vertebrates, the brain is the first major organ to differentiate into characteristic parts. The anterior end of the neurocoel enlarges and bends forward (*ventral flexure*) around the anterior tip of the notochord (Fig. 3.31). It soon divides into the anterior *prosencephalon* (forebrain), the short intermediate *mesencephalon* (midbrain), and the longer posterior *rhombencephalon* (hindbrain), the three primary portions of the brain identifiable in all vertebrate embryos. The prosencephalon, which becomes the *telencephalon* and the *diencephalon*, gives rise to the *infundibulum*, the *optic recess* and *chiasma*, the single *epiphysis*, and the thin-walled *anterior choroid plexus*. Ultimately the olfactory nerves also arise in part from the prosencephalon. The other parts of the brain are somewhat delayed in their differentiations.

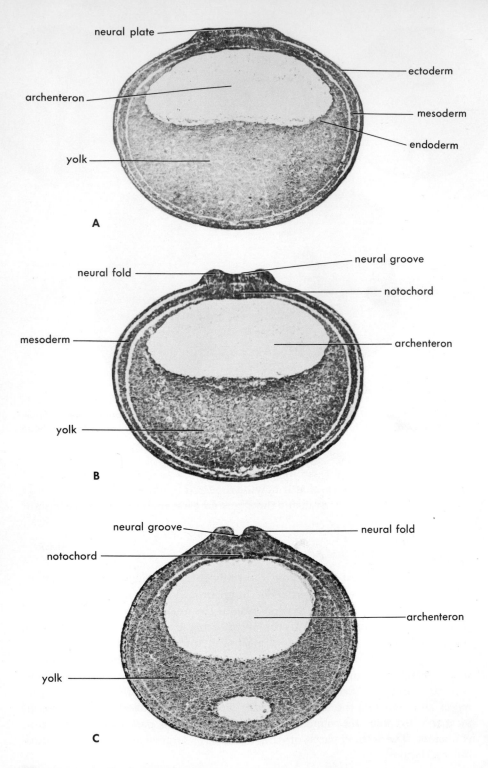

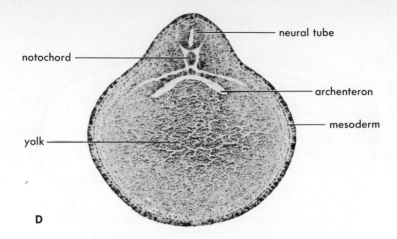

Fig. 3.29 Transverse sections of frog neurula: A, formation of neural plate; B, formation of neural folds; C, closure of neural folds; D, early neural tube. (C, D from General Biological Supply House, Chicago, Ill.)

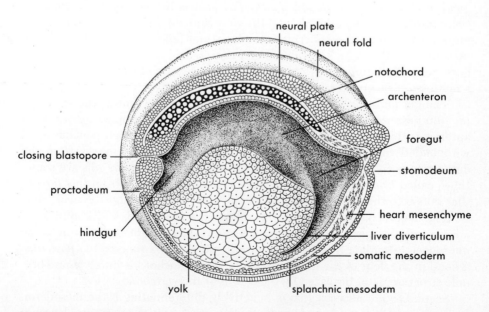

Fig. 3.30 Sagittal section of open neural fold stage in frog. (From R. Rugh, *The Frog*, McGraw-Hill, New York, 1951. Adapted from Huettner.)

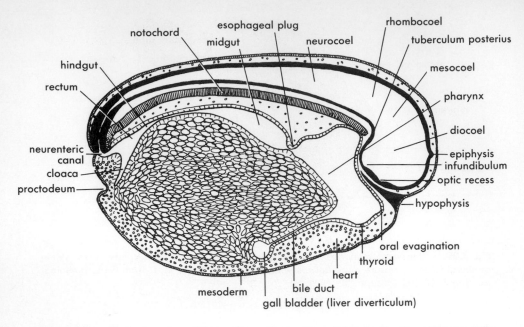

Fig. 3.31 Sagittal section of 3-mm. frog embryo. (From R. Rugh, *The Frog*, McGraw-Hill, New York, 1951.)

On either side of the head six *visceral arches,* separated by vertical *visceral grooves,* develop from the gill plates. The arches become parts of the head (*mandibular arch, hyoid arch,* and the four *branchial arches*). Each arch has an outer covering of ectoderm, an endodermal lining, and an intermediate mesoderm within which develop *blood vessels* and *nerves.* Arches III to VI give rise to the temporary *external gills* characteristic of the aquatic stage in amphibian development.

The gut joins the stomodeum anteriorly to form the mouth and the *proctodeum* posteriorly to form the *anus* (Fig. 3.32). In between and toward the anterior is the enlarged *pharynx,* with lateral vertically placed pouches lined with endoderm (*visceral pouches*) that join the visceral grooves from the outer ectoderm to form *visceral clefts* (those associated with gills are sometimes called *branchial clefts*). The *liver* is a ventral pocket from this *foregut* that cuts into the yolk. Derivatives of the *midgut* and *hindgut* appear later.

The major axiate structure at this time is the notochord, which appears as a large rod of apparently vacuolated cells dorsal to the gut and ventral to the neurocoel, extending from the neurenteric canal to the *tuberculum posterius,* a bend in the floor of the mesencephalon. The notochord is purely an embryonic structure, later displaced by the *centra* of the *vertebrae.*

Second to the nervous system in actively differentiating is the mesoderm. It gives rise, first as mesenchyme, to the substance of the visceral arches (hence the gills), to the *somites* (*epimere*), to the *nephrotome* (*intermediate*

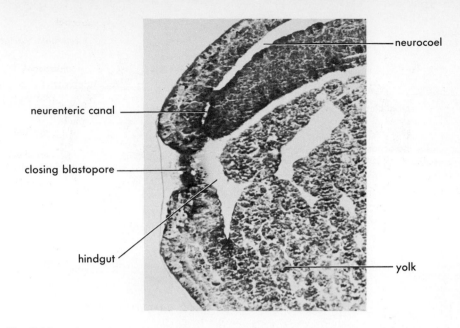

Fig. 3.32 Sagittal section through posterior of 3-mm. frog embryo, showing closure of blastopore and early formation of anus while neurenteric canal persists.

cell mass) (*mesomere*), and to the *lateral plate (hypomere)* (Fig. 3.33). Since the most differentiated mesodermal structures are the most anterior, one can see the progressive steps in differentiation in any embryo at this time by studying the mesodermal derivatives from the anterior toward the posterior (Fig 3.34).

The mesomere is the source of the early embryonic kidney, the *pronephros*. A more advanced kidney develops later in the same general region, slightly more posteriorly, but even this kidney is not as advanced as that of higher vertebrates. The splitlike cavity that appears in the hypomere, creating an outer double membrane *(somatopleure)* and an inner double one *(splanchnopleure)* adjacent to the yolk, is the beginning of the *coelom* (Fig. 3.35).

The *heart* first arises as a longitudinal tube ventral to the pharynx, and its mesodermal parts are continuous with the hypomeric mesoderm of the pharynx (Figs. 3.34, 3.36). The *pericardium* develops from somatopleure, the *myocardium* (heart muscle) from splanchnopleure, and the *pericardial cavity* from the coelom of the anterior body region (Fig. 3.37). The lining *endocardium* of the heart arises either from pinched-off endoderm of the overlying pharynx or from cells migrating inward from the encircling myocardium. The single tubular heart of the early frog embryo is reminiscent of the hearts of lower forms and is a stage through which all vertebrate hearts pass in development. It begins to pulsate at the 5-mm. stage (Figs. 3.37, 3.38) before its development into the three-chambered organ typical of the adult.

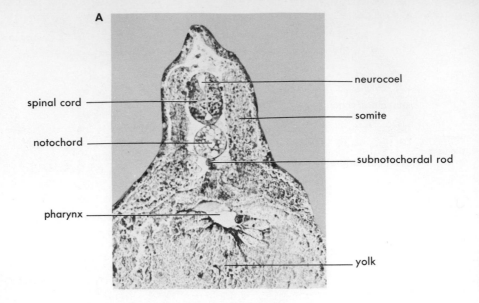

A

spinal cord

notochord

pharynx

neurocoel

somite

subnotochordal rod

yolk

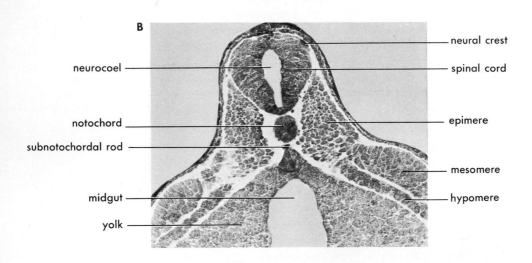

B

neurocoel

notochord

subnotochordal rod

midgut

yolk

neural crest

spinal cord

epimere

mesomere

hypomere

Fig. 3.33 Transverse sections showing early mesodermal derivatives of frog embryo: A, near origin of liver; B, at mid-body level.

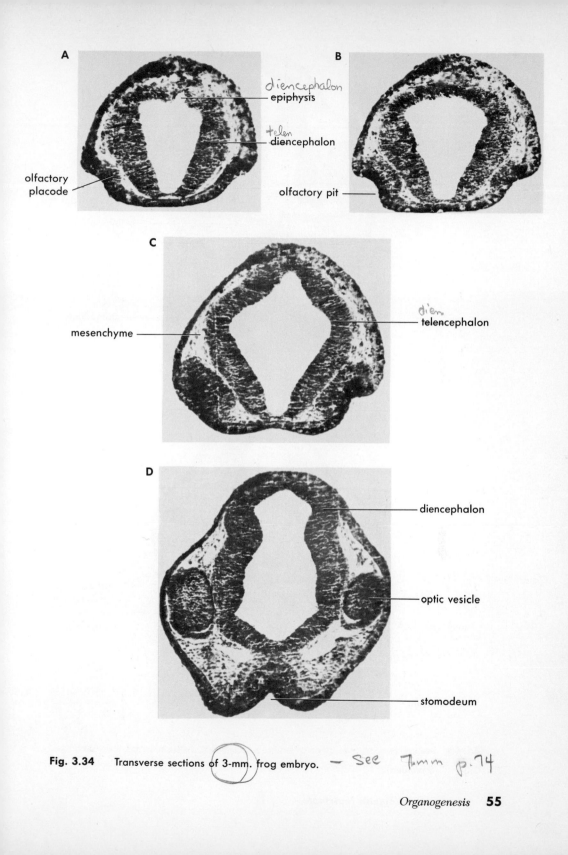

A — diencephalon
epiphysis

telen
diencephalon

olfactory
placode

B — olfactory pit

C — mesenchyme

dien
telencephalon

D — diencephalon

optic vesicle

stomodeum

Fig. 3.34   Transverse sections of 3-mm. frog embryo. — see 7mm p.74

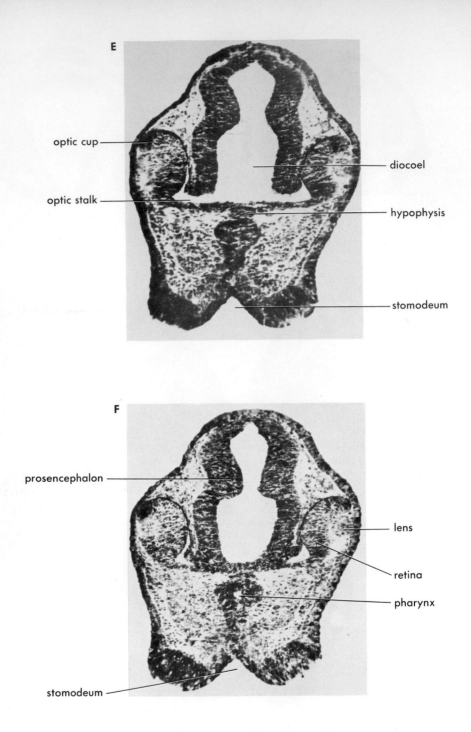

Fig. 3.34 (continued)

G

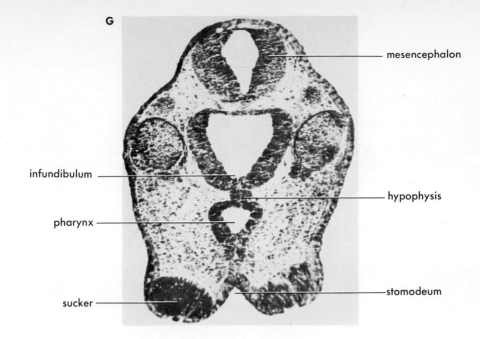

mesencephalon

infundibulum

hypophysis

pharynx

stomodeum

sucker

H

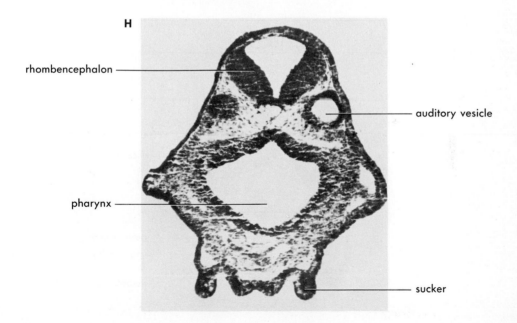

rhombencephalon

auditory vesicle

pharynx

sucker

Fig. 3.34 (*continued*)

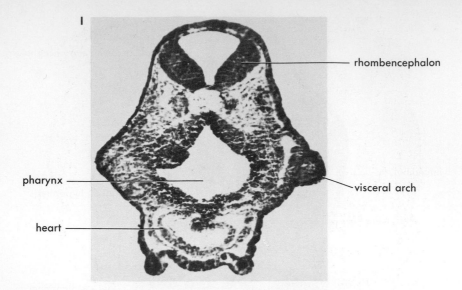

I

rhombencephalon

pharynx

visceral arch

heart

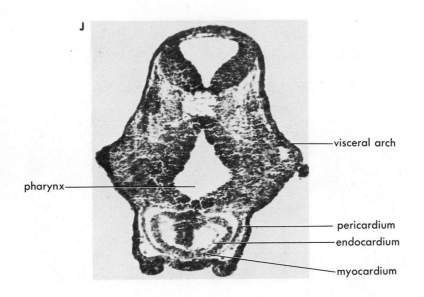

J

visceral arch

pharynx

pericardium

endocardium

myocardium

Fig. 3.34   (*continued*)

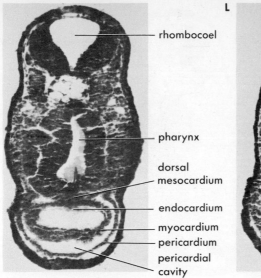

K

rhombocoel

pharynx

dorsal
mesocardium

endocardium

myocardium

pericardium

pericardial
cavity

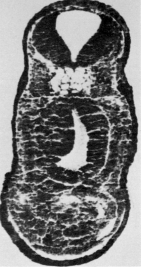

L

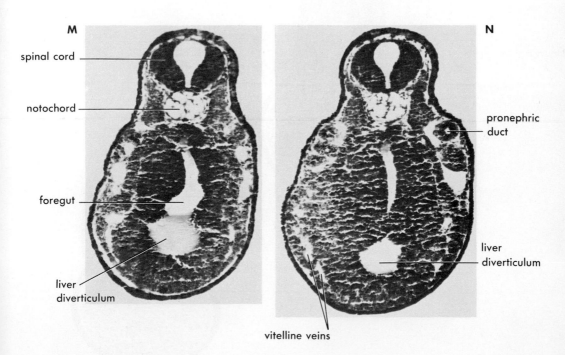

M

spinal cord

notochord

foregut

liver
diverticulum

N

pronephric
duct

liver
diverticulum

vitelline veins

Fig. 3.34   (continued)

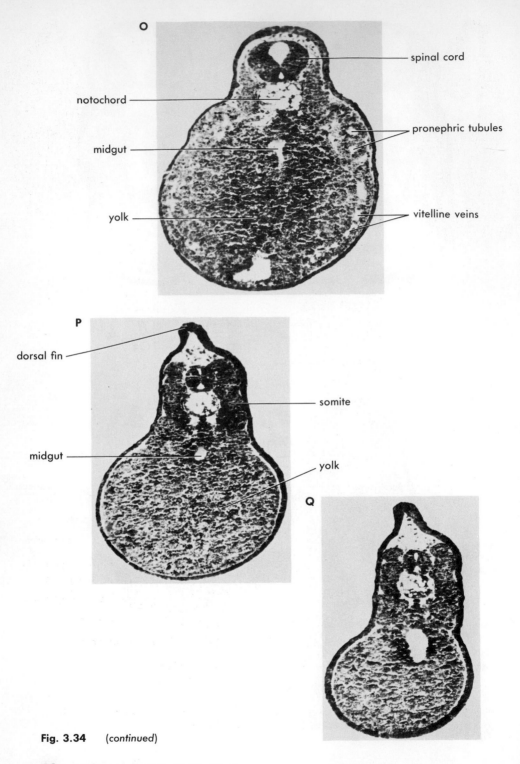

O

spinal cord

notochord

pronephric tubules

midgut

yolk

vitelline veins

P

dorsal fin

somite

midgut

yolk

Q

Fig. 3.34   (*continued*)

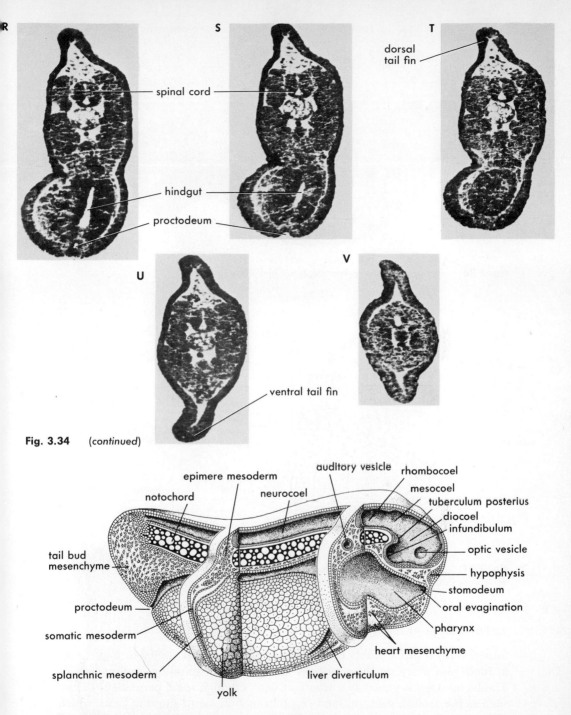

Fig. 3.34 (continued)

Fig. 3.35 Three-dimensional diagram of tail bud (4-mm.) stage in frog. (From R. Rugh, *The Frog*, McGraw-Hill, New York, 1951. Adapted from Huettner.)

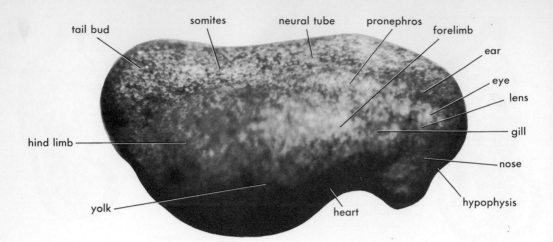

Fig. 3.36   Regions of organ primordia in tail bud stage in frog.

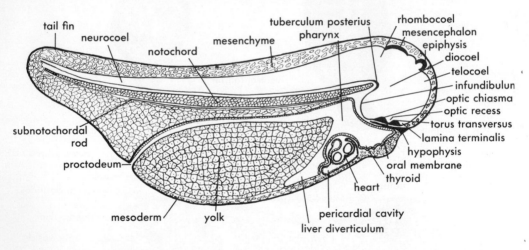

Fig. 3.37   Sagittal section of 5-mm. frog embryo. (From R. Rugh, *Laboratory Manual of Vertebrate Embryology*, 5th ed., Burgess, Minneapolis, 1961.)

Later embryo or larva

Superficially a *larva* differs from an early embryo in its ability to move, take in food, and carry on the processes of digestion, respiration, and excretion. The larval stage is generally a transient one, although some permanent larvae, such as the axolotl, necturus, and cryptobranchus, exist. The frog larva, which appears at the 6-mm. stage (at *hatching*), is commonly called the *tadpole* and has certain recognizable features (Figs. 3.39–3.43). At first external gills are

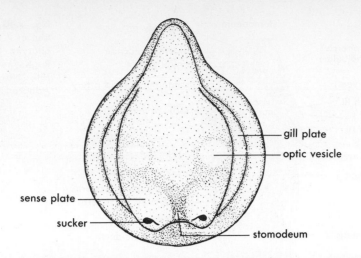

Fig. 3.38 Frontal view of 5-mm. frog embryo. (From R. Rugh, *Laboratory Manual of Vertebrate Embryology*, 5th ed., Burgess, Minneapolis, 1961.)

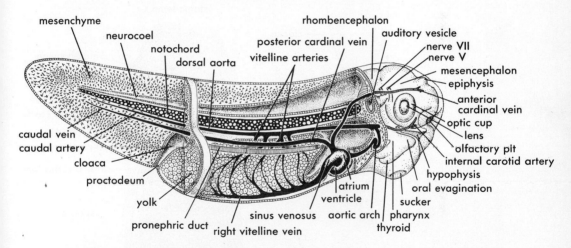

Fig. 3.39 Three-dimensional diagram of 7-mm. tadpole. (From R. Rugh, *The Frog*, McGraw-Hill, New York, 1951. Adapted from Huettner.)

apparent, but soon the *operculum,* a posterior growth of one of the visceral arches, covers them, except for a small pore, the *spiracle,* through which water taken into the mouth escapes to the outside. The tadpole is an actively feeding vegetarian, with horny jaws, rasping *papillae,* and temporary lips. It breathes by gills, digests by a long coiled gut, excretes by primitive (pronephric) kidneys, and moves by active muscular contractions and a whiplashing tail (the superficial cilia, the main organs of movement for the early neurula, are no longer present). Its eyes are functional.

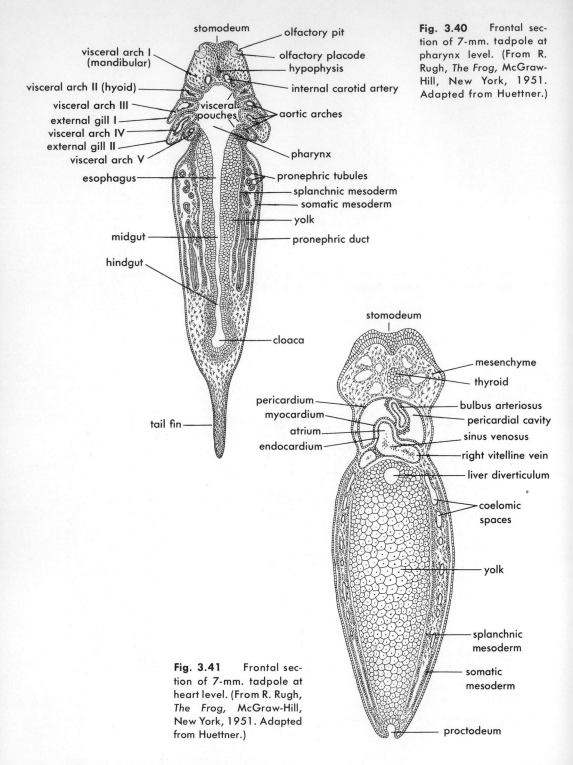

stomodeum
olfactory pit
visceral arch I (mandibular)
olfactory placode
hypophysis
visceral arch II (hyoid)
internal carotid artery
visceral arch III
external gill I
visceral pouches
aortic arches
visceral arch IV
external gill II
visceral arch V
pharynx
esophagus
pronephric tubules
splanchnic mesoderm
somatic mesoderm
yolk
midgut
pronephric duct
hindgut
cloaca
tail fin

Fig. 3.40 Frontal section of 7-mm. tadpole at pharynx level. (From R. Rugh, *The Frog*, McGraw-Hill, New York, 1951. Adapted from Huettner.)

stomodeum
mesenchyme
thyroid
pericardium
bulbus arteriosus
myocardium
pericardial cavity
atrium
sinus venosus
endocardium
right vitelline vein
liver diverticulum
coelomic spaces
yolk
splanchnic mesoderm
somatic mesoderm
proctodeum

Fig. 3.41 Frontal section of 7-mm. tadpole at heart level. (From R. Rugh, *The Frog*, McGraw-Hill, New York, 1951. Adapted from Huettner.)

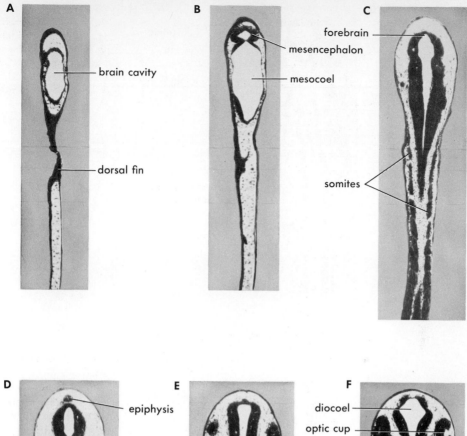

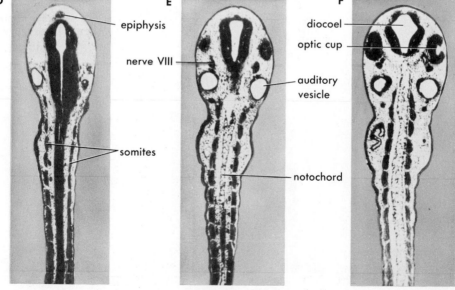

Fig. 3.42 Frontal sections of 7-mm. tadpole.

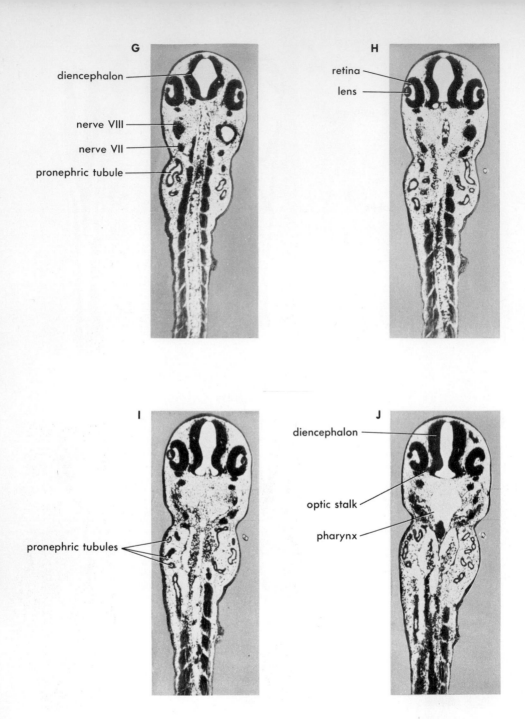

Fig. 3.42 (continued)

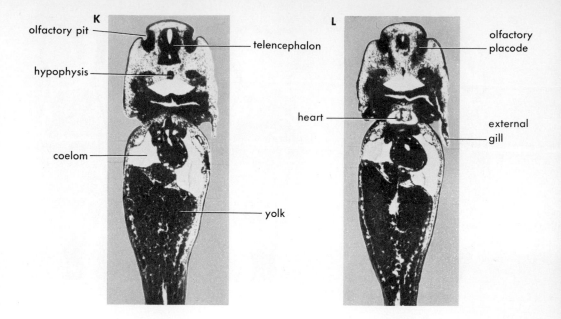

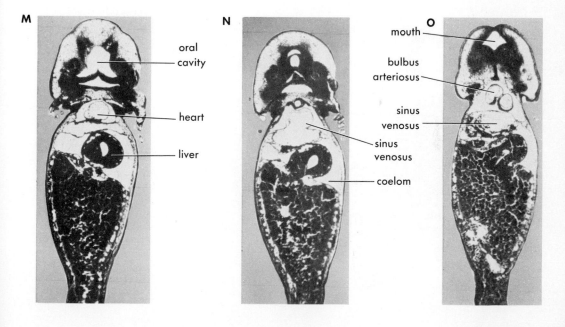

Fig. 3.42 (continued)

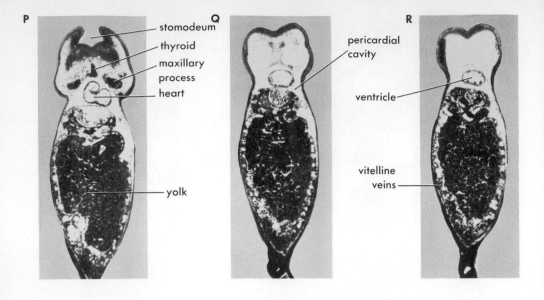

P

stomodeum
thyroid
maxillary
process
heart

yolk

Q

pericardial
cavity

R

ventricle

vitelline
veins

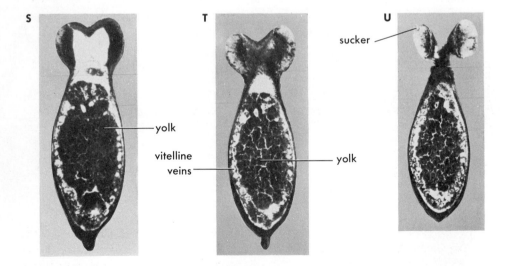

S

yolk

T

vitelline
veins

yolk

U

sucker

Fig. 3.42 (continued)

68 THE FROG: *An Aquatic Vertebrate*

Fig. 3.43   Fully formed tadpole, with external gills and long tail.

Adult

The tadpole is an aquatic organism with persistent embryonic structures that disappear when it emerges from the water to a terrestrial existence (Fig. 3.44). Gills give way to *lungs,* and pronephric kidneys to mesonephric kidneys; the horny jaws are lost, the mouth widens, and the gut shortens; the *gonads* appear; forelimbs and then hind limbs develop as the tail recedes and disappears, so that the animal can crawl out onto the land; and the diet changes from herbivorous to omnivorous, with emphasis on insects and worms. In a period of a few days the embryonic larva becomes an adult frog, albeit a very small and weak one at first. Its departure from an aquatic environment is complete, except that its skin must be kept moist at all times and that it invariably returns to the water to produce its succeeding generation.

Such a *metamorphosis* is typical of those forms making a major adjustment from water to land during development. In *Rana pipiens* metamorphosis occurs in 75 to 90 days from the time of fertilization, so that eggs laid in the spring become terrestrial frogs by fall, able to hibernate and become sexually mature for the next spring.

■ **Derivatives of the Ectoderm**

Nervous system

In the 2.5-mm. embryo there are two adjacent thickenings in the mid-ventral floor of the forebrain, the optic chiasma and, anterior to this, the *torus transversus.* An imaginary line from the depression between these thickenings (the optic recess) to just anterior to the epiphysis (region of the choroid plexus) marks off the telencephalon, the anterior division of the forebrain. Directly opposite the epiphyseal evagination, and below the notochord, is the evagination known as the infundibulum. Above the infundibulum, at the point where the brain bends around the notochord, the brain floor is slightly thickened

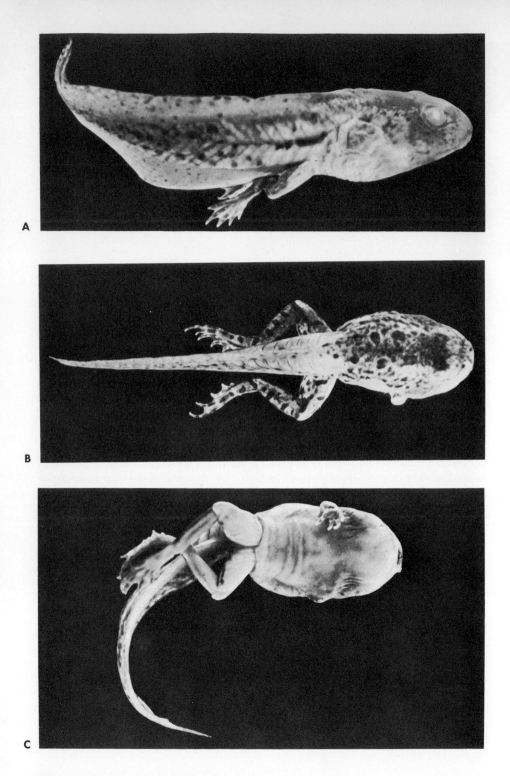

A

B

C

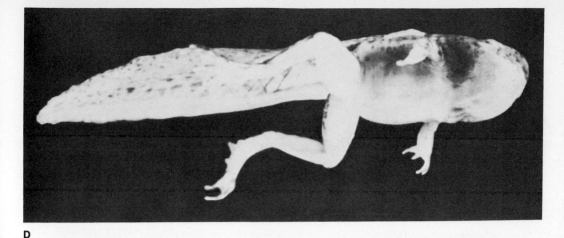

D

Fig. 3.44 Steps in metamorphosis of frog (*Rana pipiens*): A, with paired hind legs only (lateral view); B, with right forelimb bulge (dorsal view); C, with fully formed right forelimb and left forelimb bulge (ventral view); D, with both pairs of legs, just before emergence from water to terrestrial existence (ventral view).

into the *tuberculum posterius*. An imaginary line from the tuberculum dorsally to a position just anterior to an extensive dorsal thickening of the brain marks off the diencephalon, the second division of the forebrain. The mesencephalon is a wedge-shaped portion (in lateral view) having the dorsal thickening as its anterior-posterior limit and tapering ventrally to the tuberculum posterius. Posterior to this region, and entirely dorsal to the notochord, is the rhombencephalon, which extends to the *spinal cord*. In all of these sections a cavity is designated by the suffix -*coel*, as diocoel, rhombocoel, etc., whereas the neural tissue that thickens to form the brain substance carries the suffix -*cephalon*, as telencephalon, mesencephalon, etc. Eventually the central cavities are almost obliterated, to remain only as brain vesicles.

The optic vesicles arise in that part of the forebrain below and lateral to the anterior tip of the notochord. The hypophysis develops close to but below the infundibulum between the pharyngeal endoderm and the brain.

The ultimate disposition of the embryonic nervous system is as follows (Figs. 3.45–3.47):

PROSENCEPHALON (subdivided into telencephalon and diencephalon)

1. The telencephalon forms the paired *cerebral hemispheres*, with the (first and second) *lateral ventricles* as their cavities.

2. The *lamina terminalis*, which represents the anterior end of the original neural tube, remains as a commissure between the cerebral hemispheres.

3. The optic chiasma remains as the region where optic nerve fibers partially cross, to continue into the brain as *optic tracts*.

4. The mid-dorsal wall of the diencephalon anterior to the epiphysis thins

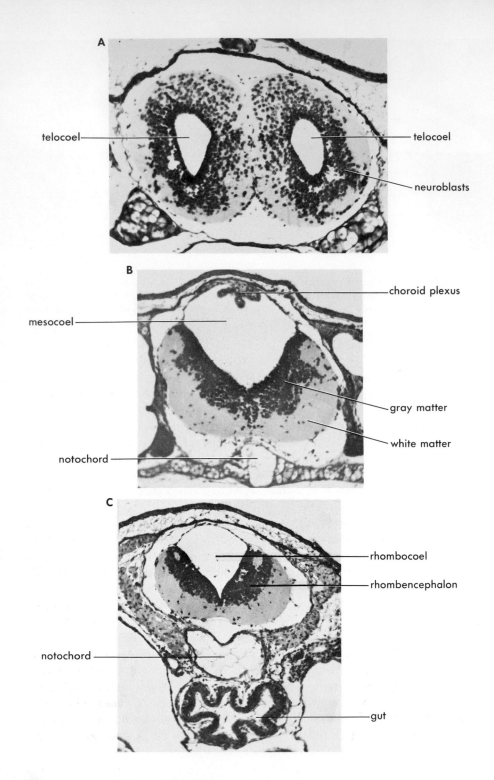

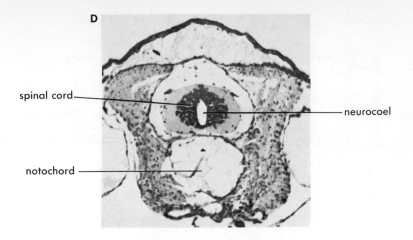

Fig. 3.45 Transverse sections showing neural development in tadpole: A, telencephalon; B, mesencephalon; C, rhombencephalon; D, spinal cord.

and vascularizes, forming the anterior choroid plexus. Its folds project into the diocoel, or *third ventricle*.

5. The *foramen of Monro* opens from the diocoel into each of the lateral ventricles.

6. The hypophysis joins the infundibulum to form the *pituitary* gland (Fig. 3.48).

MESENCEPHALON (not subdivided)

1. The mesocoel becomes the *aqueduct of Sylvius*, connecting the diocoel with the rhombocoel.

2. The ventral and lateral walls thicken to form the *crura cerebri*.

3. The dorsal walls bulge to form the *optic lobes* (not to be confused with the diencephalic optic vesicles).

RHOMBENCEPHALON (not subdivided as in higher forms)

1. The rhombencephalon, continuous with the spinal cord, becomes the *cerebellum,* and the rhombocoel becomes the *fourth ventricle.*

2. The dorsal wall thins out and invaginates to form the *posterior choroid plexus.*

SPINAL CORD.   The spinal cord consists of the neural tube and neurocoel posterior to the brain. As the cells in its walls multiply, it becomes laterally compressed, so that its roof and floor are relatively thin.

The bulk of the neural tissue is neural ectoderm, which gives rise to both *neuroblasts* and supporting *spongioblasts.* At the 7-mm. stage some of the neuroblasts begin to differentiate into *neurons* of the *gray matter* and into more laterally situated neurons known collectively as the *white matter* because of the fatty sheath of *myelin* (Fig. 3.45). The spongioblasts differentiate into *ependymal* and *neuroglial* cells. Ependymal cells line the central canal of the cord.

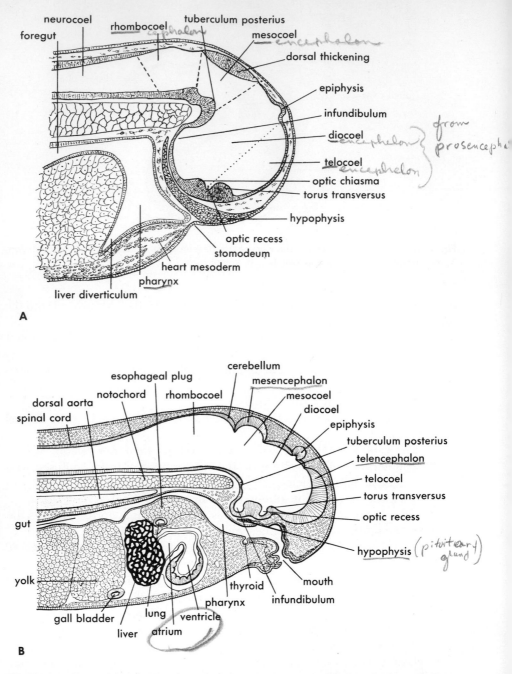

Fig. 3.46   Sagittal sections showing development of brain and anterior structures in tadpole: A, at 7 mm.; B, at 11 mm. (From R. Rugh, *The Frog*, McGraw-Hill, New York, 1951.)

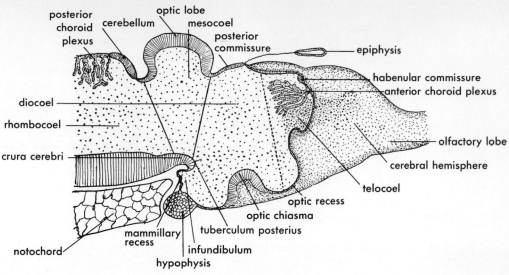

A

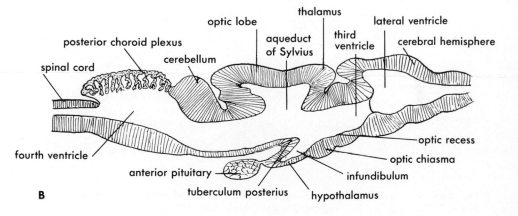

B

Fig. 3.47 Sagittal sections showing late development of tadpole brain: A, premetamorphosis; B, adult. (From R. Rugh, *The Frog*, McGraw-Hill, New York, 1951.)

Derivatives of the Ectoderm **75**

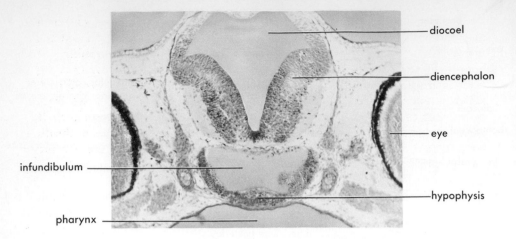

Fig. 3.48   Transverse section showing formation of pituitary gland in frog.

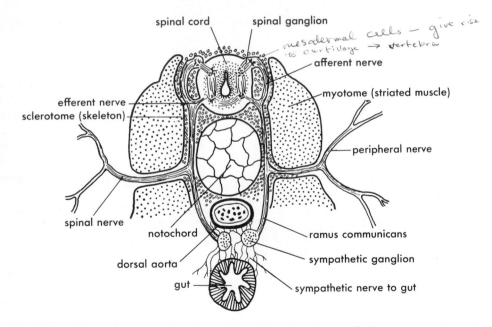

Fig. 3.49   Transverse section showing relation of spinal and sympathetic nervous systems in frog. (From R. Rugh, *The Frog,* McGraw-Hill, New York, 1951.)

NERVES.   Cells are proliferated from the walls of the neural folds into the space between them and the overlying ectoderm, where they cluster into *neural crests.* The crests are continuous at first but rapidly organize into segmented pairs between the paired mesodermal somites. These masses of neural ectoderm give rise to the paired spinal nerves, parts of some of the cranial nerves, the sympathetic system, and some of the pigmentation.

The tadpole, with its elongated tail, has 40 pairs of spinal nerves, of which only the anterior 10 pairs remain in the adult. Unlike some of the cranial nerves, spinal nerves have no connection with placodes. The neuroblast cell bodies of each crest make up a *spinal ganglion* (Fig. 3.49). Fibers growing from each ganglion to the dorsal margin of the spinal cord form a *dorsal root,* which is entirely afferent (sensory) in function. A *ventral root* arises from neuroblasts in the ventral part of the cord itself and is efferent (motor). It joins some fibers from the dorsal crest in a common connective tissue sheath for a short distance and then goes its separate way. The afferent tracts bring impulses from the skin and sense organs while the efferent tracts go to the muscles.

The sympathetic system develops from cells that migrate ventrally from the neural crest to each side of the *dorsal aorta,* where they give rise to the *sympathetic ganglia* (Fig. 3.49), which comprise the *sympathetic trunk.* Fibers extending from a sympathetic ganglion to a spinal ganglion form a *ramus communicans.* Other fibers extend from the sympathetic ganglia to the viscera.

The cranial nerves also arise in pairs, but not exclusively from cranial crests (Table 3.2 and Fig. 3.50). In some instances their derivation is associated

Table 3.2   Cranial nerves

NERVE		ORIGIN	DESTINATION	TYPE
I	olfactory	telencephalon	olfactory organ	afferent
II	optic	diencephalon	retina	afferent
III	oculomotor	mesencephalon	superior rectus, inferior rectus, median rectus, and inferior oblique eye muscles	efferent
IV	trochlear	mesencephalon	superior oblique eye muscle	efferent
V	trigeminal	rhombencephalon and first crest segment and placode (semilunar)	ophthalmic, maxillary, and mandibular regions	mixed
VI	abducens	rhombencephalon (neuroblasts of medulla)	lateral rectus eye muscle	efferent
VII	facial	rhombencephalon and second crest segment and placode	hyomandibular region	mixed
VIII	acoustic	rhombencephalon and second crest segment and placode	inner ear	afferent
IX	glossopharyngeal	rhombencephalon and third crest segment and placode	visceral arches II and III, mouth, tongue, and pharynx	mixed
X	vagus	rhombencephalon and fourth crest segment and placode	lateral line and visceral arches IV and V	mixed
			viscera	efferent

with *placodes,* ectodermal patches near the surface of the head that may be contiguous with the crest segments but lie between them and the surface. It has been suggested that the placodes are vestigial sense organs. In a 4-somite embryo sectioned frontally, the following nerves may be identified: *trigeminal* (V), from the first segment and placode; *acousticofacial* (VII and VIII), from the second segment and placode; *glossopharyngeal* (IX), from the third segment and placode; *vagus* (pneumogastric) (X), from the fourth segment and placode.

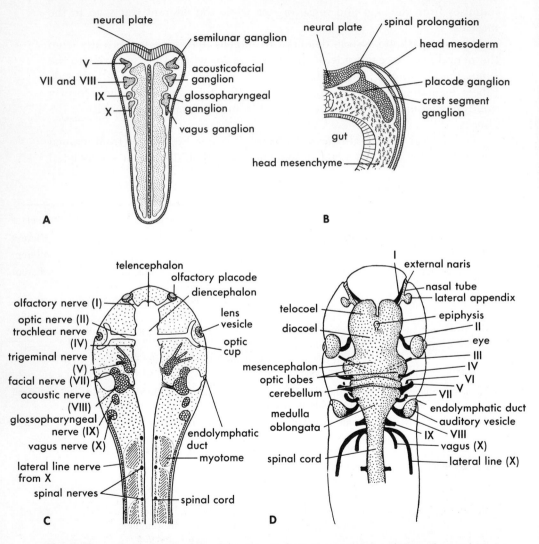

Fig. 3.50   Development of cranial nerves in frog: A, origins; B, relation of neural crest segment and placode; C, relations of sense organs to cranial ganglia; D, brain, sense organs, and cranial nerves at 12 mm. (From R. Rugh, *The Frog,* McGraw-Hill, New York, 1951.)

Eyes

The optic vesicle, an outpocketing of the floor of the diencephalon toward the lateral head ectoderm, is the first indication of eye development. The bulge is not spherical; the dorsal side grows fastest and makes contact with the head ectoderm. The material of the optic vesicle then invaginates to form a double-layered *optic cup*. The head ectoderm proliferates off into the optic cup, forming a *lens placode*, which becomes a *lens vesicle* and finally a spherical *lens* with only a remnant of its original cavity (Figs. 3.51, 3.52). In the meantime, the head ectoderm closes over.

The optic cup connects with the rest of the brain ectoderm by means of a ventral tubular stalk. This *optic stalk* has in it an inverted, elongated groove known as the *choroid fissure*. Through this groove nerves and blood vessels pass into the optic cup and thence to the *sensory layer* of the *retina*, which lines the cup. The outer layer of the cup is the *pigmented layer* of the retina. The choroid fissure closes to form the *choroid knot*, from which the *iris* arises.

Obviously the sensory portions of the eye derive from ectoderm. However, the mesoderm also contributes eye components. Specifically the origins of the eye are as follows:

ECTODERM.   Sensory layer of retina (consists of rods and cones as well as neuroblasts) and nonsensory pigmented layer of retina; optic nerve; lens; cornea, outer portion.

MESODERM.   Choroid; sclera (cartilaginous); aqueous and vitreous humor (may come in part from ectoderm); cornea, vascular and connective tissue portions; eye muscles.

Ears

The frog has no real outer ear, merely a *tympanic membrane* (ear drum) exposed directly on the lateral head surface.

The middle ear consists of the *tubotympanic cavity*, derived from the pharynx as a remnant of the first visceral pouch, between the mandibular and hyoid arches. This cavity, vestigial in the frog, becomes the *auditory (Eustachian) tube*. The *columella (plectrum)* is a rodlike cartilaginous connection between the inner *auditory capsule* and the tympanic membrane across the *tympanic cavity*. The inner end of the columella plugs the opening of the *fenestra ovalis*, and the outer end is associated with the *tympanic ring*, a cartilaginous ring around the tympanic membrane derived from the *palatoquadrate* bone.

The inner ear or *membranous labyrinth* arises from an invagination of the *auditory placode* that closes over to form a very small sac, the *auditory vesicle (otocyst)*, about 0.2 mm. in diameter, on the side of the rhombencephalon (Fig. 3.53). The *endolymphatic duct*, a structure of significance only in aquatic forms, connects the vesicle to the surface for a short time. The auditory vesicle divides into chambers, with septa, until eventually there are an upper, inner

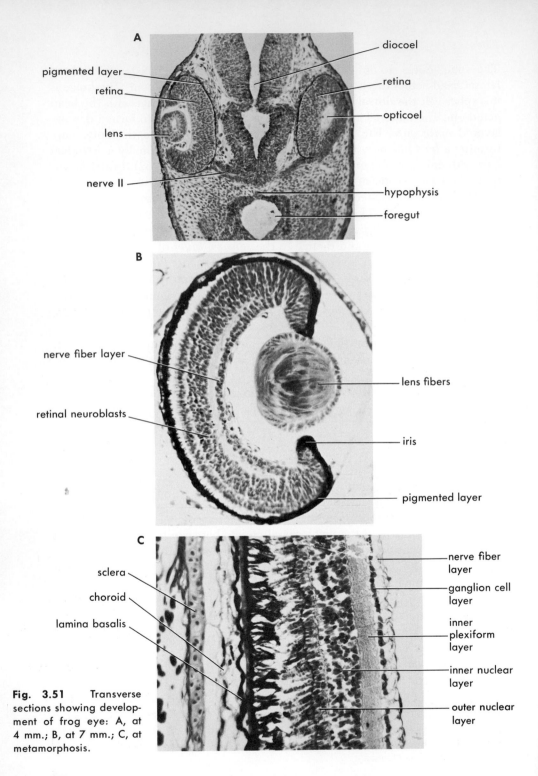

Fig. 3.51 Transverse sections showing development of frog eye: A, at 4 mm.; B, at 7 mm.; C, at metamorphosis.

A
- pigmented layer
- retina
- lens
- nerve II
- diocoel
- retina
- opticoel
- hypophysis
- foregut

B
- nerve fiber layer
- retinal neuroblasts
- lens fibers
- iris
- pigmented layer

C
- sclera
- choroid
- lamina basalis
- nerve fiber layer
- ganglion cell layer
- inner plexiform layer
- inner nuclear layer
- outer nuclear layer

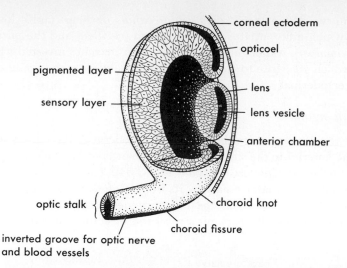

Fig. 3.52 Diagram of eye development in frog. (From R. Rugh, *The Frog*, McGraw-Hill, New York, 1951.)

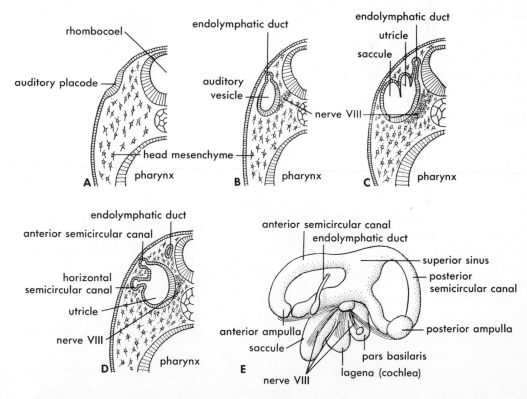

Fig. 3.53 Development of frog ear. (From R. Rugh, *The Frog*, McGraw-Hill, New York, 1951. Adapted from Krause.)

utricle (in which the three *semicircular canals* develop) and a lower, outer *saccule,* which differentiates into the *lagena* (*cochlea*) and the *pars basilaris* (*basilar chamber*). Although all of the inner ear becomes invested with mesenchyme, which gives rise to cartilage and bony labyrinth, the lining epithelium remains ectodermal.

Olfactory organs

At about the 2½-mm. stage the superficial ectoderm of the sense plate slightly above and anterior to the stomodeum disappears, and the underlying ectoderm forms a thickened *olfactory placode* (Fig. 3.54). This invaginates to form an *olfactory pit,* which later enlarges. Its lining ectoderm becomes the sensory *organ of Jacobson,* to which the olfactory nerve proceeds from the telencephalon. From the olfactory pit a solid rod of ectoderm grows toward and

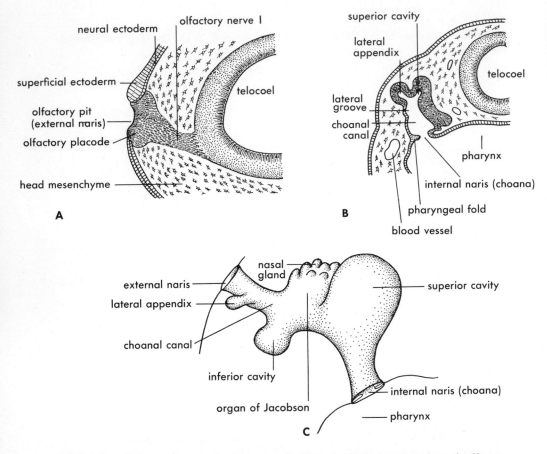

Fig. 3.54 Development of olfactory organ in frog: A, sagittal section through olfactory placode and nerve; B, transverse section through choanal canal; C, embryonic olfactory organ. (From R. Rugh, *The Frog,* McGraw-Hill, New York, 1951.)

joins the pharynx, eventually becoming a tube connecting the external and internal *nares (choana).*

Lateral line organs

At the 4-mm. stage the vagus nerve joins an elongated placode lying laterally just beneath the epidermis and extending into the tail. Clusters of sensory cells appear at intervals along this cord, grow to the surface, and develop cilia, thus becoming sensitive to vibrations in the water (Fig. 3.55). These lateral line organs are transient in aquatic forms and are lost in the metamorphosis from tadpole to frog.

■ Derivatives of the Endoderm

In the mouth the border between ectoderm and endoderm is difficult to define, for the *oral membrane* or *plate,* which separates the two germ layers, breaks through after hatching to form the mouth opening and make them contiguous. The lateral margins of the mouth are the outer edges of the mandibular arches. The *dorsal lip* has three medially placed but incomplete rows of teeth, really cornified ectoderm, which are periodically replaced, and

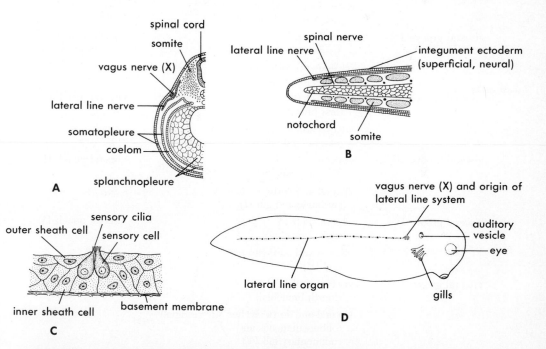

Fig. 3.55   Development of lateral line organ in frog: A, transverse section at 4 mm.; B, frontal section at 4 mm.; C, section through lateral line organ at 12 mm.; D, tadpole. (From R. Rugh, *The Frog,* McGraw-Hill, New York, 1951.)

the *ventral lip* has four rows. These horny teeth and the larval jaws are lost at metamorphosis. The adult jaws are derived largely from the mandibular arches. Permanent teeth appear on the upper jaw only and are more advanced than their predecessors. The *tongue* arises from the floor of the mouth by a proliferation of cells and is supplied with mesodermally derived muscles and blood vessels.

Table 3.3 lists the major derivatives of the pharynx, in anterior to posterior order. A frontal section through the pharynx (Fig. 3.56) reveals great differences in the degree of development of the visceral grooves, arches, and clefts. The arch occurring between grooves (or clefts) III and IV is by far the largest. It gives rise not only to the large gill, II, but also to the *systemic* (aortic) *arch* that carries the bulk of the blood to the body. Of the five visceral pouches and grooves that join to form clefts after hatching, the first (*hyomandibular*) never functions in respiration, remaining instead as the auditory tube. The arches

Table 3.3   Pharyngeal derivatives

ECTODERM	MESODERM	ENDODERM
	visceral and aortic arches I (maxillary and mandibular)	
visceral groove I	visceral cleft I (hyomandibular)	visceral pouch I (auditory tube)
	visceral and aortic arches II (hyoid; operculum)	
visceral groove II	visceral cleft II (first branchial)	visceral pouch II
	visceral and aortic arches III (carotid and gill I)	
visceral groove III	visceral cleft III (second branchial)	visceral pouch III
	visceral and aortic arches IV (systemic and gill II)	
visceral groove IV	visceral cleft IV (third branchial)	visceral pouch IV
	visceral and aortic arches V (gill III)	
visceral groove V	visceral cleft V (fourth branchial)	visceral pouch V
	visceral and aortic arches VI (vestigial) (pulmocutaneous and rudimentary gill IV)	
visceral groove VI (vestigial)	visceral cleft VI (vestigial) (fifth branchial)	visceral pouch VI

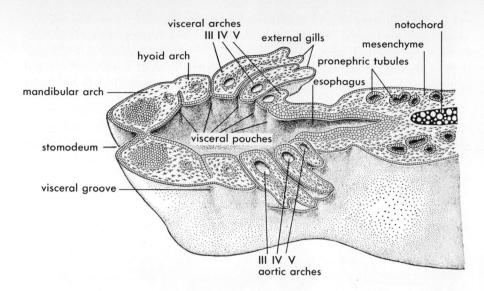

Fig. 3.56 Three-dimensional diagram of external gill stage in tadpole. (From R. Rugh, *The Frog*, McGraw-Hill, New York, 1951. Adapted from Huettner.)

between each pair of visceral clefts carry nerves and blood vessels. Water going into the mouth and out through the visceral clefts passes near these blood vessels (*aortic arches*) so that gaseous exchange may take place. The aortic arches assume great importance during the temporary life of the external gills, since they transport oxygen from the gills to the body.

The development of the external gills (Fig. 3.57) begins shortly before hatching. Although they are covered with ectoderm, they are actually projections of mesoderm, principally from the dorsal part of the third, fourth, and fifth visceral arches; the small gill from the sixth visceral arch is nonfunctional. The operculum grows backward from the hyoid arch to enclose the external gills in the *opercular chamber* (Fig. 3.58). This closes completely on the right side but remains open until metamorphosis at the posterior margin on the left side, in the spiracle. The external gills then degenerate, as *internal gills* arise (Figs. 3.58, 3.59). The two lateral opercular chambers are linked beneath the pharynx by the *opercular groove*. Water taken into the mouth passes over the gills on the right side, through the opercular groove, over the gills on the left side, and out through the spiracle. Serrated papillae, called *gill rakers* or filtering organs, develop between the pharynx and the opercular chamber on each side to filter out detritus in the water. *Velar plates*, folds of the pharyngeal wall, further separate the pharynx from both the gill rakers and the gills. At metamorphosis the gills and their accessories are completely absorbed.

The paired *thymus* glands arise from the dorsal ends of the first and second visceral pouches and are therefore endodermal. Since the dorsal part of the first pouch degenerates, the thymus comes principally from the second. After metamorphosis the thymus glands migrate toward the surface of the head and take up positions posterior to the auditory capsules and jaw articulations.

The *carotid* glands proliferate from the ventral ends of the second visceral pouches at the 10-mm. stage. The *epithelioid (postbranchial) bodies* arise

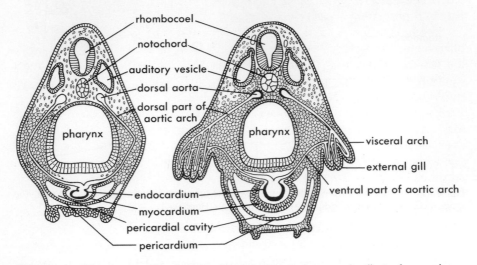

Fig. 3.57 Transverse sections showing development of external gills in frog embryo. (From R. Rugh, *The Frog*, McGraw-Hill, New York, 1951.)

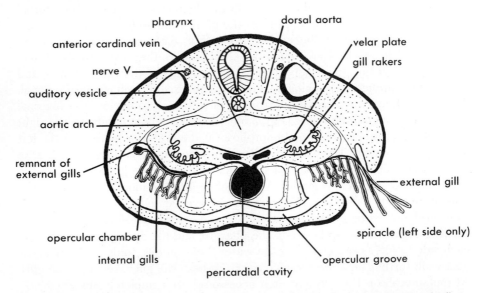

Fig. 3.58 Transverse section showing relation of pharynx to internal and external gills in 10-mm. tadpole. (From R. Rugh, *The Frog*, McGraw-Hill, New York, 1951.)

from the ventral ends of the third and fourth pouches and possibly have an endocrine function. The *ultimobranchial (suprapericardial) bodies* develop from the sixth pouches (vestigial).

The *thyroid,* an unpaired gland, begins to form by the 3-mm. stage and appears at the 10-mm. stage as a solid endodermal evagination in the floor of the pharynx, just posterior to the level of the first visceral pouch (Figs. 3.60A, 3.61). This gland assumes major importance in the critical changes that anticipate and promote metamorphosis.

The lungs arise as solid proliferations of endoderm from the floor of the pharynx just posterior to the heart region. The *glottis* connects the pharynx to the tubular *larynx* and thence to the bifurcated lung buds. These do not develop until just before metamorphosis, at which time the lungs take over respiration from the gills.

The liver, the next posterior organ derivative of the endoderm, arises very early as a ventromesial evagination of the pharyngeal floor to extend beneath the yolk mass (Fig. 3.60B,C). The most posterior diverticulum becomes the *gall bladder,* with a tubular connection (the *bile duct*) to the foregut. The *pancreas* begins as two endodermal outgrowths from the foregut, one posterior to the bile duct and one from the roof; the two join around the gut, retaining the *pancreatic duct* as the connection with the foregut. The *esophagus,* which extends from the glottis to the bile duct, differentiates into two parts, esophagus and *stomach,* just before metamorphosis. The stomach becomes very muscular and shifts to a transverse position at metamorphosis.

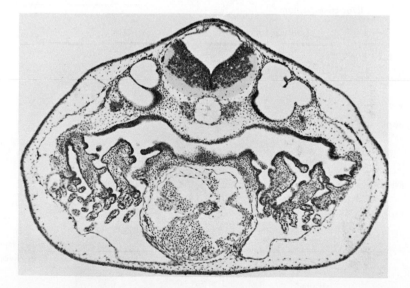

Fig. 3.59   Transverse section showing internal gill system in 11-mm. tadpole. (From General Biological Supply House, Chicago, Ill.)

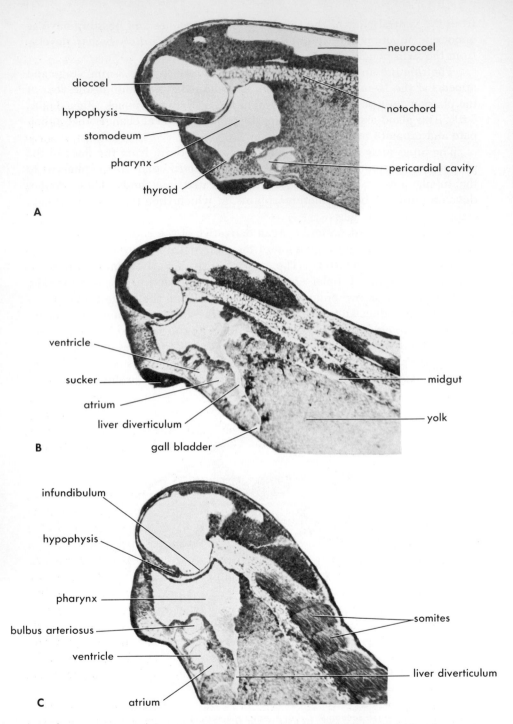

A

neurocoel

diocoel

hypophysis

notochord

stomodeum

pharynx

pericardial cavity

thyroid

B

ventricle

sucker

atrium

liver diverticulum

gall bladder

midgut

yolk

C

infundibulum

hypophysis

pharynx

bulbus arteriosus

ventricle

atrium

somites

liver diverticulum

Fig. 3.60   Sagittal sections showing derivatives of pharynx in 10-mm. tadpole.

The midgut lies directly above the yolk mass up to hatching time (Fig. 3.60B). Its roof and sides are generally only one cell in thickness. Elongation occurs at hatching, resulting in a long spiral gut in the tadpole, associated with its vegetarian diet. This elongated *intestine* is about nine times the body length, but at metamorphosis it is reduced to one third its original length. Above the midgut, between the notochord and the dorsal aorta, the *subnotochordal rod (hypochord)* of three or four cells appears at the 8-somite stage and disappears at the 13-mm. stage. It is presumably derived from the dorsal wall of the midgut. Its function is unknown.

The hindgut, between the yolk mass and the posterior body wall, gives rise to the *rectum,* a slight dilatation near the proctodeum; the anus, which is ventral to the blastopore and partially lined with ectoderm; the cloaca, an enlargement of the proctodeal region that later receives the urogenital ducts; the *urinary bladder,* which develops at metamorphosis as a ventroanterior outgrowth of the cloaca (having no direct connection with the urogenital ducts); and the *tail (postanal) gut,* a purely embryonic backward growth of the hindgut into the tail, that carries with it both the notochord and the neurenteric canal.

■ Derivatives of the Mesoderm

The mesoderm appears first at the time of gastrulation, as mesenchyme from the gray crescent (*peristomial*). The anterior ventrolateral mesoderm and some of the ventral mesoderm arise by delamination from yolk cells (*gastral*). Whatever its origin, its cells are indistinguishable. Mesenchyme is abundant and substantial and tends to fill the embryonic regions between the ectoderm and the endoderm.

The somites are the segmented plates of mesoderm on either side of the notochord from anterior to posterior (Fig. 3.60C). The most anterior pair is just posterior to the auditory vesicles, and the most posterior pair is in the extremity of the temporary tail. A total of 45 pairs develops, 13 in the body and 32 in the tail. Those in the tail are lost at metamorphosis; the first 2 in the body are incorporated into the occipital region of the head; and the 11 that remain give rise to skeleton, muscles, and dermis. At the 5-mm. stage longitudinally arranged muscle *fibrillae* appear in the inner portion (myotome) of each somite. On the outer edge is the *dermatome (cutis plate),* the precursor of the connective tissue of the skin and the muscles of the body wall and limbs. Between the myotome and the dermatome a temporary cavity, the *myocoel,* develops. Loose cells (*sclerotome*) proliferated from the somite sheath the notochord and neural tube, eventually becoming bone and cartilage.

Ventral to the somites, and of the same sheet of mesoderm, is the lateral plate. The coelom, the split in this plate that forms an outer somatic layer and an inner splanchnic layer, never becomes continuous dorsally to the midgut.

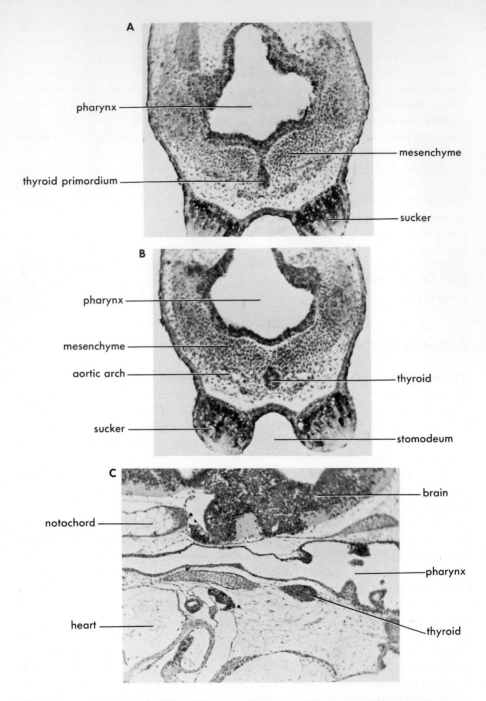

Fig. 3.61 Development of thyroid gland in frog: A, transverse section through pharynx at 3 mm.; B, transverse section through pharynx at 4 mm., showing detached thyroid; C, sagittal section through head at 11 mm.; D, section of thyroid shortly after metamorphosis.

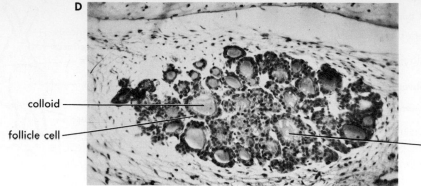

colloid

follicle cell

vacuoles
in colloid
(secreting)

Fig. 3.61 (continued)

Instead, in this region a mesodermal membrane, the *dorsal mesentery,* supports the gut. The coelom does become continuous ventrally around the yolk and gut, where the splanchnic layer eventually forms the intestinal muscles.

The *septum transversum* partitions the coelom from the pericardial cavity. The *mesocardia,* mesenteries formed by the junction of the myocardium with the somatic mesoderm mid-ventrally and with the splanchnic mesoderm mid-dorsally, suspend the heart in its cavity. Although the *ventral* mesocardium ruptures, the *dorsal* mesocardium persists as a suspensory organ. Frontal sections or reconstructed longitudinal views (Fig. 3.62) show the heart to be a single elongated tube anchored posteriorly at the *sinus venosus* and anteriorly at the *bulbus arteriosus.* Because it grows rapidly within a confined space, it curves and then folds until its original anterior region becomes the posterior and ventral muscular *ventricle* (single in the frog) and its original posterior *atrium* becomes the anterior and dorsal right and left *atria.* These changes occur early in larval development; the related vascular changes necessary for metamorphosis occur much later.

The vascular system (Figs. 3.63, 3.64) develops from *blood islands,* which arise in scattered mesenchyme and splanchnic mesoderm. The islands organize into blood vessels, some of the original cells becoming the earliest corpuscles.

The arterial system (Figs. 3.65, 3.66) consists first of the large paired dorsal aortae dorsal to the pharynx, which fuse into a single large dorsal aorta more posteriorly. This receives arterial blood from aortic arches III to VI, each of which connects the *ventral aortae,* short anterior extensions of the *truncus arteriosus,* to the dorsal aortae through a visceral arch. As each gill develops, the related aortic arch loops into it for aeration of the blood (Fig. 3.67). Visceral arch VI, which develops only a rudimentary external gill, supports only internal and vestigial gill circulation. With the loss of external gills the circulation is rerouted through direct anastomoses between the efferent (ventral aortae) and afferent (dorsal aortae) vessels. At metamorphosis the original aortic arches function as follows (Fig. 3.68): I and II are lost with the

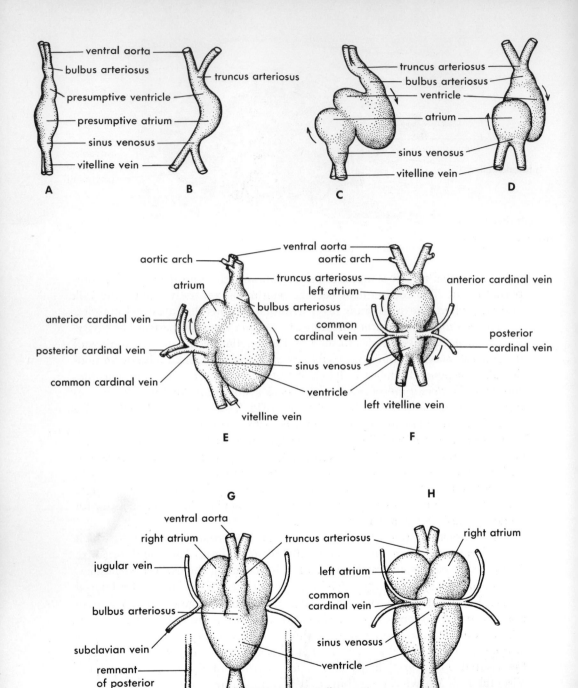

Fig. 3.62 Development of frog heart: A, right side view; B, dorsal view; C, right side view; D, dorsal view; E, right side view; F, dorsal view; G, ventral view; H, dorsal view. (From R. Rugh, *The Frog*, McGraw-Hill, New York, 1951.)

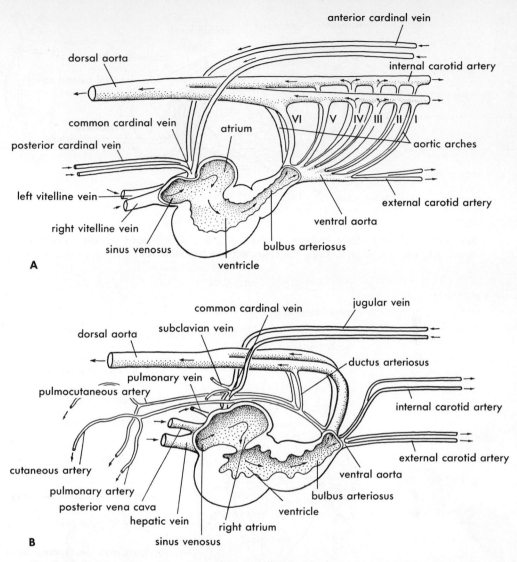

Fig. 3.63 Lateral views showing development of blood vascular system in frog embryo. A, early embryo; B, late embryo. (From R. Rugh, *The Frog*, McGraw-Hill, New York, 1951.)

gills, but extensions of the ventral and dorsal aortae, which originally incorporated parts of them, join III; III, with parts of I and II, becomes the *internal* (from the dorsal aortae) and *external* (from the ventral aortae) *carotid arteries* to the head, which give off branches to the carotid gland and to the tongue; IV becomes the systemic arch, providing arterial blood for the dorsal aorta, which feeds the *vertebral, subclavian,* and *coeliac arteries* and all of the major body parts; V disappears completely; and VI becomes the *pulmocutaneous artery* to the lungs and skin.

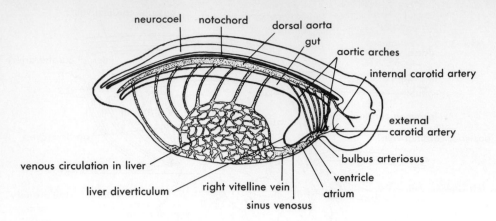

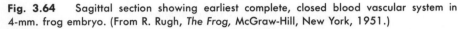

Fig. 3.64 Sagittal section showing earliest complete, closed blood vascular system in 4-mm. frog embryo. (From R. Rugh, *The Frog*, McGraw-Hill, New York, 1951.)

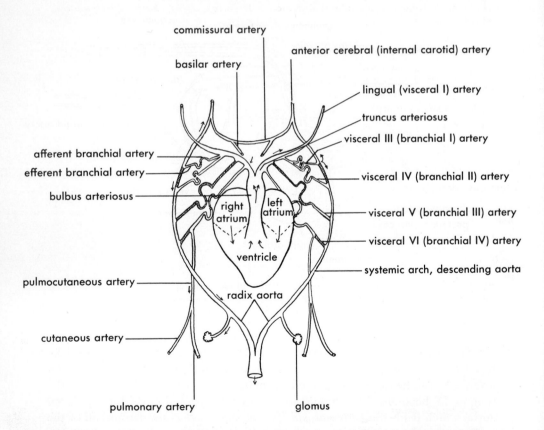

Fig. 3.65 Ventral view of arterial system of tadpole. (From R. Rugh, *The Frog*, McGraw-Hill, New York, 1951.)

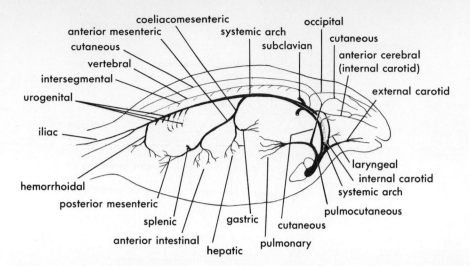

Fig. 3.66 Sagittal section showing arterial system of tadpole just before metamorphosis. (From R. Rugh, *Laboratory Manual of Vertebrate Embryology*, 5th ed., Burgess, Minneapolis, 1961.)

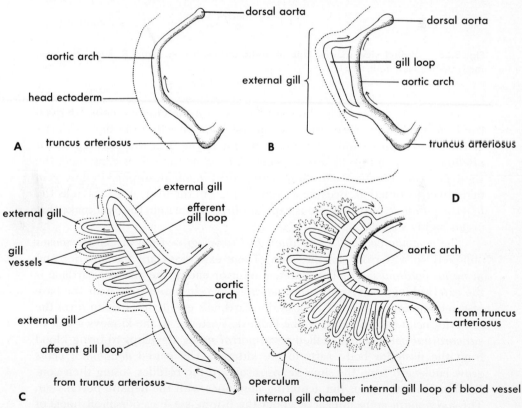

Fig. 3.67 External and internal gill circulations in tadpole. (Adapted from Maurer.)

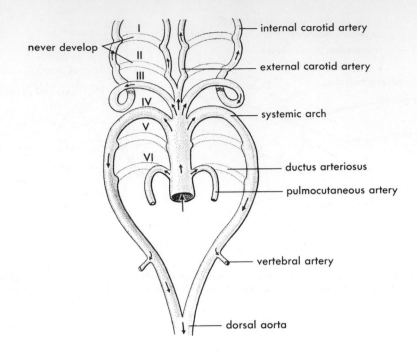

Fig. 3.68   Ventral view showing fate of aortic arches in frog. (From R. Rugh, *The Frog*, McGraw-Hill, New York, 1951.)

The venous system (Fig. 3.69) originates with the *vitelline veins,* derived from the splanchnic mesoderm to carry nutrition directly from the yolk mass to the sinus venosus and the heart. Anterior to the liver the paired *anterior vitelline veins* join to form a single *hepatic vein.* As the yolk is consumed, the right *posterior vitelline vein* disappears, and the left posterior vitelline vein takes over its function. Because it carries blood to the liver, it is known as the *hepatic portal vein.* Its numerous capillary branches within the liver make that organ highly vascular.

The *common cardinal veins (ducts of Cuvier)* grow from the sinus venosus obliquely in a dorsolateral direction. Their extensions are the *anterior* and *posterior cardinal veins.* The extreme anterior end of the anterior cardinal is the *external jugular vein;* the *internal jugular vein* issues from near the base of the common cardinal. The posterior cardinals eventually fuse to form the *posterior vena cava* anterior to the kidneys. Posterior to the kidneys a pair of *subcardinal veins,* finally called *renal portal veins,* develops to bring blood from the posterior body parts to the kidneys. The paired *abdominal veins* grow backward from the sinus venosus toward the bladder, losing their connections with the sinus but acquiring new ones with the hepatic portal vein. The *pulmonary veins* appear at about the 6-mm. stage as dorsal offshoots of the sinus venosus but later open into the left atrium.

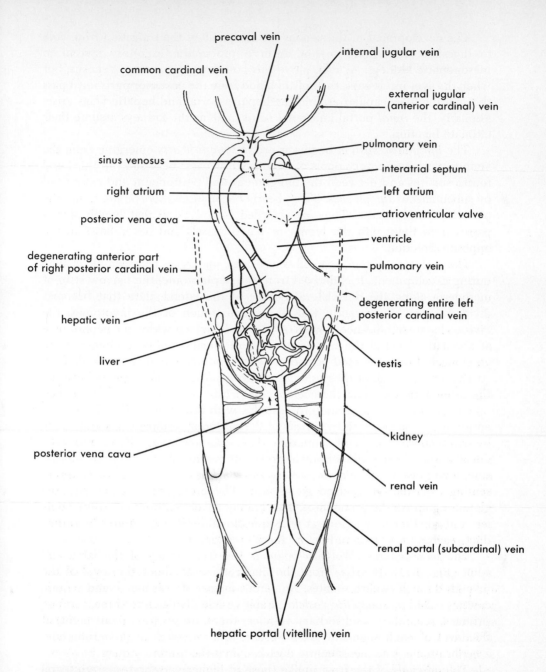

precaval vein

internal jugular vein

common cardinal vein

external jugular (anterior cardinal) vein

sinus venosus

pulmonary vein

interatrial septum

right atrium

left atrium

posterior vena cava

atrioventricular valve

degenerating anterior part of right posterior cardinal vein

ventricle

pulmonary vein

hepatic vein

degenerating entire left posterior cardinal vein

liver

testis

posterior vena cava

kidney

renal vein

renal portal (subcardinal) vein

hepatic portal (vitelline) vein

Fig. 3.69 Ventral view of venous system of tadpole. (From R. Rugh, *The Frog*, McGraw-Hill, New York, 1951.)

The development of the venous system parallels the transition from yolk to digestive tract nutrition and from a pronephric excretory system to mesonephric kidneys. At first, all vessels converge at the sinus venosus, but when the liver intervenes, the bulk of blood from the posterior parts must pass through the liver capillaries, and the hepatic portal and hepatic veins arise. Similarly, the *renal* portal and *renal veins* arise as the kidneys assume their ultimate function.

The *lymphatic system* begins as crude *lymph hearts* emerging from the venous plexi (temporary pools of venous capillaries) between the third and fourth somites and between the integument and peritoneum and connected by subcutaneous *lymph sacs*. These hearts become the *thoracic ducts* and the posterior lymph hearts. They are guarded by valves so that lymph always passes from them into the lymph or blood vessels and never flows in the opposite direction.

The excretory system, as in all vertebrates, undergoes considerable change during development. It is derived from the nephrotome, the narrow strip of mesoderm along the dorsolateral border of the lateral plate that becomes divided by or concurrently with the segmentation of the myotomes; the division has no significance. Spaces (*nephrocoels*) appear within the nephrotome at about the level of the second, third, and fourth somites, joining to form an elongated tube directed posteriorly as the *pronephric, or segmental, duct.* At the level of each of these somites, a *pronephric tubule* appears between the pronephric duct and the coelom. *Nephrostomes,* ciliated, funnel-shaped openings, connect the pronephric tubules with the coelom (Fig. 3.70). The entire mass is surrounded by sinuses of the posterior cardinal veins and finally by a pronephric capsule of connective tissue (also from mesoderm). From the dorsal aorta on each side a branch grows out toward the nephrotome on that side, giving rise to the *glomus,* a very vascular mass of tissue possibly representing a partially organized *glomerulus.* The pronephric tubules plus the glomus comprise the pronephros. This kidney never acquires an external outlet, and whether it functions at all is questionable. It degenerates before its duct reaches the cloaca and before the 20-mm. stage.

The *mesonephros* (*Wolffian body*) is the true kidney of the larva and adult (Fig. 3.71). It arises from the nephrotome at about the level of the seventh through twelfth somites. Numerous masses of cells merge and acquire cavities called *mesonephric vesicles.* Each vesicle divides into three, forming primary, secondary, and tertiary vesicles; there are several (about eight) at the level of each segment. Each vesicle then acquires a glomerulus and a nephrostome. The mesonephric duct becomes the excretory duct.

The *adrenals* of the frog, unlike those of higher vertebrates, are integral parts of the mesonephric kidneys. The *cortical* substance, which appears first at the 12-mm. stage, is a mass of anastomosing cells penetrated by blood capillaries. The *medullary* substance consists of pigmented cells from the sympathetic ganglia (ectoderm); these cells are dispersed among the cortical cells.

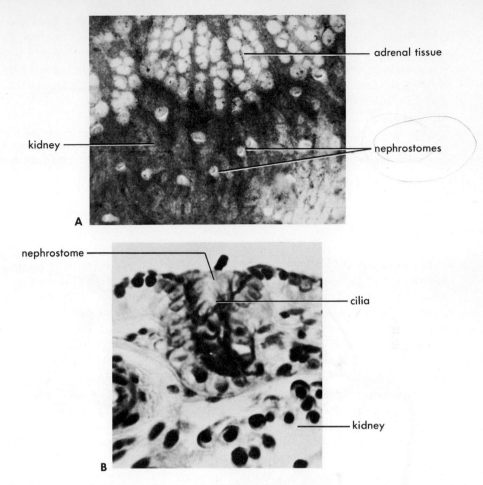

kidney

adrenal tissue

nephrostomes

nephrostome

cilia

kidney

A

B

Fig. 3.70   Nephrostomes in frog mesonephros: A, surface view; B, section of surface.

The *gonad* primordia come from the *sex cell ridge* directly dorsal to the gut. At about the time of hatching, the cluster of cells divides, and each half moves ventrolaterally to the region of the cardinal veins to form a *genital ridge*, which projects into the coelom. The genital ridge has a central cavity and is covered by peritoneum. This early gonad is indistinguishable as to sex; differentiation does not occur until after metamorphosis (see the section on reproductive systems).

The reproductive accessories largely represent vestiges of earlier development. In the male the vas deferens (and ureter) and the seminal vesicles arise from the mesonephric duct; the vasa efferentia are modified kidney tubules; and the *Müllerian duct*, nonfunctional in the male but homologous to the oviduct of the female, remains as a vestige of the pronephric duct. In the female the ureter is exclusively excretory, as the mesonephric duct. The oviduct is the

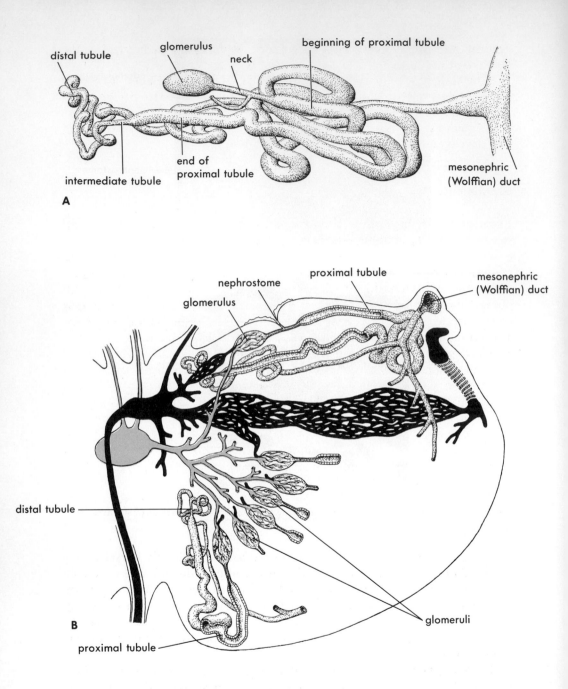

Fig. 3.71   Renal circulation in frog: A, enlargement of mesonephric tubule; B, mesonephros, with black areas representing veins and shaded areas representing arteries. (From A. K. Solomon, *Sci. American*, **207**, 101 (1962).)

original pronephric duct, with its anterior nephrostomes constituting the ciliated ostium tubae.

The skeletal system is a late larval or early adult development. There are ten skeletal segments, consisting of nine real vertebrae, derived from sclerotomal masses, and the *urostyle,* derived from the two last somites. The skull, largely cartilaginous in the larva, becomes partially bony in the adult. Skeletal parts also develop in the girdle and limbs.

▪ Experimental Embryology

Experimental embryology is almost as old as morphological embryology and is essentially a study of the reactions of developing organisms to interruptions or alterations in the various developmental processes. When one immerses an embryo in a foreign environment, extirpates a part, or exchanges parts either within the embryo itself or with another embryo, he creates a condition for observing the reactions of a system to external disturbance. Such reactions have intrinsic interest, and they may also explain the origins of the congenital anomalies and teratologies that occur in all animal phyla. The remarkable fact is that, despite tremendous variations in the environment and all the disturbances in nature, so many embryos are able to survive and develop into organisms that fit within certain limits of "normality."

The basis for sound scientific experimentation is a thorough knowledge of the normal, control situation. Those who have acquired this knowledge of amphibian development are prepared to investigate the effects of altering the development by various means. The amphibian embryo, being a cold-blooded form not requiring constant temperature, is ideal for initial experimentation.

Areas of possible interest to the student of experimental embryology follow. For detailed information, he should refer to encyclopedias and laboratory manuals on the subject.

Availability of material

Since 1928, when it was found that most amphibia could be induced by hormone treatment to lay their eggs and shed their sperm at almost any season of the year, abundant frog, toad, and salamander eggs and embryos have been available for experimentation under controlled laboratory conditions.

Experiments with the very early embryo

The effect of aging of the egg prior to fertilization; the effect of diluted sperm, foreign sperm, excess sperm, or aged sperm; the effect of alterations of the electrolytes in the environment, such as sodium and potassium, as well as of sugar and other substances; the effect of temperature; the effect of space or the number of embryos growing per unit of volume; the effect of externally applied pressure; the effect of variations in nutrition; the effect of narcosis, etc., on the development of the embryo or of specific organ systems may all be studied. Any student may divide a clump of eggs in two, taking one portion for the control and the other for experimentation in a variety of ways, and thus determine the degree of adaptation of the embryo and the persistence and efficiency of organismic influences.

As soon as a student exhibits the care and dexterity necessary for surgical procedures, he should be admitted to the excitement of this field of investigation. Eggs may be deprived of their own nuclei and yet develop with the sperm nuclei alone; unfertilized eggs may be stimulated by a gentle puncturing of their cortex to achieve artificial parthenogenesis; external pressure may be used to divert the cleavage planes from their normal course; and each cell of a two-cell stage may be tied off from the other to produce double monsters or siamese twins—identical twins apparently result from a similar separation of early blastomeres.

Experiments with the early embryo

The cells of an embryo may be separated by mechanical or chemical means and observed in their efforts to rejoin and reorganize into functional entities; areas of the blastula and gastrula may be extirpated and their relative influences on further development determined (this is how the "organizer" was discovered); areas on the surface of the egg or embryo may be stained with vital, nontoxic dyes and studied throughout development so that maps may be made of prospective regions of organ formation; the ability of the embryo to heal or repair wounds under a variety of conditions may be explored; embryos may be fused together as conjoined twins; organ primordia may be extirpated or transplanted and the embryo's adjustment to the losses or additions studied; chromosome studies may be made upon growing parts or regions, by the application of either certain chemicals or special lighting situations; and genetic variations of hybrids may be compared with those of pure lines.

Endocrine factors in development

It is known that the thyroid, the pituitary, and possibly the adrenal glands have much to do with normal development. Any of these glands may be surgically removed or transplanted during early development, before they have differentiated and become active and functional, and the effects of the deprivation or addition noted. For instance, the addition of thyroid extract or iodine to the environment of the tadpole hastens its metamorphosis tremendously. The loss of its thyroid primordium renders it a permanent tadpole, never to undergo metamorphosis.

Experimentation yields valuable information about biological adjustments, but one can truly understand the processes of normal development only by studying the normal embryo. Despite countless volumes of reports of experimental findings, investigators are still seeking knowledge of the nature of those forces that hold cells together in the integrating process of differentiation toward a perfectly functioning entity, the organism. The experimental method is valuable and exciting, but it should not be stressed to the point of obscuring the object under study—the normal embryo.

THE CHICK:

A Shelled Vertebrate

■ Introduction

Since the original and surprisingly accurate observations on the chick embryo by Malpighi (1672), Wolff (1759), and von Baer (1828), it has come to be the most thoroughly understood and described of all embryos. It is available all over the world, at all seasons of the year, and can be studied in laboratories with even the most modest equipment. Because the embryonic development of the chick is representative of that of all birds and reptiles, and because knowledge of it leads to an understanding of the relationships of the extra-embryonic membranes, the circulation, and the early respiration in mammals, every course in embryology should have as its core a study of chick development.

A brief survey of the major steps in the development of the chick embryo follows.

COPULATION. At insemination the cock provides *spermatozoa* to fertilize all the *ova* maturing for the next 20 to 30 days. The spermatozoa migrate up the *oviduct* and fertilize the ova before they enter the *uterus*. In the most pro-lific hens, an ovum matures daily, and a spermatozoon enters it during the formation of the *first polar body*, a process that is initiated or stimulated by *ovulation*. Fertilization occurs prior to the deposition of the outer membranes.

PASSAGE THROUGH THE OVIDUCT. The time required for the fertilized ovum to move down the oviduct to the uterus is 12 to 24 hours. In transit it picks up additional membranes. (The *vitelline membrane*, from the ovary, already encloses all of the *yolk*.) Two types of *albumen*, two shell membranes, and finally the shell are deposited. The outer shell does not solidify until it meets the outside air.

CLEAVAGE. Cleavage progresses to at least the 32-cell stage within the oviduct. It is discoid and incomplete; the protoplasm is in the form of a disc, the *germinal disc*, that always floats to the upper surface of the egg, and the yolk is never divided as it is in the frog.

BLASTULATION. At the 64-cell stage or shortly after, the central cells become elevated above the yolk, producing a cavity, the *blastocoel*, while the marginal cells remain contiguous with it. The region directly over the blastocoel is called the *area pellucida* because it is transparent. The peripheral region in direct contact with the yolk is called the *area opaca*. The *blastula* stage generally appears in the uterus.

GASTRULATION. Involution of the surface of the blastula results in a new cavity, the *archenteron*. The point of initial involution is the *blastopore*. The egg is usually laid at this stage and must be incubated at 103°F. if it is to develop further. The finished egg measures about 40 mm. in diameter, but the germinal disc, which constitutes the living protoplasm of the embryo, measures only about 3 mm. in diameter. Since unfertilized eggs, with all the essential membranes in the proper relationship, are also laid, it is impossible to identify fertilized eggs until there is evidence of embryonic development.

FIRST DAY OF INCUBATION. The embryo has a *primitive streak* and is for the first time identifiable as an embryo. The *notochord* arises anteriorly to *Hensen's node;* the *neural folds* form and close; the *foregut* and the *heart* primordium appear; and *blood islands* develop in the posterior area opaca.

SECOND DAY OF INCUBATION. Although the embryo is actually lifted off the yolk, the two regions remain functionally connected by a *yolk stalk*. The head is flexed ventrally; three primary *brain* areas are apparent; the eyes are well developed; the foregut is closed; the heart is S-shaped; the primitive streak is much reduced; and the *amnion* begins to fold back over the head.

THIRD DAY OF INCUBATION. The embryo shows pronounced cephalization, with *cranial, cervical,* and *pontine flexures;* the brain cavities are distinct; the eyes and ears are well formed; and four *visceral pouches*, three complete *aortic arches*, and the wings are apparent.

FOURTH DAY OF INCUBATION. The *proctodeum,* four *visceral grooves,* and five aortic arches are evident.

EIGHTH DAY OF INCUBATION. The embryo exhibits a definite birdlike contour.

TWENTIETH DAY OF INCUBATION. The remains of the yolk are withdrawn into the body through the yolk stalk; the shell is perforated for respiration; and the *lungs* begin to function.

TWENTY-FIRST DAY OF INCUBATION. A chick hatches out.

SEXUAL MATURITY. The male matures at 4 to 5 months, and the female at 4 to 10 months.

With this schedule in mind, the student can anticipate the processes discussed in detail throughout the chapter.

■ **Reproductive Systems**

Male

The paired *testes* are white ellipsoid organs about 2 inches long and 1 inch in diameter. They are internal, even though the body temperature of the cock may be 106° F., a temperature much too high for the survival of mammalian spermatozoa. Each testis consists of many coiled *seminiferous tubules* (Fig.

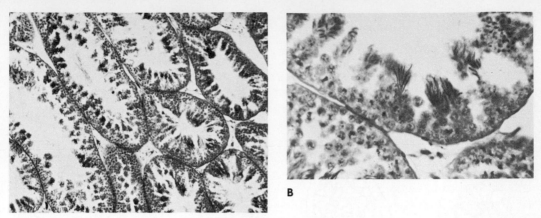

Fig. 4.1 Section of rooster testis: A, seminiferous tubules; B, tubules showing, from outside in, maturation stages from spermatogonia to spermatozoa, with tails in lumen (high power).

4.1), connected with each other and in turn with the *vasa efferentia* and *epididymis*, through which the mature spermatozoa are discharged into the *vas deferens* and then into the *cloaca*. In between the sperm-bearing tubules is abundant connective tissue, the *interstitial tissue*, which not only supports the tubules but also produces the male hormones that give rise to the secondary sex characters. A fold of coelomic epithelium, the *mesorchium*, suspends each testis from the dorsal body wall.

Spermatogenesis, the production of mature spermatozoa, is continuous (Fig. 4.2). The most primitive male sex cells are the *spermatogonia*, which adhere closely to the walls of the seminiferous tubules. Although they tend to divide frequently, clusters of them in each tubule stop dividing and grow into *primary spermatocytes*. Two rapid mitotic divisions convert each primary spermatocyte into two equal and smaller *secondary spermatocytes* and then into four very small *spermatids*. No more divisions occur, but each spermatid undergoes a metamorphosis in which the nucleus, with its distinct chromatin threads, becomes a very compact, dark-staining mass of elongated chromatic material concentrated in the head of a mature spermatozoon. Thus each original spermatogonium gives rise to four mature spermatozoa by a process of growth followed by two mitotic divisions and a metamorphosis. Throughout reproductive life the seminiferous tubules contain spermatogonia undergoing mitosis and awaiting possible differentiation into primary spermatocytes. Since cells at the same maturation stage appear in groups, it is likely that all the mitotic descendants of a single spermatogonium remain in close proximity and develop simultaneously.

The mature spermatozoon is very long and slender, with a distinguishable head, middle piece, and tail. The nucleus, carrying all of the hereditary influences of the male, is in the head. The top of the head is pointed, forming

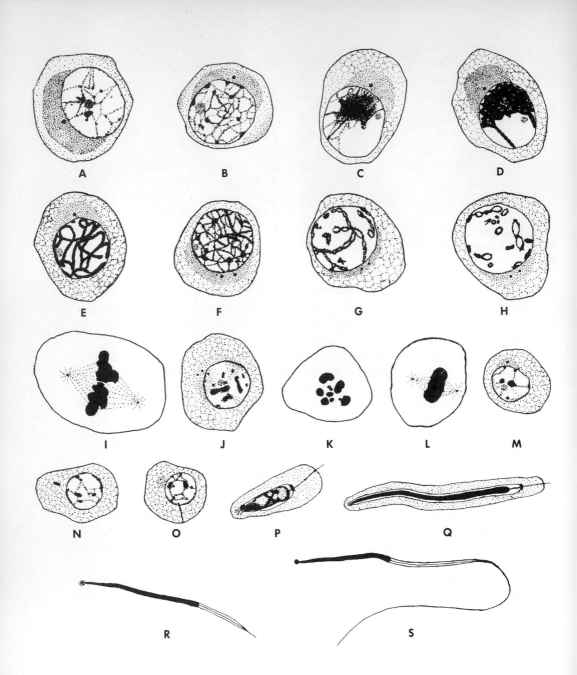

Fig. 4.2 Spermatogenesis in rooster: A, resting spermatocyte; B, early spireme; C, synaptene stage; D, bouquet stage; E, pachytene stage; F, diffuse stage; G, strepsinema breaking up into tetrads; H, diakinesis; I, primary spermatocyte division (side view); J, resting secondary spermatocyte; K, secondary spermatocyte division (polar view); L, secondary spermatocyte division (equatorial view); M, resting spermatid; N–R, several stages in transformation of spermatid into spermatozoon; S, spermatozoon. (From R. A. Miller, *Anat. Record*, **70**, 155 (1938).)

an *acrosome,* or *perforatorium,* which probably aids in the penetration of the egg surface. The middle piece, or neck, contains *centrioles* from the spermatid stage, which aid in setting up the early mitotic spindles for cleavage. The tail contains a central axial filament surrounded, except at the tip, by a protoplasmic sheath.

Female

Although the female chick embryo develops two *ovaries,* the right one and its oviduct degenerate, so that only the left ovary and oviduct mature and function (Fig. 4.3). This single ovary becomes excessively large, probably in compensation for the loss of the other, and matures ova at an average approaching one per day for many months after sexual maturity. The *mesovarium,* a double epithelial membrane, suspends the ovary from the dorsal body wall.

The female genital tract consists of the following parts, with the functions indicated (Fig. 4.4). The *ostium tubae (infundibulum),* the frilled, ciliated, funnel-shaped upper end of the oviduct, receives the *primary oöcyte.* The *magnum,* the convoluted upper glandular portion of the oviduct, secretes the heavy albumen that twists around the ovum to form a *chalaza* at each end. The first two cleavages may occur in this portion of the oviduct, during a 3-hour transit. The *isthmus,* or lower glandular portion of the oviduct, secretes the thinner albumen and a double shell membrane of matted organic fibers. Cleavage proceeds from the 8-cell stage to the blastula during a 3- to 4-hour transit of the isthmus. The short, saclike, glandular *uterus* secretes the three-layered shell and retains the ovum for 4 to 24 hours, depending upon when it arrives. Since eggs are usually laid in early morning, gastrulation and endoderm formation may take place even before laying. The *vagina* is a mere passageway to the cloaca and thence to the outside, where the shell immediately hardens.

Most of the egg cells in the mature ovary are *oögonia,* in the earliest stage of *oögenesis* (egg development). A cluster of nurse cells, known as *follicle cells,* encloses each oögonium, and the oögonium and follicle cells together constitute the *Graafian follicle* (Figs. 4.5, 4.6). Immediately surrounding the oögonium, and secreted by it, is a very thin noncellular membrane, the vitelline membrane. Outside this membrane is a second one, traversed by delicate radiating striations (*zona radiata*) and derived from the follicle cells, which comprise the next layer. Finally the highly vascular connective tissue *theca folliculi* encircles the primordial Graafian follicle. The theca folliculi is continuous with the ovarian *stroma,* giving it substance to support the numerous nests of primitive ova and follicle cells.

The follicle cells derive nutriment from the theca folliculi and transfer it through the zona radiata to the oögonium, aiding it in its accumulation of yolk (deutoplasm). Thus the oögonium grows into a primary oöcyte with a small nucleus and a limited amount of cytoplasm but an enormous storage of yolk that provides food for the embryo during its 21 days of confinement in a shell. The oöcyte bulges from the surface of the ovary and, when it attains

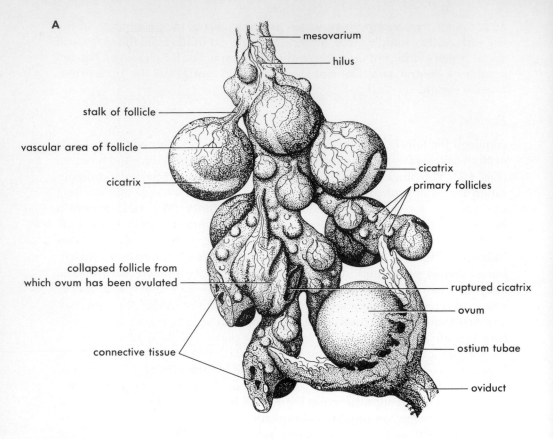

A

mesovarium

hilus

stalk of follicle

vascular area of follicle

cicatrix

cicatrix

primary follicles

collapsed follicle from
which ovum has been ovulated

ruptured cicatrix

ovum

connective tissue

ostium tubae

oviduct

Fig. 4.3 Bird ovary, showing ova in varying stages of maturation: A, with ostium tubae engulfing recently ovulated ovum; B, with ruptured follicles apparent. (A from O. E. Nelsen, *Comparative Embryology of the Vertebrates,* McGraw-Hill, New York, 1953; B from M. W. Olsen.)

a size too great for its sheaths, ruptures from its follicle and lies briefly within the peritoneal cavity. Then the ostium tubae, which lies close to the ovary, draws the oöcyte into its cavity by means of ciliary action. Within the oviduct the nucleus divides, but all the yolk remains with one nucleus, forming a *secondary oöcyte,* while the other nucleus is discarded as a first polar body. A second and similar division occurs at the time of fertilization, with the formation of the mature ovum and the elimination of a *second polar body,* while the first one divides. Thus one primitive oögonium gives rise to a single mature ovum and three polar bodies, whereas one primitive spermatogonium gives rise to four mature spermatozoa; and yet growth, two divisions, and metamorphic changes are involved in both processes of maturation. At hatching, the female chick has all the oögonia it will ever have. Some 7 days before hatching a few of the oögonia begin to grow, and others mature in a continuous stream throughout the hen's reproductive life.

Fig. 4.3 *(continued)*

In the early Graafian follicle the cell destined to become an ovum is indistinguishable from any other cell except for its position, in the center of a cluster of similar cuboid and granular follicle cells surrounded by the concentric fibers of the theca folliculi. Then a concentrated mass of protoplasm, the *yolk nucleus,* appears at one side of its nucleus and begins to form yolk, a substance composed of about 50% water, 42% solids, and 8% salts. The yolk nucleus first organizes the *white yolk,* a very thin layer consisting of numerous small, nonuniform spheres containing fine granules and presumably deposited during the nighttime period of relaxation and low blood pressure. A thicker layer of *yellow yolk,* consisting of much larger and rather uniform spheres, is deposited during the daytime period of activity and higher blood pressure. As these yolk layers surround the nucleus, it moves away from the center of the cell to the periphery, leaving behind it a stream of white yolk. This stalk of white yolk extending from the center of the ovum to the peripheral nucleus is the *latebra,* and its continuation beneath the nucleus is the *nucleus of Pander.* A fully mature egg has eight or more rings of alternating white

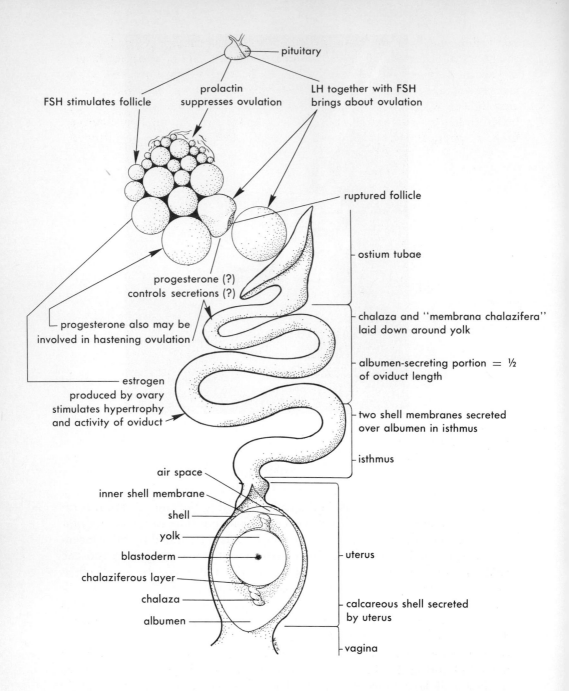

Fig. 4.4 Chart showing effects of pituitary gland on ovum and passage of ovum down oviduct in chicken. Ovulation ordinarily does not occur until ovum in oviduct has been laid. (From O. E. Nelsen, *Comparative Embryology of the Vertebrates*, McGraw-Hill, New York, 1953.)

and yellow yolk, interrupted only by the latebra, the nucleus of Pander, and the germinal disc. Although there is no sharp demarcation between the layers of yolk, or between the yolk and the protoplasm of the germinal disc, they are present and distinguishable in normal eggs. Since the germinal disc is very light in weight, so that it floats to the top, it can be located in an egg boiled to hardness in one position. During maturation the nucleus changes from a spherical structure about 9 microns in diameter to a flattened

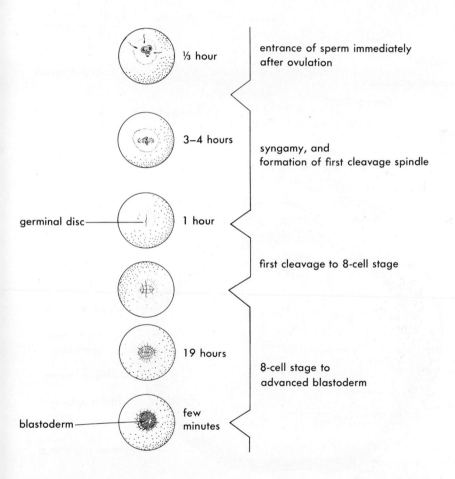

⅓ hour — entrance of sperm immediately after ovulation

3–4 hours — syngamy, and formation of first cleavage spindle

germinal disc — 1 hour

first cleavage to 8-cell stage

19 hours — 8-cell stage to advanced blastoderm

blastoderm — few minutes

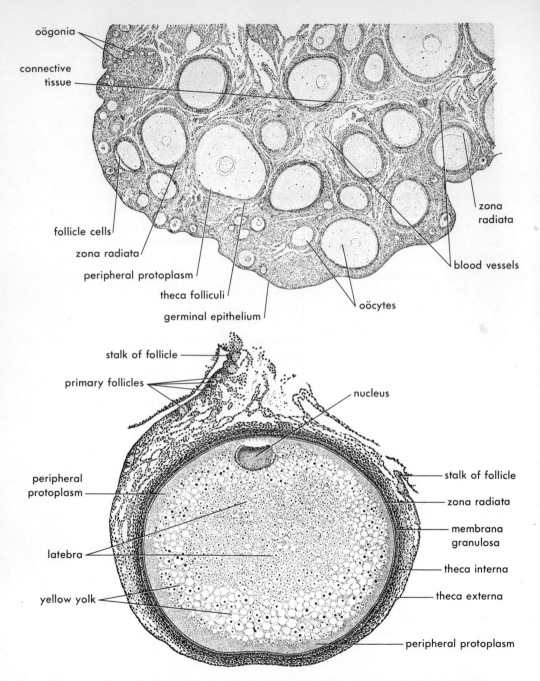

Fig. 4.5 Sections of bird ovaries: A, chicken ovary, showing oögonia and primary oöcytes (small black dots within oöcytes are yolk); B, pigeon ovum. (A from A. E. Huettner, *Fundamentals of Comparative Embryology of the Vertebrates*, rev. ed., Macmillan, New York, 1949; B from F. R. Lillie and H. L. Hamilton, *Lillie's Development of the Chick*, 3rd ed., Holt, Rinehart & Winston, New York, 1952.)

structure over 400 microns in diameter and 70 microns thick. The diameter of the ovum itself grows from about 4 mm. to about 40 mm. in 10 days, owing to the accumulation of yolk.

▪ Maturation and Fertilization

In the primitive oögonium the nucleus is central and spherical, with a distinct chromatic network. During development to the primary oöcyte stage it enlarges tremendously and moves outward to lie next to the vitelline membrane, which compresses it into a flattened shape. Its wall becomes quite thin and irregular, and toward its center nucleoli and a cluster of eight chromosome tetrads (derived by two splittings of a single chromosome) appear. Just before ovulation, the eight tetrads range themselves upon a mitotic spindle with its main axis perpendicular to the egg surface. Then the wall of the nucleus disintegrates, and the contained protoplasm mixes with some nearby white yolk. Each tetrad divides into a pair of dyads, one dyad going to each of the mitotic poles. Just as the oöcyte passes into the ostium tubae, which usually contains a suspension of active spermatozoa, the most peripheral dyads are pinched off in a bud of cytoplasm that protrudes into the *perivitelline space* between the vitelline membrane and the oöcyte. This minute fragment, containing half the chromatin material, is the degenerate nucleus known as the first polar body. It is discarded, leaving a secondary oöcyte. Fertilization stimulates the chromosomes within the oöcyte nucleus to reorganize almost immediately in preparation for another mitosis, and the two homologous members of each of the eight dyads migrate along the mitotic axis toward opposite poles, so that sixteen discrete chromosomes result. Again the mitotic spindle is oriented at right angles to the surface, this time close to the position of the first polar body. Again a protoplasmic bud containing half the chromosomes forms and is pinched off. This is the second polar body. Thus the nucleus divides twice to reduce its chromosome content from 32 (eight tetrads) to eight, which is the haploid condition of the egg *pronucleus*. Fusion with the similarly haploid sperm pronucleus at fertilization restores the diploid condition. If fertilization does not occur, the ovum probably remains in metaphase.

In sluggish, heavily yolk-laden ova, *polyspermy*, the invasion of the ovum by many spermatozoa, is common. It is believed that extra spermatozoa are always present in the hen's egg, tending to migrate away from the single successful sperm pronucleus that first reaches the egg pronucleus and fuses with it. Although some of these surplus spermatozoa may attempt to form centers for division, they quickly disintegrate and have no effect on development.

It seems doubtful that the haploid male chromosomes intermingle immediately with the haploid female chromosomes, but with the first cleavage they become indistinct from each other. The first cleavage spindle forms at the site of the egg pronucleus, which is near the center of the germinal disc and near the periphery of the egg. The axis of this mitotic spindle differs from

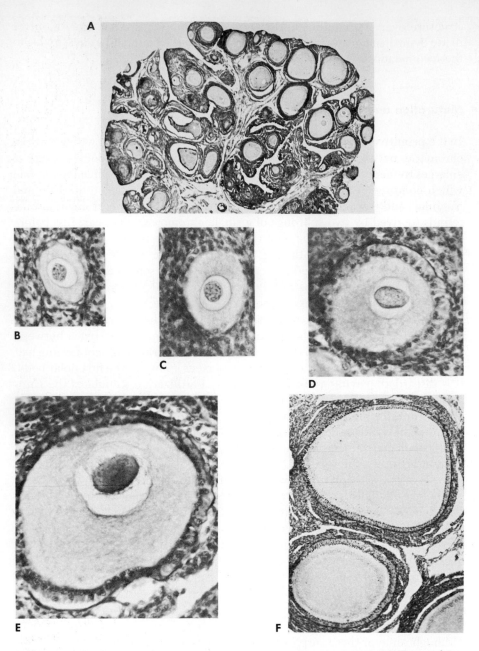

Fig. 4.6   Development of ovum in chicken: A, section of ovary showing follicles in various stages of growth (low power); B, early oögonium; C, later oögonium; D, still later oögonium, with ring of follicle cells; E, oögonium enlarging rapidly; F, oögonia accumulating yolk; G, margin of oögonium, showing follicle cells contributing yolk (high power); H, margin of oögonium, showing abundant yolk granules and follicle cells becoming distinct from yolk (high power); I, margin of primary oöcyte, showing yolk, distinct layer of follicle cells, and theca interna.

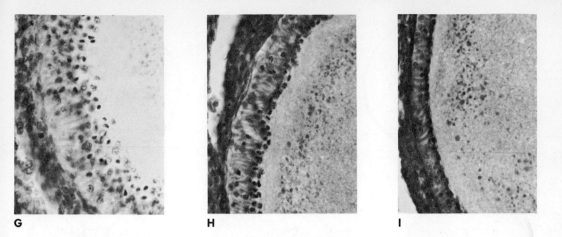

G   H   I

Fig. 4.6 *(continued)*

those of oögenesis in being parallel to the surface of the egg, so that there is no more discarding of nuclear or protoplasmic material.

■ **Cleavage**

Despite its size, the fertilized hen's egg is a single cell, with a single nucleus derived by the fusion of the haploid pronuclei from the spermatozoon and the ovum and situated near the center of a small amount of peripherally located protoplasm, the germinal disc. Cleavage does not include the huge mass of inert yolk but is limited to the small disc of protoplasm lying dorsal to it. Hence it is known as discoid cleavage.

The margin between the germinal disc and the surrounding white yolk is indistinct, but at no point is the protoplasm in contact with the yellow yolk. The general distribution of the protoplasm resembles an umbrella, with the handle extending into the latebra and the convex covering representing the germinal disc near the surface. Cleavage divides the protoplasm, independently of the yolk, into progressively smaller units that eventually give rise to the multicellular embryo and all its extraembryonic structures.

The first cleavage furrow appears as a vertical slit near the center of the germinal disc about 3 hours after fertilization, while the ovum is in the oviduct (Figs. 4.4, 4.7, 4.8A,B, 4.9). As it extends in two directions, a second furrow appears, generally at right angles to the first. The third cleavage furrow follows shortly. It is radial, at right angles to the second, but the resultant eight cells, or *blastomeres*, are quite irregular in contour. Since none of these cleavage furrows extends to the margin of the germinal disc, none of the early blastomeres is completely surrounded by a cell membrane; in fact, each of the eight blastomeres of the third cleavage is contiguous with other cells both peripherally and beneath the surface.

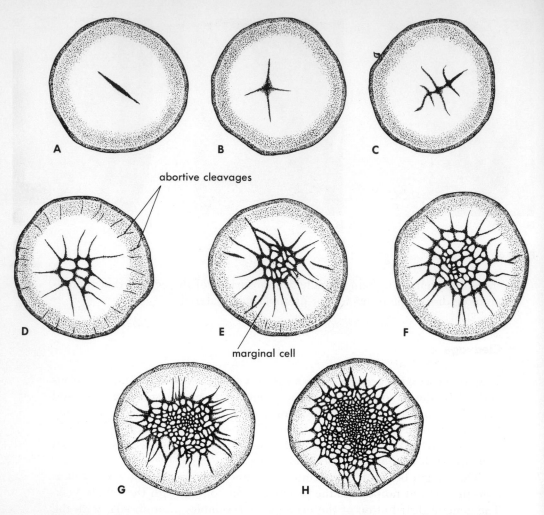

Fig. 4.7   Cleavage in chicken egg. (From O. E. Nelsen, *Comparative Embryology of the Vertebrates,* McGraw-Hill, New York, 1953. C adapted from Olsen; A, B, D–H adapted from Patterson.)

■ Blastulation

Circumferential and radial furrows further divide the germinal disc superficially, and then horizontal furrows cut away the superficial cells from the underlying white yolk and enclose them completely in cell membranes. These membranes give the cells a degree of rigidity, and they become slightly elevated, leaving a slitlike space, the blastocoel (*segmentation cavity*), above the yolk (Fig. 4.8C–G). With the appearance of the blastocoel, the egg

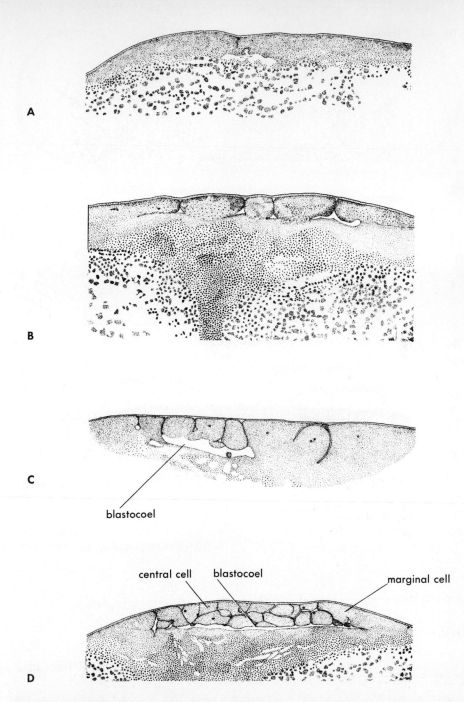

A

B

C

blastocoel

central cell   blastocoel   marginal cell

D

Fig. 4.8   Sections showing cleavage in chicken egg. (A–G from O. E. Nelsen, *Compara-tive Embryology of the Vertebrates,* McGraw-Hill, New York, 1953. Adapted from Patterson. H from F. R. Lillie and H. L. Hamilton, *Lillie's Development of the Chick,* 3rd ed., Holt, Rine-hart & Winston, New York, 1952.)

Fig. 4.8 (continued)

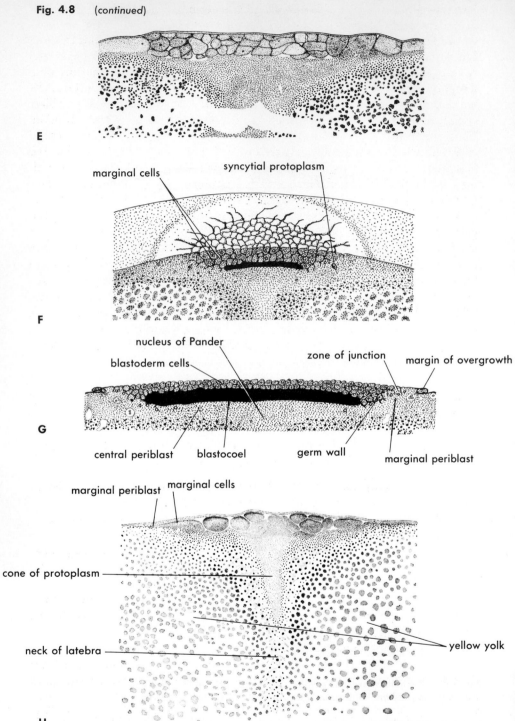

E

marginal cells

syncytial protoplasm

F

nucleus of Pander

blastoderm cells

zone of junction

margin of overgrowth

G

central periblast   blastocoel   germ wall   marginal periblast

marginal periblast   marginal cells

cone of protoplasm

yellow yolk

neck of latebra

H

becomes a blastula (*discoblastula*), and the germinal disc becomes a *blasto-derm*. The early blastoderm is two cells thick at most.

Additional horizontal cleavage furrows divide the blastoderm into three or four layers, with the central cells bounded by cells only partially separated from each other by radial cleavage furrows. Outside these actively dividing marginal cells is a layer of free protoplasm, the *periblast,* which adjoins the white yolk. Except for occasional degenerating sperm nuclei, the periblast contains no nuclei until the marginal cells provide them by mitotic division. Then continuing cleavage transforms some of the marginal cells into central cells, and some of the nucleated periblast cells into marginal cells, so that the blastoderm grows. (Some of the scattered periblast nuclei migrate to peri-blast in the floor of the blastocoel, which organizes into the central, or sub-germinal, periblast and shortly disappears.) The central cells overlying the blastocoel constitute the clear area pellucida. The marginal cells, close to the yolk and darkened by yolk particles, make up the area opaca. The outer marginal cells, connecting the blastoderm and the periblast, form the *germ wall.* As the blastoderm enlarges, cells at its edge are lifted off the yolk to form a *margin of overgrowth.* Cells beneath the margin of overgrowth and ad-joining the yolk form a *zone of junction.* The blastula, then, includes a blasto-derm with central elevated pellucid cells, an active cellular germ wall, a rapidly expanding margin of overgrowth, and a zone of junction consisting of a syncytium of scattered nuclei; a central blastocoel; and yolk. The shape of the entire body is spherical or oval.

■ Gastrulation

Gastrulation, the critical process that results in the differentiation of the primary germ layers, involves the following changes:

1. A thinning of the posterior third of the blastoderm, at 20 to 21 hours after fertilization, and an increase in the size of the blastocoel.

2. A freeing of the posterior margin of the blastoderm to form a small slit, the blastopore, with the *dorsal lip of the blastopore* as its upper edge.

3. An involution, or inturning, of cells at the dorsal lip of the blastopore, with movement anteriorly beneath the outer cells, so that two cell layers, the outer *ectoderm* and the inner *endoderm,* appear.

4. A convergence, or lateral compression, of the cells at the sides of the dorsal lip of the blastopore to form a column-like primitive streak in the blastoderm.

5. A peripheral expansion of the entire blastoderm.

6. The appearance of *mesoderm* as loose *mesenchyme,* which arises from the sides and posterior margin of the primitive streak as well as from the fused blastoporal region, between the ectoderm and endoderm.

The blastoderm has been described as a spherical disc of cellular proto-

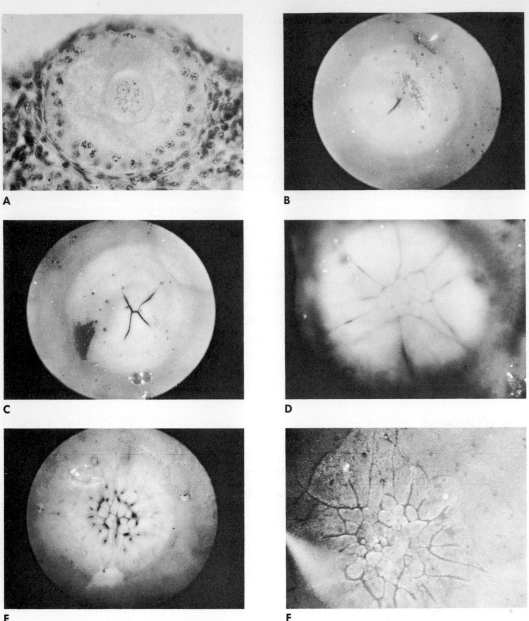

Fig. 4.9 Maturation, fertilization, and early cleavage of chicken egg: A, follicle just before ovulation; B, egg with first cleavage furrow (from isthmus); C, 4-cell stage (from isthmus); D, 16-cell stage (from uterus); E, 32-cell stage (from uterus); F, approximately 100-cell stage; G, late cleavage (256 or more cells); H, section of ovum just before ovulation, showing chromatin near center of disintegrating nucleus; I, section of newly ovulated ovum, showing first polar body; J, section of fertilized egg, showing male and female pronuclei near second polar body; K, section of egg with first cleavage furrow; L, section of egg late in first cleavage. (From M. W. Olsen.)

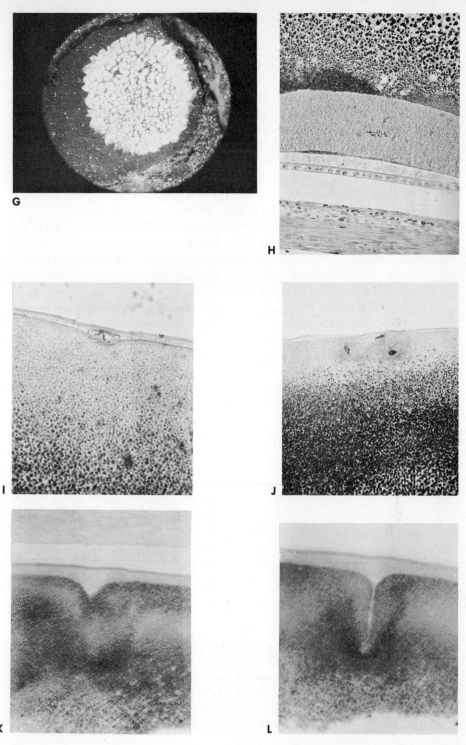

plasm above a blastocoel, with its syncytial margins in contact with the yolk (zone of junction) and extending over it (margin of overgrowth). This description applies to all but the posterior margin of the blastoderm, where there is no zone of junction to connect the cellular blastoderm with the noncellular yolk; instead there is a small slit, the blastopore, separating the two regions. The first indication that gastrulation is about to occur (20 to 21 hours after fertilization) is a thinning of the posterior third of the blastoderm, resulting from the forward migration of some cells (Fig. 4.10). The identification of the "posterior" position is based on subsequent developments. If one holds an egg with the blunt end of the shell toward the left, he can assume that the embryo will almost always develop at right angles to the main axis of the egg, with its head facing away from him. Therefore, the thinning of the blastoderm will occur on the side nearest to him. The thinning is most obvious at the posterior margin of the blastoderm, which may become only one cell thick. The cells from the posterior region pile up increasingly toward the anterior margin, where they may form a layer seven or eight cells thick. During this cell migration and re-arrangement, the blastoderm expands in all directions except posteriorly, and the blastocoel also grows, although not so rapidly.

The cells at the thin posterior margin of the blastoderm, which are separated from the yolk by the blastopore, are freer than those of the zone of junction, and for some reason they begin to roll inward and forward beneath the blastoderm. This involution, or inturning, is typical of gastrulation and creates the dorsal lip of the blastopore. Thus cells derived from the outer blastoderm move inside the blastocoel. Because of their new location, they are called endo-derm. The cells remaining outside are called ectoderm, even though some of them, particularly those toward the posterior margin, later roll inward to become endoderm. The distinction is merely one of position.

The invasion by endoderm transforms the blastocoel into the archenteron (*gastrocoel, subgerminal cavity*) and the egg into the *gastrula*. The sheet of endoderm spreads from the blastopore in all directions within the archenteron and comes to lie close under the ectoderm. However, there is no possibility of fusion of the two layers because their movement is generally in opposite directions. While the inner endoderm moves anteriorly and laterally, some of the outer ectoderm still moves posteriorly toward the blastopore. The convergence (*confluence, concrescence*) of ectoderm cells at the relatively small blastopore soon closes it, but not until an adequate number of cells has entered.

Since the cells of the gastrula comprise a continuous sheet, movements in one region affect all others. During involution the blastoderm continues to expand by mitosis, and the involution and expansion account for the change in general shape of the area pellucida during primitive streak formation. The mitotic index is greatest at the rim of the area pellucida and anterior to the primitive streak and least in the streak itself. Most of the posterior half of the area pellucida eventually rolls into the blastopore to contribute to the streak and to the early mesenchyme. Evidence of these movements is gained by placing

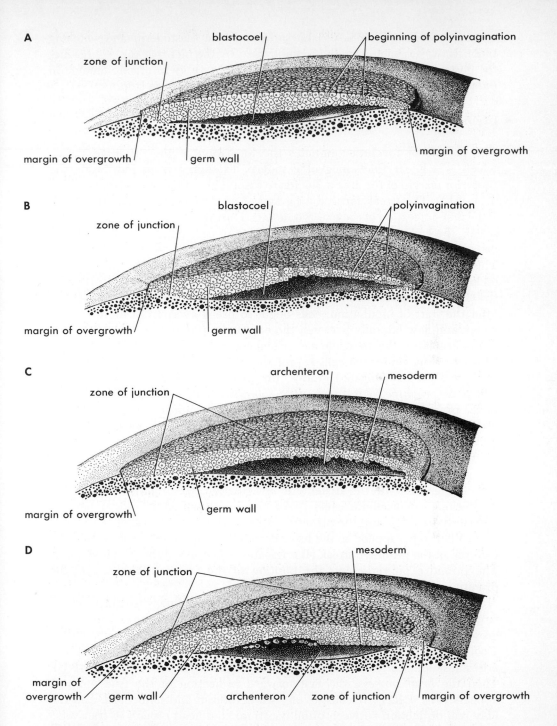

Fig. 4.10 Gastrulation in chicken egg. (From A. E. Huettner, *Fundamentals of Comparative Embryology of the Vertebrates*, rev. ed., Macmillan, New York, 1949.)

minute granules or stains on the surface of the blastoderm and watching them. However, such a study is complicated by the fact that the egg reaches the gastrula stage before it is laid and with the sudden, drastic change in temperature at laying, development may slow down or even stop.

■ Laying to 33 Hours Incubation

The process of involution initiates the formation of the primitive streak, which is a linear thickening of ectoderm extending from just inside the posterior margin of the area pellucida to a point about halfway across it (Figs. 4.11–4.14). The streak forms during and after closure of the blastopore and is the first suggestion of the embryonic axis. During formation of the primitive streak, the endoderm remains as a thin layer of cells lying over the yolk and extending peripherally to the zone of junction, where it merges with the yolk. The ectoderm extends farther out in the margin of overgrowth. Although the endoderm may make limited contact with the ectoderm of the primitive streak, it never fuses with it, and laterally it is quite separate. About 14 hours after the start of incubation, cells begin to break away from the primitive streak and flow laterally between the ectoderm and endoderm to form the third germ layer, the mesenchyme, or embryonic mesoderm (Figs. 4.15, 4.16). This lateral movement of cells is probably the reason for the appearance in the streak of an elongated groove, the *primitive groove,* on each side of which are *primitive folds,* terminating anteriorly in a clump of cells, Hensen's node, or the *primitive knot.* Hensen's node surrounds a depression, *the primitive pit.* At its posterior end the primitive streak flares out laterally into a *primitive plate.*

It is possible to homologize chick structures with frog structures as follows: the primitive folds with the coalesced lateral lips of the blastopore; the primitive groove with the archenteric invagination; the primitive pit with the undeveloped neurenteric canal (since the notochord and embryo develop anteriorly from it); and the primitive plate with the dorsal lip of the blastopore. Vital stains applied to the blastoderm during gastrulation show that the material of the primitive streak all originates at the site of the primitive plate. The primitive pit represents the position of the future *midbrain,* and the primitive plate the position of the future *anus.*

The embryo begins to develop anteriorly to, and in line with, the primitive streak, incorporating its material. Thus, as embryonic structures appear and grow, the primitive streak recedes posteriorly and disappears. The notochord, a column of undifferentiated cells derived from and beneath the ectoderm, arises just anteriorly to Hensen's node (Figs. 4.11B,C,G, 4.13, 4.14B,C). Then the *head process,* the first forward projection of the true embryo, appears (Fig. 4.12A). It consists of both ectoderm and notochord, and the only real distinction between primitive streak and head process in transverse sections taken at this time is the presence of the notochordal cells. Mesenchyme cells move laterally from the elongating head process, as well as later-

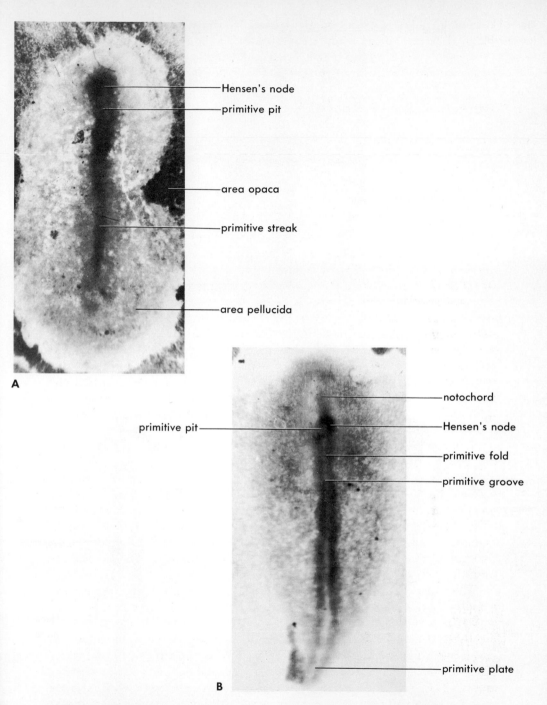

Fig. 4.11   Dorsal views showing development of chick embryo from 14 to 30 hours: A, at 14 hours; B, at 15 hours; C, at 16 hours; D, at 22 hours; E, at 24 hours; F, at 26 hours; G, at 30 hours.

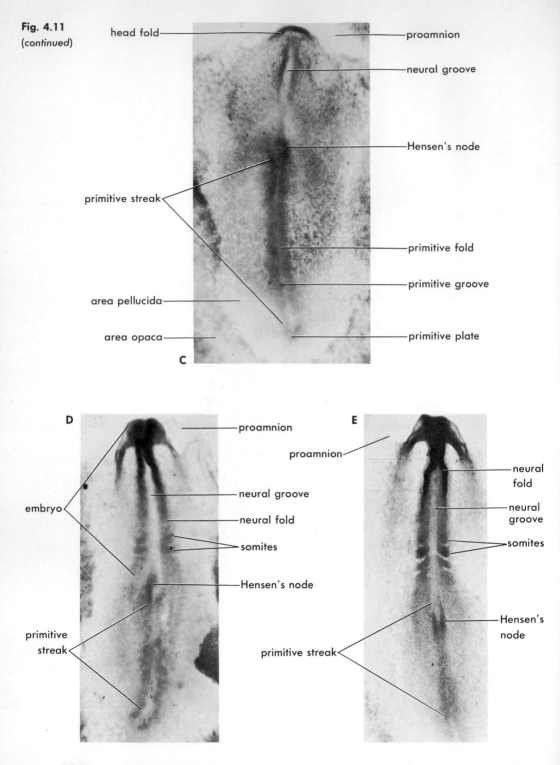

Fig. 4.11
(*continued*)

head fold — proamnion

neural groove

Hensen's node

primitive streak

primitive fold

primitive groove

area pellucida

area opaca — primitive plate

C

D proamnion

neural groove

neural fold

embryo — somites

Hensen's node

primitive streak

E proamnion

neural fold

neural groove

somites

Hensen's node

primitive streak

Fig. 4.11
(*continued*)

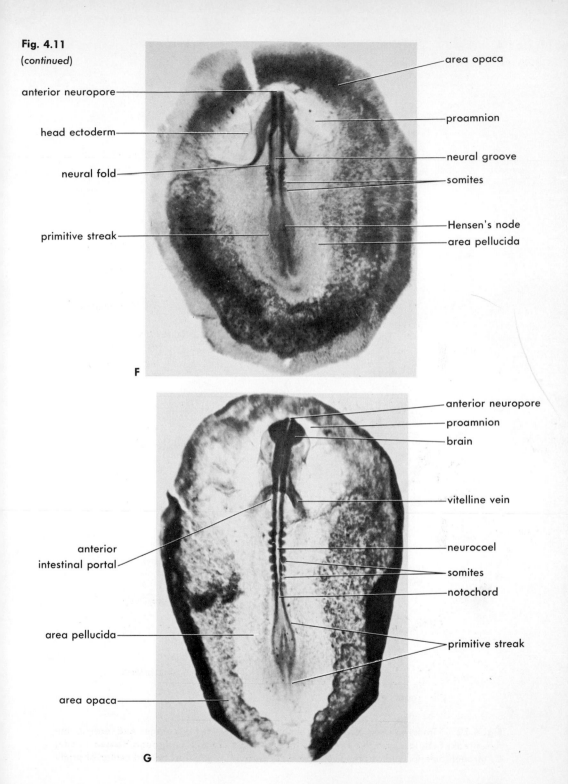

anterior neuropore

head ectoderm

neural fold

primitive streak

area opaca

proamnion

neural groove

somites

Hensen's node
area pellucida

F

anterior neuropore
proamnion
brain

vitelline vein

anterior
intestinal portal

neurocoel

somites

notochord

area pellucida

primitive streak

area opaca

G

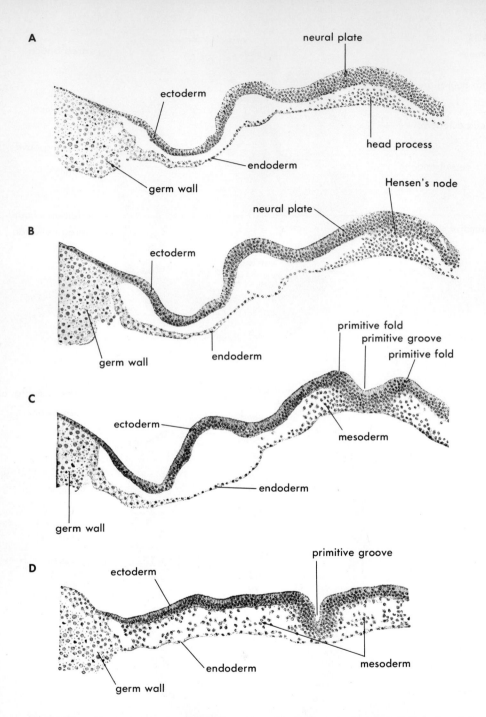

Fig. 4.12 Transverse sections of chick embryo at primitive streak stage: A–E, early primitive streak; F–H, late primitive streak; A, through head process; B, through Hensen's node; C, through anterior end of primitive groove; D, through region just behind center of primi-

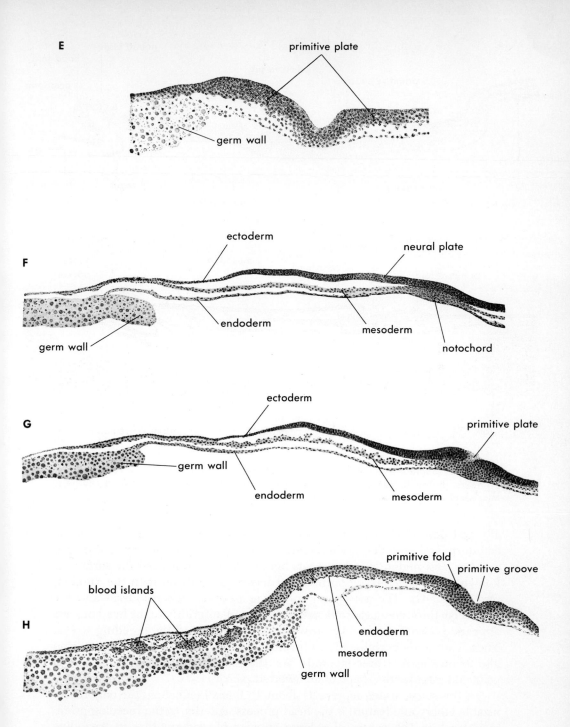

E, primitive plate / germ wall

F, ectoderm / neural plate / germ wall / endoderm / mesoderm / notochord

G, ectoderm / primitive plate / germ wall / endoderm / mesoderm

H, primitive fold / primitive groove / blood islands / endoderm / mesoderm / germ wall

tive streak; E, through primitive plate; F, through head process; G, through primitive pit; H, through region just behind center of primitive streak. (From F. R. Lillie and H. L. Hamilton, *Lillie's Development of the Chick*, 3rd ed., Holt, Rinehart & Winston, New York, 1952.)

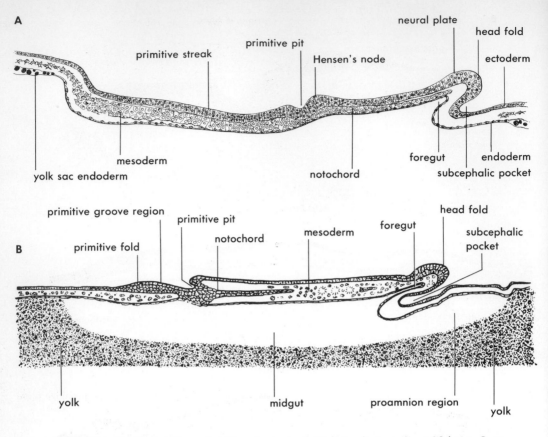

Fig. 4.13   Sagittal sections of chick embryo at primitive streak stage: A, at 18 hours; B, at 24 hours. (B from R. Rugh, *Laboratory Manual of Vertebrate Embryology*, 5th ed., Burgess, Minneapolis, 1961.)

ally and posteriorly from the primitive streak, into the space between the ectoderm and endoderm. No mesenchyme is present anteriorly to the head process. This region, which appears lighter than the rest from the surface, is known as the *proamnion* (although it has nothing to do with the amnion) (Fig. 4.11C–G). The mesoderm spreading between the ectoderm and the endoderm throughout the area pellucida except anteriorly to the head process appears as two flat winglike growths, merging behind the receding streak. Then it expands peripherally to invade the area opaca, making that region also triploblastic (three-layered). As the mesoderm develops, the area pellucida assumes the shape of an inverted pear.

At this stage, which represents about 15 hours incubation, the only recognizable embryonic feature is the head process, anterior to the receding primitive streak in the center of a large circular blastoderm that is expanding rapidly down over the yolk. There is no distinction between intraembryonic and extraembryonic structures, that is, between the embryo and its mem-

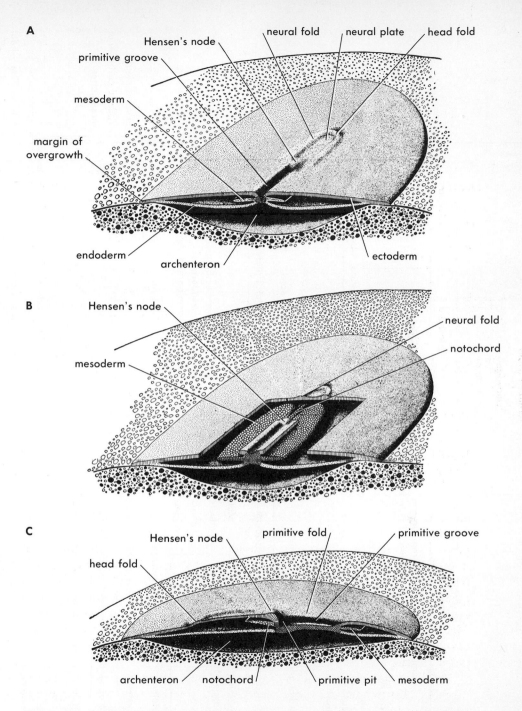

Fig. 4.14   Relation of primitive streak to chick embryo: A, transverse section; B, transverse section with ectoderm removed; C, sagittal section. (From A. E. Huettner, *Fundamentals of Comparative Embryology of the Vertebrates,* rev. ed., Macmillan, 1949.)

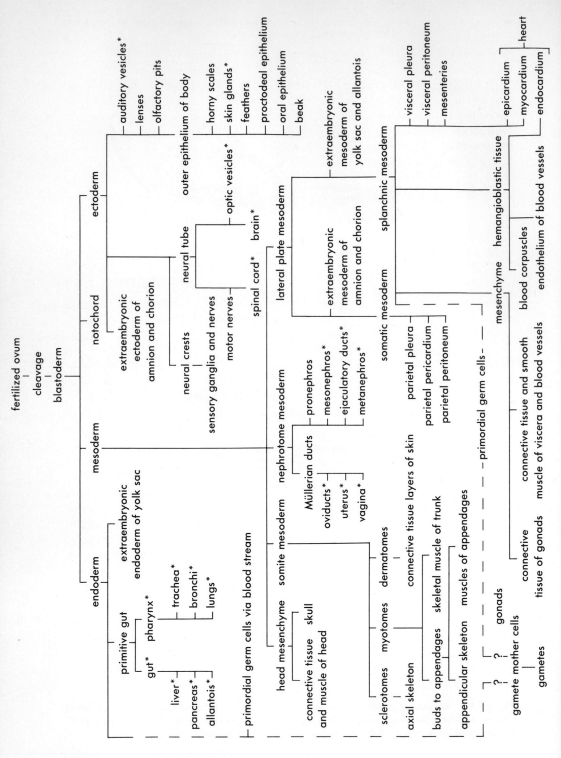

branes. During the next few hours, however, the embryo grows rapidly, projects upward and forward from the yolk, and, by an undercutting of the contiguous membranes, begins to be delimited from the extraembryonic regions.

An ectodermal thickening, the *neural (medullary) plate*, develops anteriorly to the primitive streak and above the notochord (Figs. 4.13, 4.14A). Its anterior projection is the *head fold*. A thin layer of endoderm, continuous with the rest of the embryonic endoderm, lines the fold, forming the early foregut. The ectodermal pocket that appears beneath the head fold, as a result of its outward thrust, is the *subcephalic pocket*.

Derivatives of the ectoderm

The neural plate is the precursor of the central nervous system. As it grows forward, too rapidly to remain flat on the yolk, it also grows backward at the expense of the primitive streak. Its posterior extension appears to flare out around the anterior end of the primitive streak as the streak recedes, and when the streak disappears, the neural plate is complete. This means that neural development proceeds from anterior to posterior. Therefore, progressive stages in neural development are evident from posterior to anterior in any embryo, the most posterior being the least advanced.

Soon after the head fold begins to project forward, there develops in the center of the thickened neural plate a longitudinal groove, the *neural groove*, the sides of which are the neural folds (4.11C–G, 4.14, 4.17–4.19). The groove deepens, and the folds elevate and then come together above the groove to fuse and form an elongated tube, the *neural tube*. Fusion begins just posteriorly to the anterior end of the neural plate, at a point where the midbrain will develop, and continues posteriorly. Anteriorly the folds remain unfused until the 12-somite stage. The anterior opening in the tube is the *anterior neuropore*.

The thick ectoderm of the neural plate becomes the lining of the neural tube, and the thin ectoderm lateral to the plate remains as the body covering. When the neural folds meet, the neural plate ectoderm fuses and separates from the outer ectoderm, so that almost immediately two ectodermal layers appear. Simultaneously some of the neural plate ectoderm breaks off on each side into the space between the neural tube and the overlying ectoderm. This at first forms a continuous rod from anterior to posterior but shortly is segmented into the *neural crests*.

The ectoderm of the neural tube gives rise to the neural tissue of the *spinal cord* and brain, and the cavity of the tube becomes the *neurocoel* and the

Fig. 4.15 Derivation of body parts in chick. Chart shows origin of epithelial parts of organs; asterisks indicate secondary supporting investments of mesenchyme. (Adapted from B. M. Patten, *Embryology of the Chick*, McGraw-Hill, New York, 1953.)

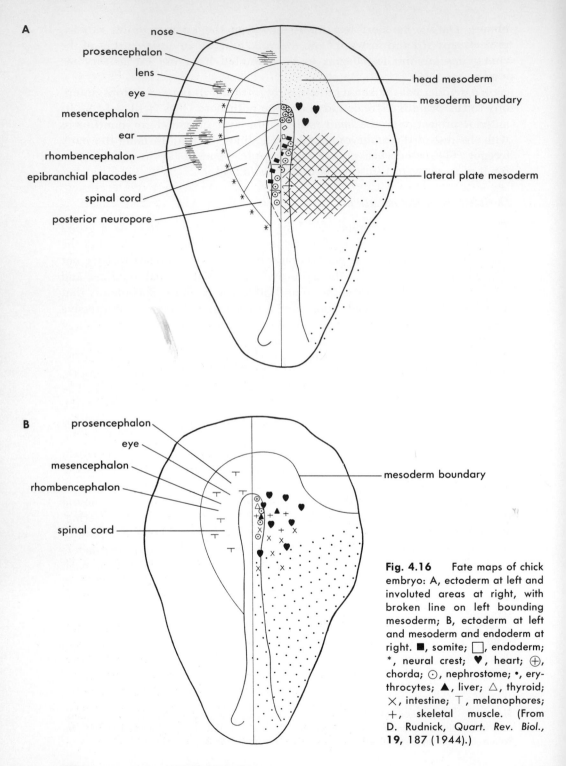

A

- nose
- prosencephalon
- lens
- eye
- mesencephalon
- ear
- rhombencephalon
- epibranchial placodes
- spinal cord
- posterior neuropore

- head mesoderm
- mesoderm boundary

- lateral plate mesoderm

B

- prosencephalon
- eye
- mesencephalon
- rhombencephalon

- spinal cord

- mesoderm boundary

Fig. 4.16 Fate maps of chick embryo: A, ectoderm at left and involuted areas at right, with broken line on left bounding mesoderm; B, ectoderm at left and mesoderm and endoderm at right. ■, somite; □, endoderm; *, neural crest; ♥, heart; ⊕, chorda; ⊙, nephrostome; •, erythrocytes; ▲, liver; △, thyroid; ✕, intestine; ⊤, melanophores; +, skeletal muscle. (From D. Rudnick, *Quart. Rev. Biol.,* **19**, 187 (1944).)

primary cavities of the brain. In the embryo these parts of the central nervous system are continuous and indistinguishable until the paired mesodermal *somites,* the primitive muscle blocks, appear. The first somites to develop are the most anterior, and since it is known that the first four pairs lie in the head, their position identifies the portion of the neural tube that is to be brain. For a time the embryo appears to be about half brain.

As the first four somite pairs appear, the anterior neural tube begins a transformation. The anterior neuropore closes (*anterior cerebral suture*), and just posteriorly to it the neural tube expands into two large lateral bulges, the *optic vesicles* of the *forebrain (prosencephalon)* (Figs. 4.11G, 4.20A,B). The anterior end of the notochord is just behind and beneath the forebrain. Immediately posterior to the forebrain are the smaller lateral bulges of the midbrain (*mesencephalon*). The *hindbrain (rhombencephalon)* extends from the midbrain to the level of the fourth pair of somites. Six to 12 somite pairs appear as the neural tube differentiates into the three primary brain regions. Still the brain is little more than an elongated tube with paired lateral pockets.

Derivatives of the endoderm

As the head fold pushes forward, the foregut elongates, and its wall forms a roof, sides, and floor. This early foregut becomes the *pharynx* (Fig. 4.13B), and sections reveal that its floor is made up of columnar cells and its roof of a thin layer of flat cells, all endoderm. Directly beneath the thickest portion of the neural plate, the endodermal floor of the foregut meets the outer ectoderm to form the *oral membrane (plate).* Simultaneously the related ectoderm pushes inward in a depression, the *stomodeum.*

Derivatives of the mesoderm

Mesoderm is the origin of the circulatory system, the urogenital system, and the skeletal and connective tissue systems. It occurs in the embryo as either *mesothelium,* which is membranous, or *mesenchyme,* which is more loosely distributed. Both arise from either ectoderm or endoderm. The considerable mesenchyme in the head derives from three sources: migrating parietal cells (ectoderm); cells proliferating from the foregut (endoderm); and head ectoderm.

Concurrently with the development of the brain and gut, important changes take place in the mesoderm. The lateral mesoderm is at first a thick sheet of cells on each side of the embryo that thins out peripherally. The thickest portion of each lateral sheet forms a solid rod extending alongside the notochord, ventrolateral to the neural tube. At about 21 hours incubation, a break appears in both rods just anteriorly to the primitive streak, giving the first indication of segmentation of the mesoderm into somites (Fig. 4.21A). The first pair of somites lies directly behind the position of the future

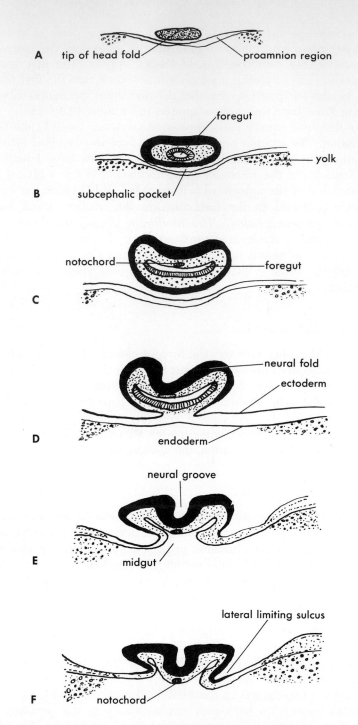

Fig. 4.17 Transverse sections of 18- to 20-hour chick embryo. (From R. Rugh, *Laboratory Manual of Vertebrate Embryology*, 5th ed., Burgess, Minneapolis, 1961.)

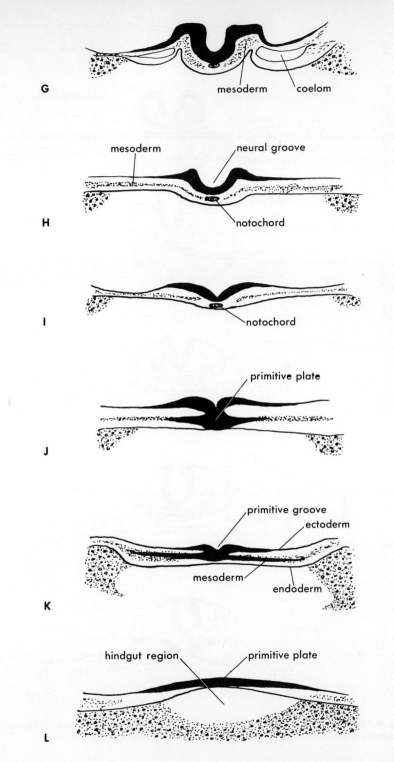

G

mesoderm coelom

mesoderm neural groove

H

notochord

I

notochord

primitive plate

J

primitive groove

ectoderm

K

mesoderm endoderm

hindgut region primitive plate

L

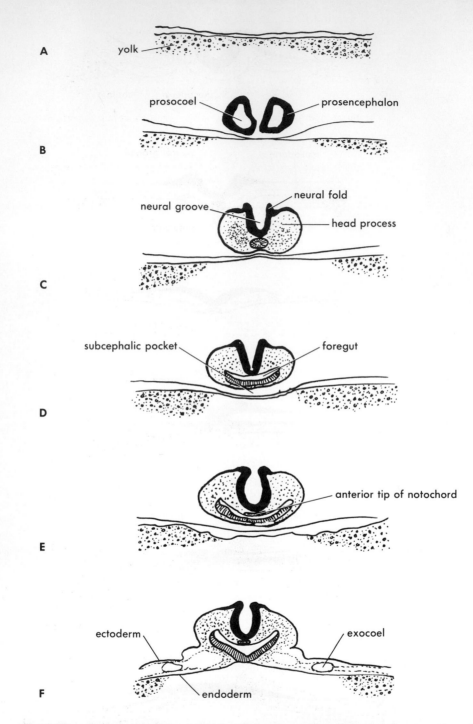

Fig. 4.18 Transverse sections of 24-hour chick embryo. (From R. Rugh, *Laboratory Manual of Vertebrate Embryology*, 5th ed., Burgess, Minneapolis, 1961.)

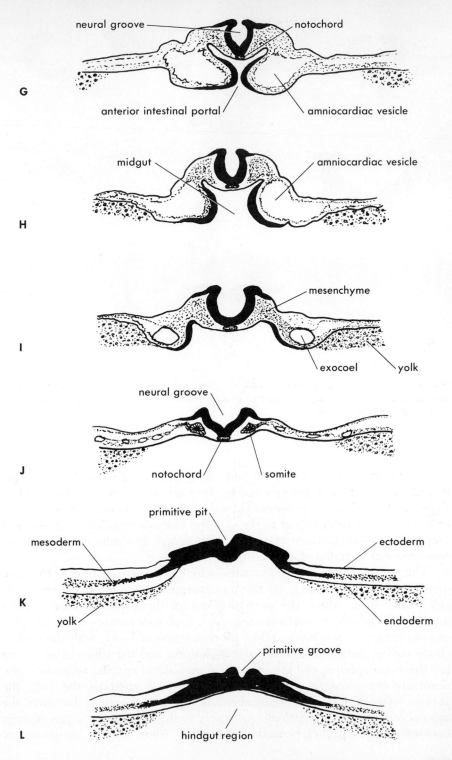

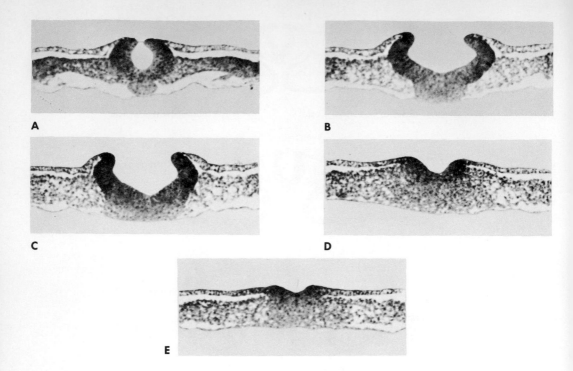

Fig. 4.19 Transverse sections of 24-hour chick embryo: A, through posterior part of neural tube; B, through anterior part of primitive streak; C, D, through primitive streak; E, through primitive groove.

auditory vesicles. From this point posteriorly paired segmental breaks in the mesoderm form blocks that give rise to other somites (Figs. 4.11D–G, 4.21B–F). At 24 hours four to six somite pairs are apparent. Shortly central cavities or lumens (*myocoels*) appear in the somites. Since incubation time does not take into account the stage of development at laying, somite number is a far more accurate criterion of age during the first 4 days.

The mesoderm next to the somites, which is somewhat thicker than the more peripheral mesoderm, is the unsegmented *nephrotome* (*intermediate cell mass*), from which the excretory system develops. Its cavity is the *nephrocoel.* Outside the nephrotome is the *lateral plate* mesoderm, which splits into an outer *somatic* layer and an inner *splanchnic* layer, with the *coelom* (body cavity) between. The somatic mesoderm and the adjacent ectoderm are the *somatopleure,* and the splanchnic mesoderm and the adjacent endoderm are the *splanchnopleure.* As the mesoderm encircles the yolk, the coelom extends into the extraembryonic regions, where it becomes the *exocoel* (*extraembryonic coelom*). Anteriorly to the first somites a pair of large coelomic spaces pushes beneath the foregut. They are the *amniocardiac vesicles,* so-called because their mesoderm gives rise to both the amnion around the embryo and the *pericardium* around the heart.

The blood islands arise as mesenchymal masses in the area opaca, first behind and then alongside the embryo, at about 24 hours. *Lacunae* within them merge to form the blood vessels, while their mesodermal substance differentiates into the epithelial lining of the vessels and into the blood cells (some of which acquire hemoglobin and become red) (Fig. 4.22). The development of the blood vessels gives the region of the area opaca involved a mottled appearance and transforms it into the *area vasculosa* (Fig. 4.23).

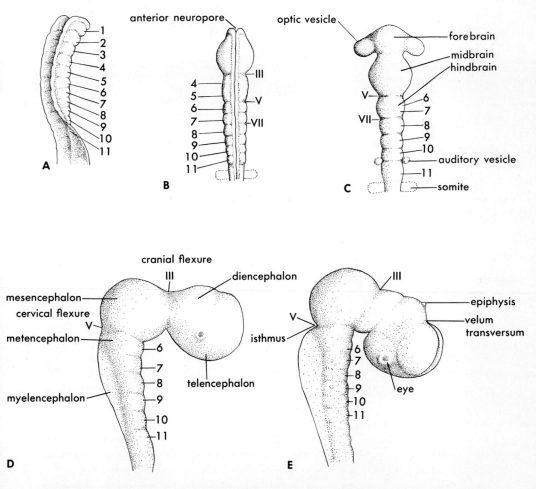

Fig. 4.20   Lateral views showing brain development in chick embryo: A, at 24 hours (4 somites); B, at 27 hours (7 somites); C, at 36 hours (14 somites); D, at 50 hours (26 somites); E, at 80 hours (36 somites). Arabic numerals denote neuromeres, and Roman numerals denote interneuromeric grooves.

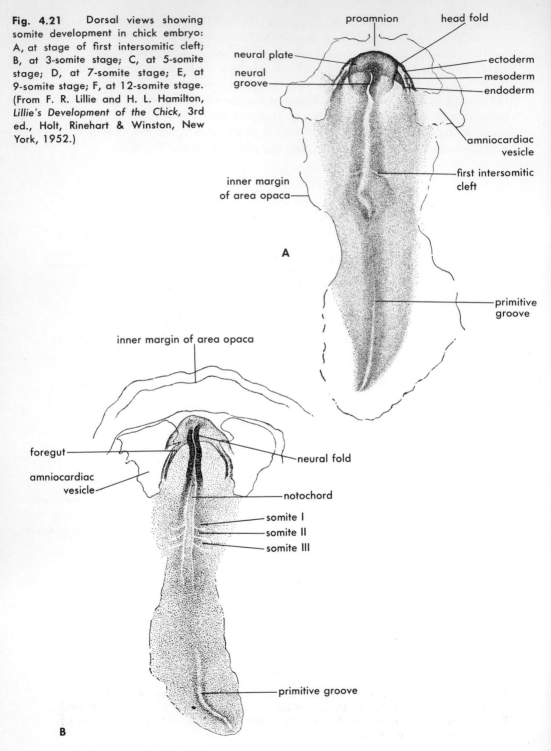

Fig. 4.21 Dorsal views showing somite development in chick embryo: A, at stage of first intersomitic cleft; B, at 3-somite stage; C, at 5-somite stage; D, at 7-somite stage; E, at 9-somite stage; F, at 12-somite stage. (From F. R. Lillie and H. L. Hamilton, *Lillie's Development of the Chick*, 3rd ed., Holt, Rinehart & Winston, New York, 1952.)

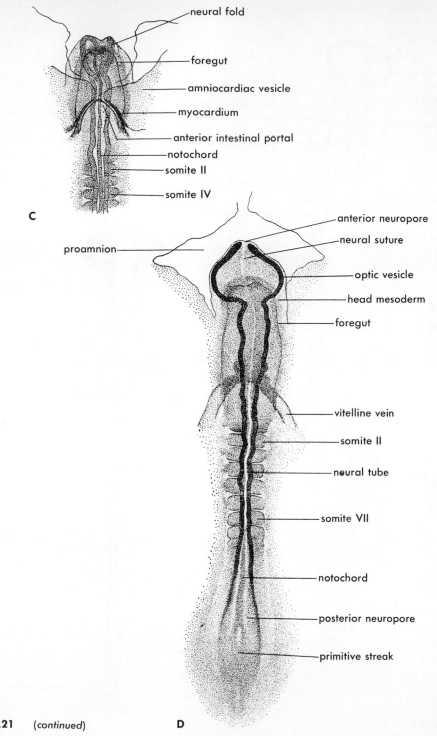

neural fold

foregut

amniocardiac vesicle

myocardium

anterior intestinal portal

notochord

somite II

somite IV

C

proamnion

anterior neuropore

neural suture

optic vesicle

head mesoderm

foregut

vitelline vein

somite II

neural tube

somite VII

notochord

posterior neuropore

primitive streak

Fig. 4.21 (continued) D

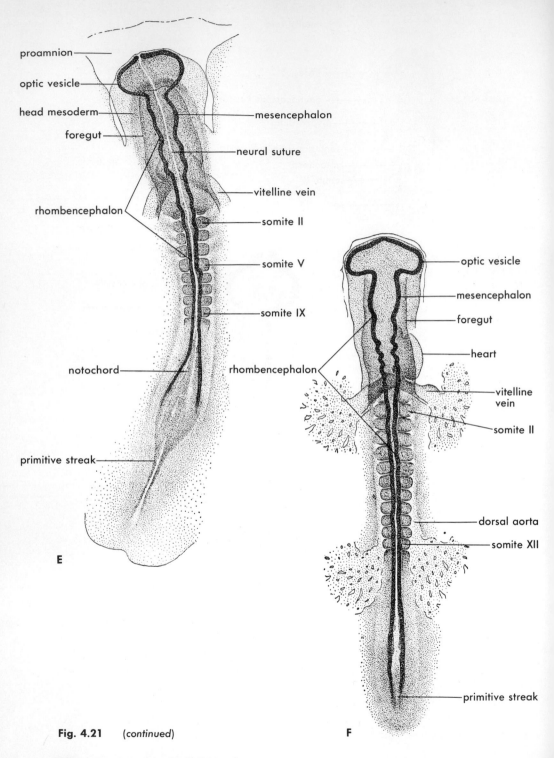

proamnion

optic vesicle

head mesoderm

foregut

mesencephalon

neural suture

vitelline vein

rhombencephalon

somite II

somite V

somite IX

notochord

primitive streak

E

optic vesicle

mesencephalon

foregut

heart

rhombencephalon

vitelline vein

somite II

dorsal aorta

somite XII

primitive streak

F

Fig. 4.21 (*continued*)

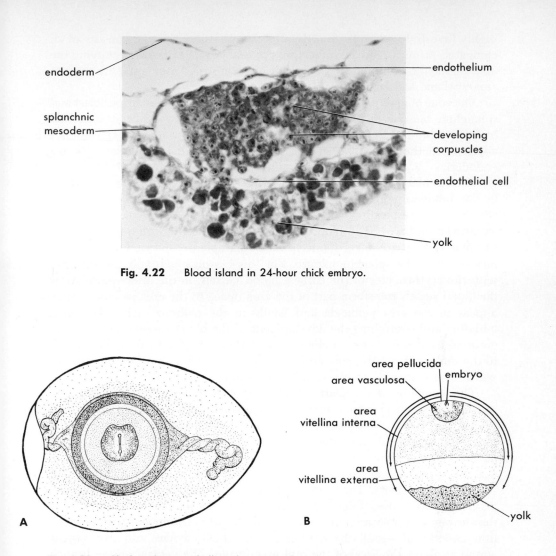

Fig. 4.22 Blood island in 24-hour chick embryo.

Fig. 4.23 Chick embryo in shell: A, longitudinal section at 24 hours; B, transverse section at 50 hours, with albumen removed. (From R. Rugh, *Laboratory Manual of Vertebrate Embryology*, 5th ed., Burgess, Minneapolis, 1961.)

The blood vessels of the area vasculosa anastomose in a network having as its outer boundary an encircling vein known as the *sinus* (*vena*) *terminalis.* Just beyond the sinus terminalis the endoderm follows the ectoderm closely, and the two layers comprise a ring, the *area vitellina interna.* Outside this ring the single layer of ectoderm extends over the yolk in the *area vitellina externa,* which includes the margin of overgrowth and the zone of junction. The names of both areas (designated together as the area vitellina) derive from their close association with the yolk. Their cells are, in fact, highly invested with yolk. Shortly after laying, then, the egg consists of an elongated primitive streak, indicating the embryonic axis and occupying the area pellucida, bounded by the rather circular area vasculosa, two rings of area vitellina, and finally the uncovered yolk.

The zone of junction actually consists of white yolk invaded by periblast and splanchnic mesoderm. The periblast eventually digests the surrounding yolk to form a thin layer of endoderm, the *yolk sac endoderm,* separate from but adjacent to the yolk. The splanchnic mesoderm lies above the yolk sac endoderm.

The circulatory system originates as three distinct divisions, which develop in the following sequence: extraembryonic (for nutrition); accessory (or allantoic, for respiration and excretion); and embryonic (for distribution within the embryo). The blood islands, which differentiate into the blood vascular system, are never found in the somatopleure but are limited to the mesoderm of the splanchnopleure. For this reason much yolk intermingles with the erythrocytes of the earliest blood vessels, in the area opaca. After the blood vessels transform part of the area opaca to the area vasculosa, they appear in the area pellucida and finally in the embryo itself. The forces initiating and controlling the development of the blood vascular system integrate all these vessels into a closed circuit that carries nutrition and oxygen to the embryo from the yolk and excretory materials from the embryo outward. The system is continuous by 26 hours.

The formation of the heart probably involves the most intricate developmental changes. The organ consists of a lining (*endocardium*) from a thin-walled pair of embryonic blood vessels, a muscular wall (*myocardium*) from the innermost splanchnic mesoderm, a cavity (*pericardial cavity*) from a cutoff portion of the coelom, and its surrounding mesoderm (pericardium). Although it arises from bilateral structures and movements, it is a single elongated tube suspended in a cavity. The fusion of the paired primordia into the single tube proceeds posteriorly. (Figs. 4.24, 4.25A, 4.26). So does the development of the surrounding myocardium. Anteriorly the heart is continuous with a single, thin endothelial vessel, the *ventral aorta,* which divides into two ventral aortae at about the level of the oral membrane. The ventral aortae branch into the first aortic arches connecting dorsally with paired *dorsal aortae.* Posteriorly the heart joins the fusion of two large venous (*vitelline,* or *omphalomesenteric*) vessels coming from the yolk (Fig. 4.11F,G). Since its muscle develops from splanchnic mesoderm, for a time both a *dorsal mesocardium* and a *ventral mesocardium* support it in its cavity. The ventral mesocardium soon ruptures, however, leaving the heart suspended by the dorsal mesocardium and anchored anteriorly and posteriorly by paired vessels. Because of its secure attachment at either end, when the heart begins to grow rapidly, it twists upon itself. Thus it forms its chambers and assumes the characteristic shape of the adult heart. Its posterior part becomes the *sinus venosus* and the adjoining atrium, and the anterior two thirds become the *ventricle* and the *bulbus arteriosus,* which leads to the ventral aorta.

The heart begins to pulsate as it forms. The earliest movements are fibrillar contractions along the right margin of the developing ventricle, which coalesce to involve the entire right side of the ventricle. The next movements occur on the left side of the ventricle, prior to the division of that structure and as the atrium is becoming morphologically distinct. Then the atrial walls begin to contract, at a slightly faster rate than the walls of the ventricle, so that soon the atrium controls the ventricular pulse. Shortly, and even before the sinus venosus is distinguishable, blood corpuscles are forced through the primitive circulatory system. When the sinus differentiates, into both endocardium and myocardium, it has a still higher pulse rate and finally assumes control of the contractions of both the atrium and the ventricle. From this time on the cardiac pulsations are regular, rhythmic, and correlated.

If one opens the developing chick egg at about 26 hours, he can witness the earliest beatings of the heart mass. If he quickly excises the blastoderm, places it in warm saline, and observes it under the dissection microscope, he will see that this mass beats rhythmically even before it is a formed heart. Aristotle named this phase the *puntum saliens* (springing point). The beat is initiated at the sinoatrial and atrioventricular nodes, the first of which is known as the *pacemaker* of the heart. The heart beat rate is regulated by the carbon dioxide content of the blood and in birds stabilizes at about 200 counts per minute. If the embryonic heart is removed and cut into several pieces, and if these pieces are properly fed and protected against infection, each may continue to beat for several decades, a period far beyond the life expectancy of the chicken. The heart is a magnificent organ, apparently indefatigable, and the cessation of its activity invariably means the death of all other organs and the organism itself.

The circulation of a 26-hour chick embryo is as follows: The simple tubular heart pumps blood anteriorly into the ventral aorta, which becomes paired, and thence to the paired first aortic arches, which connect dorsally with the paired dorsal aortae. These carry blood posteriorly below the somites and the spinal cord, giving off *intersegmental arteries,* and finally turn outward as paired *vitelline arteries* toward the yolk. In the area vasculosa the outgoing arterial vessels connect with the incoming venous vessels in a capillary plexus and then converge into one of the two *vitelline veins* taking blood to the embryo and into its heart.

At the end of the first day of incubation, these derivatives of the primary germ layers are present:

ECTODERM: head fold, neural tube, neural crests, and optic vesicles.

ENDODERM: foregut, in head region only.

MESODERM: six pairs of somites, nephrotome, lateral plate mesoderm divided into somatic and splanchnic layers and coelom, pericardial cavity and heart rudiments, embryonic and extraembryonic blood vessels and corpuscles, area vasculosa with sinus terminalis, and area vitellina (interna and externa).

In addition, the separation of the embryo from its extraembryonic membranes and vascular network is beginning.

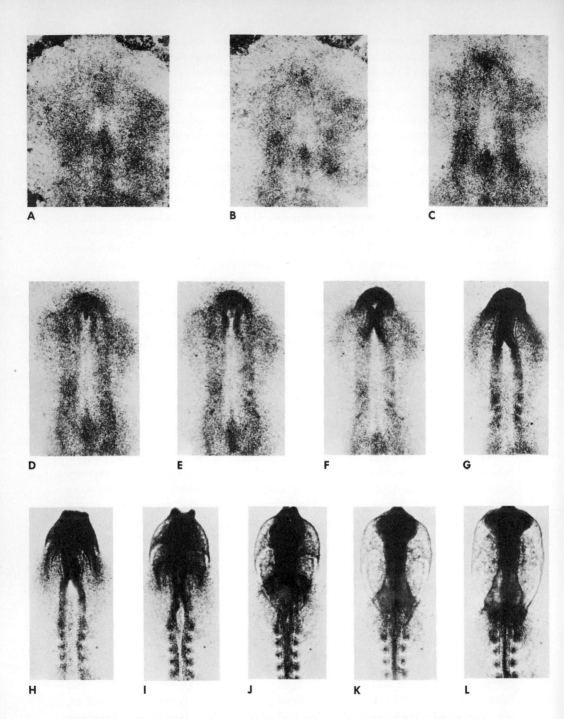

Fig. 4.24 Ventral views showing heart development in chick embryo. Numbers in right heart-forming regions indicate specific cell clusters. (From R. L. DeHaan, *Carnegie Inst. Wash. Yearbook*, 1960.)

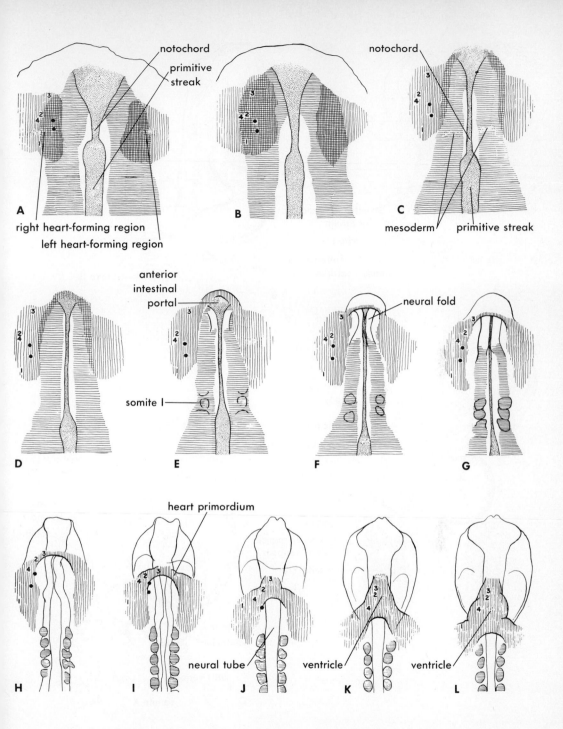

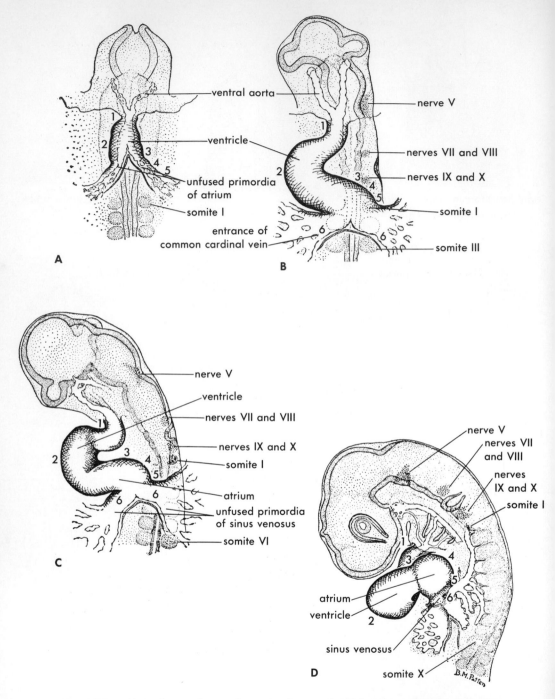

Fig. 4.25   Ventral views showing heart development in chick embryo: A, at 9-somite stage; B, at 16-somite stage; C, at 19-somite stage. Arabic numerals indicate specific regions. (From E. C. Hoff, T. C. Kramer, D. DuBois, and B. M. Patten, *Am. Heart J.*, **17**, 470 (1939).)

152   THE CHICK: *A Shelled Vertebrate*

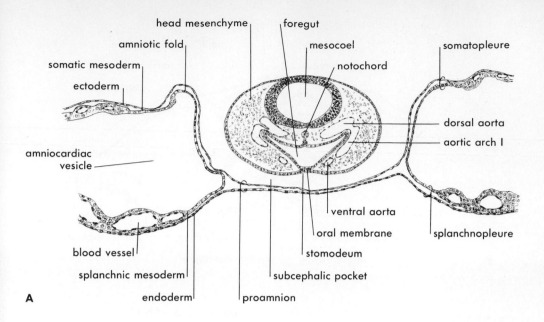

A

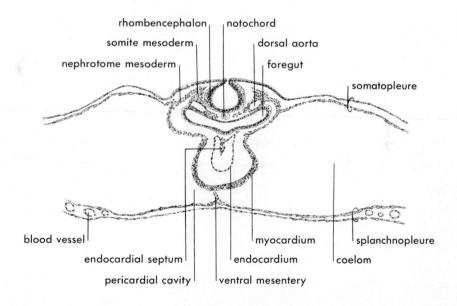

B

Fig. 4.26 Transverse sections of 7- to 10-somite chick embryo: A, through subcephalic pocket; B, through rhombencephalon; C, slightly anterior to anterior intestinal portal; D, through anterior intestinal portal.

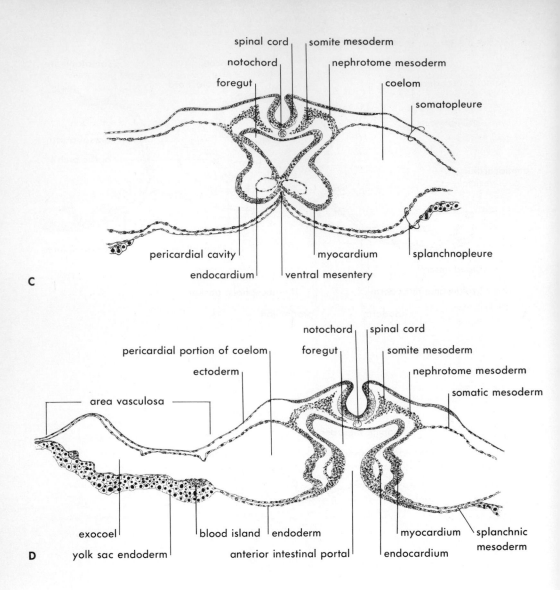

C

D

Fig. 4.26 (continued)

Between 33 and 72 hours incubation the chick embryo undergoes its major differentiations (Figs. 4.27–4.32). By 72 hours it has separated from the yolk, has rotated to lie on its left side, has developed all its extraembryonic membranes, and has acquired its organ primordia from ectoderm, endoderm, and mesoderm.

Separation from extraembryonic structures

The first indication of the separation of the embryo from its yolk is the forward projection of the head fold, resulting in the formation of the sub-cephalic pocket. The innermost recess of the pocket is the *anterior limiting sulcus*. As growth continues, the pocket extends laterally on both sides beneath the embryo, in the *lateral limiting sulci,* and eventually forms the *posterior limiting sulcus,* thus completing an encircling groove beneath the embryo and pinching it off from the underlying yolk much in the manner of a drawstring. The time interval from the first appearance of the anterior limiting sulcus beneath the head to the completion of the posterior limiting sulcus beneath the tail is about 27 hours.

In transverse sections the presence of thickened masses of mesoderm in the body wall somatopleure at the level of the sulci distinguishes the embryo from the extraembryonic structures. In certain regions the thickening is extreme, forming limb buds.

The embryo grows lengthwise in both directions as the somatopleure closes in under it, so that the anterior and posterior extremities of the gut are cut off from the yolk and become tubular. The opening from the *yolk sac* into the foregut is the *anterior intestinal portal,* and that from the yolk sac into the *hindgut* is the *posterior intestinal portal.* Eventually only the *midgut* retains a connection with the yolk, the yolk stalk. However, at no time does yolk pass through the stalk until just before hatching, when the little yolk that remains is drawn into the midgut, which finally closes off also. The yolk nutrition is digested outside the embryo and is carried by the vitelline veins to the embryonic vascular system and thence to the developing tissues.

Rotation

At the first appearance of an embryonic axis, the embryo lies flat on the yolk, with obvious bilateral symmetry. As it elongates and separates from the yolk, it starts rotating, probably to accommodate itself to the limited space. The rotation begins at the anterior end at about 14 hours incubation and ends with the embryo lying on its left side (dextral torsion) at 4 days. Simultaneously the brain bends, so that when the entire body has rotated 90° the general form of the embryo is that of a reversed question mark. The first bend in the brain is the cranial flexure, involving the mesencephalon (Figs. 4.20D, 4.32). This flexure, which results from the rapid growth of the prosencephalon, is per-

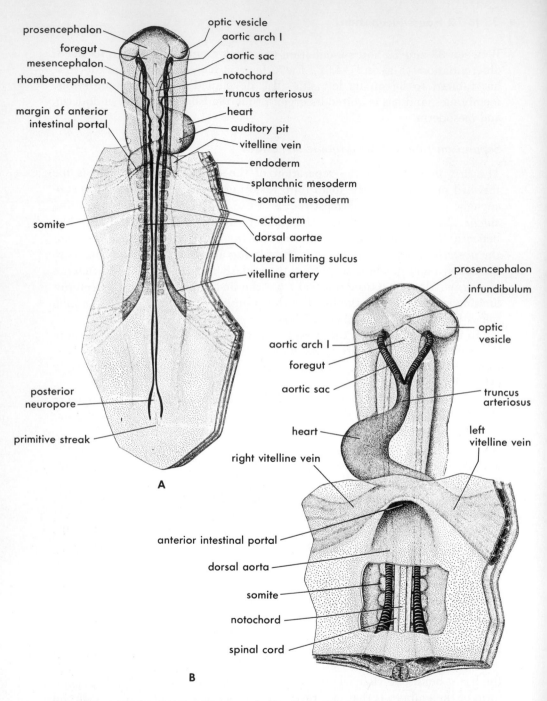

Fig. 4.27 Chick embryo at 33 hours: A, dorsal view; B, ventral view of anterior portion. (From A. E. Huettner, *Fundamentals of Comparative Embryology of the Vertebrates*, rev. ed., Macmillan, New York, 1949.)

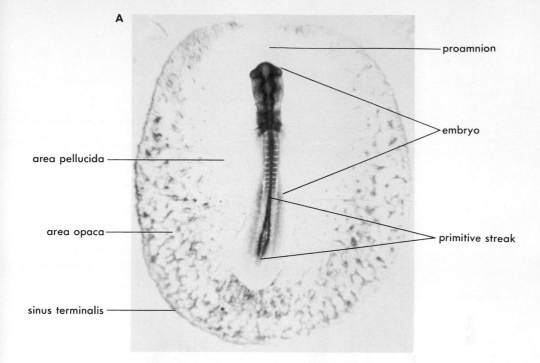

Fig. 4.28   Chick embryo at 33 hours: A, dorsal view; B, dorsal view showing heart development; C, ventral view showing heart development.

manent. Shortly a second bend, the cervical flexure, occurs at the point where the head and body join. This flexure is only embryonic. The second flexure extends the first so far that the anterior tip of the head actually points posteriorly, with the prosencephalon folded back against the ventral aspect of the throat. A third bend, the pontine flexure, occurs at the level of the *myelencephalon* (the posterior part of the rhombencephalon) at 72 hours. Ultimately the posterior end of the embryo also bends ventrally, and by 96 hours the embryo not only is on its left side but also has the exaggerated C shape characteristic of all amniote vertebrates.

Embryonic membranes

Each of the extraembryonic membranes—amnion, *chorion, allantois,* and yolk sac—forms in essentially the same way and has the same primary functions in all amniotes. The amnion and chorion arise from somatopleure (ectoderm and mesoderm), and the allantois and yolk sac from splanchnopleure (endoderm and mesoderm). All except the chorion connect with the embryo through the *umbilical stalk.*

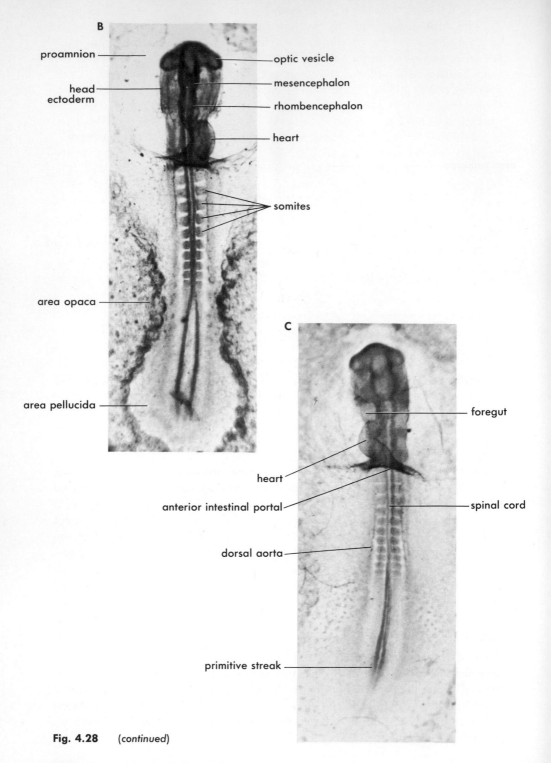

B

proamnion

head
ectoderm

optic vesicle

mesencephalon

rhombencephalon

heart

somites

area opaca

area pellucida

C

foregut

heart

spinal cord

anterior intestinal portal

dorsal aorta

primitive streak

Fig. 4.28   (*continued*)

The amnion and chorion develop simultaneously, the amnion from the original somatopleure of the area pellucida and the chorion from more lateral extensions of somatopleure. While the somatopleure pushes inward as sulci beneath the embryo, its extraembryonic portion lifts upward to fold over the embryo. The first fold appears at the anterior end (at 30 hours), in connection with the early development of the head fold and the anterior limiting sulcus. This *anterior amniotic fold* curves backward over the head and is continuous with *lateral amniotic folds*, which appear next, and eventually with a *posterior amniotic fold* (at 3 days). At about the 27-somite stage the uncovered embryo is visible only through an oval situated posteriorly. The folds meet and fuse above the embryo, producing two saclike membranes around it. The outer one, with its mesoderm toward the embryo and its ectoderm away from it (the characteristic arrangement of somatopleure), is the chorion. It encloses both embryo and yolk. The inner one, with its ectoderm toward the embryo and its mesoderm away from it, is the amnion. It covers a fluid-filled cavity, the *amniotic cavity,* that encloses only the embryo. The amniotic fluid protects the embryo from mechanical shocks and jarring and reduces the possibility of desiccation.

Since the embryo rotates as the amnion and chorion form, the fusion of the somatopleuric folds occurs over its right side rather than over its dorsal surface. Accordingly, the fold from the left (under) side must extend clear around the embryo to the right (upper) side. The fold from the right side is therefore shorter and thicker than the one from the left. A knot of tissue, the *amniotic raphe,* marks the point of fusion of the amnion above the embryo and remains throughout embryonic life.

The yolk sac differentiates progressively, and its tissue attains its maximum development at the end of incubation. It consists of yolk sac splanchnopleure, always intimately associated with yolk, and is continuous with the developing gut by way of the yolk stalk. The yolk sac splanchnopleure is in contact with the chorion except where the exocoel or the allantois intervenes. Yolk sac septa in the endoderm of the yolk sac splanchnopleure produce enzymes that digest the yolk, and nutrition passes through the numerous blood vessels to the embryo.

The allantois is an outgrowth of the hindgut appearing at 60 hours just anteriorly to the region of the *cloacal membrane* and extending into the exocoel. Its lining is gut endoderm, and its covering is very vascular splanchnic mesoderm. The allantois functions as a respiratory and excretory organ until hatching (even though the chick may pierce its membranes and breathe from the air space of the shell before hatching); through the *chorioallantoic membrane,* which is adjacent to the shell membranes, it removes oxygen from the environment and discharges gaseous and liquid wastes. For these purposes it carries two *umbilical (allantoic) arteries* and two *umbilical (allantoic) veins,* with the left umbilical artery persisting throughout incubation. The allantois also takes part in the absorption of the albumen.

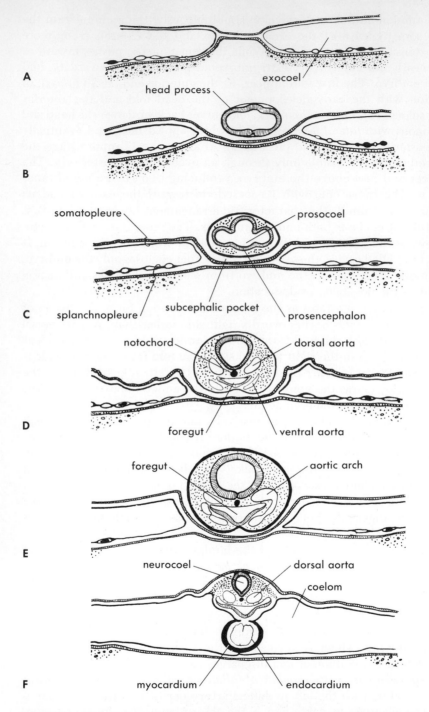

Fig. 4.29 Transverse sections of 33-hour chick embryo. (From R. Rugh, *Laboratory Manual of Vertebrate Embryology*, 5th ed., Burgess, Minneapolis, 1961.)

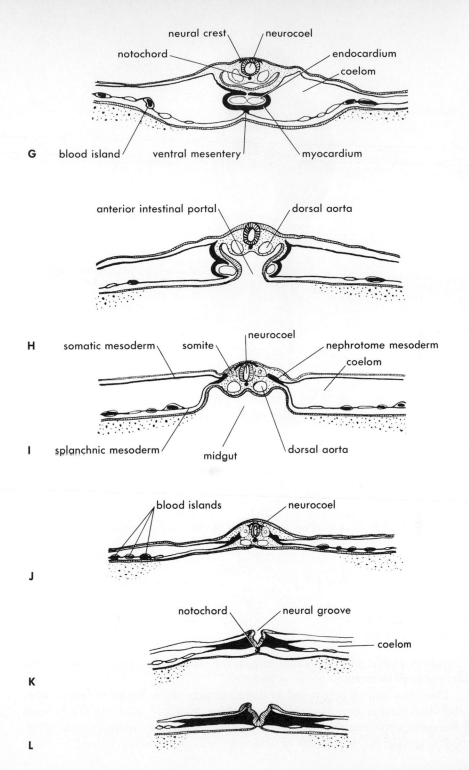

G

neural crest · neurocoel
notochord
endocardium
coelom
blood island · ventral mesentery · myocardium

anterior intestinal portal · dorsal aorta

H

somatic mesoderm · somite · neurocoel · nephrotome mesoderm
coelom

I

splanchnic mesoderm · midgut · dorsal aorta

blood islands · neurocoel

J

notochord · neural groove
coelom

K

L

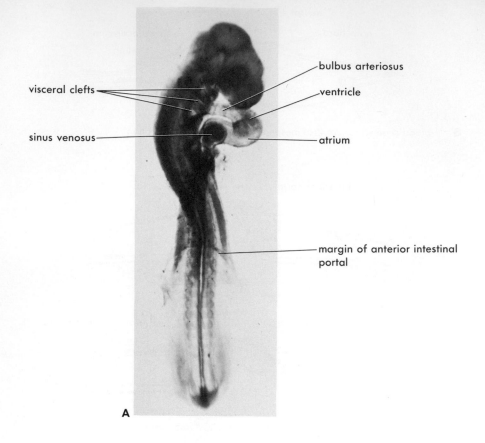

visceral clefts

bulbus arteriosus

ventricle

sinus venosus

atrium

margin of anterior intestinal portal

A

Fig. 4.30   Dorsal views showing development of chick embryo from 40 to 60 hours: A, at 40 hours; B, at 44 hours; C, at 48 hours; D, at 60 hours.

Derivatives of the ectoderm

NERVOUS SYSTEM.   The brain, the spinal cord, and the cranial and spinal nerves are all derivatives of the ectoderm.

The brain, which originated as three sections of the anterior neural tube, subdivides further into five major parts (Figs. 4.20C,D, 4.33). In the process it becomes apparent that the neural tube ectoderm is metameric (as is the somite mesoderm). It consists of *neuromeres*, concentrations of neural tissue

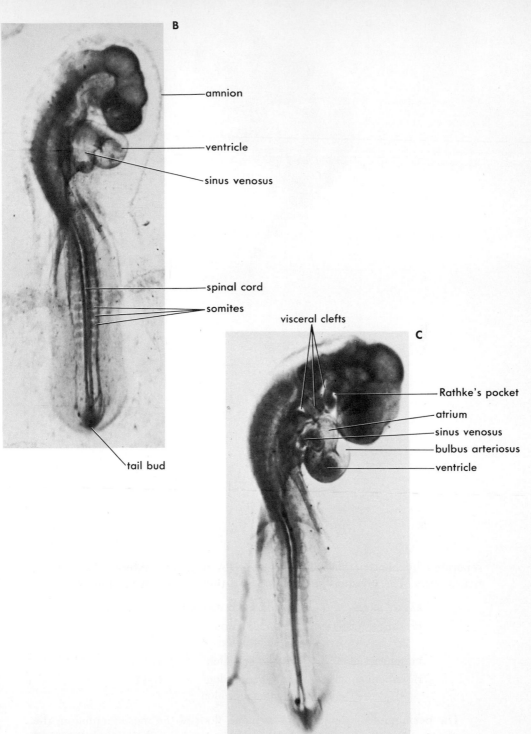

Labels on figure B:
amnion
ventricle
sinus venosus
spinal cord
somites
tail bud

Labels on figure C:
visceral clefts
Rathke's pocket
atrium
sinus venosus
bulbus arteriosus
ventricle

Fig. 4.30 (continued)

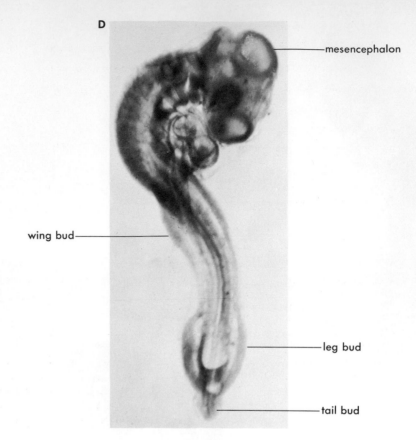

D

mesencephalon

wing bud

leg bud

tail bud

Fig. 4.30   *(continued)*

separated by constrictions. The brain arises from the anterior 11 pairs of neuromeres. The divisions of the brain and their origins are as follows:

EARLY BRAIN	COMPLETED BRAIN	NEUROMERES
prosencephalon	telencephalon	1–3
	diencephalon	
mesencephalon	mesencephalon	4, 5
rhombencephalon	metencephalon	6–11
	myelencephalon	

The permanent cranial flexure is in the floor of the mesencephalon, the transient cervical flexure at the junction of the myelencephalon and the spinal

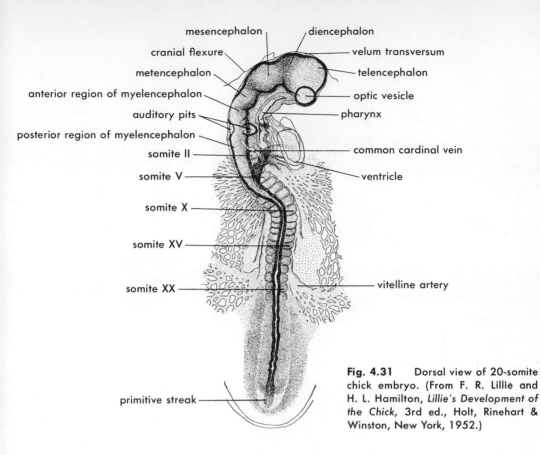

mesencephalon
cranial flexure
metencephalon
anterior region of myelencephalon
auditory pits
posterior region of myelencephalon
somite II
somite V
somite X
somite XV
somite XX
primitive streak

diencephalon
velum transversum
telencephalon
optic vesicle
pharynx
common cardinal vein
ventricle
vitelline artery

Fig. 4.31 Dorsal view of 20-somite chick embryo. (From F. R. Lillie and H. L. Hamilton, *Lillie's Development of the Chick,* 3rd ed., Holt, Rinehart & Winston, New York, 1952.)

cord, and the pontine flexure, last to develop, in the floor of the myelencephalon. Since the various flexures direct the anterior end of the brain forward and downward, a considerable portion of the prosencephalon occupies a prechordal position, whereas the mesencephalon and rhombencephalon are suprachordal.

As the brain differentiates, its cellular wall grows at the expense of its central cavity and eventually reduces it to narrow ventricles that are continuous within the brain and with the central canal of the spinal cord. The prosencephalon develops first, and most actively, of the brain divisions, with tremendous lateral bulges from its floor (the optic vesicles), constrictions in its roof that demarcate the *telencephalon* from the *diencephalon,* and thickenings and thinnings in its roof and lateral walls. Its posterior limit extends from the anterior margin of the dorsal thickening to the *tuberculum posterius,* an invagination in the floor at the anterior end of the notochord (Fig. 4.33).

The first signs of differentiation are the large paired optic vesicles. As they appear, a downgrowth of head mesenchyme somewhat constricts the prosencephalon from the rest of the brain. The result is paired lateral sacs

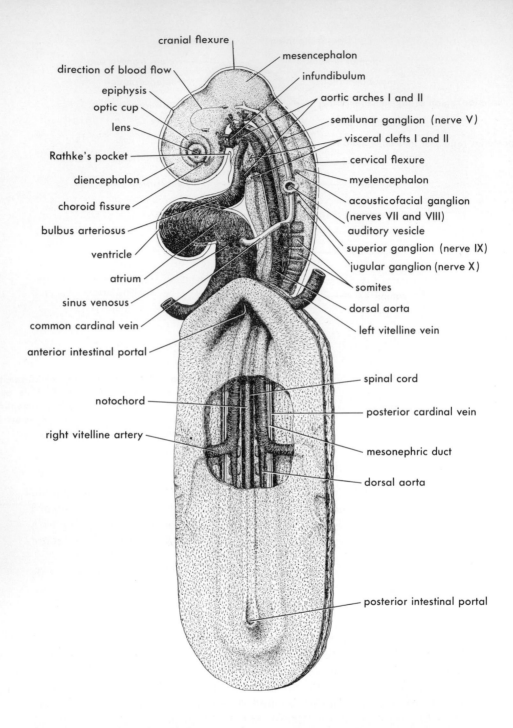

cranial flexure
mesencephalon
direction of blood flow
infundibulum
epiphysis
aortic arches I and II
optic cup
semilunar ganglion (nerve V)
lens
visceral clefts I and II
Rathke's pocket
cervical flexure
diencephalon
myelencephalon
choroid fissure
acousticofacial ganglion
(nerves VII and VIII)
bulbus arteriosus
auditory vesicle
ventricle
superior ganglion (nerve IX)
atrium
jugular ganglion (nerve X)
sinus venosus
somites
common cardinal vein
dorsal aorta
anterior intestinal portal
left vitelline vein

spinal cord
notochord
posterior cardinal vein
right vitelline artery
mesonephric duct
dorsal aorta

posterior intestinal portal

Fig. 4.32 Ventral view of 48-hour chick embryo. (From A. E. Huettner, *Fundamentals of Comparative Embryology of the Vertebrates*, rev. ed., Macmillan, New York, 1949.)

having tubular connections with the brain, the *optic stalks*. The *optic recess* is a depression in the prosencephalon floor, and the slight thickening between it and the closed anterior neuropore is the *lamina terminalis*.

The second change in the prosencephalon is its superficial division into the telencephalon (anterior) and the diencephalon (posterior). At about 20 hours incubation a slight thickening develops in the roof. This is the *velum transversum*. An imaginary line from the velum transversum to the optic recess marks the boundary between the telencephalon and the diencephalon. The most prominent derivative of the roof of the diencephalon at this time is the *epiphysis* (pineal body), which appears as an evagination just posterior to the velum transversum. The *infundibulum* is a pocket in the diencephalon floor beneath the anterior end of the notochord and just anterior to the tuberculum posterius. The differentiations in the walls of the prosencephalon are difficult to detect before 72 hours.

The mesencephalon is easily identified in sagittal sections, since its roof is rather uniformly thick and bulging. Its rapid growth leads to the development of the cranial flexure. The anterior and posterior boundaries of the mesencephalon extend from the anterior and posterior limits of its dorsal thickening to the tuberculum posterius. The posterior limit of the roof is a deep constriction, the *isthmus*. The lateral walls expand somewhat to form the *optic lobes*.

The rhombencephalon is the longest division of the early embryonic brain, involving six pairs of neuromeres and the first four pairs of somites. There is little differentiation in this region before 72 hours. The short *metencephalon* (anterior, only one neuromere) has a thick roof, whereas the long *myelencephalon* (posterior, five pairs of neuromeres and four pairs of somites) has a very thin roof.

The paired neural crests, which extend the length of the embryo, give rise to 12 pairs of cranial nerves and 38 pairs of spinal nerves, with the numerous associated *ganglia* (Figs. 4.25B,C,D, 4.34). In addition, they give rise to the sympathetic ganglia, to some interganglionic mesenchyme, and to *chromatophores* and *sheath cells*. Since the most anterior crests differentiate first, transverse sections of the embryo from posterior to anterior show progressive stages in nerve development. The differentiating cells, or *neuroblasts*, are very delicate and sensitive.

The neural crests in the head may be topographically divided into those developing anteriorly to the ear (*preotic*) and those developing posteriorly to the ear (*postotic*). The preotic crests begin to form at about the 6-somite stage. Ganglionic masses appear as enlargements of the crests both in the head (cranial) and in the body (spinal). Mesenchyme develops from the interganglionic regions and moves between the masses, particularly in the head; thus some mesoderm arises from neural ectoderm.

By the 8-somite stage the preotic neural crests are complete. By the 10-somite stage the preotic masses form elongated condensations of deeply staining cells that become the *semilunar* and *acousticofacial* cranial ganglia.

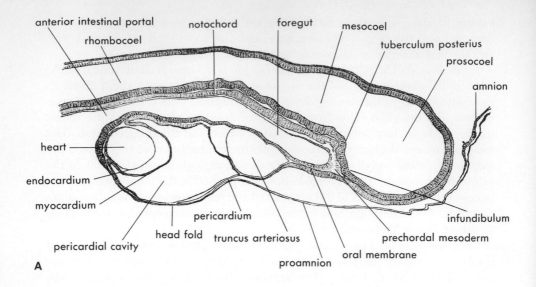

A

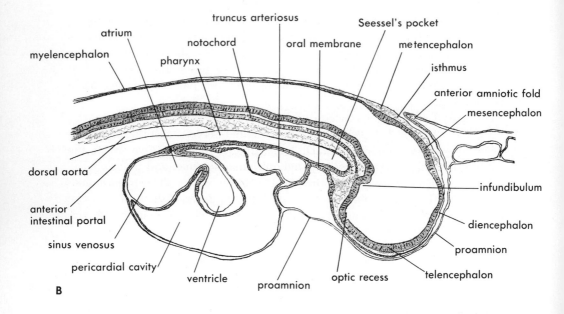

B

Fig. 4.33 Sagittal sections showing brain and heart development in chick embryo: A, at 13-somite stage; B, at 18-somite stage; C, at 22-somite stage; D, at 30-somite stage. (A, B from F. R. Lillie and H. L. Hamilton, *Lillie's Development of the Chick,* 3rd ed., Holt, Rinehart & Winston, New York, 1952.)

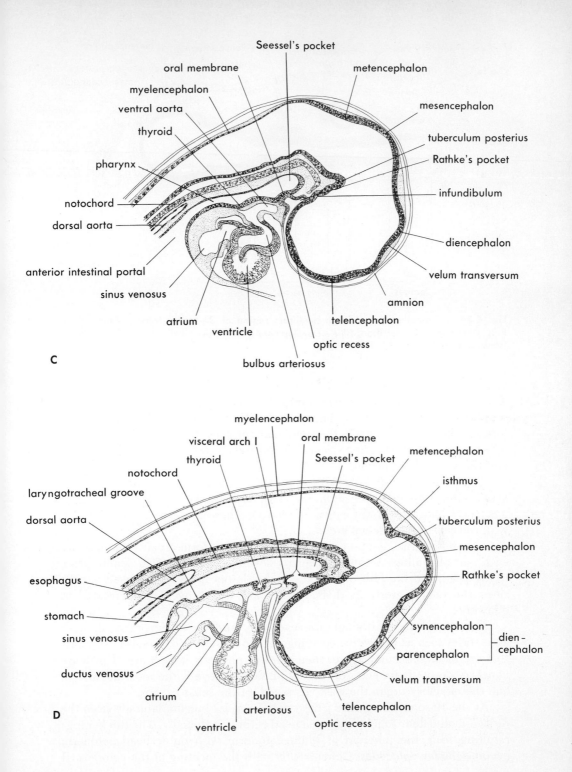

C

oral membrane
myelencephalon
ventral aorta
thyroid
pharynx
notochord
dorsal aorta
anterior intestinal portal
sinus venosus
atrium
ventricle
bulbus arteriosus
optic recess
telencephalon
amnion
Seessel's pocket
metencephalon
mesencephalon
tuberculum posterius
Rathke's pocket
infundibulum
diencephalon
velum transversum

D

myelencephalon
visceral arch I
thyroid
notochord
laryngotracheal groove
dorsal aorta
esophagus
stomach
sinus venosus
ductus venosus
atrium
ventricle
bulbus arteriosus
optic recess
telencephalon
velum transversum
parencephalon
synencephalon
dien-cephalon
Rathke's pocket
mesencephalon
tuberculum posterius
isthmus
metencephalon
Seessel's pocket
oral membrane

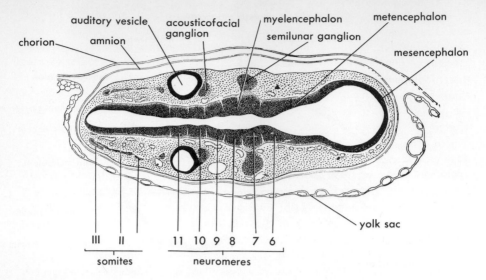

Fig. 4.34 Frontal section through hindbrain region of 36-somite chick embryo. (From F. R. Lillie and H. L. Hamilton, *Lillie's Development of the Chick,* 3rd ed., Holt, Rinehart & Winston, New York, 1952.)

The acousticofacial, which grows into the second *visceral (hyoid) arch* and supplies the *acoustic* (VIII) and *facial* (VII) *nerves,* assumes prominence first. By the 27-somite stage, the semilunar supplies the *trigeminal nerve* (V), which branches into the first visceral (*mandibular*) arch, the *maxillary process,* and the *ophthalmic* region.

The postotic crests give rise to the *superior* and *petrosal ganglia,* which supply the *glossopharyngeal nerve* (IX), and to the *jugular* and *nodose ganglia,* which supply the *vagus nerve* (X). These are associated primarily with the remaining visceral arches.

As somites arise, neural crest cells aggregate to form a pair of ganglia for each pair of somites. A total of 42 pairs develops. The first four somite pairs, in the head, and the fifth pair, in the body, do not have well-formed ganglia since the neural crests in their vicinity are not so well differentiated as elsewhere.

SENSE ORGANS. Although the eye, ear, and olfactory organ all have accessories such as protective coverings, blood vessels, and structural supports that are of mesodermal origin, their sensory portions, which are of primary concern, derive from ectoderm. At 72 hours the eye is the most advanced, and the olfactory organ the least advanced, of the sense organs.

At the 10-somite stage the paired optic vesicles bulging laterally from the diencephalon floor touch the lateral head ectoderm dorsally. The thickenings resulting from the junction of brain ectoderm with outer head ectoderm become the *lens placodes.* Concurrently with the meeting of the ectodermal layers, the lateral margin of each vesicle invaginates to form a double-layered cup, the *optic cup*, which contains the lens thickening. As the optic cup expands inward, its lining, the *sensory layer of the retina*, thickens and comes into close contact with its outer, *pigmented layer*, thus almost obliterating an intermediate extension of the brain cavity into the eye. Meanwhile, the lens thickening also invaginates to form a cup, the *lens cup*, with its aperture to the outside (Fig. 4.32). In an embryo of about 30 somites, therefore, two cups appear in a head section, the lens cup within the double-layered optic cup. The optic cup is not exactly spherical, for it has an inverted groove in its floor. This groove, the *choroid fissure*, is a transitory structure through which the optic nerve passes from the diencephalon into the optic cup to spread out over the retina. The groove also encloses the blood vessels associated with the retina. The differentiation of the eye is an excellent example of cooperative development among the primary germ layers. It involves not only brain and head ectoderm but also mesoderm, which gives rise to the connective tissue layers (*sclera* and *choroid*) and to the under layers of the *cornea*.

Just anteriorly to the first pair of somites and at the level of the eleventh pair of neuromeres, a pair of circular condensations of ectoderm, the *auditory placodes*, appear. At about the 14-somite stage (34 hours), each placode invaginates to form an auditory (*otic*) vesicle (or *otocyst*) (Fig. 4.34). Each vesicle enlarges ventrally, closes, and acquires a cluster of cells, the *otolith*, and an elongated neck, the *endolymphatic duct*. The base of the vesicle thickens and joins the acoustic nerve (VIII).

The *olfactory placodes* appear as ectodermal thickenings anterior to the eyes at about the 28-somite stage. They give rise to the sensory epithelium of the nose. The placodes invaginate to form *olfactory pits*, with a lining of five or more cell layers. Olfactory nerves grow from each pit to the telencephalon.

Derivatives of the endoderm

The entire alimentary canal develops from splanchnopleure; it is lined with endoderm and invested with mesoderm, which forms its muscles, blood vessels, connective tissue, and outer covering mesothelium. However, ectoderm breaks through from the outside at the stomodeum (mouth) and proctodeum (anus) to line the cavity at either end. This ectoderm is continuous with the endoderm lining the major portion of the gut, and the two germ layers are indistinguishable.

Arbitrary subdivisions of the gut are the foregut (from the stomodeum to and including the *liver* primordium), the midgut (open to the yolk), and the hindgut (from the midgut to the proctodeum). Throughout its length splanchnic mesoderm attaches its mid-dorsal surface to the dorsal body wall, forming the *dorsal mesentery*. As the embryo elongates, and as the sulci undercut it on all sides, the gut acquires a floor except at the midgut region, which remains open over the yolk for some time. The lateral limiting sulci contribute to the formation of a *ventral mesentery* where the gut becomes tubular.

For a time the two mesenteries separate the coelom into bilateral halves. The ventral mesentery soon ruptures, however, except at the liver and extreme posterior end, leaving the gut suspended in the coelom (in the *peritoneal cavity*) by the dorsal mesentery.

The stomodeum arises as an ectodermal thickening ventral to the foregut and not quite terminal. It thins (at the 12-somite stage), invaginates, and breaks through the oral membrane (at the 30-somite stage) to form the lining of the mouth or buccal cavity. Simultaneously with the rupture, a forward-directed pouch, *Rathke's pocket,* appears in the head ectoderm anterior to the stomodeum (Fig. 4.33C,D).

The pharynx is simply the portion of the foregut in the head. Temporary structures arising in this region during embryonic development reflect ancestral influences. Specifically, the visceral arches and *visceral clefts* that function in respiration in aquatic forms develop into parts of the jaws and hyoid apparatus in the chick.

When the oral membrane ruptures, an anterior extension of the pharynx remains as *Seessel's pocket* (the *preoral gut*), a transitory cavity with no known function. Just posteriorly to the mouth the pharynx expands laterally into the first visceral (*hyomandibular*) pouches. They grow to the outer ectoderm, fuse with it, and break through to the outside at about 48 hours incubation. A second and similar pair of visceral pouches grows out just posteriorly to the auditory vesicles. Third and fourth pairs follow at almost equidistant intervals. All reach the ectoderm by 48 hours (Figs. 4.30C, 4.32), but the fourth pair does not break through. A slight dorsoventral invagination of head ectoderm directly opposite the point of contact of each visceral pouch prior to breakthrough forms the visceral groove. The opening from pouch to groove is the visceral cleft. Each cleft provides a junction of head ectoderm with foregut endoderm. The masses of mesenchyme between the visceral pouches constitute the visceral arches. Each visceral arch contains an aortic arch (leading from the ventral aorta to the dorsal aorta and clearly identifiable in sections) and a branch of a cranial nerve.

The arrangement of the arches and clefts is as follows:

> visceral arch I (mandibular)
> visceral cleft I (hyomandibular)
> visceral arch II (hyoid)
> visceral cleft II
> visceral arch III
> visceral cleft III
> visceral arch IV
> visceral pouch IV (does not break through)
> visceral arch V

An abortive fifth visceral pouch may appear. Although it never reaches the ectoderm, a portion of it may develop into the *ultimobranchial body*. All the arches and pouches have homologues in higher vertebrates and give rise to important permanent structures.

The *thyroid gland* arises as a single, mid-ventral evagination in the floor of the pharynx between the second visceral pouches. At about the 12-somite stage, the endoderm cells destined to line the thyroid become columnar, and at the 26-somite stage they form a spherical depression and then a sac (Fig. 4.33C,D). By 72 hours the sac separates from the floor of the pharynx.

The respiratory tract arises at about the 23-somite stage as a single, mid-ventral, elongated, posteriorly directed groove, beginning just behind the thyroid primordium. The groove squeezes off from the foregut as the *laryngo-tracheal groove*. Its posterior end expands to form the paired lung primordia. The original connection of the groove with the foregut is at the level of the *esophagus*.

By 72 hours the esophagus is a narrow tube just posterior to the pharynx, identified by the opening into the laryngotracheal groove. The esophagus leads directly into the spindle-shaped *stomach*, as yet undifferentiated.

The liver has two endodermal origins, one above and the other below the fork of the joining vitelline veins, in the vicinity of the anterior intestinal portal. It becomes the reservoir for the *ductus venosus* at the junction of the two veins. The liver primordia are evident by the 26-somite stage, and by the 30-somite stage they form anastomosing hepatic lobules that eventually destroy part of the ductus venosus. The floor of the foregut between the liver primordia is the transient *ductus choledochus (common bile duct)*.

The *pancreas* has three origins, all endodermally lined. One is dorsal to the foregut, two are ventral, and all three are closely associated with the posterior liver diverticulum.

At 72 hours the midgut is still open over the yolk sac and gives no indication of differentiation. Its limits are the anterior and posterior intestinal portals.

A fold of yolk sac splanchnopleure beneath the tail bud provides an *anal tube* that is the posterior extremity of the hindgut. Just anteriorly and mid-ventrally, at the proctodeum, the ectoderm thickens to form the cloacal membrane. When the hindgut floor is nearly complete, the allantois develops anteriorly to the cloacal membrane, as a mid-ventral saccular evagination into the exocoel. Except for these changes, there is very little differentiation in the hindgut region before 72 hours.

Derivatives of the mesoderm

The ultimate disposition of the mesoderm is as follows:

Somites: dermis, voluntary muscles, skeleton.
Nephrotome: excretory system and some reproductive ducts.
Lateral plate: pericardium, pleura, peritoneum, coelom, exocoel.
Blood islands: blood vessels and investing layers.
Head mesenchyme: head muscles (partly also from crests).

Since the most anterior somite pairs develop first, an embryo incubated for at least 21 hours exhibits progressive stages in somite differentiation from posterior to anterior. Approximately 35 pairs of somites are apparent at 72 hours. A total of 52 pairs is present at 6 days incubation, but the last 10 pairs are purely embryonic. Each somite consists of the following parts:

POSITION	DESIGNATION	CELLS	DISPOSITION
outer	dermatome	high columnar	dermis
middle	sclerotome	spherical, mesenchymal core	axial skeleton (bone and cartilage)
inner	myotome	high columnar	voluntary muscles (except in head)

The *dermatome* and *myotome* are continuous, the myotome being in fact the inner margin of the dermatome. It curls back under the dermatome to form the *dermomyotomic plate* with the myocoel inside (Fig. 4.35). The *sclerotome*, the major portion of the somite, moves toward the notochord and envelops it and the neural tube, eventually giving rise to the axial skeleton. As these transformations take place, the myotome cells orient their axes in an anteroposterior direction in anticipation of differentiation into elongate, spindle-shaped voluntary muscle cells and fibers. Certain of the myotomes send growths into the limbs to form the appendage muscles, while others send growths into the ventral body wall to form other voluntary muscles. The myotomes have these specific destinations:

  1–4: cephalic, occipital region of skull; lose identity.
  5–16: prebrachial, between skull and wings.
  17–19: brachial, muscles of wings.
  20–25: body muscles between wings and legs.
  26–32: muscles of legs.
  33–35: reduced muscles of cloaca.
  36–42: caudal, rudimentary.
  43–52: embryonic, vestigial; degenerate by 8 days.

The location of the vertebral column is determined first by the axial notochord and then by its sclerotomal sheath, since the *sclerotomes* give rise to *vertebrae*. (In the skull there are only four pairs of sclerotomes, which aid in the derivation of the occipital region.) Although both the somites and the *vertebrae* are metameric, they are not parallel. Instead, each vertebra consists of sclerotome from two somites—the caudal portion of one and the cephalic portion of the one just behind it (Fig. 4.36). Thus each vertebra actually lies between two myotomal bundles that have separated from somites; and each intervertebral fissure, between adjacent vertebrae, is level with a myotome.

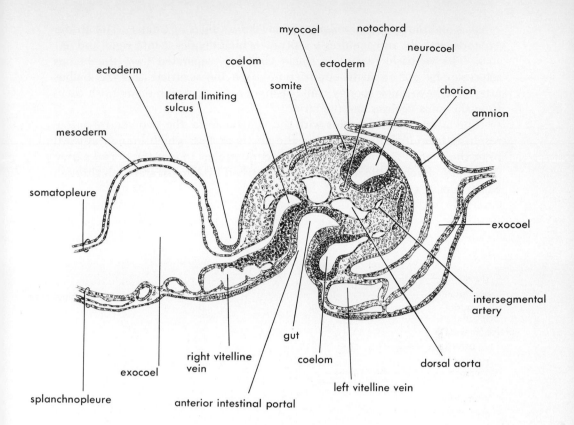

Fig. 4.35 Transverse section through somite V of 23-somite chick embryo, showing gut and embryonic membrane development.

Intersegmental arteries and spinal nerves arise between the myotomes at the level of each vertebra. Frontal sections even show superficial, ectodermal intersomitic clefts. The centra of the vertebrae completely displace the notochord. Eventually the neural arches and transverse processes (also from sclerotome) join the centra to enclose the spinal cord.

The 44 vertebrae of the chick are as follows: cervicals, 16 (including the atlas and axis); thoracics, 5; lumbars, 6; sacrals, 2; and caudals, 15. The pelvic girdle includes these: thoracic, last 1 only; lumbar, all 6; sacral, both; caudal, first 5 (the last 4 caudals constitute the *pygostyle*). The *sternum* derives from two longitudinal cartilaginous bars. They unite in the mid-line to form the *keel* (*carina*), to which the large pectoral muscles are attached.

By 65 hours the heart has advanced considerably over its 33-hour condition (Figs. 4.25C,D, 4.37). The sinus venosus receives three veins, the ductus venosus and the paired *common cardinal veins* (*ducts of Cuvier*). The atrium expands laterally and acquires a septum, which divides it into right and left atria. The ventricle remains a single chamber, separated from the bulbus arteriosus by only a slight constriction. Both the ventricle and the bulbus arteriosus have thick spongy walls of myocardium, which distinguish them from the sinus venosus and the atria.

The arterial system begins with the ventral aorta, the two ventral aortae resulting from its bifurcation, and the aortic arches, which branch upward from the ventral aortae through the visceral arches to join the dorsal aortae (Fig. 4.38). Each aortic arch may be identified by the visceral arch through which it passes as follows:

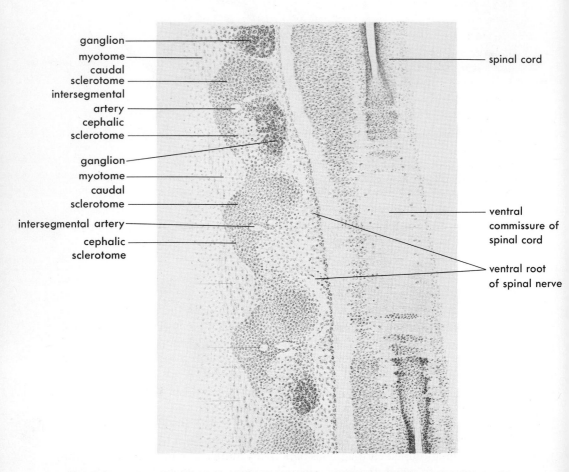

Fig. 4.36   Frontal section of vertebral primordia in 5-day chick embryo. (From F. R. Lillie and H. L. Hamilton, *Lillie's Development of the Chick*, 3rd. ed., Holt, Rinehart & Winston, New York, 1952.)

AORTIC ARCH	VISCERAL ARCH	TIME OF APPEARANCE	DISPOSITION
I	I (mandibular)	10 somites (30 hours)	disappears at 3 days
II	II (hyoid)	19 somites (40 hours)	disappears at 4 days
III	III	26 somites	common carotid arteries
IV	IV	36 somites	systemic arch
V	V	96 hours	disappears
VI	VI	120 hours	pulmonary arteries

When the first and second aortic arches disappear, the remaining anterior projections of the ventral aortae become the *external carotid arteries*, and the remaining anterior projections of the dorsal aortae become the *internal carotid arteries*. The left fourth aortic arch disappears, and the right enlarges to become the huge *systemic arch*. The sixth aortic arches function as the *ducti arteriosi (ducts of Botallus)* until just before hatching. Then the dorsal connection with the right arch vanishes, and the ventral portions become the paired *pulmonary arteries*.

At about 50 hours the paired dorsal aortae fuse, from the level of the sinus venosus posteriorly to about the level of the fifteenth somite, to form a single large dorsal aorta. The intersegmental arteries branch from the dorsal aortae dorsolaterally between the somites to join *intersegmental veins*. The vitelline arteries arise from the dorsal aortae posterior to the fusion to carry blood out onto the yolk (Figs. 4.39, 4.40).

The venous system brings blood from the yolk through the vitelline veins,

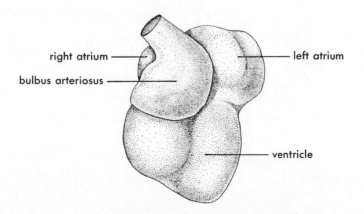

right atrium

left atrium

bulbus arteriosus

ventricle

Fig. 4.37   Ventral view of heart of 33-somite chick embryo. (Adapted from Masius.)

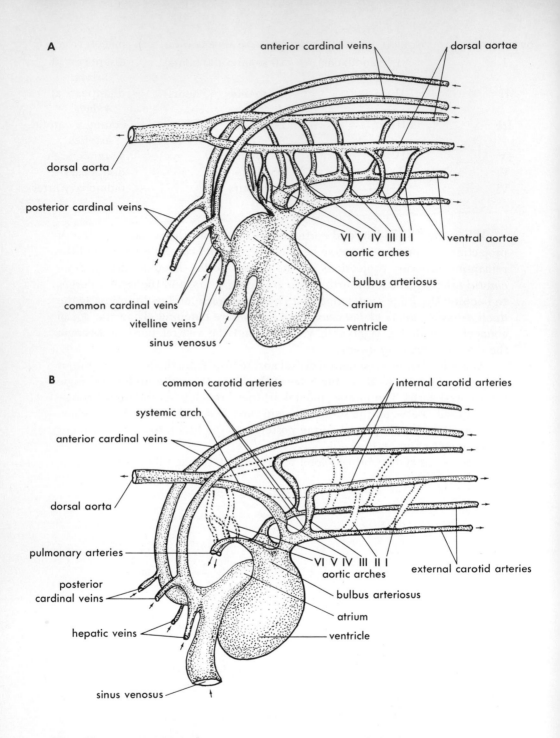

Fig. 4.38   Lateral views showing aortic arch development in chick embryo: A, at 60 hours; B, at hatching.

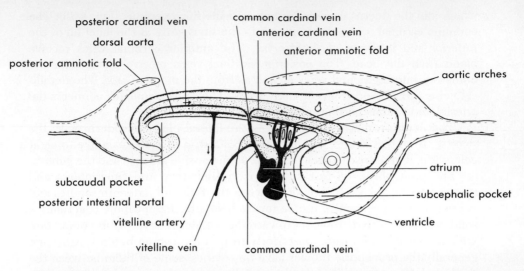

Fig. 4.39 Lateral view of vascular system of 48-hour chick embryo. (From R. Rugh, *Laboratory Manual of Vertebrate Embryology*, 5th ed., Burgess, Minneapolis, 1961.)

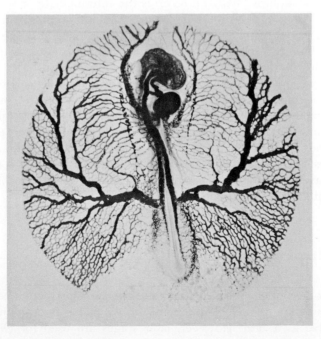

Fig. 4.40 Dorsal view of vascular system of 48-hour chick embryo. (From General Biological Supply House, Chicago, Ill.)

which join the ductus venosus leading into the sinus venosus (Fig. 4.38). The common cardinal veins, also leading into the sinus, arise at the junction of the *anterior* and *posterior cardinal veins*. The anterior cardinal veins receive blood from the head. The posterior cardinal veins receive blood from the numerous intersegmental veins as well as from the *mesonephros*. The umbilical veins carry blood from the body walls. The sinus terminalis connects the arterial and venous portions of the vitelline circulation.

The nephrotome, which connects the lateral plate mesoderm with the somites, from the fifth to the thirty-third, is a strip of mesoderm five to eight cells wide. It gives rise to each of the three successive kidneys and the *gonads*.

The *pronephros,* or first kidney, is rudimentary and functionless and degenerates at 4 days. It extends between the fifth and sixteenth somites and consists of one *pronephric tubule* for each somite. Each tubule is actually a solid cord of cells that grows out toward the ectoderm, severing its connection with the somite, and turns posteriorly to join the tubule behind. Although generally the pronephric tubules have no cavities, some of them between the tenth and sixteenth somites may have slight lumens that open into the coelom through *nephrostomes,* and some of the posterior tubules may be associated with primitive *glomeruli*. The continuous cord formed by the junction of the adjacent pronephric tubules is the *pronephric duct*. It continues to grow posteriorly beyond the pronephric tubules and becomes the *mesonephric duct* when the next kidney appears.

The mesonephros (*Wolffian body*) is the intermediate or second kidney, developing between the fourteenth and thirtieth somites and functioning from 5 to 11 days. Instead of one tubule for each somite, as in the pronephros, there are four to eight *mesonephric tubules* per somite, with the larger number likely in the posterior portion of the mesonephros. The mesonephric tubules have lumens, *Bowman's capsules,* and glomeruli and communicate with the mesonephric duct. Only the tubules between the twentieth and thirtieth somites are functional, however; they have no nephrostomes, as do the anterior ones, and rely exclusively on their glomeruli to excrete wastes.

The mesonephric duct proceeds posteriorly, reaching the cloaca at 60 hours (31-somite stage) and becoming tubular at 72 hours. It is rudimentary in the female but forms the vas deferens in the male; thus, although it is excretory in origin, it assumes a reproductive function.

▪ After 72 Hours Incubation

The first 4 days of chick development are the most instructive because by 96 hours incubation the chick has most of its major organs and is clearly recognizable as a bird. However, later stages are used for chorioallantoic grafting in experimental embryology and are also of some interest with regard to specific organ systems.

At the end of the third day the embryo has the general shape of a reversed question mark, due in part to the cervical flexure (Figs. 4.41–4.43). With cephalization, or the accelerated growth of the anterior end, the head enlarges until at 4 days it represents almost half the bulk of the embryo. The mesencephalon is particularly prominent so that the head appears to have an anterior protuberance. Each eye occupies almost half the side of the head. The rest of the body shows only the beginning limbs (wings and legs) and bulging viscera. At 7 days a *beak* forms on the head, the *external auditory meatus* is evident, the cervical flexure begins to straighten out, the limbs are distinguishable, and feather follicles appear. By 9 days the embryo is definitely recognizable as a chick, and the body parts are catching up with the head in development.

At 14 days the embryo lies along the longitudinal axis of the shell with its head toward the air chamber. The head is overly large and well developed and is bent toward the breast, usually tucked under the right wing. The *egg tooth* develops, and the head turns so that the tooth lies against the shell membrane. The amniotic fluid decreases rapidly between 17 and 19 days and is entirely gone by 20 days. The remains of the yolk sac are drawn into the midgut, which closes off completely; the ducti arteriosi begin to degenerate, so that more blood goes to the lungs; and the chick may be heard chirping within its shell.

Embryonic membranes

At 4 days the chorion and amnion are closed over the embryo, the yolk sac covers most of the yolk, and the allantois fills the exocoel (Fig. 4.44A). At 5 days muscle fibers appear in the amnion, and it begins to rock gently, preventing adhesion of the embryo to any extraembryonic structures. Meanwhile, the splanchnic mesoderm of the allantois fuses with the mesoderm of both the outer chorion (in the chorioallantoic membrane) and the inner amnion. By 11 days the allantois all but envelops the embryo (Fig. 4.44B).

The albumen sac is first obvious at 9 days and surrounds the albumen by 11 days (Fig. 4.44B–D). It is really an accessory sac formed by the chorion, and between it and the yolk is the yolk sac. The albumen usually becomes very viscous and is absorbed by 16 days. At 20 days the yolk sac, with a small amount of residual yolk, slips into the midgut through the umbilical stalk, taking the albumen sac with it, and the gut closes.

Derivatives of the ectoderm

NERVOUS SYSTEM. The development of the brain is very complicated. Accordingly, the following discussion covers only its major derivatives appearing between 4 and 10 days incubation.

Telencephalon. The telencephalon expands into two enormous *cerebral hemispheres* anterior to the lamina terminalis (Fig. 4.45), and the lateral walls thicken to become the *corpora striata.* The paired cavities of the cerebral hemi-

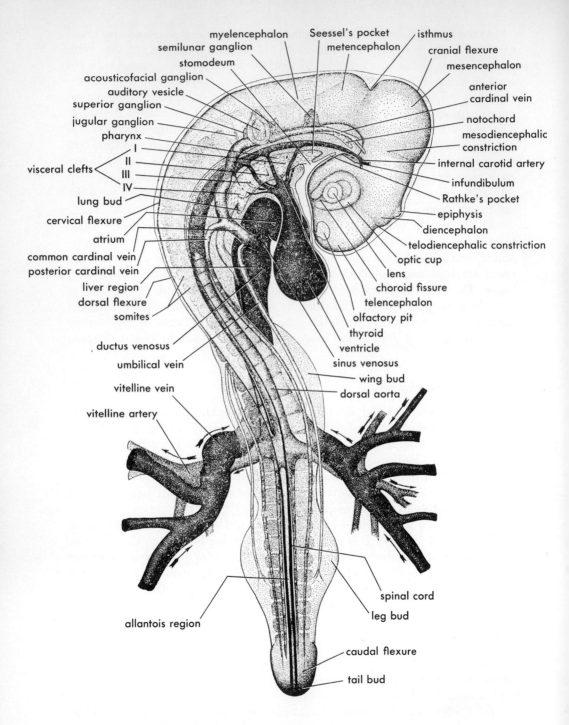

Fig. 4.41   Dorsal view of 72-hour chick embryo. (From A. E. Huettner, *Fundamentals of Comparative Embryology of the Vertebrates*, rev. ed., Macmillan, New York, 1949.)

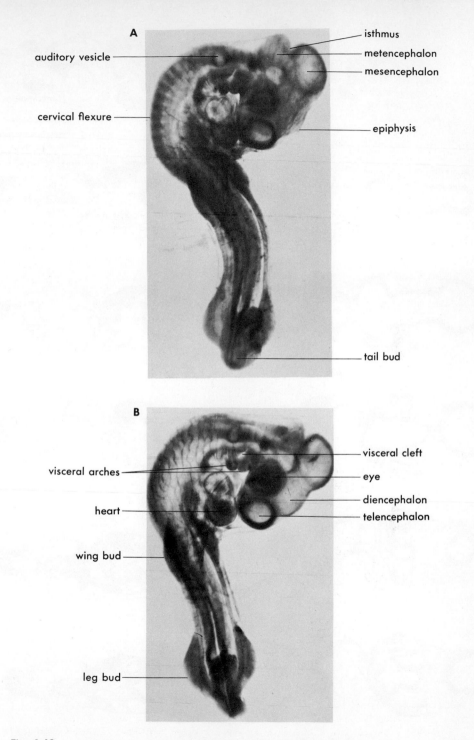

A

auditory vesicle

cervical flexure

isthmus

metencephalon

mesencephalon

epiphysis

tail bud

B

visceral arches

heart

wing bud

leg bud

visceral cleft

eye

diencephalon

telencephalon

Fig. 4.42   Dorsal views of chick embryo: A, at 72 hours; B, at 96 hours.

A

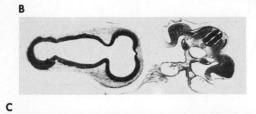

B

G

C

H

D

I

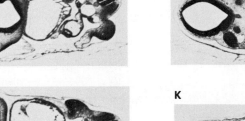

E

J

F

K

L

Fig. 4.43 Transverse sections of 72-hour chick embryo.

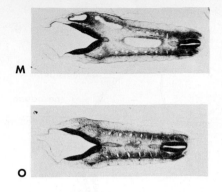

Fig. 4.43   *(continued)*

spheres are the (first and second) *lateral ventricles.* They open into the *third ventricle* through the *foramina of Monro.* The *paraphysis* is an evagination in the roof dorsal to the velum transversum, and the *anterior commissure* develops within the lamina terminalis (Fig. 4.46). The *olfactory lobes* and *tracts* develop much later.

Diencephalon. The epiphysis is an elongated pocket growing out from the anterior roof of the diencephalon (Figs. 4.20E, 4.45, 4.46), and the *posterior commissure* is a thickening in the posterior roof. In the floor are the thickening *optic chiasma,* the bulbous infundibulum, the beginnings of the *mammillary tubercles,* and the tuberculum posterius. (Late in incubation the infundibulum and Rathke's pocket join to become the *pituitary gland.*) The walls of the diencephalon thicken to form the optic *thalami* (epi-, meso-, and hypothalami), and its cavity becomes the third ventricle.

Mesencephalon. The two large optic lobes distinguish the mesencephalon. The *aqueduct of Sylvius,* its cavity, connects the third and *fourth ventricles.* The floor thickens as nerve tracts develop to and from the brain.

Metencephalon. The roof of the metencephalon gives rise to the *cerebellum,* which overlies the fourth ventricle. The cerebellum acquires folds by about 10 days. Its floor, which carries major nerve tracts, is the *pons Varoli.*

Myelencephalon. The roof of the myelencephalon becomes even thinner than before and forms folds, while its lateral walls and floor thicken considerably. Its cavity becomes the *medulla oblongata.*

Neuroblast cells, which derive from the primitive neural ectoderm and differentiate into *neurons,* form the basis of the nervous system. They first appear concentrated in two main regions, the neural tube and the neural crests, or the ganglia derived from the crests.

In the early neural tube elongated epithelial (neuroblast) cells extend from the neurocoel, or central canal, to the periphery, and between their inner ends are the more rounded germinal neural ectoderm cells. Each neuroblast has a distinct cell body. As it differentiates, it develops a long *axon,* or axis cylinder, and, generally in the opposite direction and close to

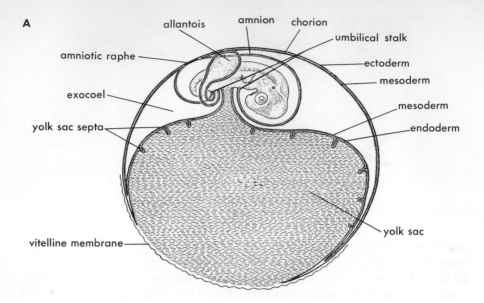

A

allantois · amnion · chorion
amniotic raphe
umbilical stalk
ectoderm
exocoel
mesoderm
mesoderm
yolk sac septa
endoderm

yolk sac

vitelline membrane

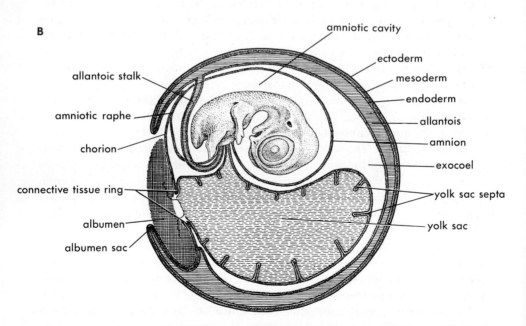

B

amniotic cavity
allantoic stalk
ectoderm
mesoderm
amniotic raphe
endoderm
allantois
chorion
amnion
exocoel
connective tissue ring
yolk sac septa
albumen
yolk sac
albumen sac

Fig. 4.44   Interrelations of embryonic membranes in chick embryo: A, at 4 days; B, at 9 days; C, at 12 days; D, at 14 days. (A–C from F. R. Lillie and H. L. Hamilton, *Lillie's Development of the Chick,* 3rd ed., Holt, Rinehart, & Winston, New York, 1952; D from R. Rugh, *Laboratory Manual of Vertebrate Embryology,* 5th ed., Burgess, Minneapolis, 1952.)

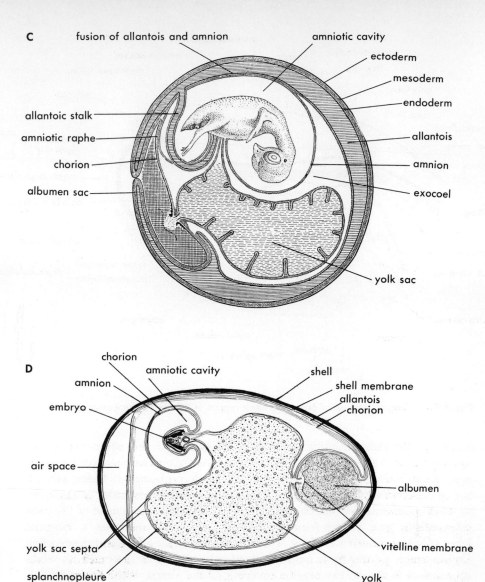

C

fusion of allantois and amnion

amniotic cavity

ectoderm

mesoderm

endoderm

allantoic stalk

amniotic raphe

chorion

albumen sac

allantois

amnion

exocoel

yolk sac

D

chorion

amniotic cavity

amnion

shell

embryo

shell membrane

allantois

chorion

air space

albumen

yolk sac septa

splanchnopleure

vitelline membrane

yolk

Fig. 4.44 (*continued*)

the nucleus, a cluster of *dendrites*. The neural tube neuroblasts become quite typical neurons, whereas the ganglionic neuroblasts (from the crests) become bipolar, spindle-shaped neurons with outgrowths from both ends, the dendrites being modified into long axonic extensions.

The central canal of the spinal cord is at first a vertical slit, with a very thin roof and floor and thick lateral walls composed of the elongating neuroblast cells interspersed with supporting *neuroglial cells* and nerve fibers. The

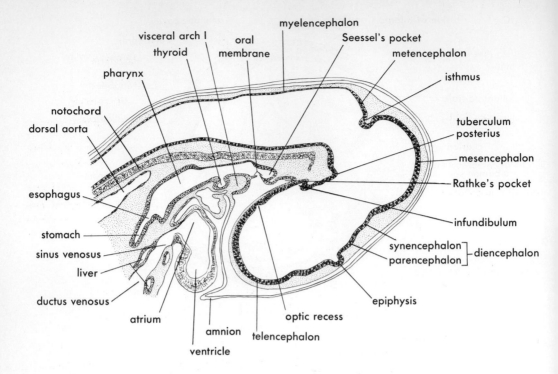

Fig. 4.45   Sagittal section of brain and heart region of 39-somite chick embryo.

nuclei of the differentiating neuroblasts cluster near the neurocoel as the *ependyma,* and the neuroblasts bordering directly on the neurocoel acquire cilia. Neuroblasts in the cord may give rise to efferent (motor) tracts, ascending or descending fibrous tracts, commissures between the sides of the cord, or short commissural connections within the cord. By 4 days most of the cord substance is *gray matter* (neuroblasts and neuroglia), and then a marginal layer of *white matter* develops, which consists of ascending and descending fibrous tracts arising from neuroblasts at other levels of the cord; its white appearance is due to the myelin covering of the axons. With the rapid cellular growth of the cord substance, the neurocoel becomes round and reduced in size.

The cranial nerves, which arise metamerically, differ from the spinal nerves in that they do not have *dorsal* and *ventral roots.* Further, some of the cranial nerves are purely sensory (for example, the olfactory nerve), others are purely motor (for example, the oculomotor nerve), and still others are mixed (both sensory and motor). Their origins and dispositions are as follows.

I. Olfactory. The ectodermal head epithelium gives rise not only to the sensory epithelium of the *naris,* but also to neuroblasts that grow toward and join the olfactory lobe of the telencephalon at about 6 days as the olfactory nerve. The fibers are not myelinated, and no ganglion forms.

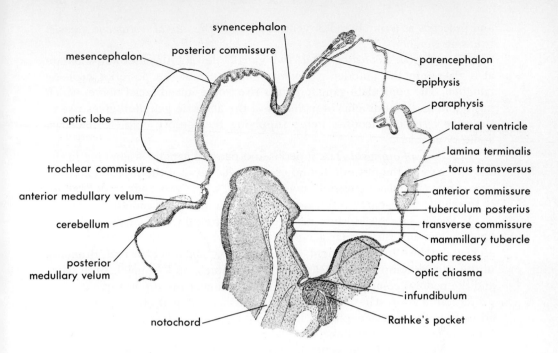

Fig. 4.46 Sagittal section of brain of 7-day chick embryo. (From F. R. Lillie and H. L. Hamilton, *Lillie's Development of the Chick,* 3rd ed., Holt, Rinehart & Winston, New York, 1952. Adapted from von Kupffer.)

II. Optic. The optic nerve, sensory only, arises from the retina, with axons covering the retinal cells, extending toward the optic stalk, and invading and following the choroid fissure to its origin in the diencephalon at 4 days. At the floor of the diencephalon some fibers cross over to the opposite side of the brain (in the optic chiasma) to become associated with the optic tract on that side. The fibers of the optic tract are myelinated.

III. Oculomotor. The oculomotor nerve, primarily motor, derives from almost mid-ventral neuroblasts of the mesencephalon at about 60 hours. It grows to the orbit of the eye, where it innervates the eye muscles (except the *superior oblique muscle).*

IV. Trochlear. The trochlear nerve, primarily motor, arises at 4 days from the dorsal surface of the brain near the isthmus (mesencephalon) and supplies the superior oblique eye muscle.

V. Trigeminal. The semilunar ganglion, associated with the metencephalon at the side of the fourth ventricle, gives rise to the trigeminal nerve at 3 days. It is both motor and sensory and sends branches to the eye, mandible, and maxilla.

VI. Abducens. The abducens nerve arises from the metencephalon at 4 days and proceeds as a purely motor ventral nerve to the *lateral rectus eye muscle*. It has no ganglion.

VII and VIII. Acousticofacial. Two ganglia develop together and separate at 4 days into the anterior *geniculate ganglion* and the posterior *acoustic ganglion.* The geniculate ganglion gives rise to the mixed facial nerve, which has hyoid and mandibular branches, and the acoustic ganglion gives rise to the purely sensory acoustic nerve supplying the sensory epithelium of the auditory vesicle.

IX. Glossopharyngeal. The superior and petrosal ganglia originating in the anterior part of the postotic neural crests at the level of the myelencephalon give rise to the mixed glossopharyngeal nerve, which proceeds to derivatives of the third visceral arch (muscles of pharynx, tongue, and mouth) by 3 days.

X. Vagus. The mixed vagus nerve develops from divided ganglia at 4 days. One component, the jugular ganglion, lies above the fourth and fifth visceral arches, and the other component, the nodose ganglion, is ventral to it. Branches of the vagus (sympathetic) reach the heart, lungs, and stomach by 6 days, and the nodosal component moves to a position near the *thymus gland.*

XI. Accessory. The accessory nerve, associated with the vagus nerve, arises from the myelencephalon at 4 days but develops like a spinal nerve. It is purely motor and supplies the head-turning muscles.

XII. Hypoglossal. The ventrolateral aspect of the myelencephalon, at the level of the fourth pair of somites, gives rise to the hypoglossal nerve, a motor tract to the tongue, at 4 days. It has no ganglion.

All of the spinal nerves are mixed nerves, and most of them consist of both somatic (voluntary) and splanchnic (involuntary) nerve tracts. The dorsal somatic root develops from the bipolar neurons of the spinal ganglia, whereas the ventral somatic root arises as an outgrowth from neurons of the spinal cord itself (Figs. 4.47, 4.48). Peripherally to the fusion of these two roots a *ramus communicans* joins the nerve with the sympathetic (splanchnic) system. A total of 38 pairs of spinal nerves develops.

The sympathetic components probably derive from cerebrospinal or vagus ganglia and migrate posteriorly, establishing metameric connections with the somatic spinal nerves. By the fourth day the beginnings of the sympathetic system are apparent as clusters of cells dorsolateral to the dorsal aorta. These clusters actually form a longitudinal cord and are therefore distinguishable from mesenchyme (Fig. 4.49). Later, similar clusters of similar cells appear ventrally to the dorsal aorta, near the gut, and finally the sympathetic trunk moves to the mid-line near the ventral roots of the spinal nerves. Since a pair of sympathetic ganglia arises adjacent to the vagus ganglia and in association with each pair of spinal nerves, a total of 39 pairs, all connected, develops. Through plexi the sympathetic system controls the visceral organs.

EYES.   At 72 hours the optic cup consists of the thick inner sensory layer of the retina, the thin outer pigmented layer of the retina, and, outside the pigmented layer, the two mesodermally derived connective tissue sheaths, the inner choroid and the outer sclera. Cartilage is visible in the sclera

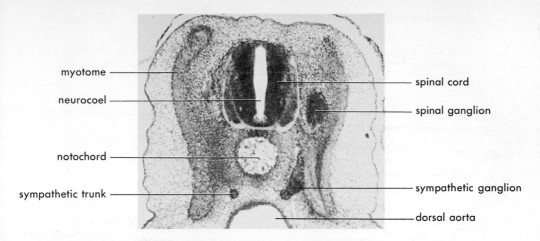

myotome

neurocoel

notochord

sympathetic trunk

spinal cord

spinal ganglion

sympathetic ganglion

dorsal aorta

Fig. 4.47   Transverse section of spinal cord of 96-hour chick embryo.

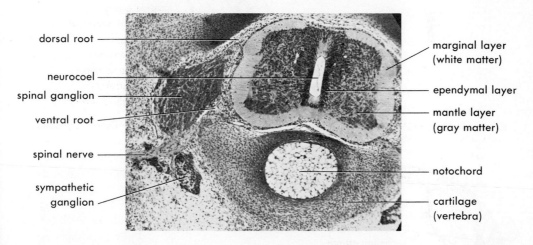

dorsal root

neurocoel

spinal ganglion

ventral root

spinal nerve

sympathetic
ganglion

marginal layer
(white matter)

ependymal layer

mantle layer
(gray matter)

notochord

cartilage
(vertebra)

Fig. 4.48   Transverse section showing spinal ganglion in 8-day chick embryo.

by 8 days. The sensory layer of the retina includes an inner marginal layer, rods and cones, and finally axons of the neuroblasts comprising the optic nerve. The two retinal layers are continuous in the rim of the optic cup, which gives rise to the *iris* and the *ciliary processes,* and in the choroid fissure, which connects the optic cup to the diencephalon. By 7 days they show two distinct zones as in the adult eye. The thick sensitive portion of most of the optic cup is the *pars optica,* and the insensitive portion at the edge of the cup is the *pars caeca.* The *ora serrata* separates the two zones.

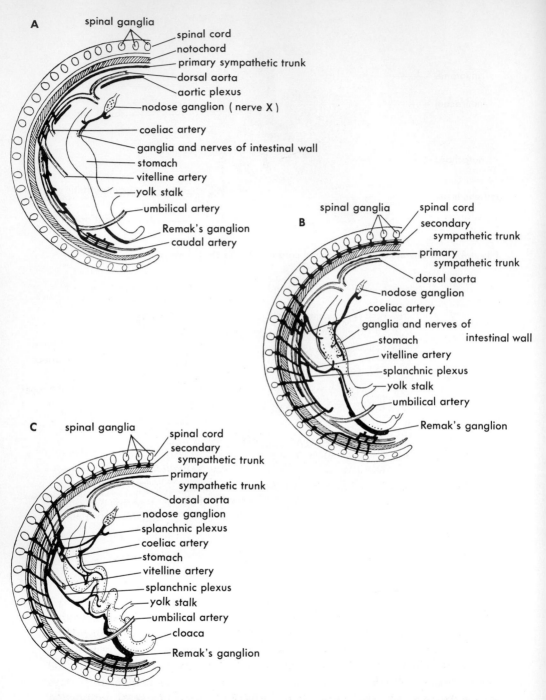

Fig. 4.49 Lateral views of sympathetic nerves in chick embryo: A, at 4 days; B, at 6 days; C, at 10 days. (From F. R. Lillie and H. L. Hamilton, *Lillie's Development of the Chick*, 3rd ed., Holt, Rinehart & Winston, New York, 1952. Adapted from His.)

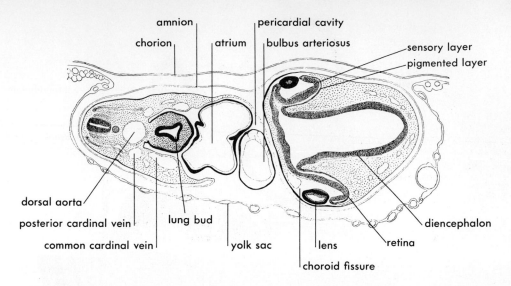

amnion
pericardial cavity
chorion
atrium
bulbus arteriosus
sensory layer
pigmented layer
dorsal aorta
posterior cardinal vein
common cardinal vein
lung bud
yolk sac
lens
retina
diencephalon
choroid fissure

Fig. 4.50 Transverse section through eye and heart region of 35-somite chick embryo. (From F. R. Lillie and H. L. Hamilton, *Lillie's Development of the Chick*, 3rd ed., Holt, Rinehart & Winston, New York, 1952.)

The lens, which arises as a thickening and then an invagination of head ectoderm, shortly breaks away to form a small, complete sac within the optic cup (Fig. 4.50). Although at first the walls of the sac are rather uniformly thin, the innermost wall rapidly thickens through the elongation of its cells. At 4 days lens fibers are organizing, and the *lens vesicle* is being obliterated (Fig. 4.51). By 8 days the lens is a biconvex mass, with a reduced crescent-shaped vesicle and a covering epithelium derived from the thin outer lens cells. As the lens develops, it moves deep inside the optic cup, where it is supported by the ciliary processes. The space between the lens and the outer ectoderm is the *anterior chamber,* and that between the lens and the iris is the *posterior chamber. Vitreous humor* from the retina fills the cavity behind the lens.

The cornea, on the surface of the lens, derives from both head ectoderm and infiltrating mesenchyme, which provides it with a thin vascular bed. The stroma of the iris also comes from mesenchyme. The upper and lower eyelids and the *nictitating membrane* are all covered with ectoderm but invested with abundant mesenchyme.

The optic nerve enters the eye at the *pecten,* or pigmented vascular plate, which is the nonfunctional "blind spot." At 4 days its axons cover the retina. At 8 days the optic nerve and the blood vessels nourishing the retina occlude the tubular optic stalk.

EARS. The ear develops from the auditory vesicle (lined with ectoderm), the first visceral (hyomandibular) cleft (ectoderm and endoderm), and the mesenchyme between the endodermal pouch and the ectodermal groove

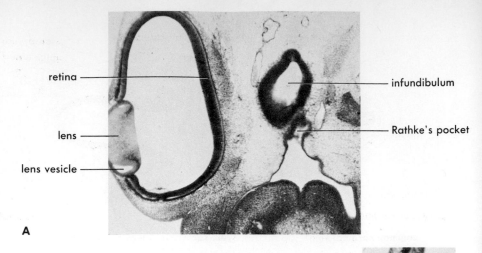

retina —

lens —

lens vesicle —

— infundibulum

— Rathke's pocket

A

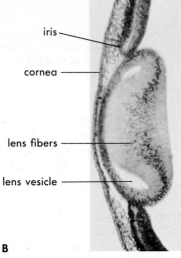

iris —

cornea —

lens fibers —

lens vesicle —

Fig. 4.51   Frontal sections showing eye development
in 96-hour chick embryo (B at high power).   **B**

that meet to form the cleft. As the auditory vesicle closes off from the outside, the ectodermal portion of the cleft becomes the external auditory meatus.
The endodermal portion of the cleft gives rise to the *auditory (Eustachian)*
tube and the *tympanic cavity,* while the mesenchyme forms the outer covering of the membranous *tympanum.* The *bony labyrinth,* the *perilymphatic*
fluid, and the *ossicles* of the middle ear also derive from mesenchyme.

In the early embryo the endolymphatic duct opens into the dorsolateral
part of the expanding auditory vesicle, but as the vesicle enlarges, the duct
connection shifts to a median lateral position (Figs. 4.52, 4.53). As a result,
the vesicle has superior and inferior portions. Ultimately the junction of the
duct with the vesicle is almost ventral, involved with the *utricle, saccule,* and

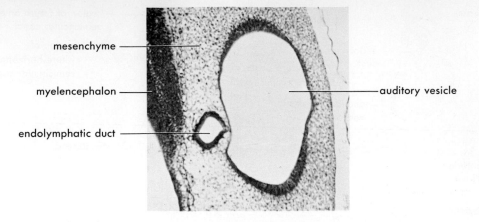

mesenchyme

myelencephalon

endolymphatic duct

auditory vesicle

Fig. 4.52   Frontal section showing ear development in 96-hour chick embryo.

lagena. The *semicircular canals* arise as folds in the superior part of the auditory vesicle, whereas the utricle, saccule, lagena, and *cochlear ducts* arise from the inferior part. The acoustic nerve enters the ventrolateral wall of the vesicle.

OLFACTORY ORGANS.   Between 4 and 8 days the olfactory pit deepens and changes shape, owing to the development of the mouth, the brain, and other parts of the head (Figs. 4.54, 4.55).

Derivatives of the endoderm

The limits of the oral ectoderm are the roof of the mouth above the *glottis* and the floor just in front of the tongue. The beak is made up of cornified epidermis peripheral to the mouth. At 6 days incubation the single temporary egg tooth, for breaking the chick out of its shell, appears near the tip of the upper jaw. It is fully formed by 14 days and is worn away shortly after hatching. Although all modern birds are otherwise toothless, every bird embryo has a ridge inside the margin of its jaw at about 6 days. This ridge is probably an evolutionary remnant of toothed ancestry.

The tongue has an ectodermal covering and a mesodermal (muscular) core. It arises from two outgrowths in the pharyngeal floor, one anterior to the thyroid gland and the other posterior to it. The posterior primordium involves the ventral portions of the second and third visceral arches. When the thyroid duct closes off, the two tongue parts merge, and with the forward growth of the head and neck, they elongate. The four pairs of *oral glands* (lingual, mandibular, palatine, and an unnamed pair at the angle of the mouth) all originate at about 8 days as solid ingrowths. They acquire cavities and become branched shortly after 11 days. There are no glands on the surface of the tongue.

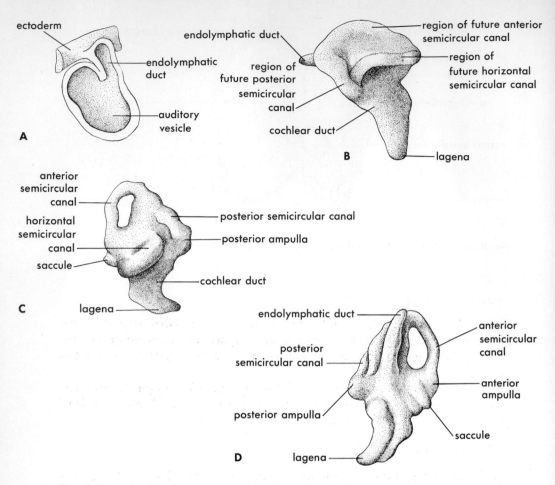

Fig. 4.53 Ear development in chick embryo: A, at 96 hours; B, right ear at 6 days 17 hours; C, D, left ear at 7 days 17 hours; E, right ear at 8 days 17 hours; F, right ear at 11 days 17 hours (C–F adapted from Röthig and Brugsch.)

At 4 days the thyroid is completely disconnected from the floor of the pharynx (Figs. 4.56–4.58). During the next 3 days it divides into two lobes, with a connecting isthmus, and each lobe moves posteriorly alongside the trachea to lie near the junction of the *common carotid* and *subclavian arteries*.

The paired lung buds form the *main bronchi*, which lengthen and expand into the air passages of the two lungs. The lungs in turn connect with *air sacs*, which begin to invade the abdomen and most of the long bones at 96 hours (Fig. 4.59). The abdominal air sacs are posterior extensions of the main bronchi, whereas the cervical, interclavicular, anterior thoracic, and posterior thoracic air sacs develop from branches of the main bronchi. All of these respiratory structures are lined with endoderm, invested with thick mesenchyme, and

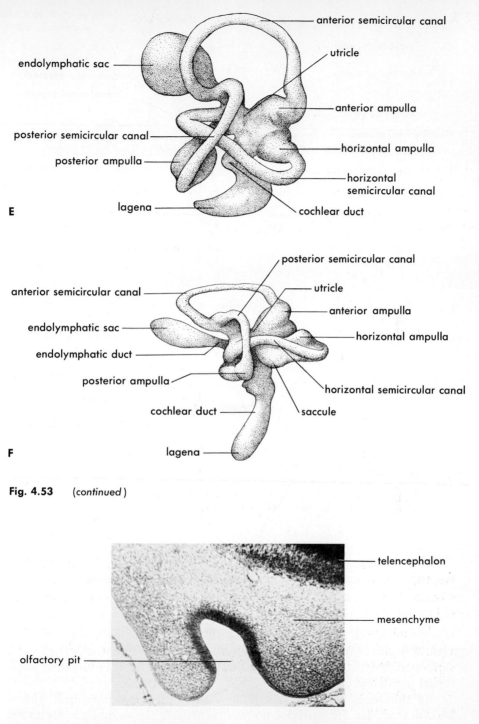

E

anterior semicircular canal

utricle

endolymphatic sac

anterior ampulla

posterior semicircular canal

horizontal ampulla

posterior ampulla

horizontal
semicircular canal

lagena

cochlear duct

F

posterior semicircular canal

utricle

anterior semicircular canal

anterior ampulla

endolymphatic sac

horizontal ampulla

endolymphatic duct

posterior ampulla

horizontal semicircular canal

cochlear duct

saccule

lagena

Fig. 4.53 (*continued*)

telencephalon

mesenchyme

olfactory pit

Fig. 4.54   Transverse section through olfactory organ of 96-hour chick embryo.

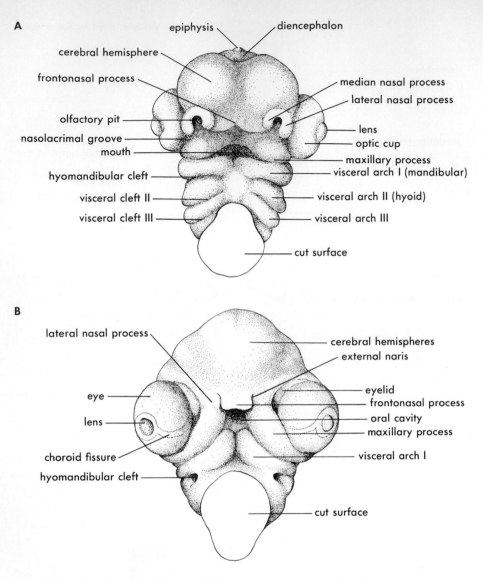

Fig. 4.55   Development of face in chick embryo: A, at 4 days; B, at 5 days.

covered by a thin layer of mesothelium. By 11 days the lungs are lateral and ventral to the esophagus and fill the *pleural cavities.* Eventually their outer surfaces fuse with the lining of the pleural cavities, so that they lose their meso-thelial peritoneal covering.

As the lungs and air sacs differentiate, the laryngotracheal groove becomes tubular. Its posterior portion, ventral to the esophagus, forms the *trachea,* and its anterior portion forms the *larynx,* which opens into the

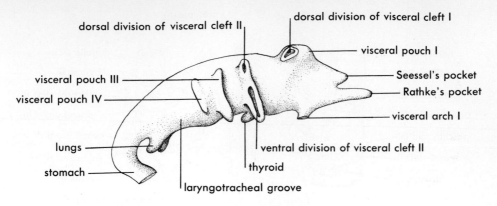

dorsal division of visceral cleft II

dorsal division of visceral cleft I

visceral pouch I

visceral pouch III

Seessel's pocket

visceral pouch IV

Rathke's pocket

visceral arch I

lungs

stomach

ventral division of visceral cleft II

thyroid

laryngotracheal groove

Fig. 4.56 Derivatives of pharynx in 72-hour chick embryo.

pharynx through the glottis. The trachea elongates as the neck grows. By 8 days both the larynx and the glottis are temporarily obstructed by cells.

The paired thymus glands arise at 7 or 8 days from upper portions of the third and fourth visceral pouches, which join to become elongated, lobular, and bulky structures on either side of the neck (Fig. 4.57). They atrophy with sexual maturity. The ultimobranchial bodies, posterior to the thyroid, arise from the fifth pair of visceral pouches.

The esophagus elongates with the growth of the neck (at 6 days). Its cavity is completely occluded posteriorly to the glottis at 7 days but opens again at 11 days. The *crop* is an enlargement of the esophagus near the base of the neck. By 5 days the stomach is subdivided into the digestive *proventriculus* and the muscular *gizzard*, and by 7 days these two regions are histologically distinct (Fig. 4.60). By 12 days they are capable of functioning.

Beyond the stomach is the *duodenum*, with its liver and pancreatic diverticuli (Fig. 4.61). The liver, which arises as two outgrowths from the midgut, develops a further extension or third derivative from its posterior primordium. As the hepatic lobules from all the primordia surround and invade the ductus venosus, the liver becomes the most vascular organ of the body. It contains no mesenchyme, consisting only of hepatic cells and blood vessels and their endothelial membranes. The *gall bladder* arises from the posterior liver rudiment by 72 hours (Figs. 4.58G, 4.60), and by 5 days many of the hepatic lobules have cavities as in the adult liver (Fig. 4.62).

The ductus choledochus connects the two major liver diverticuli and the gall bladder with the duodenum (Fig. 4.58H, 4.60). The two ventral primordia of the pancreas surround the ductus choledochus and enter it through ducts, but the dorsal pancreatic diverticulum opens directly into the duodenum. At 96 hours all the pancreatic primordia appear as solid budlike outgrowths, which intermingle but do not fuse, within abundant mesenchyme. The pancreas eventually fills the loop of the duodenum.

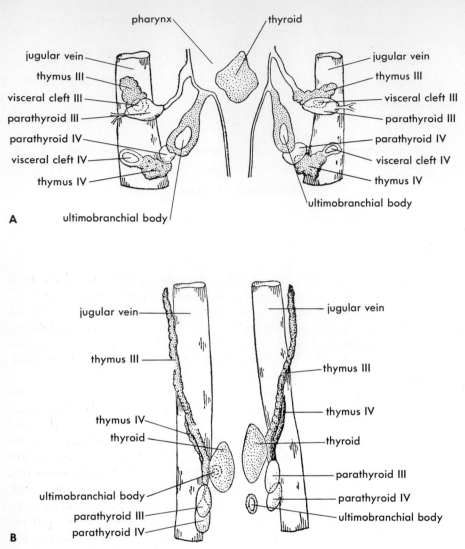

Fig. 4.57 Derivatives of pharynx in chick embryo: A, at 7 days; B, at 8 days. (From F. R. Lillie and H. L. Hamilton, *Lillie's Development of the Chick,* 3rd ed., Holt, Rinehart & Winston, New York, 1952. Adapted from Verdun after Maurer.)

Posteriorly to the duodenum, the gut lengthens and loops. The *small intestine* extends outside the body as the yolk stalk, and the *large intestine* leads from it to the cloaca (Figs. 4.63, 4.64).

The cloaca has three major parts: the terminal proctodeum; the intermediate *urodeum,* a chamber that receives the urinary and genital ducts; and the *coprodeum,* which is the terminus of the *rectum.* The cloacal membrane

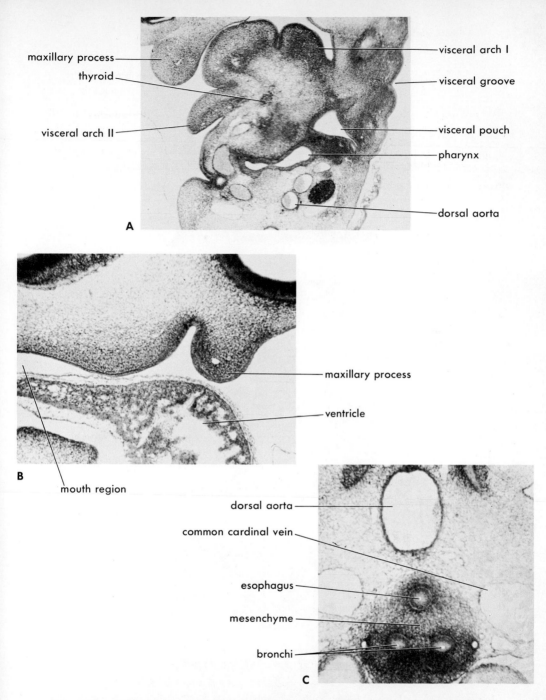

Fig. 4.58 Derivatives of pharynx in 96-hour chick embryo: A, frontal section through visceral arches; B, sagittal section through ventricle (high power); C–H, transverse sections; C, through esophagus and main bronchi (high power); D, E, at two levels slightly posterior to C; F–H, at three levels through liver and ductus choledochus.

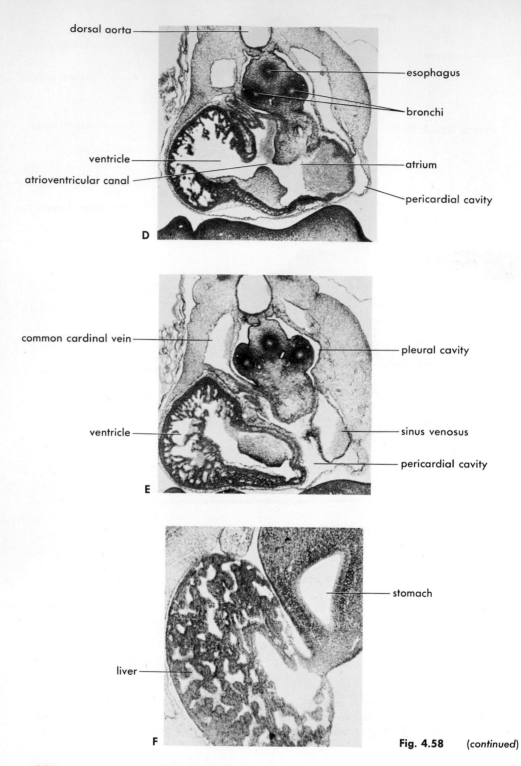

Fig. 4.58 (continued)

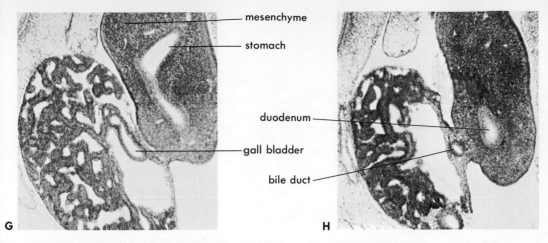

mesenchyme

stomach

duodenum

gall bladder

bile duct

G

H

Fig. 4.58 (continued)

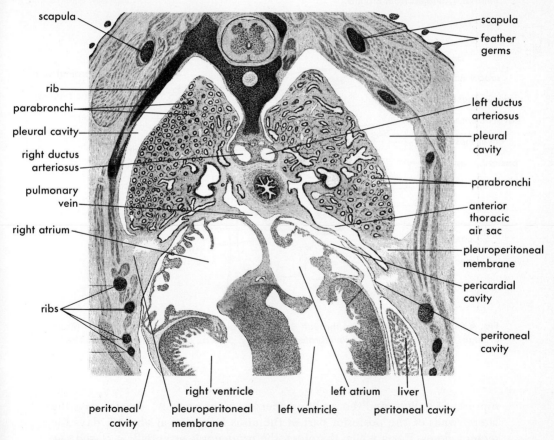

scapula

scapula

feather germs

rib

parabronchi

pleural cavity

right ductus arteriosus

pulmonary vein

right atrium

ribs

left ductus arteriosus

pleural cavity

parabronchi

anterior thoracic air sac

pleuroperitoneal membrane

pericardial cavity

peritoneal cavity

right ventricle

left atrium

liver

peritoneal cavity

pleuroperitoneal membrane

left ventricle

peritoneal cavity

Fig. 4.59 Transverse section through lungs of 11-day chick embryo. (From F. R. Lillie and H. L. Hamilton. *Lillie's Development of the Chick,* 3rd ed., Holt, Rinehart & Winston, New York, 1952.)

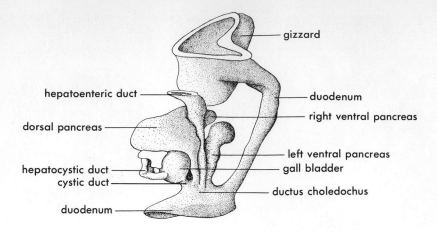

Fig. 4.60 Gizzard, duodenum, and hepatic and pancreatic ducts of 124-hour chick embryo. (Adapted from Brouha.)

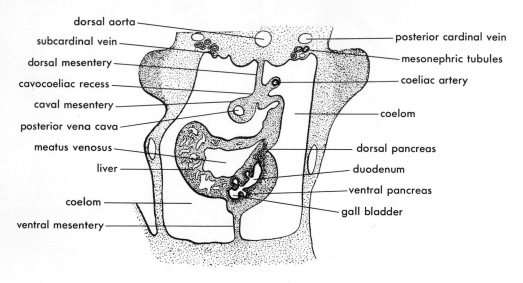

Fig. 4.61 Transverse section through duodenal region of 96-hour chick embryo. (From R. Rugh, *Laboratory Manual of Vertebrate Embryology*, 5th ed., Burgess, Minneapolis, 1961.)

ruptures at 4 days, and the resulting opening is the anus. At about 5 days the lateral walls of the posterior part of the anus fuse, and at about 7 days the rectum closes. For a while, therefore, the urodeum is essentially a closed sac. It is not until about 18 days that the large intestine is evacuated and the anus again open.

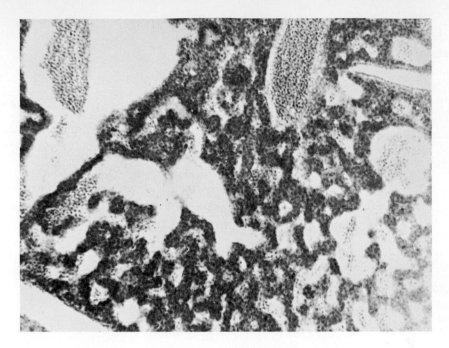

Fig. 4.62　Section of liver of 96-hour chick embryo.

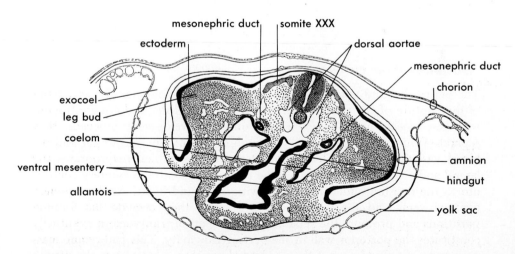

mesonephric duct　somite XXX

ectoderm　dorsal aortae

mesonephric duct

chorion

exocoel

leg bud

coelom

amnion

ventral mesentery

hindgut

allantois

yolk sac

Fig. 4.63　Transverse section through hindgut, allantois, and somite XXX of 35-somite chick embryo. (From F. R. Lillie and H. L. Hamilton, *Lillie's Development of the Chick*, 3rd ed., Holt, Rinehart & Winston, New York, 1952.)

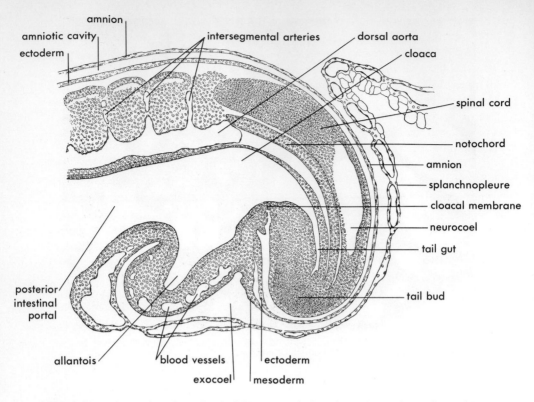

Fig. 4.64   Sagittal section of tail of 35-somite chick embryo. (From F. R. Lillie and H. L. Hamilton, *Lillie's Development of the Chick,* 3rd ed., Holt, Rinehart & Winston, New York, 1952.)

Derivatives of the mesoderm

The pericardial and peritoneal cavities arise in the same manner, as a result of the rupture of the ventral mesentery in the coelom, and are continuous with the exocoel at 72 hours incubation. As development proceeds, they separate from each other, largely through differentiation of the gut and the blood vascular system. The *septum transversum,* which incorporates the lateral and ventral mesocardia, and the remnant of ventral mesentery contribute to the division, aided by the growing liver and heart. As the common cardinal veins and the vitelline veins enlarge, they occlude the forming partitions and promote the separation. The septum transversum eventually constitutes the posterior wall of the pericardial cavity. This embryonic mass gives rise not only to part of the *pericardial membrane* but also to the *pleuropericardial membrane,* between the heart and the lungs, and to the *ligaments* of the liver.

With the completion of the lateral body walls, and the formation of the septum transversum posteriorly and the pleuropericardial membrane dorsally, the pericardial cavity finally closes off, to contain only the heart. The *pleuro-peritoneal membrane* arises from accessory mesenteries associated with the esophagus and septum transversum to separate the *pleural cavity*, containing the lungs, from the peritoneal cavity. Its development and its final position are determined to a great extent by the growth of the lung sacs into these mesenteries. At about 10 days, muscle fibers appear in the various membranes to complete the partitioning of the three body cavities.

The dorsal mesentery ultimately consists of an anterior portion (the *mesogastrium*) supporting the stomach and duodenum, a middle portion supporting the small intestine and umbilical stalk, and a posterior portion supporting the large intestine and rectum.

The *spleen* appears at 96 hours as a derivative of the dorsal mesentery near the dorsal pancreas. By 6 days it is a sizable organ located dorsally to and at the left of the stomach. It is believed that embryonic cells from the spleen enter the venous circulation to give rise to blood *corpuscles.*

The *erythrocytes* and *leucocytes* of the chick embryo arise from different sources. The *erythroblasts* (primitive erythrocytes) come from blood islands and primitive endothelium in the area pellucida, and the *myeloblasts* (primitive leucocytes) come from extravascular mesenchyme. The erythroblasts appear during the latter half of incubation. The mature leucocytes enter the blood vessels through the capillary walls. Eosinophil leucocytes may be present in the circulating blood as early as 7 days, but basophil leucocytes are not present until 14 days, when they appear together with numerous myeloblasts, eosinophil myelocytes, and eosinophil and neutrophil leucocytes in the spleen.

Intravascular phagocytic cells arise from primitive endothelium, and extravascular ones from mesenchyme. Two types of *phagocytes* pass through the primitive blood vessels of the area pellucida for about 8 days only. The *monocytes* appear very late in the incubation period.

Because of the septa in the heart, two completely independent vascular systems supply that organ, with blood flowing always in the same direction, controlled by valves. One septum divides the *truncus arteriosus* and the *bulbus arteriosus* into the ventral aortae and pulmonary arteries. It forms at 5 days and extends clear to the ventricle. Eventually the aortae and arteries become tubular (Figs. 4.65, 4.66). By 8 days the *semilunar valves* develop as endocardial thickenings within these vessels. The *interventricular septum* extends from the apex of the ventricle to the depression between the bulbus and the atrium, dividing the ventricle into chambers by 5 days. The small *interventricular foramen* that remains apparently never closes. The *inter-atrial septum* separates the sinus venosus from the *pulmonary veins.* It is not complete until after hatching. An *endocardial cushion* divides the *atrio-ventricular canal,* so that by 6 days the heart is ready for the dual circulation. The circulatory system does not function as in the adult, however, until hatching, partly because respiration within the shell is by way of the allantois

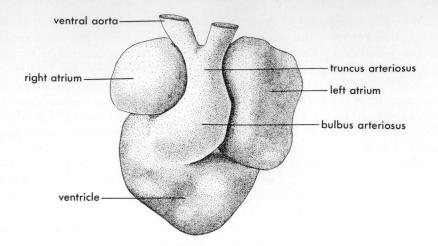

Fig. 4.65   Ventral view of heart of 38-somite chick embryo.

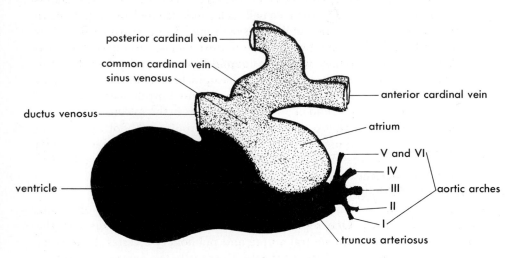

Fig. 4.66   Lateral view of heart of 96-hour chick embryo. (From R. Rugh, *Laboratory Manual of Vertebrate Embryology*, 5th ed., Burgess, Minneapolis, 1961.)

rather than the lungs (Figs. 4.67, 4.68). After the septa have formed, blood from the right ventricle passes to the pulmonary arteries, and blood from the left ventricle to the ventral aortae. The sinus venosus is incorporated into the right atrium, and the flaps between the two structures disappear.

When the transformations of the aortic arches are complete, at 5 days,

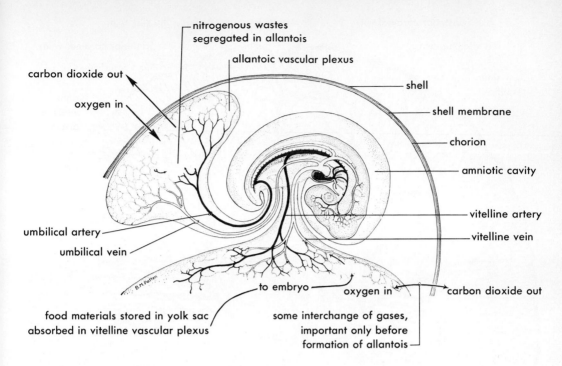

Fig. 4.67   Lateral view of vascular system of 96-hour chick embryo. (From B. M. Patten, *Am. Scientist,* **39**, 224 (1951).)

only the third, right fourth, and sixth arches remain. Later changes involving them relate principally to vessel size and to the degeneration of the sixth arches.

The internal and external carotid arteries grow as the neck lengthens and the heart moves posteriorly. The *common carotid arteries* arise from the internal carotids at the point where they join the external carotids (Fig. 4.38B). The large *subclavian arteries* to the wings develop at 4 days from the eighth intersegmental arteries but also connect with branches from the bases of the carotids. The secondary sources are the only persisting parts of the subclavians, since the intersegmental portions degenerate at 9 days.

The systemic arch grows posteriorly in the body as the dorsal aorta, giving off all the visceral arteries and the two large vitelline arteries. Paired lateral extensions associated with each intersomitic cleft probably develop. The *anterior mesenteric arteries* arise from the vitellines, whereas the *coeliac arteries* (to the stomach and its derivatives) and the *posterior mesenteric arteries* (to the large intestine) arise directly from the dorsal aorta. Numerous *mesonephric arteries* supply the glomeruli, but most of them disappear, leaving only a few *renal* and *genital arteries*. The umbilical arteries, which join the *sciatic arteries* of the legs, disappear by 8 days. The portion of the dorsal aorta posterior to the origins of the umbilicals is the short *caudal artery*.

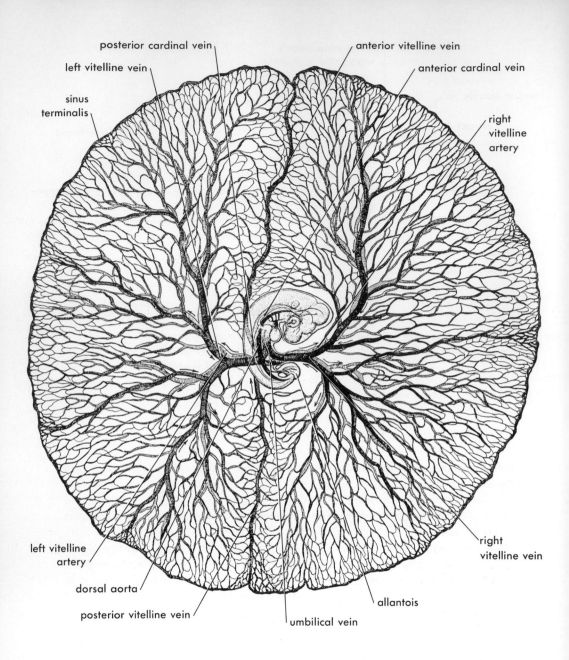

posterior cardinal vein

left vitelline vein

sinus
terminalis

anterior vitelline vein

anterior cardinal vein

right
vitelline
artery

right
vitelline vein

left vitelline
artery

dorsal aorta

posterior vitelline vein

allantois

umbilical vein

Fig. 4.68   Dorsal view of vascular system of 96-hour chick embryo. (From A. E. Huettner, *Fundamentals of Comparative Embryology of the Vertebrates*, rev. ed., Macmillan, New York, 1949.)

The venous system consists of the *posterior (inferior) vena cava* and the *precaval,* vitelline, umbilical, and *portal veins* (Fig. 4.69).

The precaval veins arise from the common cardinal veins, at the junction of the *jugular, vertebral,* and *subclavian veins.* The jugular comes from the anterior cardinal, the vertebral from the intersegmentals, and the subclavian from the posterior cardinal. The subclavians receive blood from the wings and thoracic walls.

At 3 days the two vitelline veins join in the ductus venosus above the intestine, near the dorsal pancreas. This bridge develops into an anastomosis around the gut, with the *meatus venosus* as its lower portion. At 4 days the part of the left vitelline in this region degenerates, so that blood must pass from the left vitelline, through the dorsal anastomosis, to the right vitelline, and into the meatus venosus. The gut elongates, and a second anastomosis forms between the vitellines. This one is ventral to the gut and just anterior to the anterior intestinal portal, and it degenerates along with the right vitelline. These changes transform the two vitellines into a single large S-shaped vein beginning just anteriorly to the anterior intestinal portal and ventral to the gut and turning left and forward to a position above the intestine on the right side, where it enters the liver and then the meatus venosus.

As the meatus venosus becomes part of the liver substance, it gives rise to both afferent and efferent *hepatic veins* so that by 7 days the liver is a mass of sinusoids. At this time the hepatic portal circulation is laden with yolk from the yolk sac. Small *mesenteric veins* from the dorsal mesentery join the vitellines and later become the true portal veins, carrying blood from the stomach, intestines, spleen, and pancreas.

The umbilical veins extend to the allantois at 4 days. Then the right umbilical degenerates, and the left umbilical forks to take blood from the allantois to the common cardinal vein and to the meatus venosus. The branch to the common cardinal disappears, leaving only the one to the hepatic portal circulation. This umbilical remnant persists in the adult as a link between the ventral body wall and the hepatic vein.

The posterior vena cava develops as a fusion of capillaries in the posterior part of the liver and connects the ductus venosus with the right *subcardinal vein.* The subcardinals, which arise on the median faces of the mesonephroi, enlarge and merge by 6 days in a subcardinal anastomosis. Blood from the two posterior cardinals passes through the mesonephroi, into the subcardinal anastomosis, and thence to the posterior vena cava, which empties into the degenerating ductus venosus. Posteriorly to the mesonephroi the subcardinals degenerate in favor of the posterior cardinals, but the connections between the anterior portions of the subcardinals and the posterior cardinals, at the level of the degenerating mesonephroi, remain as the *renal veins.* The posterior portions of the posterior cardinals furnish the renal portal circulation. Thus shiftings in the embryonic circulation produce vessels that have no remnants in the adult but are apparently necessary for the evolution of the adult venous system.

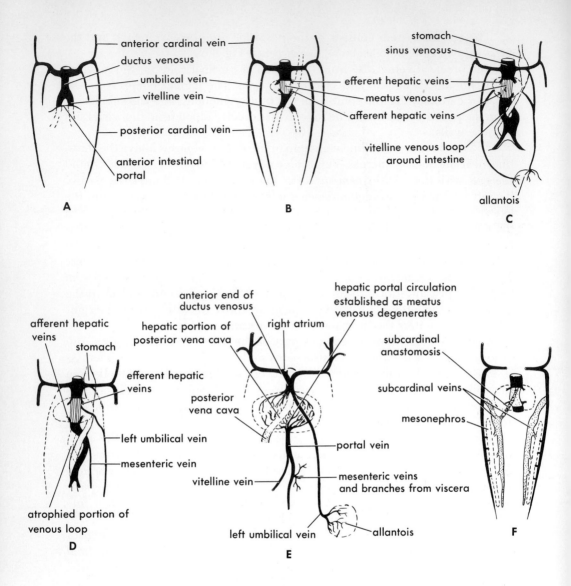

Fig. 4.69 Ventral views showing venous system development in chick embryo: A, B, at 3 days; C, at 4 days; D, at 4 to 5 days; E, at 7 to 8 days; F, at 4 to 5 days; G, at 6 to 7 days; H, at 14 days; I, at 20 to 21 days. (From O. E. Nelsen, *Comparative Embryology of the Vertebrates*, McGraw-Hill, New York, 1953. C, D, adapted from Lillie; F–H adapted from Miller.)

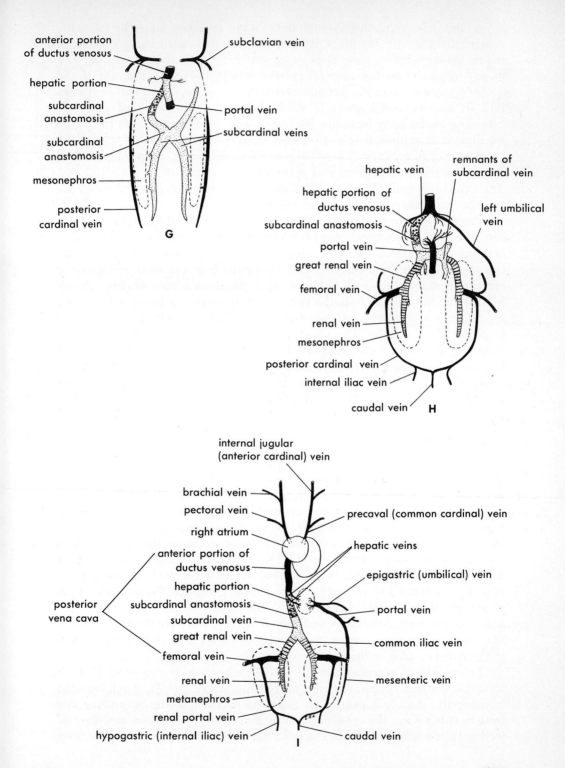

anterior portion of ductus venosus

subclavian vein

hepatic portion

subcardinal anastomosis

portal vein

subcardinal anastomosis

subcardinal veins

mesonephros

posterior cardinal vein

G

hepatic vein

remnants of subcardinal vein

hepatic portion of ductus venosus

subcardinal anastomosis

left umbilical vein

portal vein

great renal vein

femoral vein

renal vein

mesonephros

posterior cardinal vein

internal iliac vein

caudal vein

H

internal jugular (anterior cardinal) vein

brachial vein

pectoral vein

precaval (common cardinal) vein

right atrium

hepatic veins

anterior portion of ductus venosus

epigastric (umbilical) vein

hepatic portion

subcardinal anastomosis

portal vein

posterior vena cava

subcardinal vein

great renal vein

common iliac vein

femoral vein

renal vein

mesenteric vein

metanephros

renal portal vein

hypogastric (internal iliac) vein

caudal vein

I

A corpuscle circulating through the embryo at 4 days takes the following course. Upon leaving the heart, it enters the external carotid artery or one of the remaining aortic arches. Depending on which aortic arch it may enter, it passes forward into the internal carotid artery, backward into the dorsal aorta, or outward into the pulmonary artery. From the dorsal aorta it passes into an intersegmental artery, a vitelline artery, or an umbilical artery. If returning to the body from the extraembryonic regions, it travels through a vitelline or an umbilical vein. If remaining in the body, it moves toward the heart by way of an anterior cardinal vein (from the head), a posterior cardinal vein (from the mesonephros and posterior body parts), or an umbilical vein (from the body wall). From either of the last two veins, it passes through the posterior vena cava and the ductus venosus to the sinus venosus.

The sinus venosus contains a mixture of venous blood from the common cardinal veins and arterial blood from the ductus venosus. Since the vessels carrying blood (arterial) from the allantois and yolk are much greater in number and size than those carrying blood (venous) from the small but growing embryonic masses, the bulk of the blood in the sinus is aerated (from the allantois) and nutritional (from the yolk). Consequently, the blood entering the right atrium is primarily arterial, with only a small amount of venous blood from the precaval veins. The blood from the posterior vena cava, eventually truly venous, at this time is rich in oxygenated and nutrient blood, which may be even further purified in the renal portal circulation. Because of the temporary foramen between the atria, arterial-type blood passes into the left ventricle and thence to the carotid arteries, which have the purest blood. The blood of the dorsal aorta, pure in the adult, is admixed with venous blood from the right ventricle for a time.

By 8 days the heart is fully chambered, and the separation of arterial and venous blood is well advanced, with most of the blood from the heart going through the right systemic arch (the left degenerates) and the paired ducti arteriosi to the enlarged dorsal aorta.

At hatching, the allantois dries up, and the umbilical arteries and the one remaining umbilical vein disappear; the entire yolk sac circulation degenerates; and the ducti arteriosi dwindle to cords connecting the systemic arch with the pulmonary arteries, so that blood from the right ventricle goes directly to functional lungs. When the *interatrial foramen* closes, the separation of the arterial and venous blood systems is complete. Venous blood then passes into the right atrium, out through the right ventricle, and through the pulmonary arteries to the lungs, and arterial blood passes from the lungs through the pulmonary veins, into the left atrium, out through the left ventricle, and to the systemic arch or the carotid arteries.

Three sets of mesonephric tubules usually form at the level of each somite, the lowest (primary tubule) developing first (Fig. 4.70). Each joins the mesonephric duct independently. Subparts of each of the secondary and tertiary tubules are the *renal corpuscle,* the *uriniferous tubule,* and the collecting tubule associated with the duct. Although no new tubules arise after

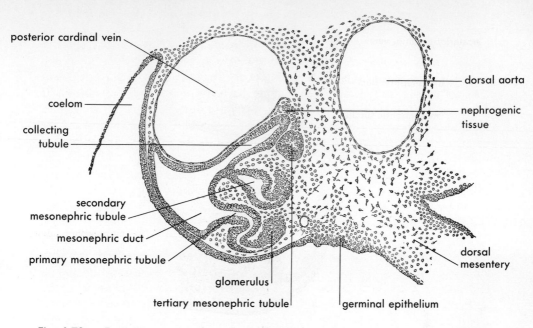

posterior cardinal vein

coelom

collecting tubule

secondary mesonephric tubule

mesonephric duct

primary mesonephric tubule

glomerulus

tertiary mesonephric tubule

dorsal aorta

nephrogenic tissue

dorsal mesentery

germinal epithelium

Fig. 4.70   Transverse section through middle of mesonephros of 96-hour chick embryo. (From F. R. Lillie and H. L. Hamilton, *Lillie's Development of the Chick,* 3rd ed., Holt, Rinehart & Winston, New York, 1952.)

the fifth day, convolution and differentiation continue until at least 8 days (Figs. 4.71–4.75), and then degeneration begins, to be completed, except for the reproduction derivatives, at about the time of hatching.

The *metanephros,* which extends only between the thirty-first and thirty-third somites, is the functional kidney from 11 days through life. It appears first at 4 days and begins to operate as the mesonephros degenerates (Fig. 4.75). At 11 days it is full of secreting tubules. The metanephros has a dual origin: its cortical portion arises from nephrogenic tissue in the nephrotome, and its medullary portion from a mesonephric diverticulum near the cloaca. The *metanephric duct,* or *ureter,* grows from the posterior end of the mesonephric duct. Since the chick has no urinary bladder, the ureter empties through the cloaca.

Each of the paired reproductive organs and ducts develops in close association with the excretory system, from a *genital ridge* on the median lateral surface of the mesonephros (Figs. 4.73–4.75). The gonad derives from the anterior (sexual) portion of the ridge, and the mesonephric duct and *Müllerian duct* from the posterior portion. In the male the anterior portion of the mesonephros remains as the *epididymis,* and the mesonephric duct as the vas deferens, and the intervening parts become the *paradidymis,* which degenerates. The Müllerian duct degenerates between 8 and 11 days, leaving no

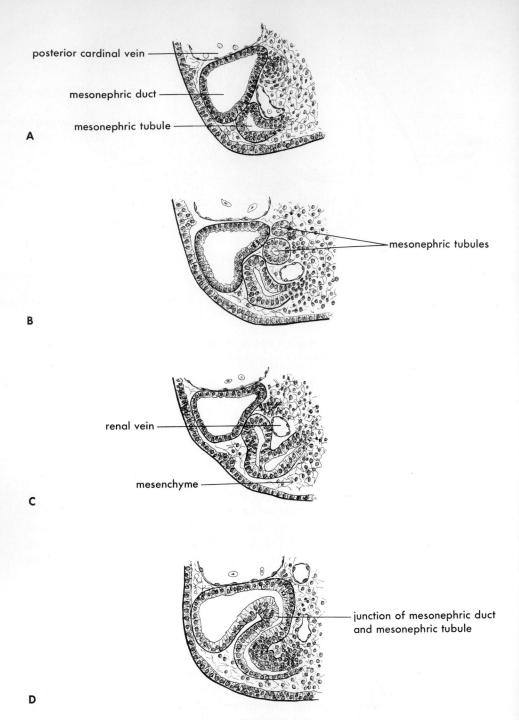

Fig. 4.71 Transverse sections showing development of mesonephric tubules in 45-somite chick embryo.

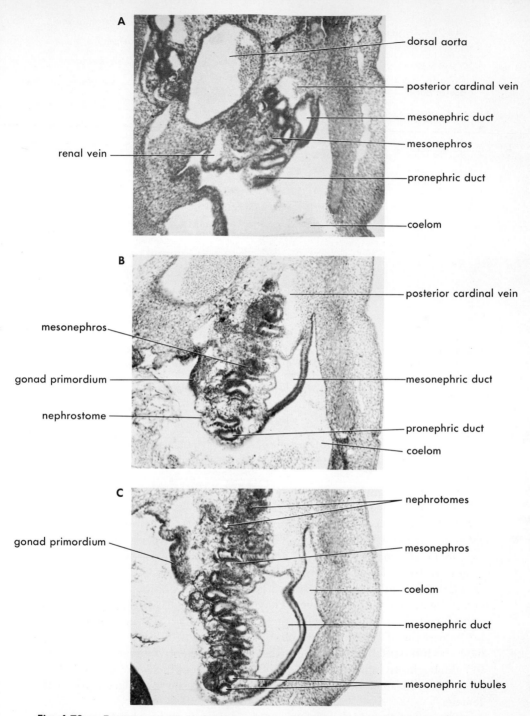

A
- dorsal aorta
- posterior cardinal vein
- mesonephric duct
- mesonephros
- pronephric duct
- coelom
- renal vein

B
- posterior cardinal vein
- mesonephros
- gonad primordium
- mesonephric duct
- nephrostome
- pronephric duct
- coelom

C
- nephrotomes
- gonad primordium
- mesonephros
- coelom
- mesonephric duct
- mesonephric tubules

Fig. 4.72 Transverse sections showing mesonephros and gonad development in 96-hour chick embryo.

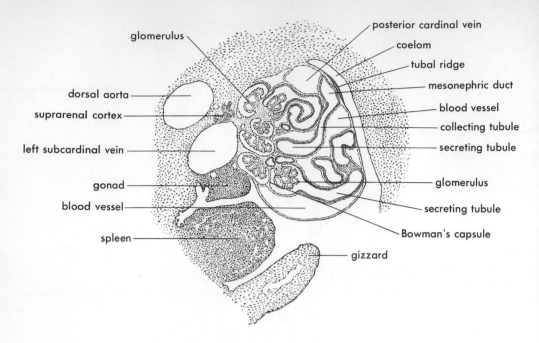

Fig. 4.73   Transverse section, at spleen level, through mesonephros and neighboring parts of 6-day chick embryo. (From F. R. Lillie and H. L. Hamilton, *Lillie's Development of the Chick*, 3rd ed., Holt, Rinehart & Winston, 1952.)

vestige. In the female it is the mesonephric duct that degenerates, whereas the Müllerian duct becomes the oviduct. The oviduct on the right side later degenerates.

Sex determination is impossible during early gonad formation, since the gonads go through an indifferent period when the cells of the prospective ovary and testis look alike. They arise from the germinal epithelium of the genital ridge at 4 days. A primordial germ cell is round and larger than an epithelial cell, its nucleus has two nucleoli, and the cytoplasm gives evidence of recent migration from the yolk region. Solid epithelial strands, the *rete cords,* form at 5 days, fill the gonad, and extend into the mesonephros to establish close contact with the renal corpuscles. They may actually arise from the Bowman's capsules of the renal corpuscles. *Sexual cords,* which also appear at 5 days, are ingrowths of germinal epithelium containing primitive germ cells. By 6 days the interstitial tissue of the male (or the connective tissue stroma of the female) begins to separate these cords from the rest of the germinal epithelium. They form the seminiferous tubules of the male or the medullary cords of the female.

The sex of the chick embryo can be determined by about 6½ days. At that time the organization of the germinal epithelium is different in male and

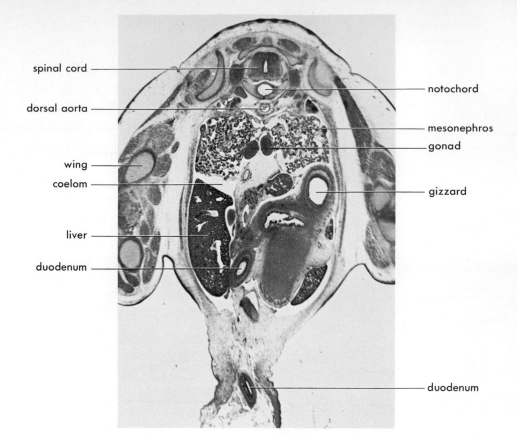

spinal cord —

— notochord

dorsal aorta —

— mesonephros

— gonad

wing —

coelom —

— gizzard

liver —

duodenum —

— duodenum

Fig. 4.74   Transverse section through mesonephroi and gonads of 8-day chick embryo.

female, the seminiferous tubules of the male are apparent, the ovaries differ in size, with the left one enlarging and the right one degenerating, and the stroma of the ovary differs from that of the testis. No real external genitalia ever appear.

The seminiferous tubules divert the rete cords toward the *hilus* of the testis, where they form the *rete testis*. By 13 days the primordial cells become active, interstitial tissue is abundant between the tubules, and the testis enlarges. By 20 days a lumen appears in each tubule. The testis is attached to the anterior part of the mesonephros, which becomes the epididymis. The vas deferens, from the mesonephric duct, connects with the testis through the epididymis, vasa efferentia, and rete testis.

The right ovary forms as a primordium and then degenerates, leaving the left ovary as the functional sex organ in the female. Secondary sexual cords, the *ovigerous cords,* develop at 6 days and force the primary sexual cords into

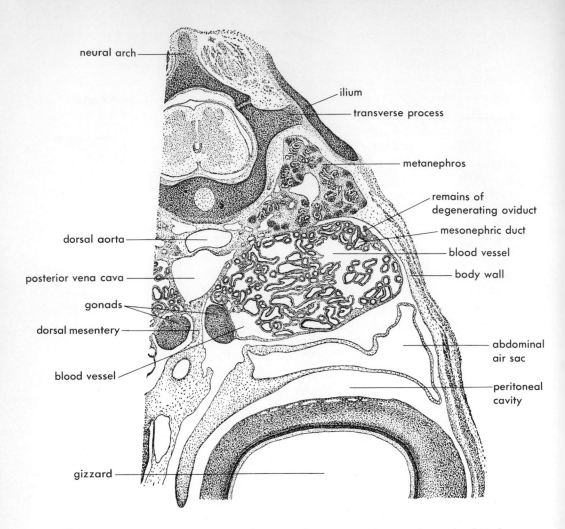

Fig. 4.75 Transverse section through metanephros, mesonephros, and gonads of 11-day male chick embryo. (From F. R. Lillie and H. L. Hamilton, *Lillie's Development of the Chick*, 3rd ed., Holt, Rinehart & Winston, New York, 1952.)

the medulla, where their germ cells degenerate. Meanwhile, the ovigerous cords, in the cortex, become follicles. Between 8 and 11 days the germinal epithelium grows rapidly, giving rise to numerous primary follicles. The germinal epithelium then not only covers the surface of the ovary but also extends into it between the connective tissue stroma. In the female the *epoöphoron* and *paroöphoron* are remnants of the mesonephros. The anterior end of the Müllerian duct forms from an epithelial fold between the genital ridge and the mesonephros. It grows posteriorly to join the cloaca by 7 days and by 12 days differentiates into the ostium tubae, glandular portions of the oviduct, and uterus.

The *suprarenal (adrenal) glands,* anterior to the mesonephroi, consist of central medullary and peripheral cortical cords, with some intermingling. The two parts probably have different origins, the cortical cells likely coming from the peritoneum (mesodermal) and the medullary cells from the sympathetic ganglia (ectodermal).

The bones, cartilage, ligaments, and joints that combine to form the skeleton arise from mesenchyme. In general, bones pass through three stages in development—an early membranous stage, a cartilaginous stage, and finally an ossification stage—although the flat bones, found largely in the skull, skip the intermediate stage.

In the membranous stage the mesenchyme merely condenses, to taper off into surrounding more loosely distributed mesenchyme. In the cartilaginous stage the cells secrete a substance that separates them from each other. The developing bones of this period are called *endochondral (cartilaginous)* bones, and some of them, particularly the long bones of the appendages, may exhibit all three stages of differentiation simultaneously. Bone deposits (*perichondrium*) around the cartilage form a cylinder, the enclosed matrix transforms into bone marrow (at around 10 days in some bones), and the two processes extend lengthwise. Outside the marrow, calcium salts are deposited in the cartilage, which is digested away by bone scavengers, the *osteoclasts,* from about 17 days. Other cells, the *osteoblasts* (bone-forming cells) then appear within the marrow. They deposit bony spicules along the lines of calcified cartilage. The chick never has epiphysial centers of ossification, as do mammals, but the ends of the bones persist as cartilage and centers of elongation. The marrow enlarges, and eventually many bones acquire extensions of the air sac system, which make the bones lighter. The bones of the chick are rather fragile, as compared with those of the mammal, owing to the greater perichondral ossification and the presence of the air sacs. The vascular supply to the bones is relatively poor, its turnover is slow, and its metabolism is low. Any chick embryo of over 11 days has membranous, chondrification, and ossification centers, representing the stages in bone development. Several of these centers may merge to become a single adult bone.

■ Experimental Embryology

Experiments with the warm-blooded chick embryo require a great deal more care and patience than those with an amphibian. Both the temperature and the humidity must be controlled, and all surgical procedures must be aseptic, since warm egg yolk is the most satisfactory medium known for bacteria culture. The basic equipment for experimentation includes a well-regulated incubator, a candler for examining the egg during development, and a means for sterilizing the surgical instruments. Ideally a complete set of slides showing developmental stages should be available for comparison with the living material.

Four general experimental techniques are most commonly used with the chick embryo. First, various substances can be injected into the large air space in the shell. This space is enclosed in a double membrane but is contiguous with the chorioallantoic membrane. The injected substances diffuse into the yolk and eventually reach the embryo. Temporary subjection of the embryo to the low oxygen level resulting from the introduction of foreign matter produces drastic changes.

The other techniques are carried out through a window in the shell. The window is made as follows: the position of the embryo is determined with the candler; the shell in this region is marked and sterilized with 70% alcohol; the air space is punctured to draw the embryo away from the shell; a rectangle about 1.5 cm. long is cut with a hacksaw or dentist's drill; and the shell is turned back to expose the embryo. Any shell fragments are removed, and sterile saline is gently dropped onto the exposed surface of the shell membrane or the embryo. The shell membrane is withdrawn with watchmaker's forceps.

The second type of experiment involves the detection of morphological movements after the application of spots of vital dye, such as Nile blue sulfate or neutral red, embedded in agar, or particles of sterile lampblack. A drawing of the stained or marked area is made immediately, and the shell window is closed with transparent tape. Movements may be observed through the tape, or, if necessary, the tape may be removed from time to time. Hensen's node, etc., may be watched for 1 or 2 days at least.

The third type of experiment is the chorioallantoic graft. The highly vascular chorioallantoic membrane is an ideal medium for the growth of transplanted organ primordia. However, the organ rudiments must come from early stages, such as 60- to 70-hour embryos. The limbs, eyes, and skin form dramatic chorioallantoic grafts. The organ is excised from the donor embryo in warm, sterile saline and pipetted onto the chorioallantoic membrane of the host embryo. The shell is then closed, or the shell window is covered with transparent tape. At 18 or 19 days incubation, the egg is opened, and the transplant is examined.

The fourth type of experiment is the interembryonic graft, in which an organ primordium is transplanted from a donor embryo into or onto a specific region of a host embryo proper, for example, into the coelom or onto the flank. A few embryologists have even transferred potentially dark-feathered organ primordia onto potentially white hosts or vice versa. Studies with transplanted neural crests have been particularly instructive.

A modification of these procedures is tissue culture. An organ is excised and placed in an artificial medium, generally containing some embryonic extracts, where it may survive and develop for a considerable period. Carrel kept chick heart tissue alive and active in culture for 23 years beyond the normal life expectancy of a chicken.

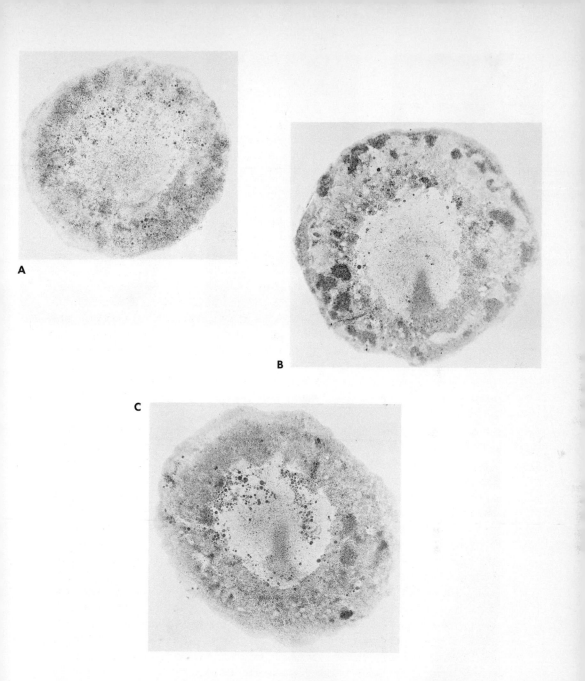

Fig. 4.76 Survey of development of chick embryo: A–I, laying to 33 hours incubation; J–Q, 33 to 72 hours incubation; R–E', after 72 hours incubation. (From F. R. Lillie and H. L. Hamilton, *Lillie's Development of the Chick,* 3rd ed., Holt, Rinehart & Winston, New York, 1952.)

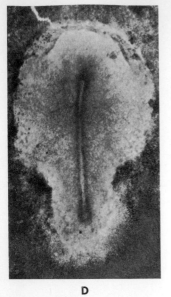

D

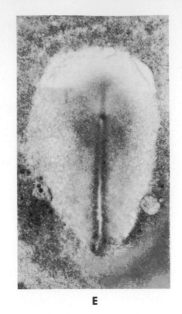

E

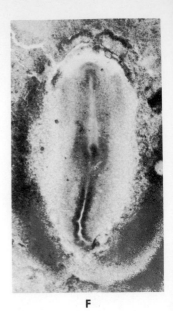

F

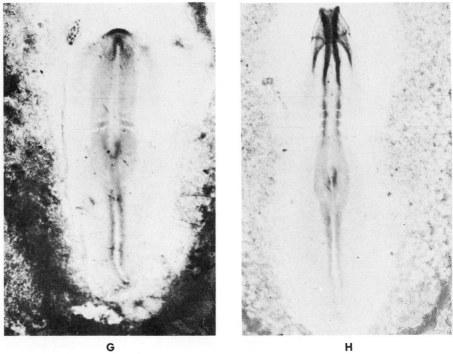

G

H

Fig. 4.76   (continued)

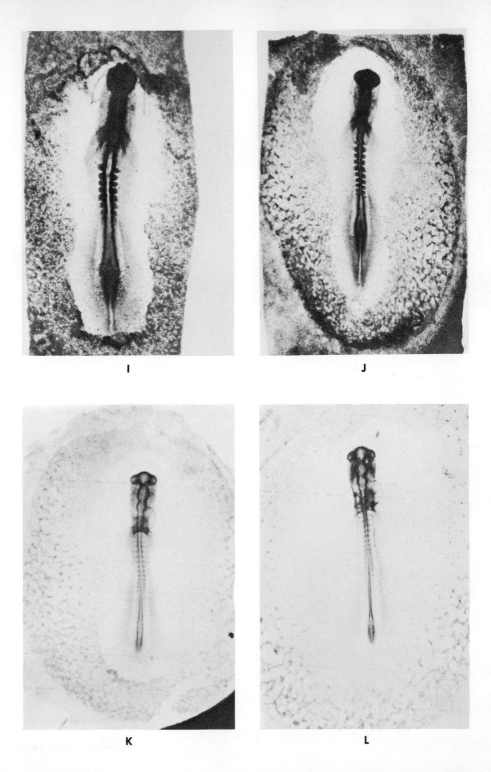

I

J

K

L

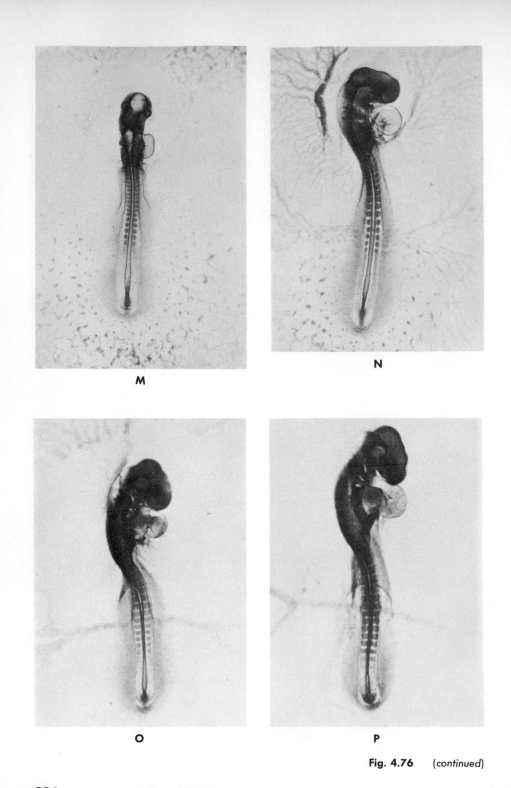

M

N

O

P

Fig. 4.76   (continued)

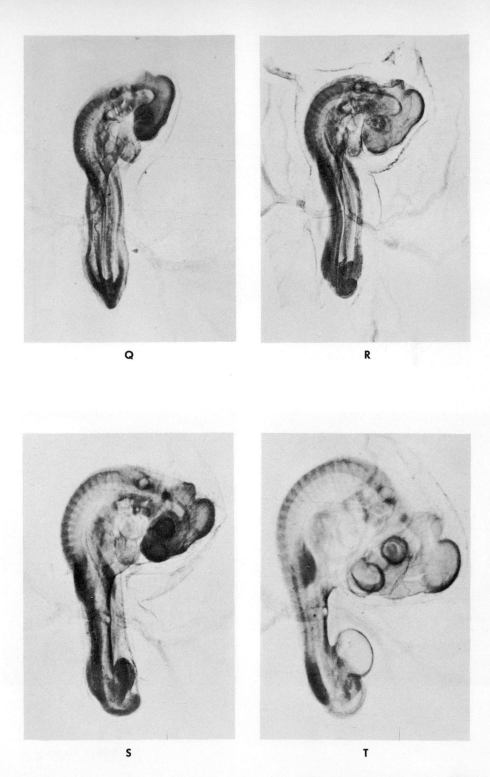

Q

R

S

T

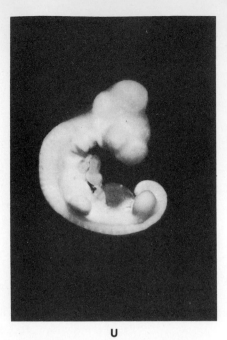

U

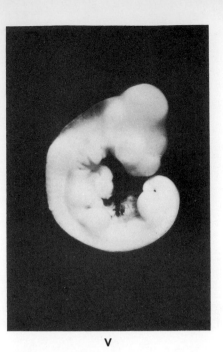

V

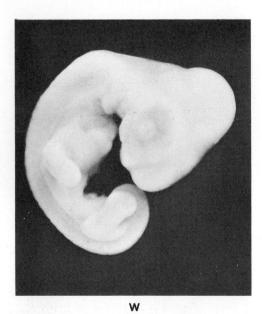

W

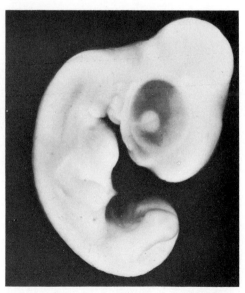

X

Fig. 4.76 (continued)

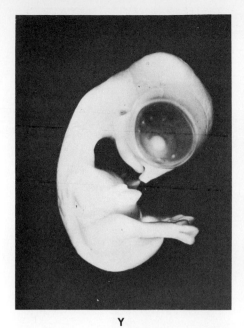

Y

Z

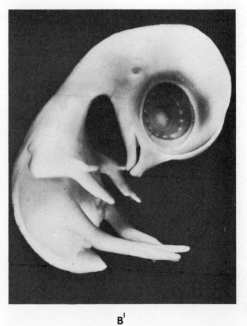

A'

B'

C'

D'

Fig. 4.76   (continued)   D'

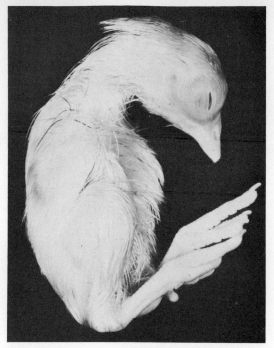

E¹

Embryonic Membranes

in Higher Vertebrates

5

In poikilothermic forms such as the fish and frog, the embryo matures early, and its sole nutriment is yolk. Consequently, the only membrane needed is a *yolk sac* for the storage of the nutriment. Higher vertebrates develop further as embryos and adapt extraembryonic membranes into organs for protection, nutrition, respiration, and excretion. The yolk sac is of secondary importance in the embryos that depend upon maternal tissues for nutrition, but it persists among all vertebrates along with the *amnion, chorion, allantois, umbilical cord,* and *placenta* as an accessory structure necessary for the normal metabolic functions of the embryo.

Although all of these membranes are disconnected from the embryo at birth, each is derived from the embryo before becoming extraembryonic. The yolk sac is part of the midgut (splanchnopleure), the allantois is part of the bladder, and the amnion and chorion are corollaries of the body wall (somatopleure).

The yolk sac is empty and small in higher mammals, but in some species it associates closely with the chorion to form a transitory yolk sac placenta. The allantois is a large and conspicuous bladder with an excretory function in ungulates and carnivores, in which it is associated with the chorion, but is vestigial in rodents and primates. The amnion encloses the embryo and the umbilical cord; it is filled with fluid that provides physical protection for the embryo. The chorion surrounds the embryo and all the other membranes, and its *villi,* fingerlike projections of its surface, invade or interdigitate with the uterine mucosal lining to form the placenta, the organ of nutrition, respiration, and excretion for the embryo. At birth the placenta is suddenly deprived of these functions, and the embryo is thrown upon its own resources, its structures assuming the operations for which they were developed.

The relationship of the chorion and the maternal uterine mucosa involves different forms and different degrees of intimacy. The more intimate the association, the greater the hemorrhage and loss of maternal tissue (*decidua*) in the birth process. The types of mammalian placentae are as follows:

1. *Diffuse,* characteristic of most ungulates (pig, horse), except ruminants

233

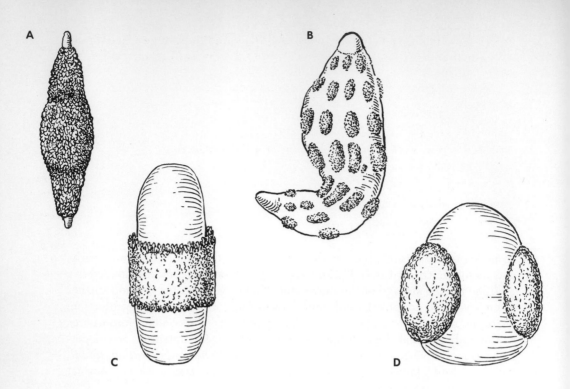

Fig. 5.1   Types of placentae: A, diffuse; B, cotyledonary; C, zonary; D, discoid. (From L. B. Arey, *Developmental Anatomy*, 6th ed., Saunders, Philadelphia, 1954.)

(cud-chewers). Many villi are scattered diffusely over the entire chorion; they do not deeply penetrate the maternal tissue, and the placenta is therefore nondeciduate.

2. *Cotyledonary*, characteristic of ruminant ungulates (cow, sheep, deer). The villi are clustered into prominent rosettes with abundant intervening smooth chorion; they are more firmly implanted than those of the diffuse placenta, and the placenta is semideciduate.

3. *Zonary*, characteristic of carnivores. The villi form a conspicuous band about the midsection of the chorion and embryo; they are securely embedded in the maternal tissue, and the placenta is truly deciduate.

4. *Discoid*, characteristic of rodents and anthropoids. The villi are all concentrated into a disc-shaped mass; they are intimately associated with the maternal tissue, and hence the placenta is deciduate.

In the pig placenta, the allantois, which has respiratory and excretory functions and also aids in nutrition, and the chorion are fused; they form jointly simple villi that fit into simple crypts in the uterine mucosa. In the mouse placenta, of a higher order, the villi establish close contact with the uterine vessels by thinning out their own vascular walls. In the primate placenta, the villi erode and invade the uterine wall so that they are actually bathed in maternal blood.

Table 5.1 lists the types of placentae and the *gestation periods* of various mammals.

Table 5.1   Types of placentae and gestation periods of mammals

ANIMAL	PLACENTA	GESTATION PERIOD, DAYS	ANIMAL	PLACENTA	GESTATION PERIOD, DAYS
opossum	none	13	pig	diffuse	115–120
mouse	discoid	20–21	goat	cotyledonary	140–160
rat	discoid	21–25	sheep	cotyledonary	144–160
mole		30	macaque monkey	discoid	147–160
squirrel		30–40	armadillo		150
rabbit	discoid	30–43	bear	zonary	210
hedgehog		31	mountain goat	cotyledonary	210
woodchuck	discoid	35–42	chimpanzee	discoid	250
kangaroo	none	39	elk	cotyledonary	250
ferret	zonary	42	marten	zonary	267–280
mink	zonary	42–76	man	discoid	270–295
red fox	zonary	52–63	cattle	cotyledonary	282
cat	zonary	60–63	deer	cotyledonary	300
dog	zonary	60–65	zebra	diffuse	300–345
lynx	zonary	63	horse	diffuse	330–380
skunk		63	whale		334–365
wolf	zonary	63	seal	zonary	340–350
guinea pig	discoid	68–71	camel	cotyledonary	389–410
beaver	discoid	94–100	giraffe	cotyledonary	400–480
lion	zonary	106	rhinoceros		488–540
tiger	zonary	106	elephant		510–730

THE MOUSE:

A Discoid Placentate

■ Introduction

Most mammals except the primates mate only when the female is ovulating and fertilization is assured. There are some forms (cat, rabbit, and ferret) in which mating stimulates ovulation. In the mouse mating occurs during *estrus* (*heat*), which usually lasts about 12 hours, and ovulation ordinarily occurs between 10 P.M. and 1 A.M. in early estrus. Through the fall and winter mice rarely mate in the daytime, regardless of the condition or susceptibility of the female. In spring and early summer they may copulate at any time. Quiet courtship (of about 15 minutes' duration) generally leads to mounting and insemination. Mountings last from 2 to 20 seconds and may be frequent. After ejaculation, both animals roll on their sides, close their eyes, and remain in a state of utter fatigue (or shock) for a few minutes. Vaginal plugs, consisting of coagulating fluid from the male, harden 3 or 4 minutes after mating and indicate successful copulation (Fig. 6.1). They disappear within a few hours.

The estrous cycle is usually short (4½ to 5½ days), although variations occur in any strain and even during the reproductive life of a single mouse. It consists of five stages, as follows: *proestrus* (½ to 1½ days), *estrus* (1 to 3 days), *metestrus 1* and *metestrus 2* (1 to 5 days), and *diestrus* (2 to 4 days). Proestrus and estrus are periods in which the ova grow actively. Diestrus, the longest stage, is a period of slow growth preceding the active or anabolic changes of proestrus. The last three stages are catabolic in the sense that they involve degenerative changes within the female genital tract.

Microscopic examination of several drops of saline injected from a flamed pipet into the vagina and immediately removed discloses the current stage of the estrous cycle (Fig. 6.2). Proestrus is characterized by a transition from leucocytes to squamous epithelial cells in the vagina; estrus is indicated by a preponderance of squamous epithelium; metestrus 1 and 2 are marked by a transition from squamous epithelium to leucocytes; and diestrus is indicated by an abundance of leucocytes. Only estrus and diestrus are clear-cut and

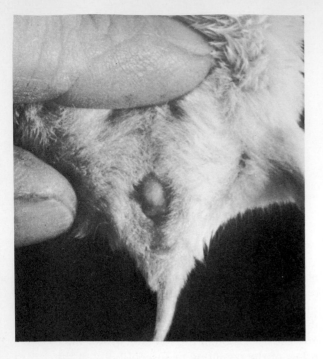

Fig. 6.1 Vaginal orifice of mouse, showing vaginal plug.

readily diagnosed. Proestrus and metestrus, which are transitional and easily confused, may be positively identified only by means of several smears taken on successive days. The external signs of estrus are so minor that they may not be noticed, but they include swelling of the *vulva* and gaping of the vaginal orifice.

The gestation period of the mouse varies somewhat with strain and treatment, but it is relatively short (18 to 21 days) and may be further shortened by stress. Litter size also differs with strain, ranging from 5 or 6 to 18 or 19; it increases up to the third litter and gradually decreases with succeeding litters. A single female may produce as many as 11 litters in 10 months, totaling 100 or more offspring. At birth, mice are hairless, and their eyes and ears are shut, but the time that they remain in this condition may be reduced by supplementing the mother's diet. Sex is determinable immediately after birth, since males have larger external genitalia and a greater distance between genital orifice and anus than females. Sex distribution is about equal under normal conditions (the ratio of males to females in the common Swiss white strain is 53 to 47; the explanation for the slight imbalance may be the same as that suggested in Chapter 8).

Although weaning may be forced at 3 to 4 weeks, healthier offspring result if it is delayed until the fifth or sixth week. Since mating rarely is possible with a female under 7 weeks of age, there is little danger of unwanted pregnancies with postponement of weaning and separation. The mother is

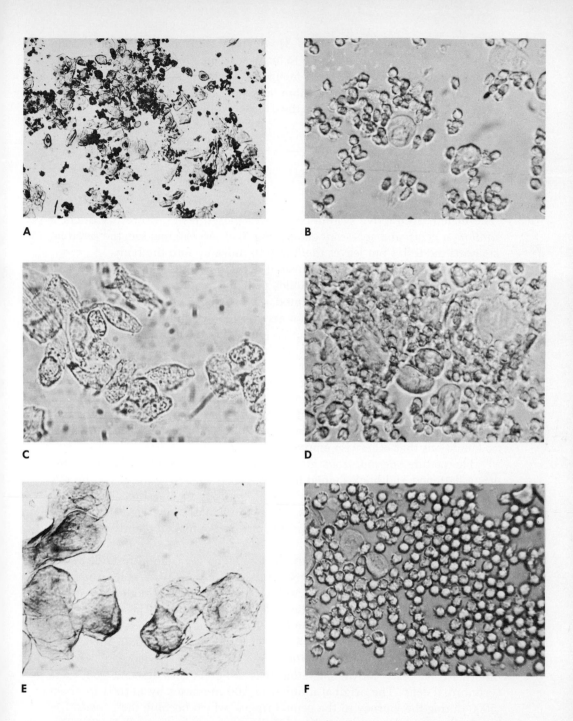

Fig. 6.2 Stages of estrus in mouse, shown by vaginal smears: A, intermediate stage, with approximately equal numbers of leucocytes and epithelial cells; B, proestrus; C, estrus; D, metestrus 1; E, metestrus 2; F, diestrus.

most actively lactating at 14 days. However, if a litter numbers more than eight, some of the young may have to begin searching for and taking solid food at this time. The final transition is facilitated if mother's milk is supplemented with dry oatmeal. Water is even more important than food and must be available at all times. The life span of the mouse averages about 3 years.

■ Reproductive Systems

Male

The male reproductive system consists of paired *testes*, excretory ducts, a *urethra*, a *penis*, and accessory glands (Fig. 6.3). An external sac, the *scrotum*, supports the testes but leaves them free to move up into the body.

The testis is a tubular gland covered with a fibrous connective tissue capsule, the *tunica albuginea*. The tunica provides septa partitioning the organ into lobes, which contain convoluted *seminiferous tubules* (Fig. 6.4), and, between the tubules, variable amounts of endocrine interstitial tissue. Each tubule has a lining of germinal epithelium lying against a basement membrane, outside of which is a thin layer of connective tissue. The germinal epithelium is made up of *sperm* cells in all stages of maturation, closely associated with large, permanent *Sertoli cells*, each of which is attached to the basement membrane. A Sertoli cell may be identified by its large size, oval shape, indented nucleus, and usually two nucleoli. In a depleted seminiferous tubule the Sertoli cells stand out. They are very stable and resistant to conditions that otherwise empty the tubule.

The mature *spermatozoon* attains a total length of up to 0.122 mm. and has a flattened and hook-shaped head. Spermatozoa are carried via the *rete testis*, the *vasa efferentia*, the tripartite *epididymis*, and the *vas (ductus) deferens* to the urethra and penis. Along the way the *ampulla*, the *seminal vesicle*, and the *coagulating, prostate*, and *bulbourethral* glands contribute their secretions.

EMBRYOLOGICAL ORIGIN OF THE TESTIS. The germ line is established at about 8 days. In either presumptive male or presumptive female some 100 alkaline phosphatase-positive cells appear in the yolk sac endoderm posterior to the primitive streak and at the base of the allantois. These cells move (perhaps independently, since they seem to be amoeboid) by way of the dorsal gut mesenchyme to the roots of the mesenchyme in the coelomic angles and by 11 days are lodged in the *genital ridges*, which start developing at 9 days in order to be ready for the migrating cells. All germ cells descend from these primordial cells. The original number of 100 increases by mitosis to about 5000 during the journey to the genital ridges, which become the *gonads*.

In the male the mitotic activity of the primordial germ cells declines toward late fetal life. Shortly before birth the cells develop into *spermatogonia*, of which there are three types, A, intermediate, and B. A is the primitive stem

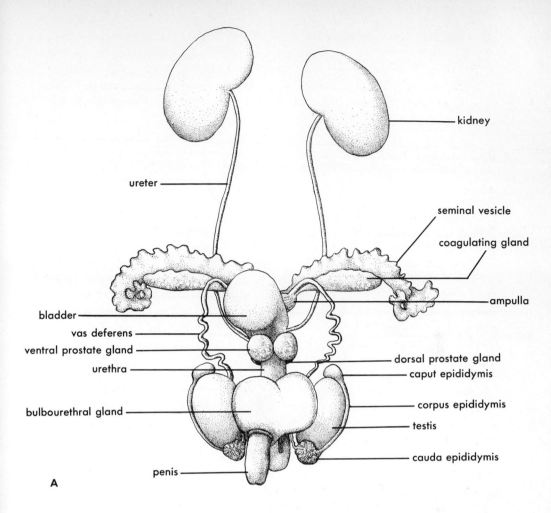

Fig. 6.3 Urogenital system of male mouse: A, ventral view; B, lateral view.

cell that not only perpetuates itself but also gives rise to the two types of advanced spermatogonia and all the succeeding maturation stages, up to mature spermatozoa.

Gonad differentiation begins between 11 and 12 days, even though the germ cells are not yet distinguishable as to sex. In the presumptive testis the germ cells are more scattered and central than in the presumptive ovary. At 13 days the testis cords can be identified.

Female

The female reproductive system consists of paired *ovaries,* coiled *Fallopian tubes,* a bicornuate *uterus,* a *cervix,* and a *vagina,* with an accessory *clitoris* and clitoral gland (Fig. 6.5).

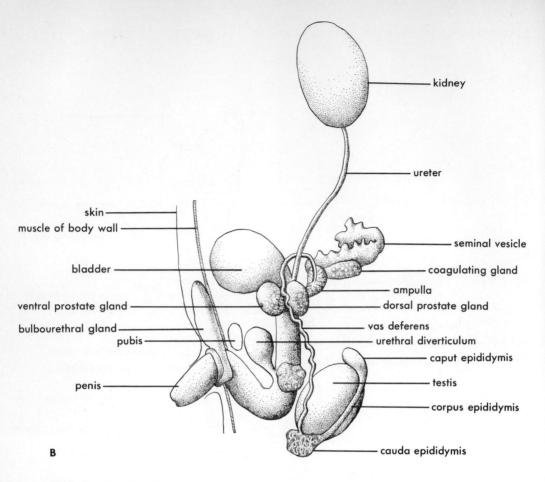

kidney

ureter

skin
muscle of body wall

bladder

ventral prostate gland

bulbourethral gland
pubis

penis

B

seminal vesicle

coagulating gland

ampulla

dorsal prostate gland

vas deferens

urethral diverticulum

caput epididymis

testis

corpus epididymis

cauda epididymis

Fig. 6.3 *(continued)*

Each ovary is very small and slightly pink in color. It is suspended from the dorsal body wall by a ligament. The ovary has an inner medullary portion, a surrounding cortex, and an outer connective tissue tunica albuginea. *Graafian follicles* in various stages of maturation are numerous, largely within the cortex, and are interspersed with ovarian stroma. As a follicle enlarges, it moves toward the surface, protruding from it shortly before ovulation (Fig. 6.6A). A ripe follicle may measure 550 μ in diameter. Five or six ripe *ova* may erupt simultaneously from the surface of a single ovary. Each carries with it some viscous *liquor folliculi*, which tends to clump the ova as they are drawn by ciliary action into the Fallopian tube. The ruptured follicles transform into the *corpora lutea* of ovulation, pregnancy, pseudopregnancy, and lactation. The mean diameter of the corpora may be as much as 450 μ, with a maximum of almost 1 mm. Any ovary contains also *atretic follicles*, which do not mature and which undergo involution and degeneration.

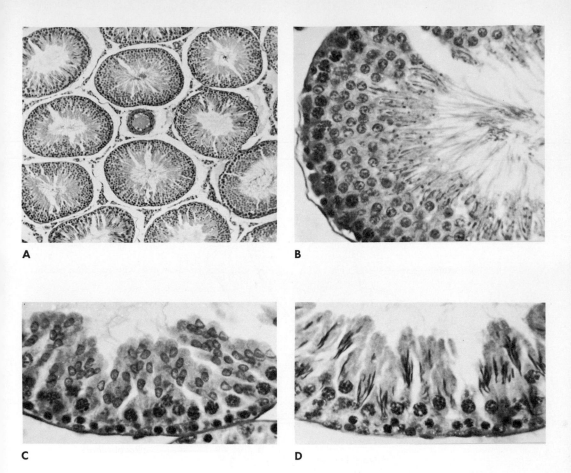

Fig. 6.4   Section of testis of male mouse: A, seminiferous tubules and interstitial tissue (low power); B, tubule showing, from outside in, Sertoli cells associated with basement membrane, spermatogonia, large primary spermatocytes, and smaller secondary spermatocytes; C, tubule showing spermatogonia, primary spermatocytes, and secondary spermatocytes undergoing transformation to spermatids; D, view toward lumen of seminiferous tubule, showing spermatogonia, primary spermatocytes, and spermatozoa (with tails in lumen) (no secondary spermatocytes or spermatids).

The Fallopian tube has a funnel-shaped and ciliated upper end, the *ostium tubae (infundibulum, ampulla)*, which all but surrounds the ovary, and four loops. The tube is lined with simple columnar epithelium, non-ciliated, and is continuous with the uterine *horn*, similarly lined. The short *corpus* of the uterus is lined with branched, tubular glands that project into the uterine cavity or *lumen* and spiral deep into the mucosa, which varies in thickness with the changes of estrus (Fig. 6.6B). The uterine wall is very muscular. The cervix is lined with stratified squamous epithelium and emerges

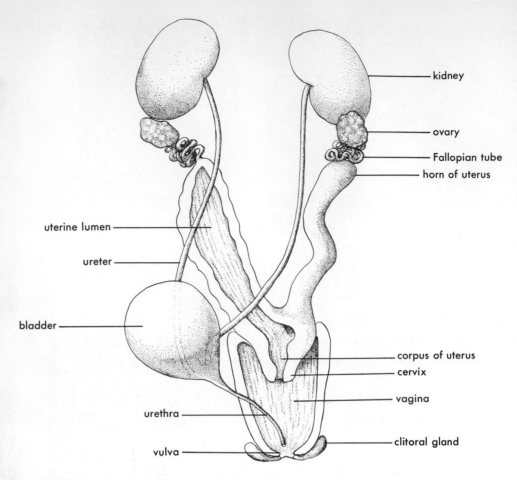

Fig. 6.5 Ventral view of urogenital system of female mouse.

in the dorsoventrally flattened lumen of the vagina. The vaginal lining, which also shows cyclic changes, is largely stratified squamous epithelium. The vagina opens to the outside through the vulva, anterior to which is the small nonerectile clitoris (the homologue of the male penis).

EMBRYOLOGICAL ORIGIN OF THE OVARY.   The ovary arises in the same manner as the testis. It is identifiable at 12½ days by the arrangement of its germ cells, which are rather evenly distributed peripherally. At 13 days five times as many ova as could ever be ovulated are present and recognizable by their early meiotic configuration. At 16 to 18 days many of these are oöcytes, which continue to grow until, just before ovulation, they begin their first meiotic division.

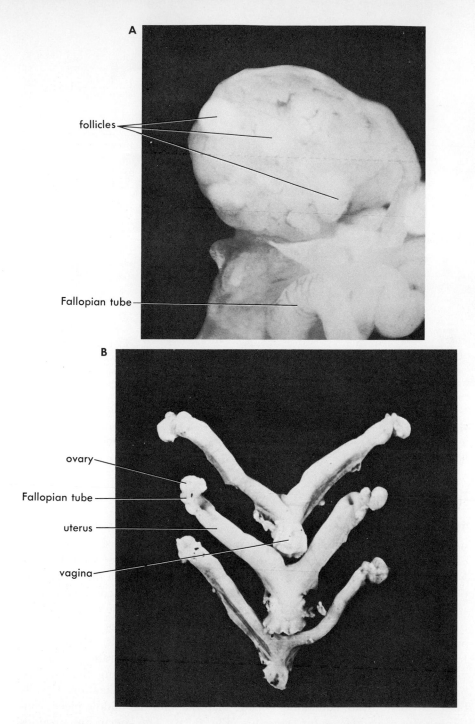

Fig. 6.6   Changes in mouse ovary and uterus with stages of estrus: A, estrus, with follicles about to rupture; B, from top down, proestrus, estrus, and metestrus-diestrus.

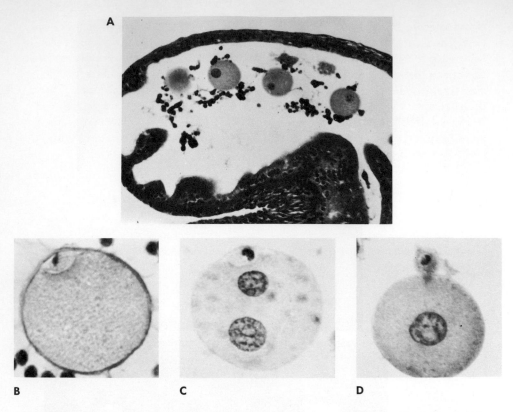

Fig. 6.7 Fertilization and polar body formation in mouse egg: A, unfertilized eggs in Fallopian tube; B, entrance of sperm; C, approach of two pronuclei and beginning polar body formation; D, extrusion of polar body (only female pronucleus shown).

▪ Fertilization

The spermatozoon retains its fertilizing capacity for 6 to 7 hours and its motility for 12 to 13 hours; the ovum is fertile for only 2 to 4 hours. Sperm cells may reach the upper end of the Fallopian tube, to meet or await the ova, within 15 minutes of copulation. The first maturation division of the ovum takes place during early estrus, and by the time of ovulation the second maturation spindle has formed (Fig. 6.7A). Fertilization causes completion of the maturation process. Each ovum is surrounded by a nonliving *zona pellucida* and an outer covering of scattered sticky *cumulus* or *follicle cells*, which clump together the ova produced by one ovary. Sperm cells penetrate these layers within a matter of minutes, the spermatozoon first reaching the *vitelline membrane* of the ovum generally being responsible for fertilization. Usually both the sperm head, containing genetic material, and the middle piece, containing the *centrioles*, enter the ovum (Fig. 6.7B). The sperm head rounds out, swells slightly, and moves toward the egg nucleus. The diameter of the ovum is 80 to 95 μ before, and 100 to 115 μ after, fertilization, the increase being due to expansion of the zona pellucida. A *perivitelline space* forms following a slight shrinkage of the egg, and the first polar body appears in this space, beneath the vitelline membrane (Fig. 6.7 C,D). Just before the first cleavage, the male and female pronuclei break down their membranes. Then their chromosomes intermingle so that every succeeding cell receives a representative portion from each maternal and paternal chromosome. Most mice have a diploid chromosome count of 40, with the male carrying both X and Y sex chromosomes.

■ Cleavage

Cleavage is total but slightly unequal. The first cleavage (Fig. 6.8 A,B) begins about 24 hours after mating and requires only 10 minutes for completion. The succeeding divisions occur at progressively shortened intervals, the

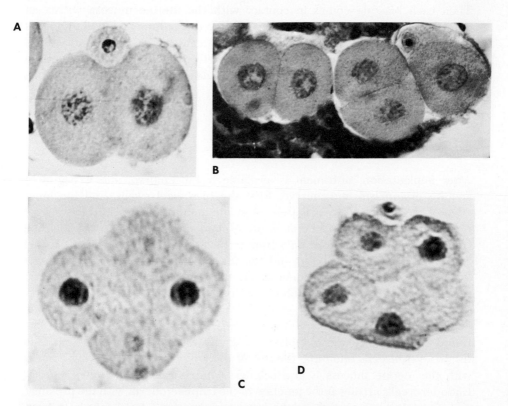

Fig. 6.8　Cleavage in mouse egg: A, telophase of first cleavage, with adjacent polar body; B, three cleaving eggs in Fallopian tube, two in two-cell stage and one showing polar body; C, four-cell stage; D, later cleavage, showing at least five cells and polar body.

second at about 36 hours (12 hours after the first) (Fig. 6.8C), the third at about 46 hours (10 hours after the second), etc. (Fig. 6.8D). These early cleavages take place in the lowest of the four loops of the Fallopian tube. The 16-cell stage (fourth cleavage), which appears about 54 hours after fertilization, is the *morula,* a solid ball of cells. It is usually found in the uppermost part of the uterus, having passed from the Fallopian tube in a cluster of similar embryos.

■ **Blastulation**

A *blastocoel* develops within the morula at about the 32-cell stage (60 hours) (Fig. 6.9). The embryo is then termed a *blastula* or *holoblastula.* A single layer of cells borders the blastocoel on every side but the one occupied by the *inner cell mass,* which is several cells thick and about five cells in diameter. Up to this stage, the early embryos are more or less clustered together, but they soon become rather evenly spaced throughout the uterine cavity. Then each blastula comes in contact with the uterine mucosa within an epithelial crypt, generally on the ventral side of the lumen (Fig. 6.9D). This contact, plus possibly some enzymatic action, causes a change in the consistency of the lining of the uterus. Epithelial cells degenerate, and the embryo embeds (implants) in the swollen mucosa (*decidua*). Meanwhile, the zona pellucida is sloughed off or dissolved.

■ **Gastrulation**

After implantation, nutriment is available to the embryo, and it begins to acquire protoplasm and enlarge. First the blastocoel swells, and the inner edge of the inner cell mass flattens. A single layer of cells on this inner edge represents the primary *endoderm (proximal endoderm)* and may be distinguished from other cells at about 4½ days from fertilization. Thereafter, the blastocoel is known as the *yolk cavity,* and the inner cell mass as the *egg cylinder* (Fig. 6.10). Except for its inner layer, the egg cylinder is *ectoderm.* The outermost layer of cells, which generally have elongated nuclei and dark-staining cytoplasm and which give off droplets of secretions into the uterine lumen, comprises the *extraembryonic ectoderm.* The central cells, which have round nuclei and clearer cytoplasm, make up the *embryonic ectoderm.* The single layer of cells bounding the rest of the yolk cavity and making contact with the uterine mucosa is also ectoderm and is called the *trophectoderm.* Endoderm cells arising at the junction of the trophectoderm with the proximal endoderm and growing along the inner surface of the trophectoderm form the *distal endoderm.* The embryo is now a true *gastrula.*

At 5 days the *proamniotic cavity* is evident in the embryonic ectoderm.

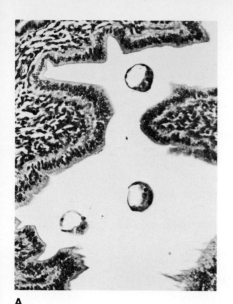

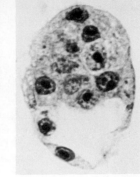

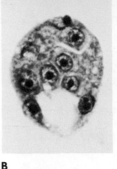

B

C

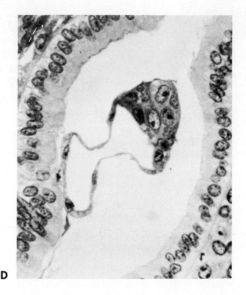

A

Fig. 6.9 Blastulation in mouse egg: A, three blastulae in uterine lumen; B, early blastula, with small blastocoel; C, later blastula; D, blastula attached to uterine wall and beginning implantation.

D

At 5½ days a similar cavity in the extraembryonic ectoderm connects with the proamniotic cavity (Fig. 6.11). Concurrently, that portion of the extraembryonic ectoderm distal to the embryonic region proliferates cells to form a new structure, the *ectoplacental cone*, which invades the uterus and is infiltrated with maternal blood.

The egg cylinder (embryo proper) elongates into, and tends to fill, the yolk cavity. In the process the proximal endoderm, between the thickening ectoderm of the egg cylinder and the yolk cavity, becomes the outer layer of the embryo. This relationship of ectoderm and endoderm in rodents is the reverse of that in most other chordates, in which the ectoderm is outside the endoderm, and is sometimes referred to as "the inversion of the germ layers."

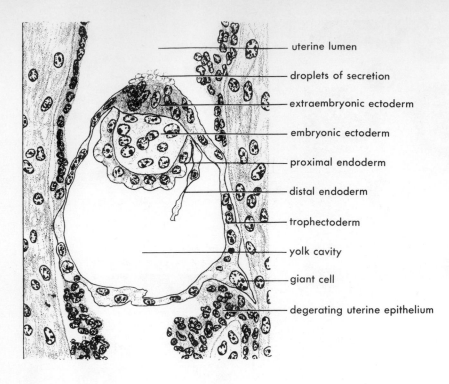

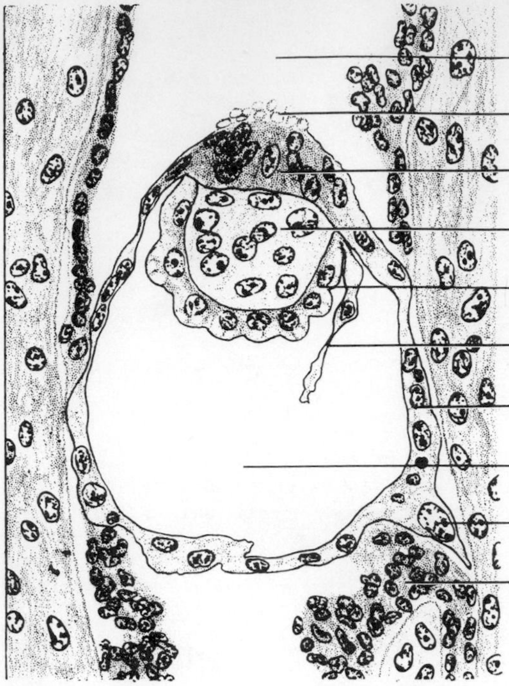
uterine lumen
droplets of secretion
extraembryonic ectoderm
embryonic ectoderm
proximal endoderm
distal endoderm
trophectoderm
yolk cavity
giant cell
degerating uterine epithelium

Fig. 6.10 Longitudinal section of mouse embryo at 4 days 15 hours after mating. (From G. D. Snell, ed., *Biology of the Laboratory Mouse,* Dover, New York, 1956.)

At 6½ days the egg cylinder extends to the opposite wall of the yolk cavity, and its inner, ectodermal layer is quite thick (Fig. 6.12). Furthermore, there is a clear demarcation between the very thick embryonic ectoderm and the thinner extraembryonic ectoderm, at the junction of which is the *posterior amniotic fold.* The distal endoderm is no longer easily distinguishable because it adheres closely to the distal wall of the yolk cavity throughout. Budding off a narrow strip of embryonic ectoderm that extends ventrally from the region of the posterior amniotic fold about halfway to the tip of the egg cylinder are the *mesenchyme* cells (primitive *mesoderm*), which become loosely dispersed between the ectoderm and the surrounding proximal endoderm. Some give rise to embryonic structures, and some to extraembryonic structures, such as the membranes around the embryo. These cells possibly contribute to the elongation of the egg cylinder, which in turn furthers their distribution. The strip of ectoderm from which they develop is the *primitive streak.*

The primitive streak indicates the posterior end of the embryo. Although implantation is in a uterine crypt, the embryonic axes are generally so oriented that the dorsoventral axis of the embryo is perpendicular to the long axis of

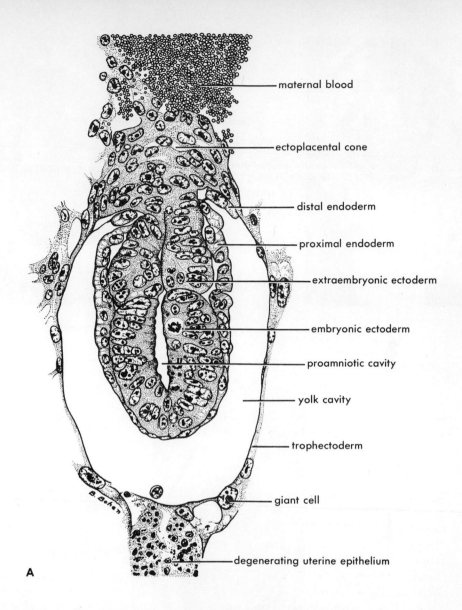

maternal blood

ectoplacental cone

distal endoderm

proximal endoderm

extraembryonic ectoderm

embryonic ectoderm

proamniotic cavity

yolk cavity

trophectoderm

giant cell

degenerating uterine epithelium

A

Fig. 6.11   Mouse embryo at 5½ days: A–C, longitudinal sections; D, transverse section. (A from G. D. Snell, ed., *Biology of the Laboratory Mouse*, Dover, New York, 1956.)

the uterus and the anteroposterior axis of the embryo is perpendicular to the *mesometrium* (the dorsal suspensory membrane of the uterus, homologous to the broad ligament in other forms). These axes, first established at 6½ days, are maintained until about 8½ days, when embryonic movement alters them.

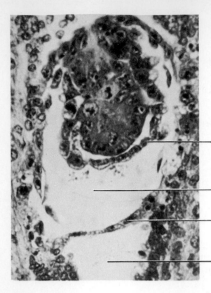

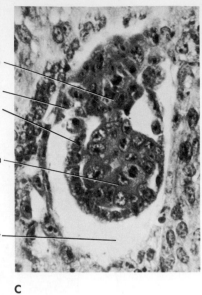

extraembryonic
ectoderm

distal endoderm

proximal endoderm

proximal endoderm

embryonic ectoderm

yolk cavity

trophectoderm

uterine lumen

yolk cavity

B

C

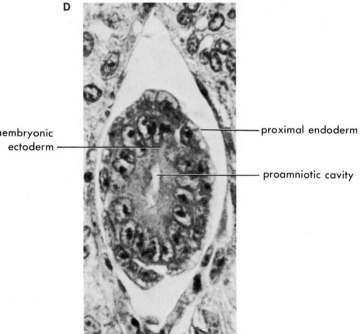

extraembryonic
ectoderm

proximal endoderm

proamniotic cavity

D

Fig. 6.11   (continued)

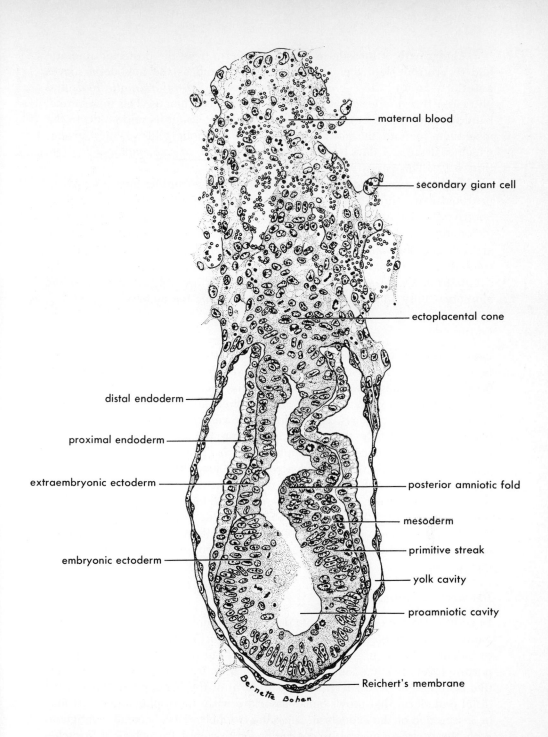

maternal blood

secondary giant cell

ectoplacental cone

distal endoderm

proximal endoderm

extraembryonic ectoderm

posterior amniotic fold

mesoderm

primitive streak

embryonic ectoderm

yolk cavity

proamniotic cavity

Reichert's membrane

Bernette Bohan

Fig. 6.12 Sagittal section of mouse embryo at 6 days 13 hours. (From G. D. Snell, ed., *Biology of the Laboratory Mouse*, Dover, New York, 1956.)

The growth of mesoderm causes ectoderm from the posterior amniotic fold to protrude into the proamniotic cavity, and as the mesoderm moves anteriorly around the egg cylinder, it forms the *lateral amniotic folds* and ultimately the *anterior amniotic fold*, which are continuous. This mesodermal band tends to constrict the entire egg cylinder at about its mid-point. In the meantime, in both the posterior and lateral amniotic folds cavities appear, which coalesce at 7 days to form the single *exocoel*, or *extraembryonic coelom* (Fig. 6.13). This cavity is lined with mesoderm.

These changes divide the egg cylinder across its middle into an upper or proximal extraembryonic region and a lower or distal embryonic region. Shortly after 7 days the regions are clearly separated by a double membrane (ectoderm and mesoderm) known as the *amnion,* with the exocoel outside the embryo and the *amniotic cavity* within its ectoderm (Figs. 6.14, 6.15). A similarly constructed membrane, the *chorion,* separates the *ectoplacental cavity* from the exocoel. The embryonic layers are still inverted, and the amniotic cavity will eventually come to lie outside the embryo.

Giant cells

Examination of the implantation site at this time shows some abnormally large cells in the area between the decidua and the embryo (Figs. 6.10, 6.11A, 6.12, 6.14). As these *giant cells* seem healthy, and as there is no accompanying evidence of hyperemia, they are accepted as normal. The first, which appear at about 4½ days, derive from the ventral trophectoderm. Others, which appear shortly thereafter, arise from the ectoplacental cone and migrate ventrally outside the trophectoderm. They develop protoplasmic processes or strands that extend across the blood-filled space between the decidua and the trophectoderm and may aid in securing the trophectoderm to the decidua. Other giant cells, with dark-staining, closely packed multiple nuclei (sometimes 10 or more), appear in the decidua near the embryo at about 7½ days. Thus three types of enlarged cells are distinguishable. Their function is uncertain, but they are believed to reinforce the embryo-decidua relationship.

Reichert's membrane

In addition to the extraembryonic membranes common to all vertebrates, the mouse has a *Reichert's membrane* (Figs. 6.12, 6.15). This structure, peculiar to rodent embryos, is a noncellular, very thin but tough, poorly staining supporting layer, elastic enough to expand with embryonic growth and protective in function, between the trophectoderm of the 6½-day embryo and the distal endoderm that grows out to associate with the trophectoderm. It may be a secretion of the endoderm. Since the trophectoderm becomes contiguous with the uterine mucosa (except at its most ventral tip, where it stretches across the uterine lumen), its identity is not clear-cut, and the Reichert's membrane is difficult to see.

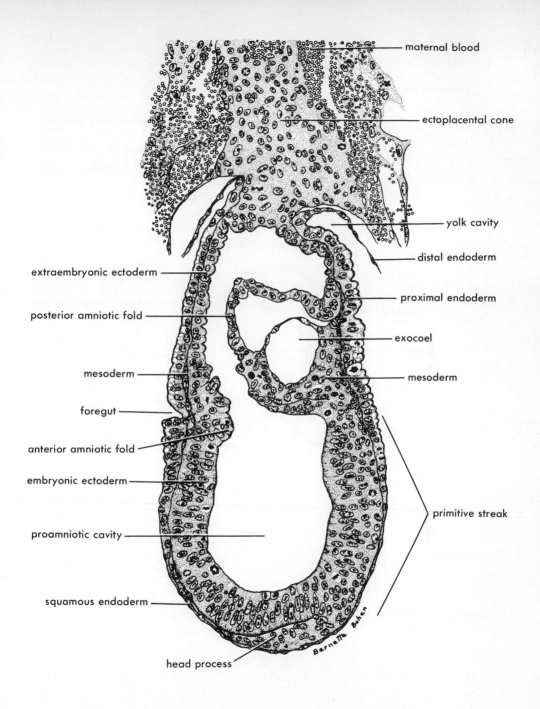

Labels on the figure:

- maternal blood
- ectoplacental cone
- yolk cavity
- distal endoderm
- extraembryonic ectoderm
- proximal endoderm
- posterior amniotic fold
- exocoel
- mesoderm
- mesoderm
- foregut
- anterior amniotic fold
- embryonic ectoderm
- primitive streak
- proamniotic cavity
- squamous endoderm
- head process

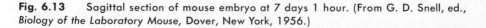

Fig. 6.13   Sagittal section of mouse embryo at 7 days 1 hour. (From G. D. Snell, ed., *Biology of the Laboratory Mouse*, Dover, New York, 1956.)

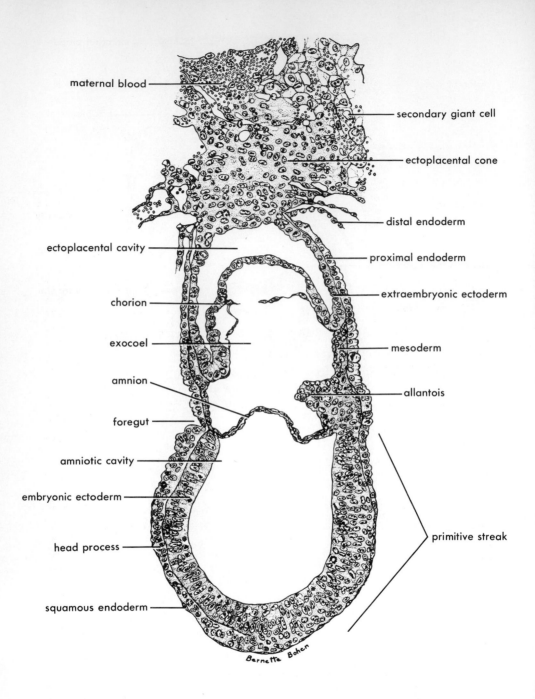

maternal blood

secondary giant cell

ectoplacental cone

distal endoderm

ectoplacental cavity

proximal endoderm

chorion

extraembryonic ectoderm

exocoel

mesoderm

amnion

allantois

foregut

amniotic cavity

embryonic ectoderm

primitive streak

head process

squamous endoderm

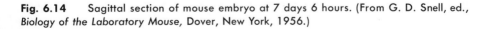

Bernette Bohen

Fig. 6.14   Sagittal section of mouse embryo at 7 days 6 hours. (From G. D. Snell, ed., *Biology of the Laboratory Mouse*, Dover, New York, 1956.)

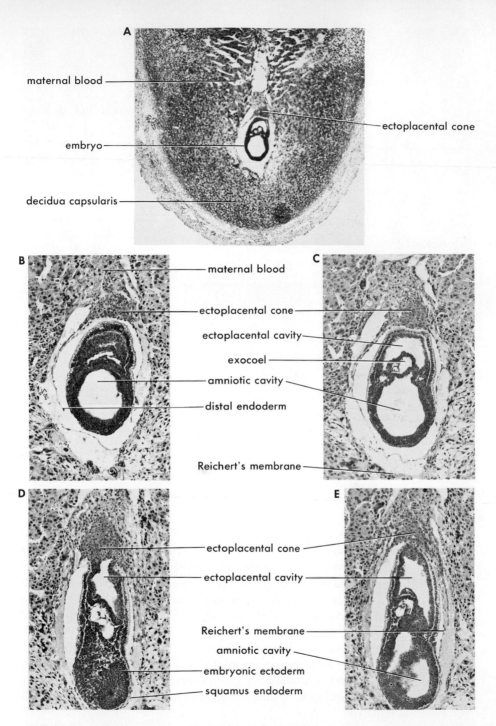

Fig. 6.15 Mouse embryo at 7½ days: A–G, longitudinal sections (A at low power); H, transverse section.

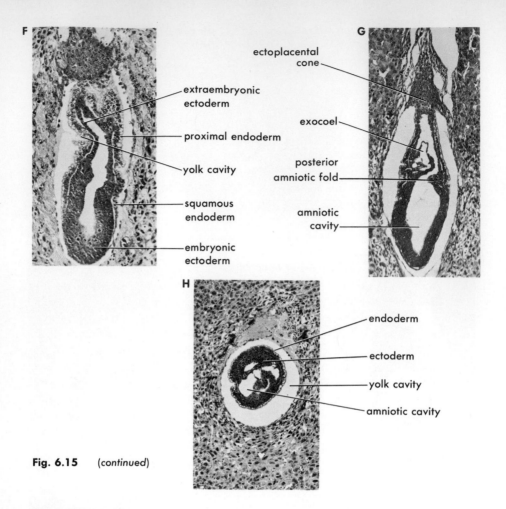

Fig. 6.15 (continued)

■ Organogenesis

The *head process*, which consists of both ectoderm and endoderm, extends anteriorly from the anterior end of the primitive streak at 7 days. At about 7½ days the elongated *notochord* develops between the ectoderm and the endoderm of this process, probably deriving from endoderm. Mesenchyme spreads outward from each side of the notochord between the ectoderm and endoderm.

The ectoderm extending anteriorly from the primitive streak above the notochord thickens to form the *neural plate*. At about 8 days a depression, the *neural groove,* which is the first sign of a central nervous system, appears in the plate. The neural groove and the primitive streak indicate the midplane of the embryo.

Extraembryonic mesenchyme from the posterior end of the primitive streak grows into the exocoel to form the *allantois* (Fig. 6.14). In the mouse it does not contain the endoderm-lined cavity found in many vertebrates; instead there are numerous small cavities in the mesoderm. The allantois fills the exocoel, obliterating it completely, and fuses with the chorion at about 8 days. It thus connects the primitive streak with the ectoplacental cone (which enlarges to become the *ectoplacenta*) and eventually provides blood vessels linking the embryo to the uterus.

The primitive streak is therefore quite extensive and is rated first as an active growth center in the mouse, since from it develop all three primary germ layers. Some authorities have tried to homologize it with the chick's primitive streak and the amphibian's dorsal lip of the blastopore as an organizing center for the embryo.

The *foregut* appears at 7 days as a notch at the anterior extremity of the columnar endoderm of the head process. This notch becomes a blind pocket, pushing inward and upward the overlying ectoderm containing the neural primordia. The anterior structures thus forced into the amniotic cavity form the *head fold*. This is the second growth center, at least in point of time, as it indicates cephalization. Further anteriorly the earliest indications of the *heart* are apparent as organizing mesenchyme, now below the level of the foregut and head fold (Fig. 6.16). During the cephalic activity another notch appears in the endoderm posterior to the primitive streak. The inverted pouch or pocket that forms is the primitive *hindgut*. The openings from the foregut and hindgut into the yolk cavity are the *anterior intestinal portal* and the *posterior intestinal portal*, respectively. As the movements that change the gut from inverted grooves to a closed tube are downward folds in the endoderm progressing from either end toward the center, the *midgut* is the last portion of the digestive tract to develop. The embryo at 7 to 8 days has an exaggerated lordosis curve in any sagittal section (Fig. 6.17), but this is rectified when the early inverted relations are corrected. The germ layers soon assume the traditional relationship of other vertebrates, with the outermost layer ectoderm or its derivatives.

The *somites* begin to appear at about 7½ days, as condensations of mesenchyme lateral and adjacent to the notochord. The first pair is anterior to the primitive streak, on either side of the notochord, and the second pair is immediately behind the first. Ultimately about 65 somite pairs develop. In the mouse, as in the chick, somite number is the best criterion of embryonic age during early development.

Lateral to the somites, the mesenchyme is extraembryonic and associated with the lining of the exocoel. At 8 days the *nephrotome* (*intermediate cell mass*) mesoderm and the *lateral plate* mesoderm are distinguishable, somewhat separated by a shallow longitudinal cleft.

The *coelom* arises in the same manner in the mouse and in the chick, as a split in the lateral plate mesoderm separating the *somatic* and *splanchnic* layers. Since the *somatopleure* is continuous with the amnion, both being ectoderm and mesoderm, the body coelom is continuous with the extraembryonic coelom (exocoel) (Fig. 6.18). The coelom is not paired in the mouse

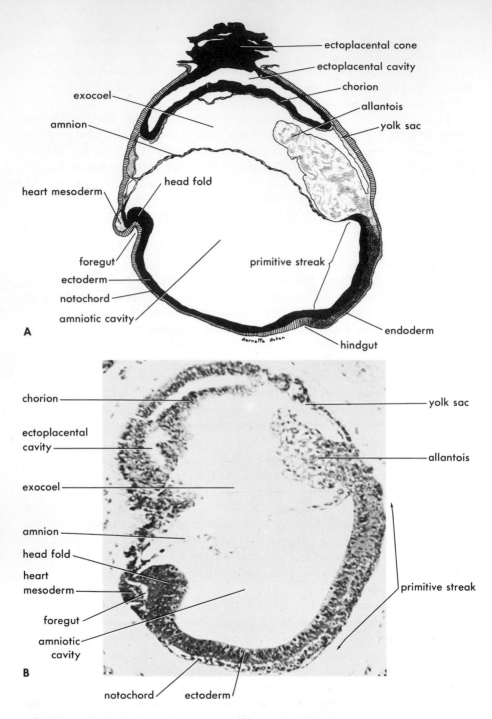

Fig. 6.16 Sagittal sections of mouse embryo at 7 days 15 hours. (A from G. D. Snell, ed., *Biology of the Laboratory Mouse*, Dover, New York, 1956.)

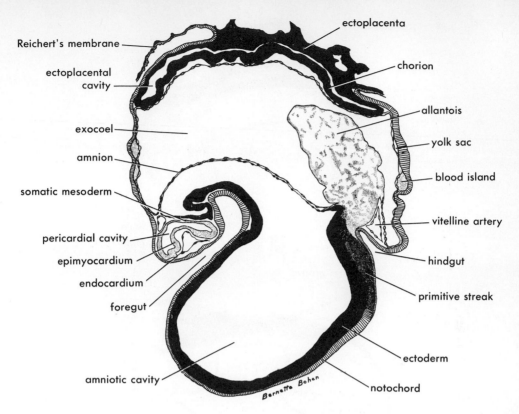

Fig. 6.17　Sagittal section of mouse embryo at 7 days 18 hours. (From G. D. Snell, ed., *Biology of the Laboratory Mouse*, Dover, New York, 1956.)

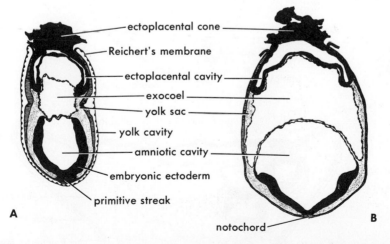

Fig. 6.18　Transverse sections showing development of extraembryonic membranes in mouse: A, at 7 days 6 hours; B, at 7 days 10 hours; C, at 8 days 10 hours, through somite VIII; D, at 8 days 11 hours, through somite IX; E, at 8 days 18 hours, through somite IX. (From G. D. Snell, ed., *Biology of the Laboratory Mouse*, Dover, New York, 1956.)

Fig. 6.18 (*continued*)

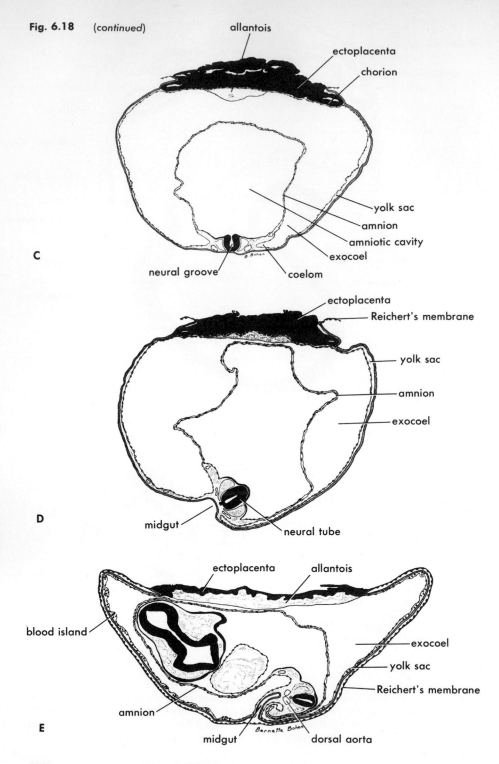

C

allantois

ectoplacenta

chorion

yolk sac

amnion

amniotic cavity

exocoel

neural groove

coelom

D

ectoplacenta

Reichert's membrane

yolk sac

amnion

exocoel

midgut

neural tube

E

ectoplacenta

allantois

blood island

exocoel

yolk sac

Reichert's membrane

amnion

midgut

dorsal aorta

as in the chick, however. Instead the two lateral wings of coelom join anteriorly in the shape of an inverted U beneath the foregut and head fold. This connection gives rise to the *pericardial cavity*, which is consequently continuous with both the body coelom and the exocoel.

The circulatory system develops from *blood islands*, early concentrations of cells in the mesoderm of the *splanchnopleure*. These form *lacunae* that coalesce into *blood vessels*, containing primitive blood cells, beginning at about 7½ days.

The heart itself begins actively differentiating at 7½ days and soon becomes structurally separated from the lateral plate mesoderm and the coelom. Between 7½ and 8 days the splanchnic mesoderm forming the ventral wall of the pericardial cavity develops into the *epicardium* (outer membrane) and *myocardium* (muscles) of the heart wall, while between the splanchnic mesoderm and the endodermal floor of the gut appear loose mesenchyme cells that become the *endocardium* or lining mesothelium of the heart cavities (Fig. 6.17). As the anterior intestinal portal moves posteriorly, the inverted U connection in the coelom becomes an inverted V, then, as the sides fuse together, an inverted Y, and finally the single pericardial cavity. The endocardial mesenchyme forms a tube and then twists to develop the various regions of the heart. Simultaneously paired dorsal aortae, with cardiac connections through visceral arches, arise and proceed posteriorly to merge into a single *vitelline (omphalomesenteric) artery* leading to the yolk sac. The artery is lost in a network of blood vessels that reorganize into the paired *vitelline (omphalomesenteric) veins*, which carry the blood back to the heart. These relations of the heart and blood vessels are characteristic of all warm-blooded vertebrates. One of the many marvels of embryology is the timing of blood vessel, corpuscle, and heart development. When all these structures are ready to function properly, the heart begins its rhythmic beat.

At 7½ days the amnion covers the dorsal surface of the embryo (Fig. 6.18B). Ultimately its folds surround the embryo, which is held in place within the fluid-containing amniotic cavity by the *umbilical cord*. Since the mouse is a discoid placentate with no real need for yolk, no *yolk sac*, or only a rudimentary one, might be expected. However, probably owing to the postulated reptilian origin of rodents, a membrane persists, homologous to the yolk sac of more primitive forms. It eventually envelops the embryo (Fig. 6.18C), as in the chick, except at the region of the midgut, and aids both in protection and in the conduction of nutriment from the placenta to the embryo by way of the umbilical (splanchnopleuric) vessels. The yolk cavity, originally the blastocoel, is between the egg cylinder and Reichert's membrane.

■ 8-Day Embryo

The 8-day mouse embryo with its four pairs of somites corresponds to about the 28-hour chick embryo. Major differences are that the mouse has so elongated as to form a relatively large lordosis curve in its body, simulating a reversed S, whereas the chick has a C shape, and that the germ layers are inverted in the mouse.

At about 8 days the mouse embryo begins to rotate, with the turning beginning almost simultaneously at both ends. Views from the dorsal side, or sections from that side, reveal that the cephalic end of the embryo rotates clockwise while the caudal end rotates counterclockwise. The developing heart aids in changing the direction of growth of the cephalic structures ventrad. Meanwhile, the *neural folds* bounding the neural groove begin to close at the mid-trunk level, forming a *neural tube* (Fig. 6.19). Bulges toward its anterior extremity indicate early brain differentiation.

The rotation is completed in the mid-trunk region at about the 12-somite stage, so that by 8½ days the once twisted body is C-shaped, with the original ventral surfaces inside the C, and the embryo is lying on its left side, with its right side toward the placenta. Transverse sections show the closed foregut and hindgut pockets; the epi-, myo-, and endocardia; the paired dorsal aortae

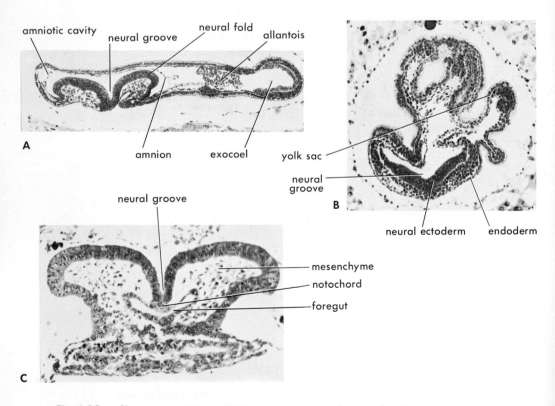

Fig. 6.19   Transverse sections of 8-day mouse embryo, showing developing neural groove.

indicating development of intraembryonic blood vessels; and an extended tail fold lying in the exocoel. The mid-trunk rotation forms, or closes off, the midgut by bringing toward each other the splanchnopleure layers from the sides.

Nutrition

Implantation at 4½ days is a cooperative process between the embryo and the uterine mucosa, which swells, becoming the decidua, and blocks the uterine crypt into which the blastula nestles from the main uterine cavity. The embryo, thus trapped, is attached dorsally by the ectoplacental cone. The decidua grows until it completely closes the uterine lumen dorsal to the embryo except for one or more small cavities. Although the lumen remains open on each side of the decidual swelling, there is no continuous passage through the length of the uterus until, at about 8 days, a new longitudinal lumen develops. This lumen is ventral to the embryo, which becomes suspended in the new cavity.

At 8½ days longitudinal sections show several newly differentiated layers in the extraembryonic, maternal uterus. The side dorsal to the embryo, where the crypt was closed, is the *decidua basalis,* unchanged uterine mucosa lying between the embryo and the remains of the original lumen. The side ventral to the embryo is the *decidua capsularis,* which consists of large and often multi-nucleate cells separating the embryo from the new uterine lumen. This layer is rather thick, but it stretches and thins with the later growth of the embryo. In close proximity to the embryo, between these zones, is the *vascular zone,* so called because of its early development of numerous blood islands and vessels. These vessels rupture at about 5½ days to flood the embryo with maternal blood. Reichert's membrane protects the embryo itself from direct contact with such normal hemorrhage, at the same time allowing soluble nutriment to pass through to the yolk sac and the embryonic circulation. The adhesion of the yolk sac to Reichert's membrane thus appears to have a functional purpose, to make close but not direct contact with the surrounding maternal blood. Eventually the decidua becomes very vascular, and some of its engorged sinusoids may rupture into the uterine lumen, producing some bleeding from the vagina at 7 to 10 days. The discrete, *discoid placenta* so prominent in the late gravid uterus is made up of the decidua basalis, the allantois, the chorion, and the ectoplacenta, all so interfused that they may be indistinguishable.

▪ Later Embryo

Beyond the ninth day the development of the mouse embryo resembles closely that of the pig or the human embryo (Fig. 6.20). When the mouse embryo becomes recognized generally as valuable material for normal mammalian embryology, it will undoubtedly displace the pig embryo to a large

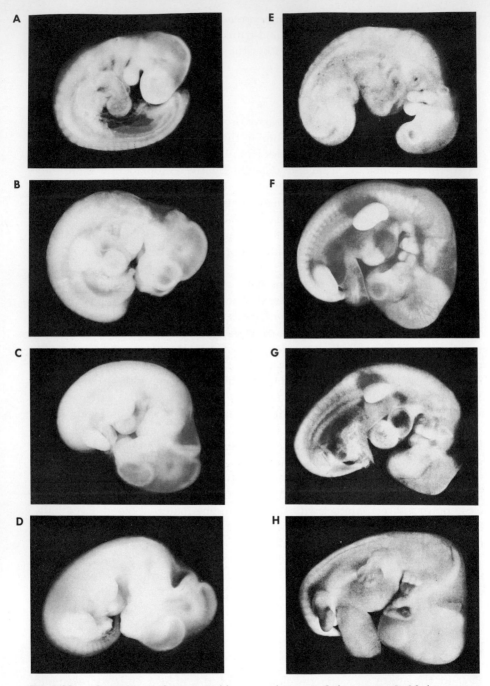

Fig. 6.20 Comparison of mouse and human embryos: A, 9-day mouse; B, 10-day mouse; C, 11-day mouse; D, 12-day mouse; E–H, human embryos at corresponding stages. (A–D from R. Alden, *Laboratory Atlas of the Mouse Embryo*, Univ. of Tennessee Medical Unit, Knoxville, Tenn.; E–H from Carnegie Institute of Washington.)

extent, even beyond the 10 mm. stage. The comparative ages of mouse and human embryos are given in Table 6.1, and the relation of age to crown-rump length and somite number in the mouse embryo is shown in Table 6.2. A description of the development of the mouse embryo from 8½ days to birth follows (Figs. 6.21–6.23).

Fig. 6.21   Gravid mouse uteri containing embryos at various stages of development: A, at 6½ to 9½ days, showing ovaries at upper ends; B, at 10½ to 14½ days, showing only one horn in each case except at extreme right, where second horn contains no embryos; C, at 13½ days, with embryos exposed; D, at 15½ to 18½ days, showing only one horn.

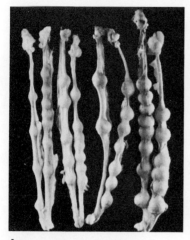

A

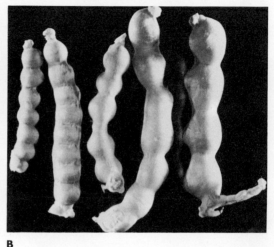

B

C

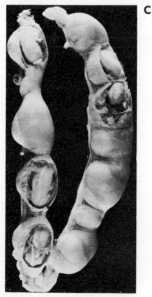

D

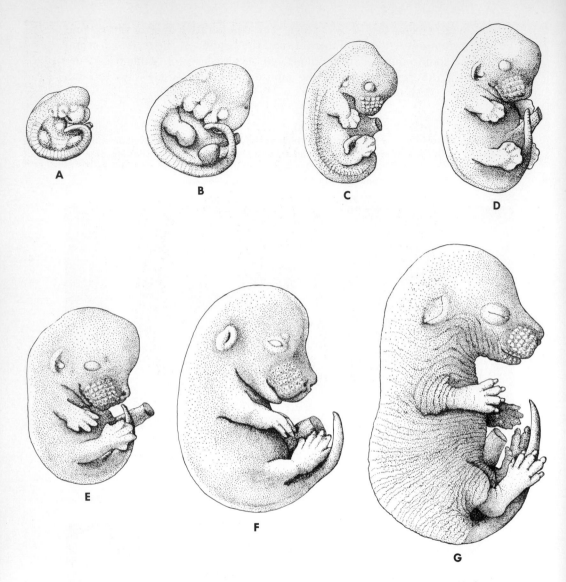

Fig. 6.22   Diagrams showing development of mouse embryo from 10½ to 16½ days.

8½ days

Neural crests appear, and the *ganglia* for nerves V to X begin to form. The *oral membrane* ruptures; *visceral arch* I and *visceral pouch* I develop; and the *thyroid* arises as a depression in the pharyngeal floor at the level of visceral pouch I. *Aortic arch* I is also evident.

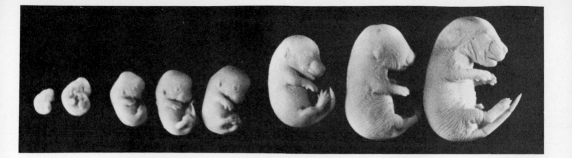

A

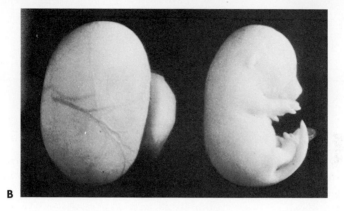

B

Fig. 6.23   Development of mouse embryo from 10½ to 17½ days: A, embryos at daily intervals, showing spurt in growth between 14½ and 15½ days; B, 15½-day mouse embryo within chorionic vesicle and its litter mate, showing size relationship and type of placenta.

Table 6.1   Comparative ages of mouse and human embryos

MOUSE AGE, DAYS	HUMAN AGE, DAYS	MOUSE AGE, DAYS	HUMAN AGE, DAYS
8	20½	11	30¾
8⅓	21	11½	33½
8½	22	12	36
8⅔–8¾	23	12½	36½
8⅘	24⅓	13–13½	38
9	25½	14½	47
9½–9⅔	26	15½	65
10	27	16½	84½
10½	28½		

AGE, DAYS	SOMITES	LENGTH, MM.
8	1–4	
8½	5–12	2
9	13–20	2.2
9½	21–25	3.3
10	26–28	3.8
10½	29–36	5.2
11	37–42	6.2
12	43–48	7.2
12½	49–51	8.9
13	52–60	9.4
13½		9.8
14½	61–64	11.2
15	65	
15½		13.7
16½		16.1

9 days

The *anterior neuropore* closes, and three primary brain vesicles are apparent. The *yolk stalk* narrows. The heart has a *sinus venosus, atrium, ventricle,* and *bulbus arteriosus.*

9½ days

The embryo (Fig. 6.24) has the C shape characteristic of all vertebrate embryos at one time or another, with an approximation of the *telencephalon* and tail. The *posterior neuropore* closes; the brain differentiates into five vesicles; the *optic vesicle* and *optic cup* are formed (Fig. 6.24A,C); the *auditory vesicle* is apparent, lateral to the *myelencephalon* (Fig. 6.24J); but there is no sign yet of the *olfactory placode*. The first and second visceral arches (mandibular and hyoid) are discernible (Fig. 6.24I,J), and sections show the *maxillary process;* the *laryngotracheal groove* is visible; *lung buds,* the dorsal *pancreas,* and the *liver* branch off the *pharynx;* the yolk stalk closes; and the *cloaca* and *tail gut* evaginate from the hindgut. Limb bud thickenings may appear anteriorly, although there is no tail bud; somites may be evident beneath the skin (Fig. 6.24F,H); and the *anterior cardinal veins* and *pronephric ducts* and *tubules* develop.

10 days

The auditory vesicle closes. Visceral pouch III forms; the thyroid has a duct; the paired lung buds extend from the laryngotracheal groove; the stomach elongates; and the *cloacal membrane* appears. The pronephric ducts reach the cloaca.

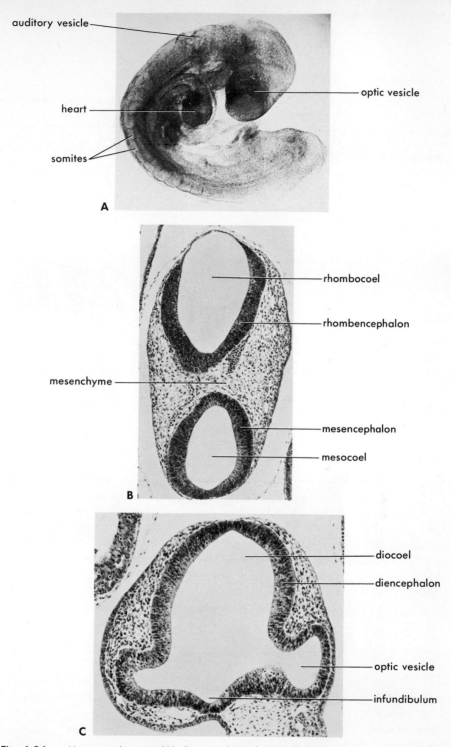

Fig. 6.24 Mouse embryo at 9½ days: A, lateral view; B–P, transverse sections (L–P at high power).

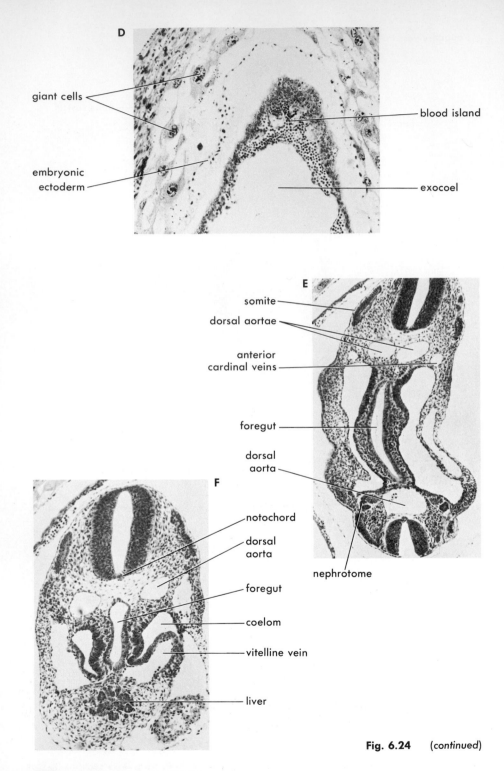

D

giant cells

blood island

embryonic
ectoderm

exocoel

E

somite

dorsal aortae

anterior
cardinal veins

foregut

dorsal
aorta

F

notochord

dorsal
aorta

foregut

coelom

vitelline vein

nephrotome

liver

Fig. 6.24   (continued)

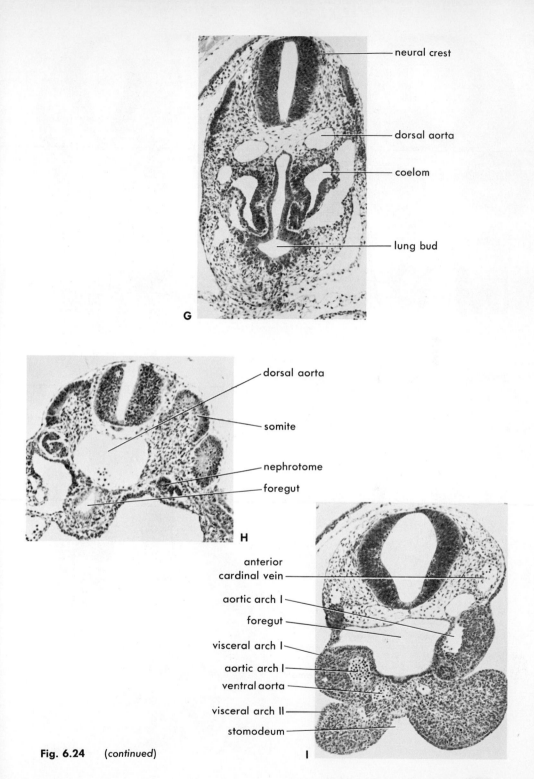

G

— neural crest

— dorsal aorta

— coelom

— lung bud

dorsal aorta —

somite —

nephrotome —

foregut —

H

anterior
cardinal vein —

aortic arch I —

foregut —

visceral arch I —

aortic arch I —

ventral aorta —

visceral arch II —

stomodeum —

I

Fig. 6.24 (continued)

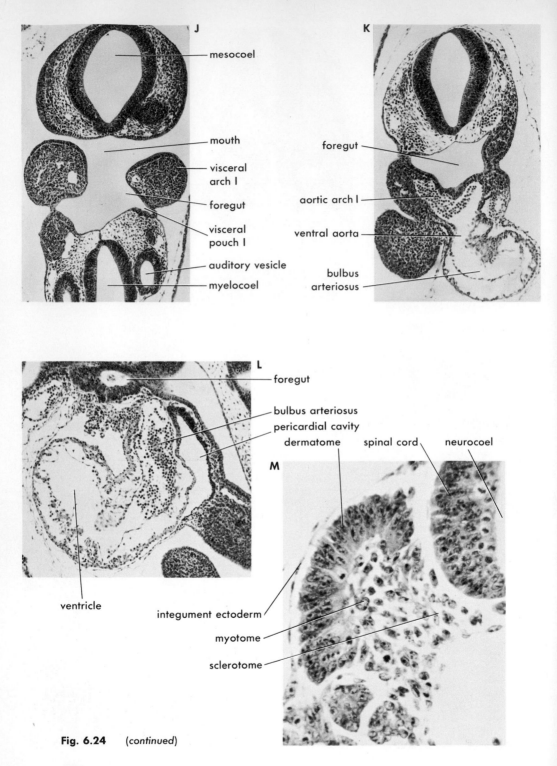

J

mesocoel

mouth

visceral arch I

foregut

visceral pouch I

auditory vesicle

myelocoel

K

foregut

aortic arch I

ventral aorta

bulbus arteriosus

L

foregut

bulbus arteriosus

pericardial cavity

dermatome   spinal cord   neurocoel

M

ventricle

integument ectoderm

myotome

sclerotome

Fig. 6.24   (continued)

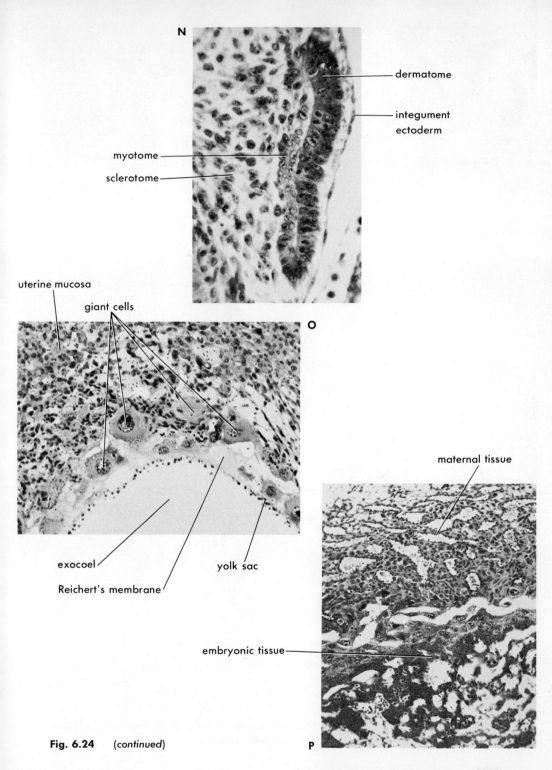

N

dermatome

integument
ectoderm

myotome

sclerotome

uterine mucosa

giant cells

O

maternal tissue

exocoel

Reichert's membrane

yolk sac

embryonic tissue

Fig. 6.24 (continued)

P

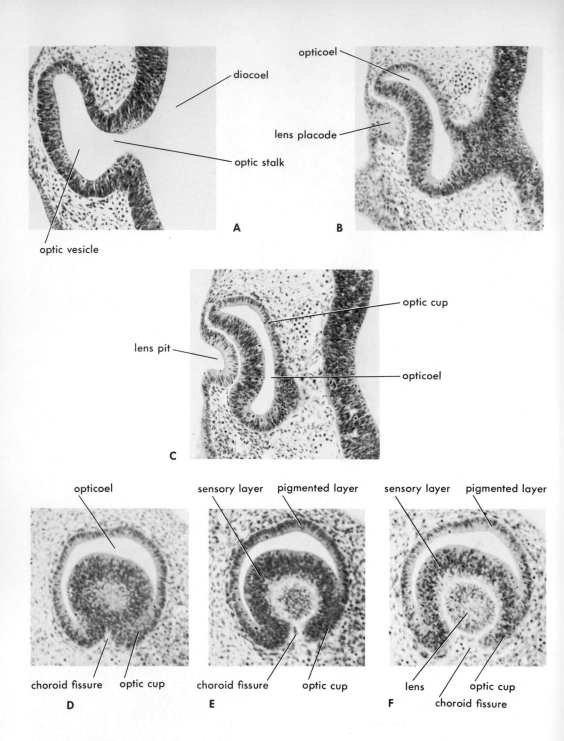

Fig. 6.25 Eye development in 10½-day mouse embryo: A–C, transverse sections; D–F, sagittal sections; G–J, transverse sections (high power).

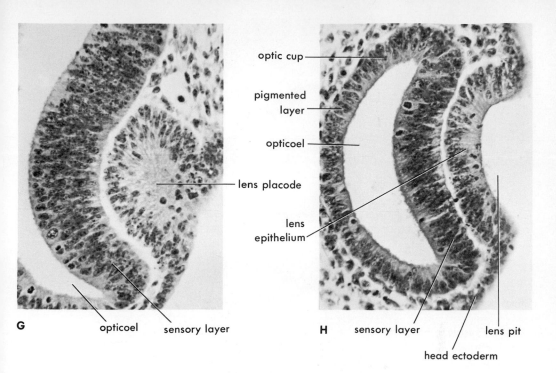

G   opticoel   sensory layer

optic cup

pigmented
layer

opticoel

lens placode

lens
epithelium

H   sensory layer   lens pit

head ectoderm

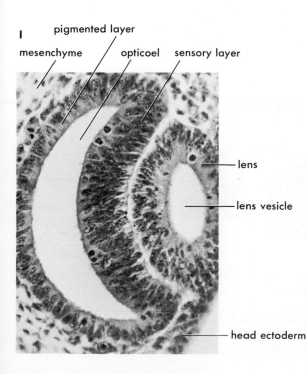

I   pigmented layer

mesenchyme   opticoel   sensory layer

lens

lens vesicle

head ectoderm

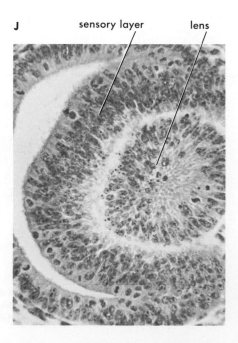

J   sensory layer   lens

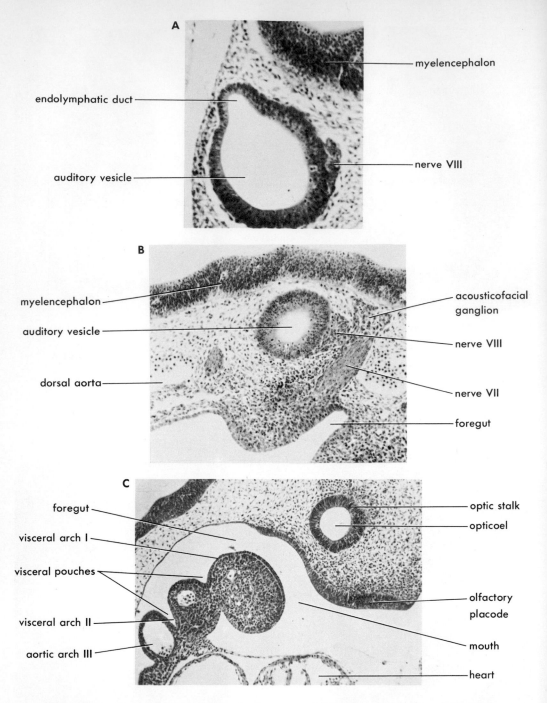

Fig. 6.26   Ear and olfactory organ development in 10½-day mouse embryo: A, transverse section showing ear; B, sagittal section showing ear; C, transverse section showing olfactory organ; D, sagittal section showing olfactory organ.

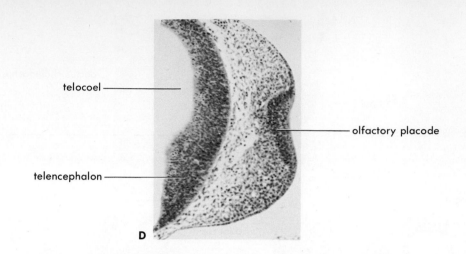

telocoel

olfactory placode

telencephalon

D

Fig. 6.26 (*continued*)

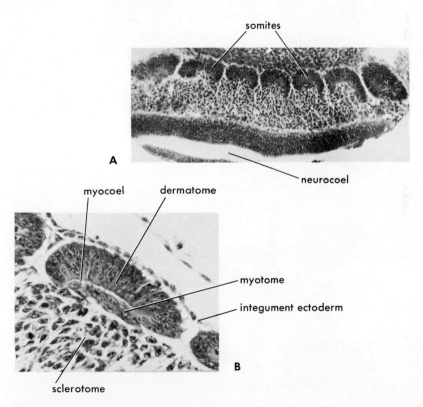

somites

neurocoel

A

myocoel

dermatome

myotome

integument ectoderm

B

sclerotome

Fig. 6.27 Somite development in 10½-day mouse embryo: A, frontal section; B, transverse section (high power).

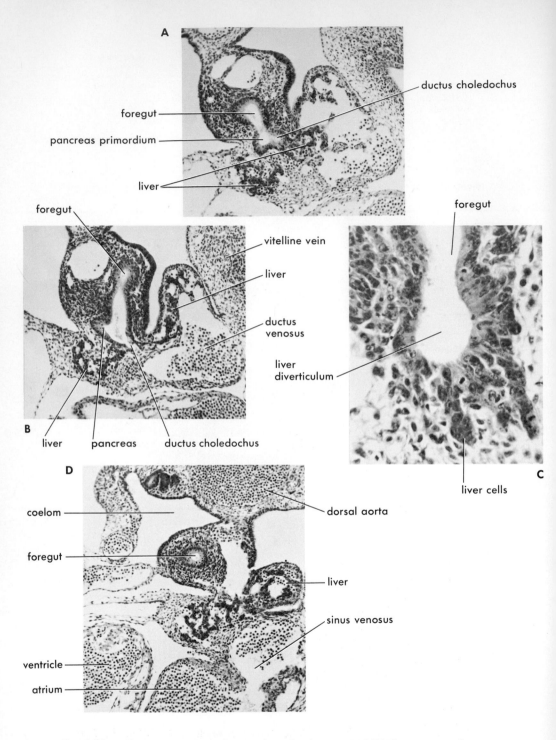

Fig. 6.28 Transverse sections showing liver development in 10½-day mouse embryo.

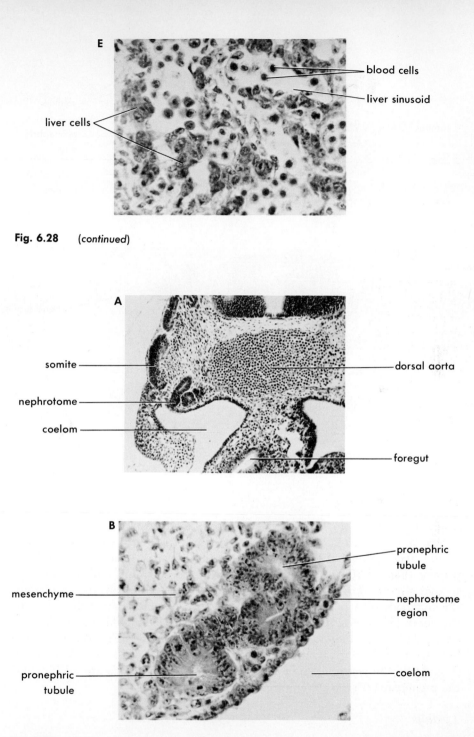

E

blood cells

liver sinusoid

liver cells

Fig. 6.28 (continued)

A

somite

nephrotome

coelom

dorsal aorta

foregut

B

mesenchyme

pronephric
tubule

pronephric
tubule

nephrostome
region

coelom

Fig. 6.29 Kidney development in 10½-day mouse embryo: A, B, transverse sections (A at low power); C, D, frontal sections.

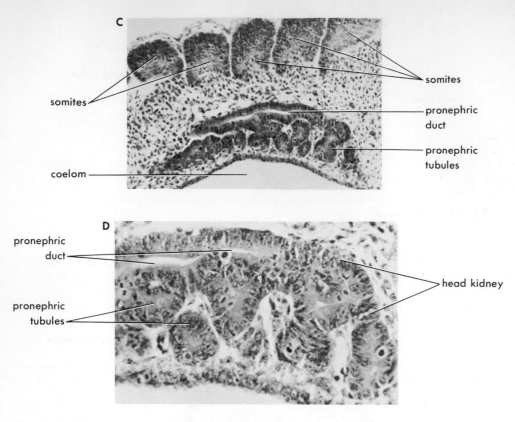

somites

somites

pronephric duct

pronephric tubules

coelom

pronephric duct

pronephric tubules

head kidney

Fig. 6.29   (*continued*)

10½ days

The *lamina terminalis* is distinct; the spinal ganglia are metameric; the optic vesicle protrudes slightly as the *lens vesicle* forms (Fig. 6.25); the *endolymphatic duct* appears (Fig. 6.26A,B); and the olfactory placode and *pit* are present (Fig. 6.26C,D). Four visceral arches are apparent, and the first and second *visceral clefts* are clearcut; the *trachea* separates from the *esophagus;* the lung buds grow posteriorly, the right one usually a little larger than the left; the ventral pancreas, *ductus choledochus* (Fig. 6.27), *hepatic* and *pancreatic ducts*, and *duodenum* form. The forelegs grow rapidly (Fig. 6.26F) as the hind leg buds emerge; somites are evident to the end of the lengthening tail (Fig. 6.28); the *septum primum* and *atrioventricular canals* are visible; and the *pronephros* (Fig. 6.29) continues to develop.

11 days

At this stage (Fig. 6.30) the *saccule* and *utricle* are distinguishable, and the endolymphatic duct is diverted dorsally. The *tongue* begins to develop; the

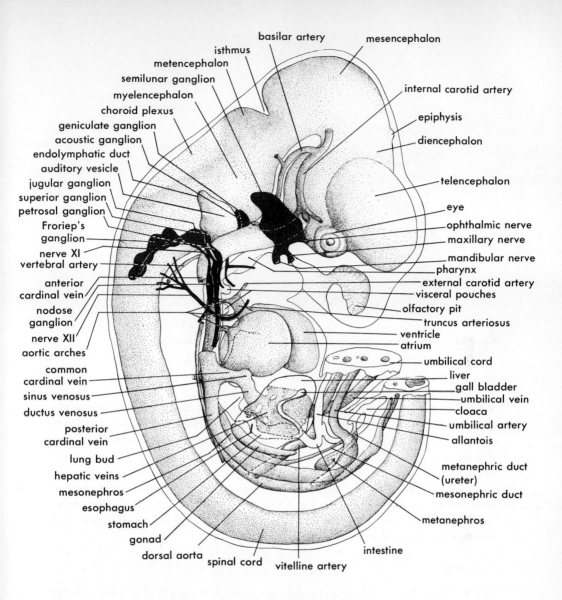

Fig. 6.30   Sagittal section of 11-day mouse embryo. (Adapted from R. Alden, *Laboratory Atlas of the Mouse Embryo*, Univ. of Tennessee Medical Unit, Knoxville, Tenn.)

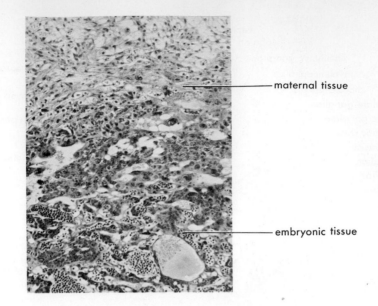

maternal tissue

embryonic tissue

Fig. 6.31   Transverse section through placenta of 11½-day mouse embryo.

thyroid duct is closed, and the thyroid is a solid block of cells; the *parathyroids,
thymus,* and *ultimobranchial body* are identifiable; the lung buds continue to
expand; the liver is lobular; the first indication of an *umbilical hernia* appears;
and the cloaca begins dividing to receive the intestinal and urogenital ducts.
Aortic arches III and IV enlarge; the vascular system includes *common
cardinal, hepatic, vitelline,* and *umbilical veins;* the *mesonephros* is a concentrated mass of solid strands, with a few *nephrostomes* anteriorly; the *metanephros* and the *suprarenal cortex* are organizing; and the gonads are well
developed but indifferent.

11½ days

At this stage (Fig. 6.31) pigment appears around the pupil of the eye (except
in albino embryos); the auditory vesicle recedes into the head and toward the
brain (Fig. 6.32); and the olfactory pit is well defined (Fig. 6.33). The *infundibulum* and *Rathke's pocket* approach each other closely (Fig. 6.34). The first
visceral cleft becomes associated with the auditory apparatus at its ventral extremity, and the *nasomaxillary fissure* develops posteriorly from the
olfactory pit. The forelegs are better differentiated than the hind ones; the
somites merge anteriorly to lose their identity but extend posteriorly into the
growing tail; skeletal elements are organizing (Fig. 6.35); the heart and liver
are well differentiated (Fig. 6.36); and the mesonephros and gonad continue
to develop (Fig. 6.37).

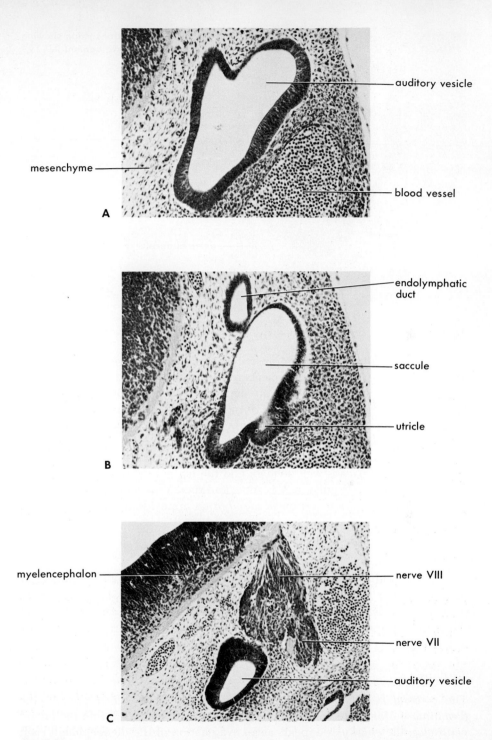

Fig. 6.32 Transverse sections showing ear development in 11½-day mouse embryo.

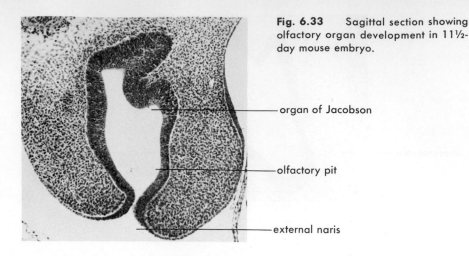

Fig. 6.33 Sagittal section showing olfactory organ development in 11½-day mouse embryo.

organ of Jacobson

olfactory pit

external naris

12 days

The *posterior choroid plexus* is present in the *fourth ventricle;* the *vitreous humor* is forming; the *cochlea* projects from the saccule, and the *semicircular canals* from the utricle; and olfactory nerves extend to the brain. Parathyroid III and the thymus have separated from visceral pouch III; Rathke's pocket has been closed into the walls of the infundibulum; the visceral pouches disappear; *arytenoid swellings* appear, and the tracheal opening into the pharynx narrows; the *bronchi* develop buds; the dorsal and ventral pancreatic rudiments fuse; the cloaca is well divided; and the tail gut vanishes. Aortic arches III and IV continue to enlarge, V is gone, and right VI is reduced; the *foramen ovale* is apparent; *pleuroperitoneal membranes* are evident; and *ureters* arise in the pelvic region.

12½ days

The *cranial* and *cervical flexures* are advanced, and the back is beginning to straighten. Hair follicles form on the sides of the face. Lens fibers appear in the lens as the lens vesicle vanishes, and the *pigmented* and *sensory layers* of the optic cup come into contact with each other, obliterating the *opticoel* (Fig. 6.38).

13 days

The *cerebral hemispheres* expand, covering part of the *diencephalon;* the *foramina of Monro* are constricted; the choroid plexus spreads into the *lateral ventricles;* the *epiphysis* appears as an evagination of the diencephalon roof; the *cerebellum* thickens; the *spinal cord* extends to the tip of the tail, and

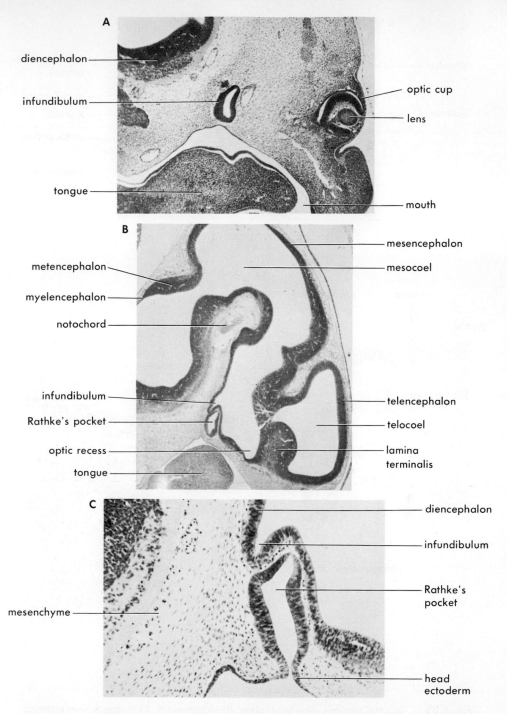

A
diencephalon
infundibulum
optic cup
lens
tongue
mouth

B
mesencephalon
metencephalon
mesocoel
myelencephalon
notochord
infundibulum
telencephalon
Rathke's pocket
telocoel
optic recess
lamina terminalis
tongue

C
diencephalon
infundibulum
Rathke's pocket
mesenchyme
head ectoderm

Fig. 6.34 Sagittal sections showing pituitary gland development in 11½-day mouse embryo (C at high power).

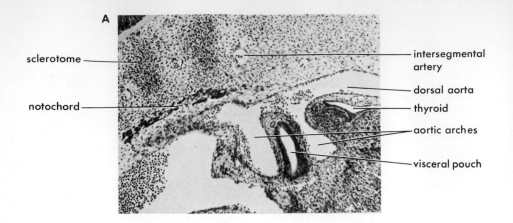

sclerotome

notochord

intersegmental artery

dorsal aorta

thyroid

aortic arches

visceral pouch

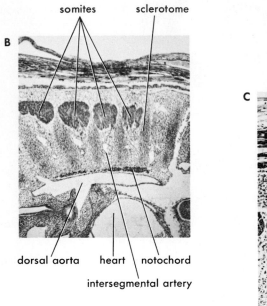

somites

sclerotome

dorsal aorta

heart

notochord

intersegmental artery

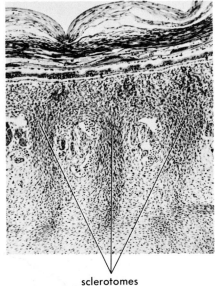

sclerotomes

Fig. 6.35 Sagittal sections showing skeletal development in 11½-day mouse embryo: A, through aortic arches, showing notochord; B, more laterally; C, showing sclerotomes that form the vertebrae (high power).

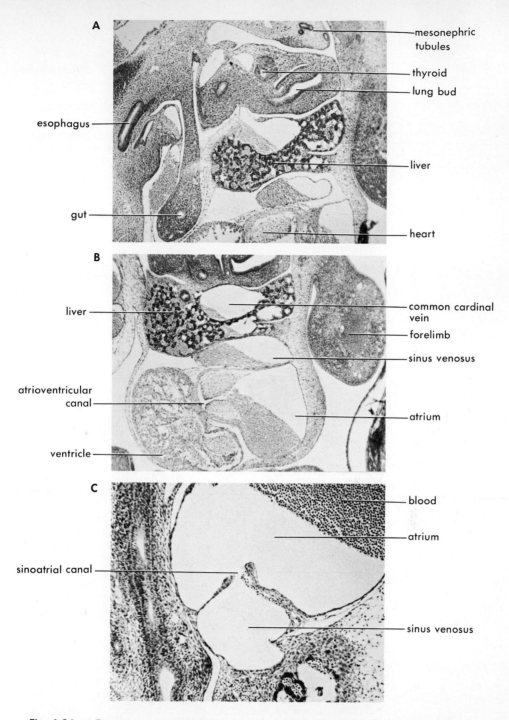

Fig. 6.36 Transverse sections showing heart and liver development in 11½-day mouse embryo (F at high power).

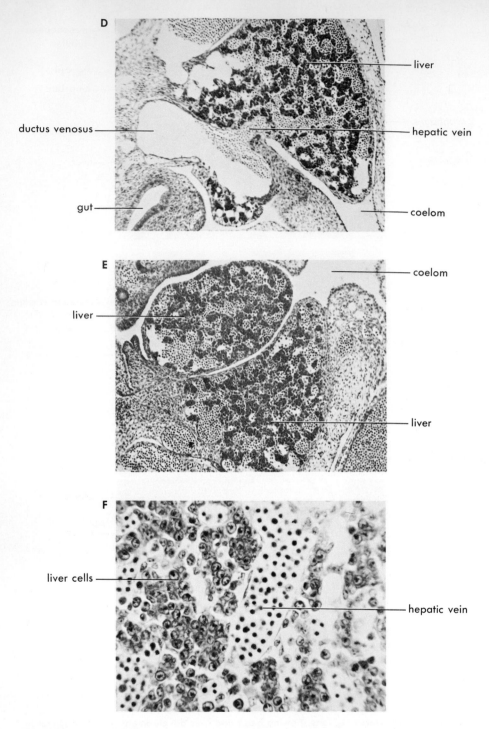

D

liver

ductus venosus

hepatic vein

gut

coelom

E

coelom

liver

liver

F

liver cells

hepatic vein

Fig. 6.36 (continued)

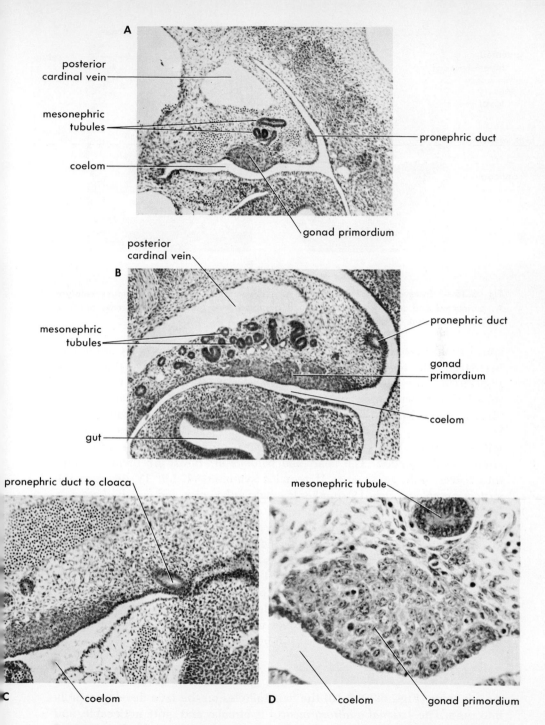

A

posterior cardinal vein

mesonephric tubules

coelom

pronephric duct

gonad primordium

B

posterior cardinal vein

mesonephric tubules

pronephric duct

gonad primordium

coelom

gut

pronephric duct to cloaca

mesonephric tubule

C

coelom

D

coelom

gonad primordium

Fig. 6.37 Transverse sections showing mesonephros and gonad development in 11½-day mouse embryo (D at high power).

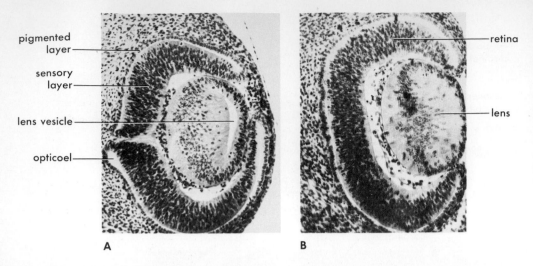

pigmented layer

sensory layer

lens vesicle

opticoel

retina

lens

A   B

Fig. 6.38 Transverse sections showing eye development in 12½-day mouse embryo: A, pigmented and sensory layers of retina approach one another to obliterate opticoel; B, retina is complete, and lens fibers appear in lens.

spinal ganglia extend to the level of somite XXXX; the fibrous part of the lens is enlarged; the *sensory layer* of the *retina* is almost 10 times as thick as the *pigmented layer;* and eyelids and eye muscles are forming. The thyroid surrounds the lower *larynx* and is lobular; parathyroid IV is separated from visceral pouch IV, and the ultimobranchial body from visceral pouch V; the tracheal entrance is closed off; the right bronchus is better developed than the left, with many buds; and the upper cloaca is divided into the *urogenital sinus* and the *rectum.* The heart and *truncus arteriosus* are divided almost into halves; only aortic arch II remains symmetrical; left IV becomes the *systemic arch,* and right IV supplies the right *subclavian* and *vertebral arteries;* left VI connects with the *dorsal aorta,* and right VI disappears, leaving a remnant as part of the *pulmonary arteries;* the dorsal aorta narrows between arches III and IV; the *posterior vena cava* collects blood from the *renal,* vitelline, and umbilical veins and incorporates the hepatic veins; the right *posterior cardinal vein* is interrupted while its left counterpart is reduced; only a few scattered anterior mesonephric tubules join ducts; sex differentiation occurs, with either spermatogonia or oögonia identifiable; ostia are apparent at the upper ends of the solid Fallopian tubes in the female; the mammary glands are cup-shaped; and the suprarenal still has no capsule.

13½ days

At this stage (Figs. 6.39, 6.40) the hair follicles on the face develop rapidly into rows. The *external auditory meatus* is circular and quite noticeable, and an early *pinna* partly covers it (Fig. 6.40C). Toes appear on the forelegs; and the umbilical hernia recedes as the intestine is withdrawn into the body.

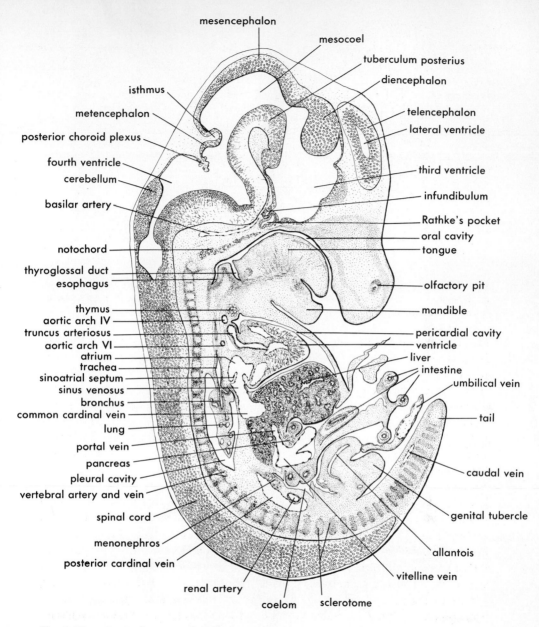

mesencephalon
mesocoel
tuberculum posterius
diencephalon
isthmus
telencephalon
metencephalon
lateral ventricle
posterior choroid plexus
fourth ventricle
third ventricle
cerebellum
infundibulum
basilar artery
Rathke's pocket
oral cavity
notochord
tongue
thyroglossal duct
esophagus
olfactory pit
thymus
mandible
aortic arch IV
truncus arteriosus
pericardial cavity
aortic arch VI
ventricle
atrium
liver
trachea
intestine
sinoatrial septum
umbilical vein
sinus venosus
bronchus
common cardinal vein
tail
lung
portal vein
pancreas
caudal vein
pleural cavity
vertebral artery and vein
spinal cord
genital tubercle
menonephros
posterior cardinal vein
allantois
vitelline vein
renal artery
coelom   sclerotome

Fig. 6.39   Sagittal section of 13½-day mouse embryo.

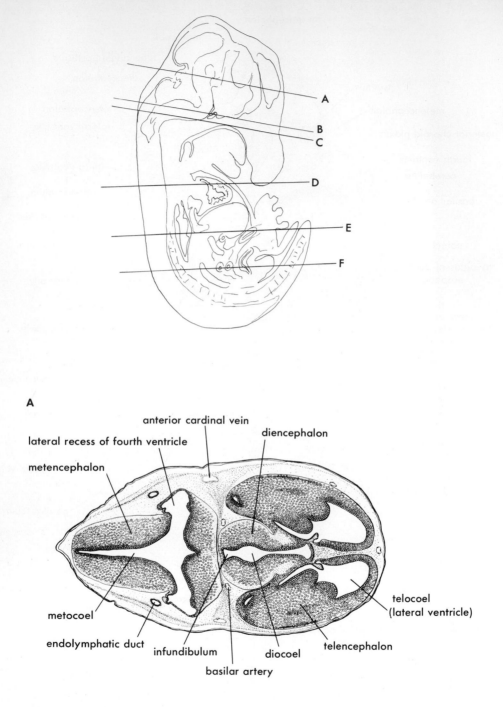

A

lateral recess of fourth ventricle

metencephalon

anterior cardinal vein

diencephalon

telocoel
(lateral ventricle)

metocoel

endolymphatic duct   infundibulum   telencephalon

diocoel

basilar artery

Fig. 6.40 Transverse sections of 13½-day mouse embryo at levels indicated on accompanying diagram.

B

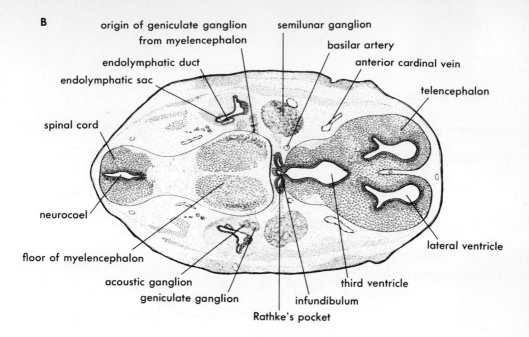

origin of geniculate ganglion from myelencephalon

semilunar ganglion

basilar artery

endolymphatic duct

anterior cardinal vein

endolymphatic sac

telencephalon

spinal cord

neurocoel

floor of myelencephalon

acoustic ganglion

geniculate ganglion

Rathke's pocket

infundibulum

third ventricle

lateral ventricle

C

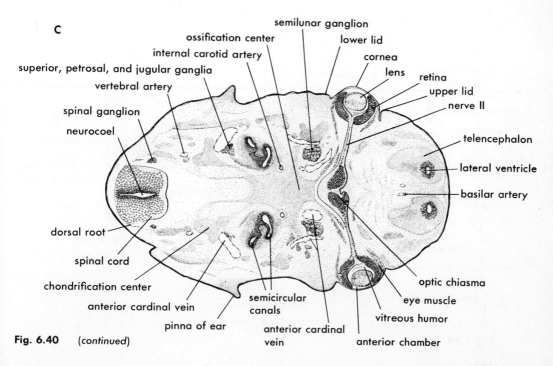

semilunar ganglion

ossification center

lower lid

internal carotid artery

cornea

superior, petrosal, and jugular ganglia

lens

retina

vertebral artery

upper lid

spinal ganglion

nerve II

neurocoel

telencephalon

lateral ventricle

basilar artery

dorsal root

spinal cord

chondrification center

anterior cardinal vein

pinna of ear

semicircular canals

anterior cardinal vein

anterior chamber

vitreous humor

eye muscle

optic chiasma

Fig. 6.40   (continued)

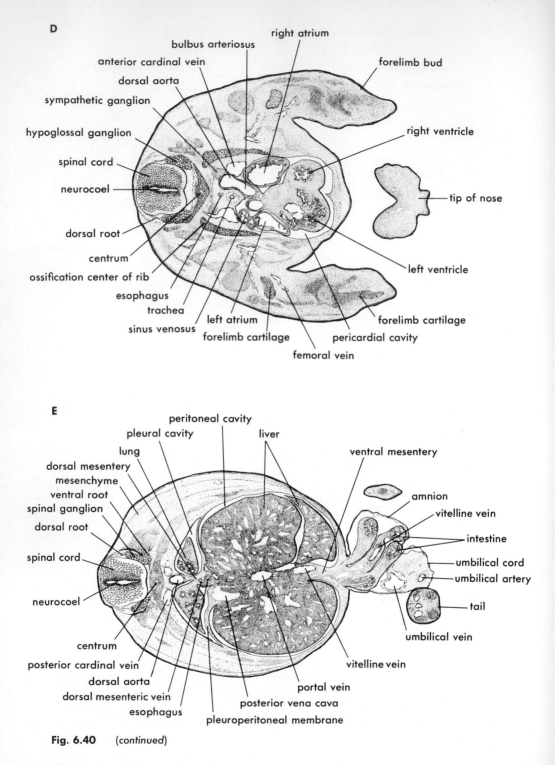

D

right atrium

bulbus arteriosus

anterior cardinal vein

forelimb bud

dorsal aorta

sympathetic ganglion

right ventricle

hypoglossal ganglion

spinal cord

neurocoel

tip of nose

dorsal root

centrum

ossification center of rib

left ventricle

esophagus

trachea

left atrium

sinus venosus

forelimb cartilage

forelimb cartilage

pericardial cavity

femoral vein

E

peritoneal cavity

pleural cavity

liver

lung

ventral mesentery

dorsal mesentery

mesenchyme

amnion

ventral root

vitelline vein

spinal ganglion

intestine

dorsal root

umbilical cord

spinal cord

umbilical artery

tail

neurocoel

umbilical vein

centrum

posterior cardinal vein

dorsal aorta

vitelline vein

dorsal mesenteric vein

portal vein

esophagus

posterior vena cava

pleuroperitoneal membrane

Fig. 6.40 (continued)

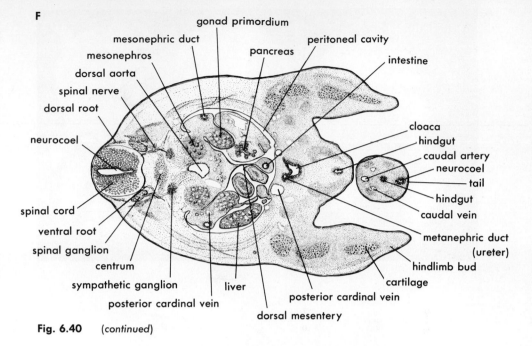

F

gonad primordium

mesonephric duct

mesonephros

peritoneal cavity

pancreas

dorsal aorta

intestine

spinal nerve

dorsal root

neurocoel

cloaca

hindgut

caudal artery

neurocoel

tail

hindgut

caudal vein

spinal cord

ventral root

spinal ganglion

centrum

metanephric duct
(ureter)

sympathetic ganglion

liver

hindlimb bud

cartilage

posterior cardinal vein

posterior cardinal vein

dorsal mesentery

Fig. 6.40   (continued)

14 days

The facial clefts close; optic fibers grow to the brain; the eye muscles are innervated; the *iris* forms; and all the ear parts are well differentiated and encapsulated. The dental equipment begins to develop; *salivary glands* are supplied with secretory ducts; the pancreas shows rapid histological differentiation with vascularization; and the cloacal membrane ruptures. Aortic arch III branches into *lingual* and *carotid arteries;* the systemic arch (IV) receives the *ductus arteriosus* from left VI, gives off the left subclavian and vertebral arteries, and continues into the dorsal aorta; the foramen ovale persists, the diaphragm is completed by the closing of the *pleuroperitoneal canals;* the mesonephros is reduced, except for the epididymis in the male; the metanephros moves posteriorly to the gonads and makes contact with the suprarenal; the ureters open into the urogenital sinus; the Fallopian tubes cross over the ureters and terminate in the pelvis; and blood vessels appear between the cortex and medulla of the ovary and spread peripherally in the tunica albuginea of the testis.

14½ days

Although the back has straightened somewhat, the elongating tail extends to touch the tip of the nose (Fig. 6.41); a snout protrudes from the face; and hair develops on the body and head. The eyes are prominent, and the pinna grows anteriorly over the external auditory meatus. Somites are no longer apparent.

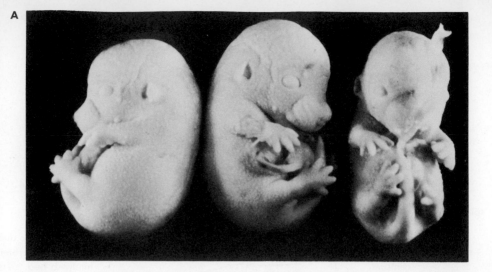

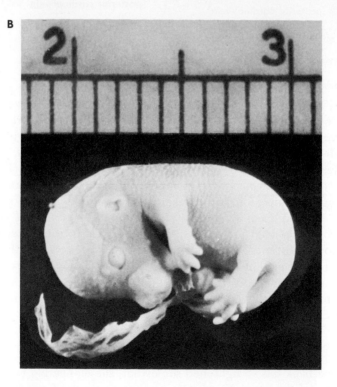

Fig. 6.41 Mouse embryos at 14½ days: A, three members of a litter; B, enlarged view of single embryo, showing its length as slightly more than 1 cm.

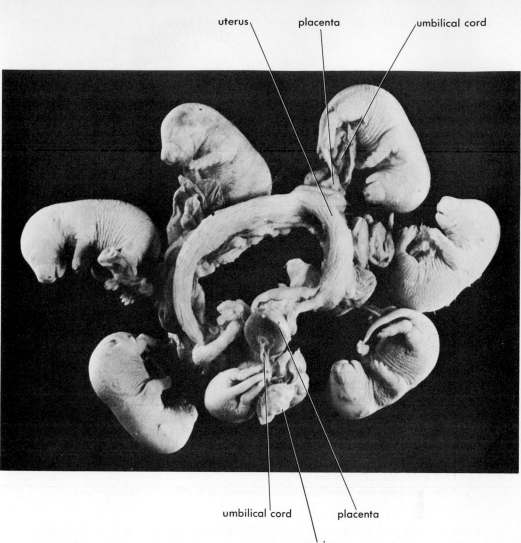

uterus   placenta   umbilical cord

umbilical cord   placenta

amnion

Fig. 6.42   Litter of seven 16½-day mouse embryos exposed on opening uterus. Each embryo has its own umbilical cord and placenta. Amniotic membranes have been removed.

15 days

The *palatine processes* meet mesially; and the eyelids are growing slowly. Dental papillae fill the mouth. The muscles become contractile.

15½ days

The embryo is filling out and appears more rounded in contour, with hair developing in many places; and the skin seems to be growing faster than the

Fig. 6.43   Lateral view showing skeletal development in 16½-day mouse embryo.

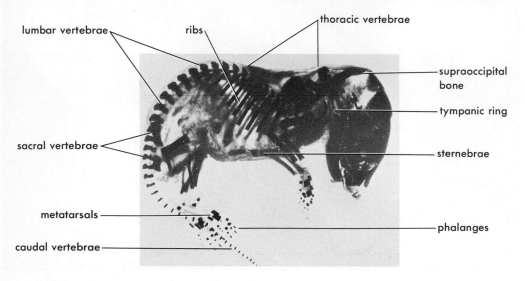

lumbar vertebrae

ribs

thoracic vertebrae

supraoccipital bone

tympanic ring

sacral vertebrae

sternebrae

metatarsals

phalanges

caudal vertebrae

Fig. 6.44   Lateral view showing skeletal development in 20½-day mouse embryo.

embryo itself, as it has many wrinkles. The major sense organs are superficially well organized, and the external auditory meatus is almost covered by the anterior growth of the pinna. Toes are apparent on both forelegs and hind legs; and the umbilical hernia is prominent.

16 days

The *palate* is complete; the *cornea* and *sclera* consist of stratified epithelium; the *endolymphatic sac* is expanding; the *pituitary* has three distinct lobes; the thyroid is a bilobed, highly vascular endocrine gland, with the parathyroids attached to it and the ultimobranchial bodies disappearing within its substance; the urogenital sinus and the rectum are completely separate; and the *perineum* is forming. Muscles are developing rapidly; laryngeal and tracheal cartilages are evident; and ossification is proceeding.

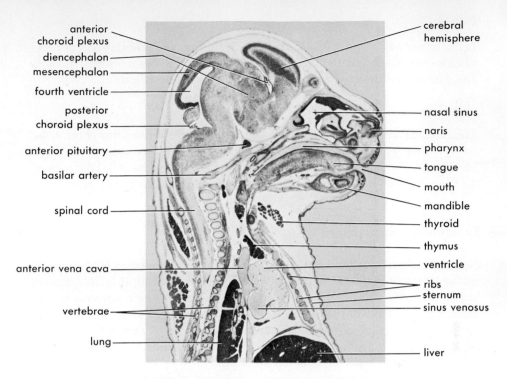

anterior choroid plexus
diencephalon
mesencephalon
fourth ventricle
posterior choroid plexus
anterior pituitary
basilar artery
spinal cord
anterior vena cava
vertebrae
lung

cerebral hemisphere
nasal sinus
naris
pharynx
tongue
mouth
mandible
thyroid
thymus
ventricle
ribs
sternum
sinus venosus
liver

Fig. 6.45   Sagittal section of anterior end of mouse embryo at birth.

16½ days

The embryo is now recognizable as a mouse (Fig. 6.42) and moves actively within the uterus. It straightens so that its front and rear feet no longer touch; and its skin wrinkling becomes extensive. Eyelids cover the eyes, and the pinna covers the external auditory meatus and may be attached anteriorly. Skeletal development is advanced (Fig. 6.43); and the umbilical hernia is less obvious than before.

17 days

The *mesencephalon* has *superior* and *inferior colliculi;* the retina shows cellular differentiation into *inner* and *outer nuclear layers;* and the middle ear structures are complete, with a *tympanic cavity* and *auditory tube.* Formation of the dental apparatus proceeds; the pancreas is like that of the adult; the liver glycogen is increased; and the gut is withdrawn from the umbilical cord. Ossification is widespread; and the embryonic membranes and the placenta are at their peak of development. The pituitary begins to control the other endocrine glands, and the suprarenals begin to control the production of glycogen by the liver.

17½ days

The crown-rump length is increased by the further straightening of the back; whiskers are distinguishable from hairs, and the skin shows marked wrinkling. The eyes are generally closed. The toes are webbed together.

18½ days

The mouse can survive if delivered and is therefore a true *fetus* (Figs. 6.44, 6.45). Its face is slightly elongated, losing the snoutlike appearance of 14½ days. The hair on the head is less conspicuous than before because it lies flat against the head, and the projecting whiskers appear more prominent as a result.

■ Experimental Embryology

No mammalian form is so suitable for embryological experimentation as the mouse or rat. It is prolific and has a short gestation period; it is inexpensive; and it is readily available. It can be bred in pure lines or numerous hybrid crosses at all seasons of the year, at temperatures from 10 to 37° C. and under other environmental variables. Its adaptability is in part due to the parasitic nature of the mammalian embryo, which lives and grows within the body of the mother at the expense of her metabolism.

For example, if a pregnant mouse is deprived of calcium, the fetuses take what they need in the way of calcium from the mother, so that her teeth decay and degenerate, her bones become brittle, etc., but, provided the deprivation of the mother is not too extreme, the fetuses survive and are delivered quite normal.

Traumatic conditions to which the pregnant mouse may be subject do not always reach and affect the embryos or fetuses. However, there is some evidence that frequent and rough handling of a mouse in early pregnancy alters the viability of the embryos. Anoxia can be conveyed to the fetuses as can, possibly, immune reactions induced in the mother. The best nonsurgical means of affecting the embryos and fetuses are by altering the mother's diet and water intake, by injecting the mother with certain dyes, and by administering ionizing radiations to the mother.

Lack of certain vitamins (for example, vitamin A) in the diet, or even an excess of such vitamins, alters the embryos in such a way as to produce congenital monstrosities. A change in the fat or protein intake directly affects the growth and viability of the offspring. The intravenous injection of dilute suspensions of Trypan blue has a severe traumatic effect on the embryos.

Ionizing radiations, such as x-rays or gamma rays, in exposure levels that are well controlled and calibrated under the direction of a radiophysicist produce congenital defects if the embryos are exposed prior to the completion of organogenesis. X-irradiation in low levels at early stages of development affects primarily the central nervous system but also the eyes, the skeleton, and often the general growth, resulting in stunted individuals. Pregnant mice exposed at 8½ days after conception to 200 r of x-rays produce fetuses exhibiting a high percentage of brain hernias, graphic congenital anomalies (examined at laparotomy at 18½ days, prior to delivery). As a rule, a mouse producing abnormal offspring kills and devours them immediately after delivery. Therefore, the investigator must dissect the pregnant mouse just before expected delivery, at 18½ or 19½ days, in order to examine the offspring.

Numerous operative procedures are possible with the mouse embryo. Fertilized eggs may be removed from the upper Fallopian tube of one mouse, treated, and then transplanted to the upper Fallopian tube or uterus of another mouse. Embryos may be surgically removed from the uterus, leaving litter mates in place to develop and be delivered, provided the techniques are aseptic. Individual fetuses may be treated by direct irradiation, by injection, or by surgical trauma and examined again some days later but before birth so that the effect of the experimental procedure may be determined.

THE PIG:

A Diffuse Placentate

■ Introduction

The estrous cycle in the pig is 21 days long. The female accepts the male only during *estrus* (heat), which lasts for 4 days. Although *ovulation* occurs at this time, coitus does not always result in fertilization.

■ Reproductive Systems

Male

The boar's reproductive system includes paired *testes,* supported in an external *scrotum,* paired ejaculatory ducts, a *urethra,* a *penis,* and accessory glands (Fig. 7.1). Mature *spermatozoa* pass from *seminiferous tubules* through short, straight *tubuli recti* into a *rete testis,* out through *vasa efferentia* into a much coiled *epididymis,* and then through a *vas deferens* to a glandular *seminal vesicle,* where they may be temporarily stored. At coitus spermatozoa, together with secretions from the seminal vesicles, the *prostate gland,* and the *bulbourethral (Cowper's) glands,* are ejaculated into the urethra and penis and thence into the *vagina* of the sow.

SPERMATOGENESIS.   The tubules of the testis connect to constitute a single duct almost 2 miles long, the walls of which produce spermatozoa continuously. Transverse sections show peripheral *spermatogonia,* often in mitosis; adjacent large *primary spermatocytes;* smaller *secondary spermatocytes;* and, toward the lumen, still smaller *spermatids* and finally tailed spermatozoa. The positional relations of the developing spermatozoa are the same in all vertebrates.

EMBRYOLOGICAL ORIGIN OF THE TESTIS.   Each of the paired testes arises as a *genital ridge* on the ventromesial face of the *mesonephros* while it is still functioning. The cells of the genital ridge enlarge and become conspicuously different from all other mesodermal cells in the vicinity. They are then identified as germinal epithelium. Many investigators believe, primarily because

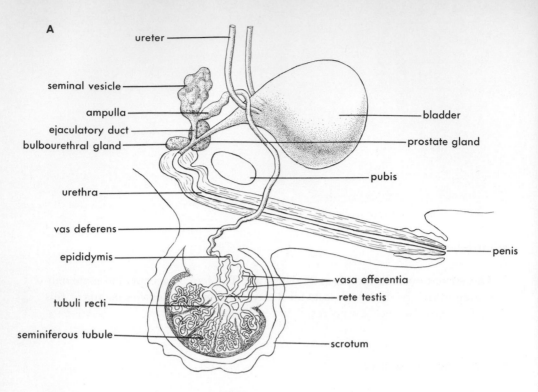

Fig. 7.1 Urogenital system of male pig: A, lateral view; B. ventral view showing positional changes during development. (B from B. M. Patten, *Embryology of the Pig*, 3rd ed., McGraw-Hill, New York, 1948. Adapted from Hertwig.)

of evidence from the chick, that these germ cells descend from primordial germ cells in the *yolk sac* endoderm, which migrate to the genital ridge before birth (or hatching). By the 18-mm. stage the genital ridges develop into *gonads,* and by the 45-mm. stage the testes are recognizable in the male.

Anterior *mesonephric tubules* remaining in the male form the epididymis, and posterior tubules, the *paradidymis*, while the *mesonephric* (*Wolffian*) *duct* becomes the vas deferens. Near its terminal end the vas deferens dilates to form the *ampulla,* and the wall of this organ evaginates to form the seminal vesicle. The remainder of the vas deferens becomes the muscular ejaculatory duct. It opens into the common *urogenital sinus,* which receives secretions from the prostate and bulbourethral glands. These fluids are necessary for the survival and functioning of the sperm. Spermatozoa, then, pass from the paired testes through the paired ducts into the common urogenital sinus and thence through the urethra and penis.

The testis is outside the *peritoneum* (the mesodermal lining of the peritoneal cavity) but for a time is supported by peritoneal folds—the *suspensory ligament* anteriorly and the *inguinal ligament* posteriorly. These ligaments arise in association with the peritoneal covering of the mesonephros. As the

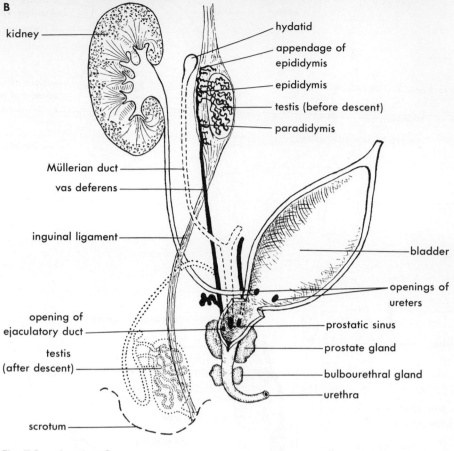

B

kidney

hydatid

appendage of epididymis

epididymis

testis (before descent)

paradidymis

Müllerian duct

vas deferens

inguinal ligament

bladder

openings of ureters

opening of ejaculatory duct

prostatic sinus

prostate gland

testis (after descent)

bulbourethral gland

urethra

scrotum

Fig. 7.1 (*continued*)

mesonephros enlarges, the developing testis gradually moves posteriorly, with the aid of the inguinal ligament, through the *inguinal canal* and into the external scrotum. The scrotal sacs, evaginations of the peritoneum, extend over the testes (which are outside the peritoneum), thereby covering them with a double layer of peritoneum. Generally the inguinal canal is obliterated after the descent of the testis.

In both the male and the female paired *Müllerian ducts* develop after, and parallel to, the mesonephric ducts. They arise along the tracts of the *pronephric ducts* and may be remnants of those ducts or derive from the substance of the mesonephric ducts. Vestiges of the Müllerian duct, in the form of a *hydatid,* are present in some males. This situation emphasizes the impossibility of early sex identification or prediction.

The external genitalia, as well as the internal sex organs, are indistinguishable as to sex early in development. A *genital tubercle* appears slightly anteriorly to the *proctodeum* by the 10-mm. stage. Shortly thereafter *genital folds*

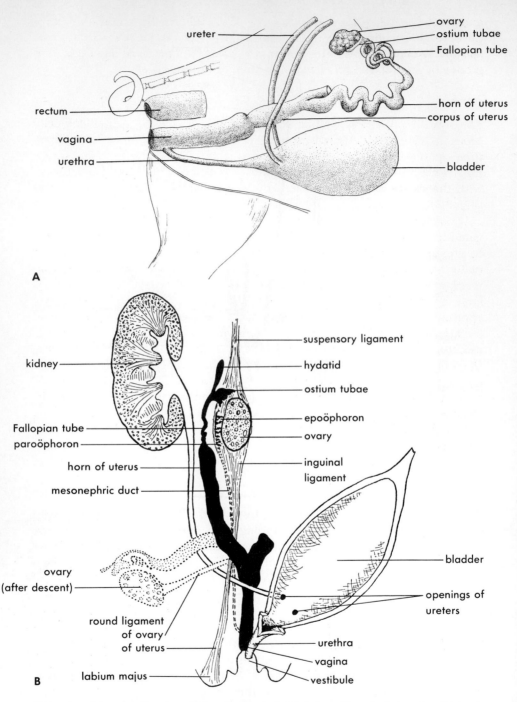

Fig. 7.2 Urogenital system of female pig: A, lateral view; B, ventral view showing positional changes during development. (B from B. M. Patten, *Embryology of the Pig*, 3rd ed., McGraw-Hill, New York, 1948. Adapted from Hertwig.)

and *genital swellings* form on either side of the tubercle. By the 18-mm. stage the tubercle is a *phallus*. By the 45-mm. stage it becomes the penis in the male, and the swellings become the scrotum. The urethra grows along a posterior groove in the penis in an elevation known as the *raphe*.

Female

The sow's reproductive system consists of paired *ovaries*, paired *Fallopian tubes*, a bicornuate *uterus*, and a vagina (Fig. 7.2). The funnel-like *ostium tubae* at the upper end of each Fallopian tube almost surrounds the ovary. Each Fallopian tube is continuous with one horn of the uterus and thence with the corpus of the uterus and the *cervix*, which opens into the vagina (Fig. 7.3).

OÖGENESIS. In an ovigerous cord of the ovary, one cell at a time is segregated to become an *oöcyte*, while the others remain as nurse or *follicle cells* to provide it with nutriment. Litter size depends on the number of oöcytes maturing simultaneously in the several ovigerous cords. The follicle cells multiply and then acquire intercellular spaces (*antra*), which fuse into a single large antrum filled with *liquor folliculi* (Fig. 7.4). The developing oöcyte appears to be suspended in this fluid on the tip of a column of follicle cells (*cumulus oöphorus*). At first the oöcyte merely enlarges, both its nucleus and its cytoplasmic mass increasing in size until its diameter is about 135 microns. In its final stages of growth, however, it acquires a *vitelline membrane* around its cell wall, a *zona pellucida* outside the vitelline membrane, and, sometimes, *zona radiata*, which appear to be canals through the zona pellucida; the thickness of the zona pellucida is approximately 15 microns, and that of the *perivitelline space*, between it and the vitelline membrane, is about the same. The oöcyte is then ready for its first maturation division, which generally occurs shortly before its liberation from the ovary (ovulation). The second

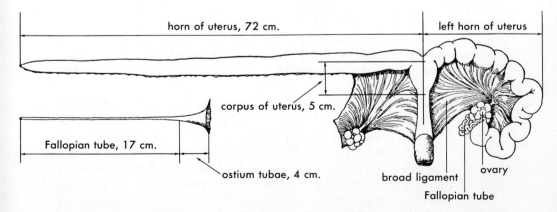

Fig. 7.3 Size relation of uterus and Fallopian tubes in adult female pig. (From G. W. Corner, *Carnegie Inst. Washington Publ. No. 276, Contribs. Embryology No. 64* (1921).)

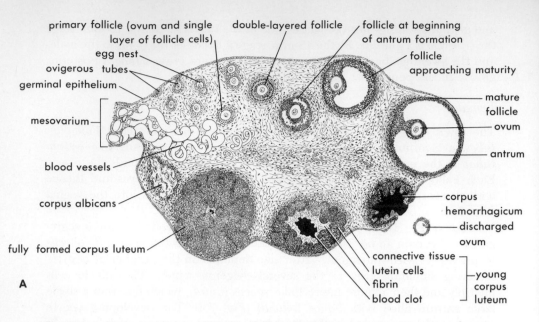

primary follicle (ovum and single layer of follicle cells)

egg nest

ovigerous tubes

germinal epithelium

mesovarium

blood vessels

corpus albicans

fully formed corpus luteum

A

double-layered follicle

follicle at beginning of antrum formation

follicle approaching maturity

mature follicle

ovum

antrum

corpus hemorrhagicum

discharged ovum

connective tissue

lutein cells

fibrin

blood clot

young corpus luteum

Fig. 7.4 Diagrams showing Graafian follicle development in pig: A, section of ovary showing, in clockwise order, sequence of origin, growth, and rupture of follicle and formation and regression of corpus luteum; B, follicle approaching maturity. (From B. M. Patten, *Embryology of the Pig*, 3rd ed., McGraw-Hill, New York, 1948.)

maturation division occurs when a spermatozoon penetrates the egg surface.

Ovulation takes place at intervals of about 21 days and stops only during pregnancy or at old age. When the oöcyte erupts from the ripe *Graafian follicle*, the empty follicle transforms to a *corpus luteum*, which persists if pregnancy ensues but degenerates otherwise (Fig. 7.4A). A persisting corpus luteum apparently inhibits ovulation during pregnancy and initiates the changes leading to lactation. Its secretions may also aid in preparing the uterus for the implantation of the developing embryo. The corpus luteum completes its development by about 7 days after ovulation and maintains its condition for another 7 or 8 days. If the ovum is fertilized, this interval permits successful implantation. If the ovum is not fertilized, the corpus luteum begins to atrophy, to be replaced by the fibrous *corpus albicans* (white because of its low vascularity).

During the period of corpus luteum formation, the uterine cells attain their maximum size and activity. Between 8 and 10 days after ovulation the uterine epithelium is secretory. Then its cells lose height and change from the columnar to the cuboid type. At 15 days after ovulation the uterine mucosa reverts to the condition characteristic of estrus. It may be that the secretory state of the uterine epithelium provides for the flotation of the embryos, allowing for their proper migration and spacing, and that the subsequent glutinous and rough condition of the uterine mucosa facilitates the attachment of the *chorion*.

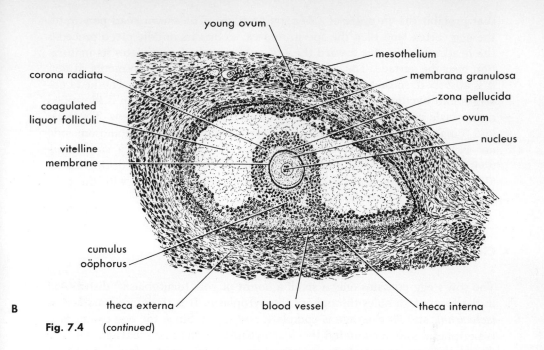

young ovum

mesothelium

corona radiata

membrana granulosa

zona pellucida

coagulated
liquor folliculi

ovum

nucleus

vitelline
membrane

cumulus
oöphorus

theca externa   blood vessel   theca interna

B

Fig. 7.4   (*continued*)

EMBRYOLOGICAL ORIGIN OF THE OVARY.   The ovaries arise in the same way
as the testes, from genital ridges on the mesonephroi that become gonads.
The rest of the female reproductive system develops from the Müllerian ducts,
which fuse just before joining the cloaca to form the single uterus and vagina.
The fused region is so short that the uterus is bicornuate. Anteriorly to the
uterus each Müllerian duct becomes a Fallopian tube, terminating in a large,
thin-walled, ciliated ostium tubae, which draws free ova into the tube at
ovulation. The *epoöphoron,* a vestige of anterior mesonephric tubules and
duct, is closely associated with the ostium.

The ovaries and their associated organs move posteriorly, laterally, and
slightly ventrally, stretching the enveloping peritoneal folds. The folds acquire
connective tissue and become the *broad ligaments.* The broad ligaments and
the *round ligaments* maintain the reproductive organs in approximate, constant position.

In the female by the 45-mm. stage, the external phallus becomes the
clitoris, a homologue of the penis, the genital folds become the *labia minora,*
and the swellings become the *labia majora.* The urogenital sinus remains as
the common chamber for the urethra and the vagina.

- **Fertilization**

Sperm entrance may occur at any point on the egg surface, but when the first
spermatozoon makes contact with the ovum, it effects instantaneous changes

that prohibit the entrance of other spermatozoa. The sperm head penetrates the egg cortex, and then the sperm rotates, so that its middle piece precedes the head, and migrates toward the egg nucleus, which completes its maturation near the surface. The sperm tail may be lost in these movements. If not, it is absorbed, so that only the head and middle piece remain. The head enlarges and becomes vesicular, and thereafter the spermatozoon is identified as the male *pronucleus,* approaching the larger female pronucleus. The male and female pronuclei unite, but as in most mammals their chromosomes do not mingle before the first cleavage. However, through every succeeding division the chromosomes from the two original sources cannot be distinguished. (The diploid chromosome number seems to be either 38 or 40, with the male producing X and Y sex chromosomes.)

■ Cleavage

The sow's egg contains only a small amount of yolk (deutoplasm) distributed in the form of globules throughout the cytoplasm. It is therefore classified as *isolecithal,* and its cleavage is complete and equal. Since the egg pronucleus is peripheral and surrounded by clear cytoplasm, the first cleavage tends to divide the egg along whatever animal-vegetal axis exists (Fig. 7.5A,F). It occurs about 2 days after copulation. The second cleavage, about 12 hours later, is at right angles to the first and may be slightly unequal (Fig. 7.5B). These two cleavages normally take place in the Fallopian tube. The third and fourth cleavages, at 3 and 3½ days, respectively, result in a solid 16-cell *morula,* which appears to have a slightly larger total volume than the original fertilized egg owing to the intercellular spaces (Fig. 7.5C,D,G,H). These last cleavages occur in the upper uterus. Table 7.1 relates the age of a pig embryo to its development from the two-cell stage on.

Table 7.1   Chronology of development°

STAGE	AGE, DAYS	STAGE	AGE, DAYS
two cells	2	1–3 somites	14
four cells	2½	6+ somites	14½
morula	3½	10+ somites	15
blastula	4¾	17+ somites	16
embryonic disc with endoderm	7–8	5 mm.	17–18
implanted blastocyst	8	7.5 mm.	18–19
elongated blastocyst	9	10 mm.	22
primitive streak	12	15 mm.	24
neural groove	13	20 mm.	28

° Measurements are crown-rump lengths.

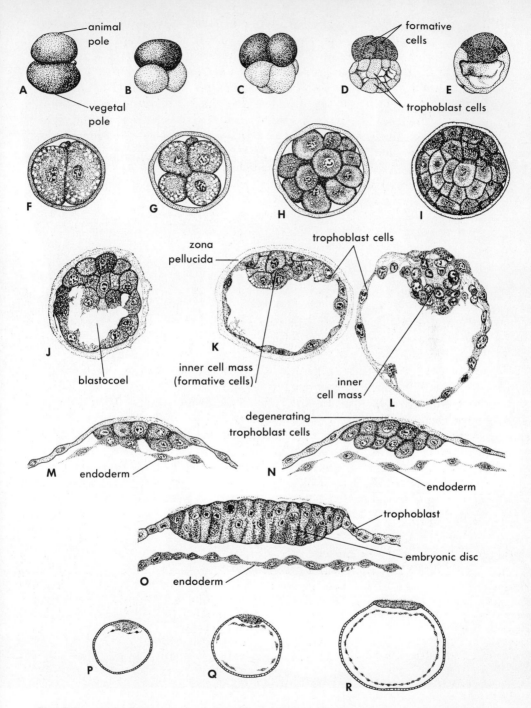

Fig. 7.5 Early development of pig embryo: A–H, early cleavages; I–L, blastula; M–R, separation of endoderm. (From O. E. Nelsen, *Comparative Embryology of the Vertebrates*, McGraw-Hill, New York, 1953.)

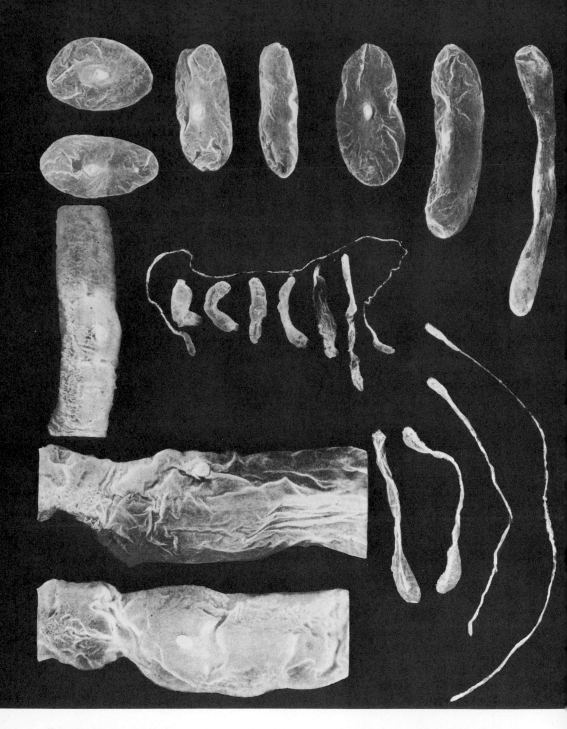

Fig. 7.6   Three litters of pig embryos showing transition from spherical blastocyst to elongated blastocyst (bottom views at high power). (From C. H. Heuser and G. L. Streeter, *Carnegie Inst. Washington Publ.* No. 394, *Contribs. Embryology* No. 109 (1929).)

■ Blastulation

A central *blastocoel* (segmentation cavity) appears at about 4¾ days, during or after the 32-cell stage, and subsequent divisions occur at progressively shortened intervals (Fig. 7.5E,I–L). The mammalian blastula is usually called a *blastocyst*, or *blastodermic vesicle*. It is still surrounded by the zona pellucida, which sloughs off just before implantation. Within the fluid-filled blastocoel and toward its apical pole, the *inner cell mass*, a cluster of cells that gives rise largely to embryonic structures, forms. The outer blastula cells, which give rise largely to extraembryonic membranes developed in association with maternal structures, comprise the *trophoblast*. As in the mouse, blastulae first appear in groups but soon disperse to allow adequate space for implantation and growth.

■ Gastrulation

As the blastocyst cells multiply, the blastocoel and the surrounding trophoblast grow faster than the inner cell mass so that it becomes proportionately smaller. At about 6 days the inner cell mass flattens into the *embryonic disc*, or *blastodisc*, and at 7 days a layer of cells identifiable as *endoderm* is proliferated from its inner margin (Fig. 7.5M–R). At this time the three types of cells may be present in the following proportion: inner cell mass, 20; endoderm, 80; and trophoblast, 470 (Heuser and Streeter, 1929). The trophoblast over the embryonic disc degenerates at implantation, and the disc itself lies at the surface. At about 9 days the blastocyst changes from a sphere to a vesicle 10 to 12 times as long as it is wide, with the embryonic disc remaining at its approximate center. Two days later it may be more than a meter in length and threadlike in diameter, with the minute disc still at its center. The long stringlike blastocyst (Fig. 7.6) is tucked and folded into the lining of the uterus, where it shortens and thickens or dilates, forming a *chorionic vesicle*.

Meanwhile the embryonic disc continues to proliferate cells. Longitudinal sections show that it graduates in thickness from two cells at one margin to three or four cells at the opposite margin. The thicker margin marks the posterior end of the embryo and is crescent-shaped from superficial view. Cells migrate from this thick margin of the embryonic disc to its opposite, thin margin and then to its mid-line to form an elongated and thickened *primitive streak*, which defines the anteroposterior axis of the embryo (Fig. 7.7A,B). Cells proliferate from the streak in all directions, and it soon develops a longitudinal *primitive groove* (Fig. 7.8). At 12 days, therefore, the pig embryo resembles the 16-hour primitive streak stage of the chick.

Mesoderm (mesenchyme) spreads outward from the primitive streak in all directions between the endoderm and ectoderm. The embryonic mesoderm, beneath the embryonic disc, and the extraembryonic mesoderm, between the

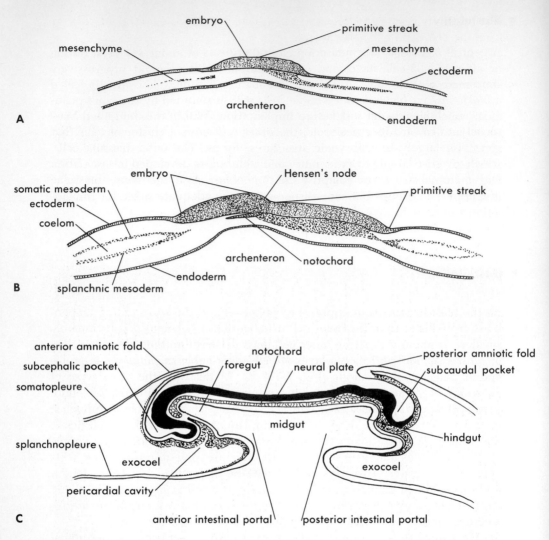

Fig. 7.7 Sagittal sections showing development of primitive streak and notochord in pig embryo.

endoderm and trophoblast, are continuous. As the mesoderm spreads peripherally, it acquires *lacunae* (intercellular spaces), which merge to split it into an outer *somatic* layer associated with the trophoblast (the two layers together constituting the *somatopleure*) and an inner *splanchnic* layer associated with the endoderm (these two layers constituting the *splanchnopleure*) (Fig. 7.7B,C). The cavity thus formed is the *coelom*. It divides into the embryonic coleom and the *exocoel*, or *extraembryonic coelom*.

The notochord develops from the anterior limit of the primitive streak (*Hensen's node*) between the ectoderm and endoderm before the mesoderm reaches this region (Fig. 7.7B,C). It is believed to arise, as does the mesoderm, from the ectoderm of the embryonic disc.

■ Organogenesis

At 12 days the ectoderm dorsal to the notochord thickens to form a *neural plate* (Fig. 7.7C). A depression, the *neural groove,* bounded by *neural folds,* appears in the plate and elongates with embryonic growth so that Hensen's node and the rest of the primitive streak recede into oblivion (Figs. 7.8C–7.10). The development of the neural plate, folds, and groove is generally most advanced anteriorly, farthest away from the primitive streak, indicating cephalic differentiation, or a distinction between brain and spinal cord or between head and body.

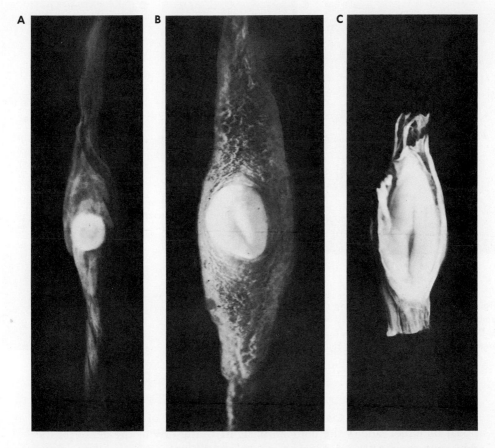

Fig 7.8   Dorsal views showing primitive groove development in pig embryo. (From C. H. Heuser and G. L. Streeter, *Carnegie Inst. Washington Publ. No. 394, Contribs. Embryology* No. 109 (1929).)

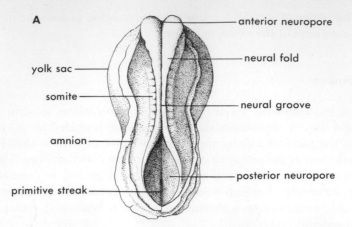

A

anterior neuropore

neural fold

yolk sac

somite

neural groove

amnion

posterior neuropore

primitive streak

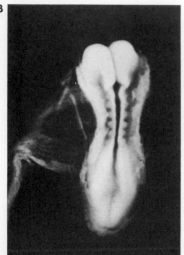

B

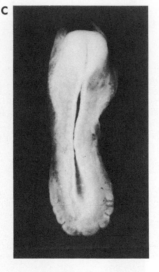

C

D

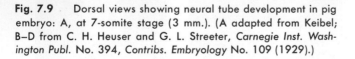

Fig. 7.9 Dorsal views showing neural tube development in pig embryo: A, at 7-somite stage (3 mm.). (A adapted from Keibel; B–D from C. H. Heuser and G. L. Streeter, *Carnegie Inst. Washington Publ.* No. 394, Contribs. Embryology No. 109 (1929).)

At about 14 days, *somites,* paired condensations of dorsal mesoderm, appear on either side of the notochord slightly anteriorly to the center of the embryonic disc. Although the first somites form at the anterior limit of the dorsal mesoderm, they move forward with the elongation of the embryo, and additional paired somites appear behind them. Thus somite number provides an accurate designation of the age of the early embryo. The *nephrotome* (*intermediate cell mass* mesoderm) joins the somites to the *lateral plate* mesoderm, which is divided by the coelom into somatopleure and splanchnopleure. At about the 7-somite stage the anterior somites differentiate into three parts: the thick dorsal portion (*myotome*), which forms the skeletal muscles; the scattered intermediate cells (*sclerotome*), which surround the spinal cord and notochord to form the skeleton; and the thickest, most lateral portion (*dermatome*), which becomes the connective tissue. As these regions separate, a temporary cavity, the *myocoel*, appears in the center of the original somite mass. The differentiation of the somites proceeds from anterior to posterior, the last somites to form being the last to differentiate.

At about the 3-somite stage (14 days) the neural folds begin closing over the neural groove to form a *neural tube,* first at mid-body level, where the fusion may be aided by somite development, and then anteriorly and posteriorly. The tube is complete except at the anterior and posterior extremities by the 11-somite stage (Fig. 7.8F,G). Last to close is the anterior tip of the groove, the *anterior neuropore,* which marks the approximate position of the future *epiphysis* (Fig. 7.10). Paired elevations due to inner condensations of mesenchyme appear on the sides of the head at 15 days. These become the *visceral (branchial) arches* (Fig. 7.11). The first two pairs are present by 16 days, and the remaining four pairs by 17 days. At 16 days the primordia of the ears and eyes are also apparent on the head, those of the ears as depressions and those of the eyes as bulbous protrusions. In the trunk region at least 17 pairs of somites exist at 16 days, lateral to the closing neural tube. The early heart appears to be outside the embryo and rather far anterior, just beneath the level of the first visceral (mandibular) arch. However, as the head develops anteriorly and the trunk posteriorly (at the expense of the primitive

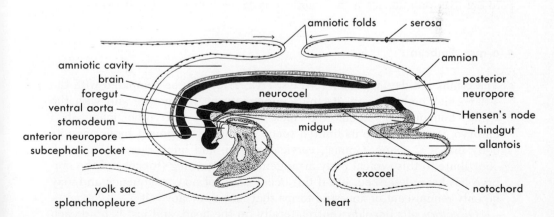

Fig. 7.10   Sagittal section of 15-somite pig embryo. (Adapted from B. M. Patten, *Embryology of the Pig,* 3rd ed., McGraw-Hill, New York, 1948.)

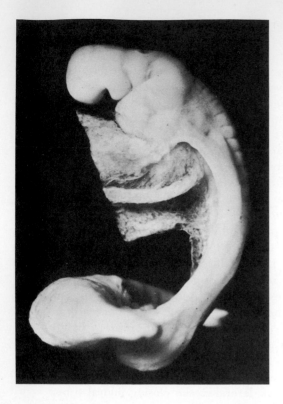

Fig. 7.11 Lateral view of 23-somite pig embryo. (From C. H. Heuser and G. L. Streeter, *Carnegie Inst. Washington Publ. No. 394, Contribs. Embryology No. 109* (1929).)

streak), and the embryo straightens out, the heart is incorporated into the embryo more posteriorly, so that at 17 days the intermediate neck region is accentuated. A slight depression, at the position of the future diaphragm, separates the heart bulge from the more posterior liver bulge. Just posterior to the liver prominence is the *umbilical cord,* with its large blood vessels.

■ 6-mm. Embryo

The 6-mm. (18-day) pig embryo (Figs. 7.12, 7.13) may be compared with the 4-day chick embryo, with its full complement of 42 somites, and with the 26-day human embryo. Like the chick embryo and every other mammalian embryo, it conforms to its limited space during development by curving its body into a C shape. Cranial, cervical, dorsal, and lumbosacral flexures all contribute to this typical body arrangement. A twisting (torsion) of the embryo has been described, but if this occurs, it is of no consequence and may be only reminiscent of ancestral forms that had abundant yolk.

Olfactory pits develop ventrolaterally on the head, and just behind each is a small *maxillary process* (upper jaw) followed posteriorly by four visceral arches—the *mandibular* arch, the *hyoid* arch, and the third and fourth arches,

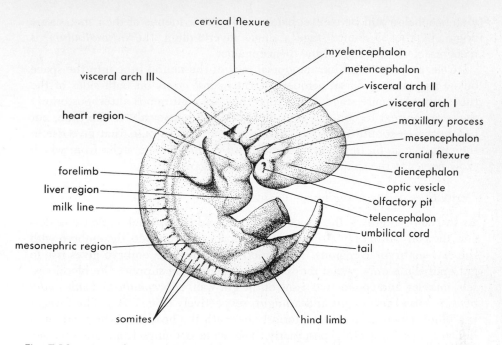

Fig. 7.12 Lateral view of 6-mm. (18-day) pig embryo.

later unidentifiable. *Visceral (branchial) grooves* between the arches demark them, the first being the *hyomandibular groove.*

The body is bulbous, owing to the development of the heart, liver, and kidney, and 36 or more pairs of somites appear along its dorsal aspect. Two pairs of mesodermal appendages are evident as stump-shaped buds, one pair at the level of the heart and the other, slightly smaller than the first, behind the umbilical cord.

Derivatives of the ectoderm

The *brain* develops from the portion of the neural tube anterior to the first pair of somites. Since the neural plate in this region is broader than elsewhere, the closing of the tube results in bulges that do not form more posteriorly. Initially 11 to 15 paired bulges, or *neuromeres,* are present. These early brain bulges coalesce into three large, primary brain vesicles (forebrain, midbrain, and hindbrain), which then subdivide into five. The *prosencephalon* (forebrain) becomes the *telencephalon* and *diencephalon,* the *mesencephalon* (midbrain) remains the same, and the *rhombencephalon* (hindbrain) becomes the *metencephalon* and *myelencephalon.*

The anterior tip of the telencephalon remains open for some time as the anterior neuropore, and the posterior tip of the myelencephalon, as the *posterior neuropore.* The mesencephalon shows no special differentiation, and the metencephalon and myelencephalon retain the evidence of their metameric origin. By the 25-somite stage a single diverticulum, the *infundibulum*, is recognizable in the floor of the diencephalon.

Cells proliferating from the dorsal part of the neural tube into the space below its covering dorsal ectoderm form *neural crests* on both sides of the tube at the 8-somite stage. For a time they are continuous anteroposteriorly and even appear to connect as compressed cell masses above the tube, but before the 10-somite stage they divide into numerous pairs that give rise to the cranial *ganglia* in the brain region and to the spinal ganglia from which grow nerves to the spinal cord and the body organs.

Derivatives of the endoderm

As the embryo grows, the exocoel expands and the splanchnopleure undercuts the body until only a tube, the umbilical cord, connects the embryo with the extraembryonic regions. The endoderm within the embryo gives rise to gut epithelium only, while the splanchnic mesoderm supplies the blood vessels, muscles, and connective tissue of the gut wall. *Subcephalic* and *subcaudal pockets* form the *foregut* and *hindgut*, respectively (Fig. 7.7C). The foregut is a blind pouch projecting anteriorly beneath the head, and the hindgut, a similar pouch projecting posteriorly. The wide openings from the yolk sac into the foregut and hindgut are the *anterior* and *posterior intestinal portals*. As the intestinal portals approach one another, the foregut and hindgut cavities lengthen, at the expense of the *midgut*. Its final connection with the yolk sac is the *yolk stalk*. Ultimately lateral folds (the *lateral limiting sulci*) close off the gut from the yolk sac entirely.

At each end of the embryo, directly opposite the foregut and hindgut limits, the ectoderm of the body surface invaginates, forming the *stomodeum* anteriorly and the *proctodeum* posteriorly. When the *oral membrane* of the stomodeum ruptures, the *mouth* appears. *Rathke's pocket* arises as an ectodermal diverticulum in the roof of the mouth. Meanwhile the ends of the gut extend into the transitory and functionless *Seessel's pocket* (*preoral gut*) and *tail* (*postanal*) *gut*.

At the 6-mm. stage certain derivatives of the primary gut levels are apparent (Fig. 7.13). The foregut gives rise to the *pharynx* and the *laryngotracheal groove*, which ends posteriorly in paired, blind *lung bud* diverticuli, and the midgut gives rise to the *esophagus* and the *stomach*, with its related outgrowths of *pancreas, liver*, and *gall bladder*. The pancreas consists of one large dorsal diverticulum and a small ventral diverticulum, often paired. The liver develops many branches and becomes invested with vascular and connective tissue. Its many tubes (*hepatic ducts*) converge near the midgut, and the single resulting duct enlarges into the gall bladder, which connects with the gut through the *ductus choledochus* (*common bile duct*). The gall bladder elongates and becomes saccular. The *intestines* are poorly developed and not yet differentiated and partially protrude from the body into the yolk stalk.

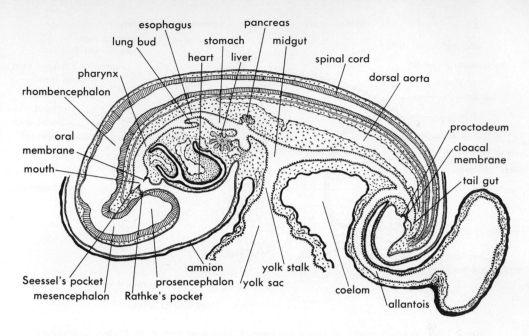

Fig. 7.13   Sagittal section showing gut development in 25-somite pig embryo. (From B. M. Patten, *Embryology of the Pig*, 3rd ed., McGraw-Hill, New York, 1948.)

The gut dilates at its caudal end, where it joins the *allantois* and the mesonephric ducts in the cloaca. Ventral to the tail the proctodeum fuses with the endoderm of the hindgut to form the cloacal membrane.

Derivatives of the mesoderm

At the 6-mm. stage the somites, early blood vascular system, and mesonephric kidneys comprise the major embryonic derivatives of the mesoderm, while outside the embryo the mesoderm is active in membrane formation. Splanchnic mesoderm covers the enlarging mesonephros and the surfaces and supporting membranes of the viscera that project into the coelom, forming a *dorsal mesentery* along with the gut and a *ventral mesentery* when the gut is complete. Somatic mesoderm lines the lateral body wall and the chorion and covers the amnion.

The circulatory system consists of a tubular heart, *blood islands,* and forming blood vessels (Fig. 7.14), all of which integrate their development so as to be ready at a precise moment to function as a closed and efficient blood vascular system. The circulatory system is particularly important because of the dependence of the mammalian embryo upon maternal sources for nutriment, oxygen, and the elimination of wastes. Until its development, nutriment

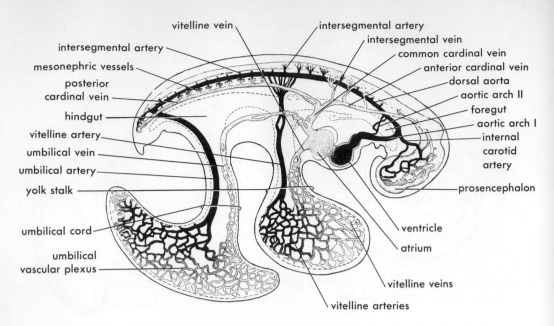

Fig. 7.14 Vascular system of young pig embryo. (Adapted from B. M. Patten, *Embryology of the Pig*, 3rd ed., McGraw-Hill, New York, 1948.)

is available to the embryo only by means of direct absorption from the maternal uterus. At the 13-somite stage the circulatory system begins to carry nutriment from the uterus through the blood vessels of the extraembryonic structures on to the growing embryonic structures.

The *endocardium* develops from mesenchymal clusters ventral to the foregut. Spaces appear in the clusters and coalesce into longitudinal tubes that fuse into a single tube on each side. These paired tubes approach each other at the 10-somite stage and fuse at the 13-somite stage into a single tube, the primitive heart. As the lateral limiting sulci meet under the embryo, the two lateral splanchnic layers close around the tubular endocardium and fuse both ventrally and dorsally. The ventral junction (*ventral mesocardium*) occurs first, and immediately thereafter the coelom breaks through it to form the *pericardial cavity* enclosing the heart. The dorsal junction (*dorsal mesocardium*) persists for some time, supporting the heart by its dorsal surface and aiding in its bifurcation. The splanchnic mesoderm surrounding the endocardium differentiates into the *myocardium*, or heart muscle, and an outer very thin but tough membrane, the *epicardium*.

The heart extends anteriorly as the *bulbus arteriosus* and posteriorly as the *sinus venosus*. While it is still a single tube, it begins to twist, largely because of its active elongation within a limited space. Its extremities are anchored by blood vessels, but the intermediate portion bends posteroventrally, and the posterior portion folds anterodorsally. The original anterior portion, thus located posteriorly, becomes the *ventricle*, and the original pos-

324 THE PIG: *A Diffuse Placentate*

terior portion, now anterior, becomes the *atrium*. Between the atrial and ventricular bulges is a constricted section through which the *atrioventricular canal* passes. The *endocardial cushion* develops along this canal, partitioning the heart in two. The *interventricular septum*, which arises at the 4-mm. stage, separates the ventricle into two parts, and the walls of the two ventricles thicken. Concurrently the atrium expands transversely to become a thin-walled chamber of two bulges overlapping the muscular ventricles. Internally the interatrial *septum primum* divides it into left and right atria, connected only by an interatrial opening, the *foramen primum*.

Clusters of mesenchyme cells appearing throughout the embryonic and extraembryonic structures at the 13-somite stage are the *blood islands*. They are the centers of development of the blood vessels, forming the blood cells and the same type of endothelium as that found in the heart. Some acquire circular connective tissue cells and fibers and smooth muscle cells and become *arteries* or *arterioles*. Others, with less mesenchyme, become *veins*.

Some of the arterial vessels join together as *ventral aortae* growing from the anterior endocardium up through the primitive visceral arches to form the *aortic arches* and turning both anteriorly and posteriorly to form the *dorsal aortae* and their extensions. Six pairs of aortic arches develop in the pig embryo. The two most anterior pairs appear by about 17 days, and the third, fourth, and sixth pairs by the 6-mm. stage. Although the first pair disappears before the others form, its ventral and dorsal parts remain in the *external* and *internal carotid arteries*, respectively. Soon after the first pair degenerates, the second pair disappears.

The arterial system consists of the ventral aortae, the aortic arches, and the carotids anteriorly, the dorsal aortae anteriorly and posteriorly, and branches of the posteriorly directed dorsal aortae, such as the *intersegmental arteries*, the *vitelline (omphalomesenteric) arteries*, and the *umbilical (allantoic) arteries*. Paired, thin-walled *anterior cardinal veins* transport blood to the heart from the head region, while similar *posterior cardinal veins* carry blood from the kidney and tail level. At their junctions are short *common cardinal veins (ducts of Cuvier)*, which empty their contents into the posterior region of the developing heart. Other afferent vessels, the paired *umbilical (allantoic) veins* and the *vitelline (omphalomesenteric) veins*, carry blood from extraembryonic regions. The umbilical veins join the common cardinals just before they enter the heart. The vitelline veins pass through the liver region and join the heart more ventrally. Innumerable small blood islands in the yolk sac and the allantois coalesce to form, respectively, the *vitelline venous plexus* and the *umbilical venous plexus*, which join both the afferent and efferent channels, completing the extraembryonic circulation. There are thus three independent but interconnected loops of blood vessels, one within the embryo, one to the yolk sac, and one to the allantois. A single corpuscle may take any of the three loops away from and back to the heart. Fluid accumulates on this closed system, and the blood begins to circulate with the first weak cardiac pulsation at about the 15-somite stage.

The *pronephros* (one of the paired pronephric kidneys) is a functionless vestige consisting of a few slightly coiled tubules located far anteriorly (around the sixth to fourteenth somites) in the early pig embryo. These tubules connect with a pronephric duct extending posteriorly in the nephrotome or lateral plate mesoderm to the cloaca. At the 16- or 17-somite stage the mesonephros arises in the nephrotome more posteriorly and mesially, with more complicated S-shaped tubules. The nephrotome at this time comprises a *nephrogenic cord* lateral to the somite mesoderm. The anterior mesonephric tubules may, like the temporary *pronephric tubules,* have *nephrostomes,* funnel-shaped openings into the coelom, but the posterior, more advanced ones do not. As the mesonephros develops, the pronephros degenerates, leaving only its pronephric duct. This joins the mesonephric tubules and is thenceforth identified as a mesonephric duct.

Embryonic membranes

The *amnion, serosa,* yolk sac, and allantois derive from the germ layers that give rise to the embryonic tissues and are continuations of these outside the embryo for purposes of protection and transport of nutrition, oxygen, and wastes (Figs. 7.15–7.17). Each contains mesoderm combined with either endoderm or ectoderm.

The amnion comes from the somatopleure and forms an enveloping membrane around the embryo in mammals as in reptiles and birds. It becomes filled with *amniotic fluid,* which bathes the embryo, preventing adhesions and contusions. In the pig the amnion begins to form at the primitive streak stage and folds together over the embryo by the 18-somite stage. Its temporary mid-dorsal point of junction with the serosa quickly breaks so that the embryo inside its amnion lies almost free within the blastocyst. The amnion expands to encircle the tubes connecting the embryo with the allantois (allantoic stalk) and with the yolk sac (yolk stalk). The resulting structure is the umbilical cord. The amnion encloses the entire body except for the region of the umbilical cord by the time the midgut has closed and the embryo has assumed its C shape.

The serosa also arises from the somatopleure. It is exactly the reverse of the amnion, having an inner layer of mesoderm and an outer layer of ectoderm, and forms simultaneously with it. The serosa is the outermost embryonic membrane, establishing intimate structural and functional relations with the maternal tissues.

The yolk sac, apparently a vestigial structure persisting from ancestral forms in which yolk was actually available, is a direct outgrowth of the midgut. Accordingly, it does not appear until the midgut is delimited. The yolk sac develops blood vessels just as if yolk were to be digested and carried to the embryo. Its distal end enlarges to almost completely fill the blastocyst at the 15-somite stage but then begins to recede. At this early, large, and active stage

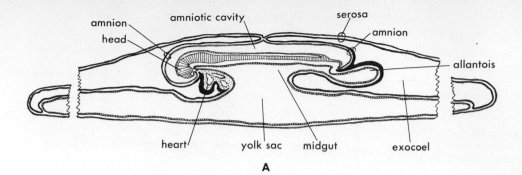

A

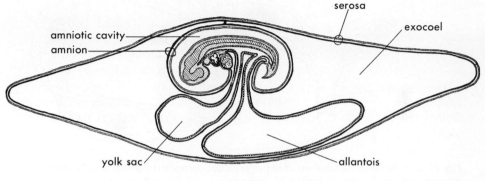

B

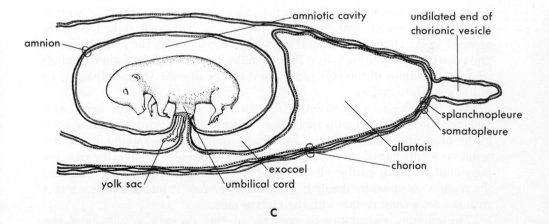

C

Fig. 7.15 Relations of embryonic membranes in pig: A, in 15- to 20-somite embryo; B, in 4- to 6-mm. embryo; C, in 30-mm. embryo. (Adapted from B. M. Patten, *Embryology of the Pig*, 3rd ed., McGraw-Hill, New York, 1948.)

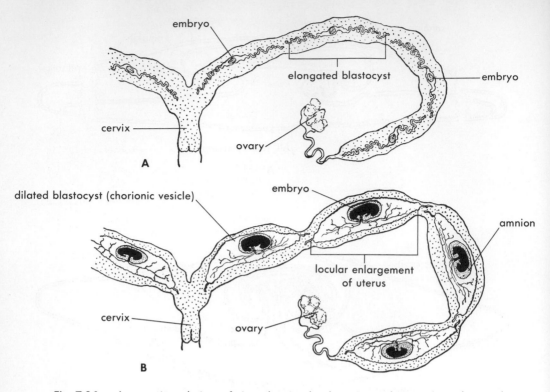

Fig. 7.16 Intrauterine relations of pig embryo and embryonic membranes: A, at elongated blastocyst stage; B, after formation of chorionic vesicles. (From B. M. Patten, *Embryology of the Pig,* 3rd ed., McGraw-Hill, New York, 1948.)

it does in fact carry diffused nutrition to the embryo through its blood vessels because of its temporary adhesion with the outer serosa, which in turn is intimately associated with the maternal tissues. The yolk stalk is slightly anterior to the allantoic stalk in the umbilical cord. When the allantois forms and enlarges to fill the blastocyst (between the amnion and the serosa), it takes over the functions of the yolk sac, so that by the 30-mm. stage only a stump of the yolk sac remains.

The allantois is a mid-ventral diverticulum of the hindgut lined with endoderm and invested with splanchnic mesoderm. It begins to form as soon as the hindgut acquires a floor. The diverticulum enlarges rapidly, becoming a full crescent-shaped sac attached to the hindgut only through the narrowing umbilical cord, until it fills the blastocyst except for the distal ends and the regions occupied by the embryo and the amnion. It makes diffuse contact with the serosa and thence with the uterine mucosa.

The *chorion,* the embryonic portion of the placenta, results from the fusion of the mesoderm of the allantois with the mesoderm of the serosa and thus consists of all three germ layers with an abundance of mesoderm. The placental relationship with the uterine mucosa is rather simple. Numerous

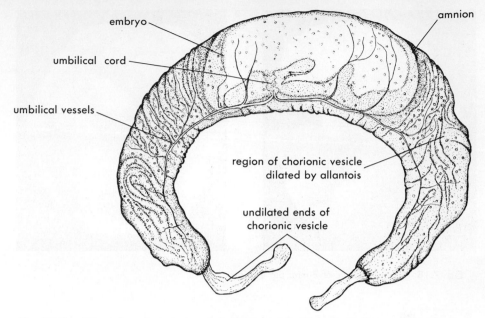

Fig. 7.17 Pig embryo in unruptured chorionic vesicle. (From B. M. Patten, *Embryology of the Pig,* 3rd ed., McGraw-Hill, New York, 1948. Adapted from Grosser.)

blood vessels in the double-layered mesoderm are in direct contact (but not connection) through the thin layer of ectoderm with the uterine capillaries. Between the folds of the chorion and those of the uterus a uterine secretion, essentially the only separation between maternal and embryonic membranes, develops. Nutriment and excretory and respiratory wastes pass across the membranes and the fluid, generally in a direction from high concentration to low so that nutriment goes to the embryo and wastes leave it. At birth the embryonic and maternal membranes easily dissociate, and there is no massive hemorrhage as in primate parturition.

10-mm. Embryo

When the pig embryo attains a length of 10 mm. (Figs. 7.18–7.23), it can be satisfactorily compared with the chick, mouse, or human embryo. Its back is not so curved as at the 6-mm. stage, owing to the continuing development of the heart, liver, and mesonephros. Pigment is apparent through the ectoderm overlying the *optic vesicles,* the first visceral arches have joined to form the *mandible* (lower jaw), and tubercles may be developing around the first visceral groove, indicating the beginnings of the ears. Approximately 44 pairs of somites are present. The limb buds are growing rapidly, and the tail is long and tapering. Between the tail and the relatively large umbilical cord is a genital tubercle.

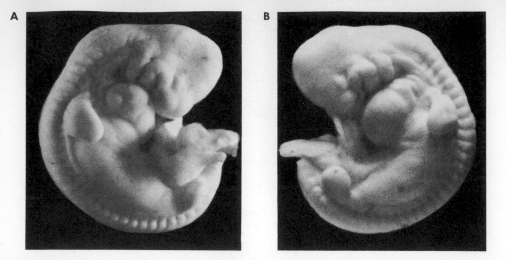

Fig. 7.18 Lateral views of 7-mm. pig embryo.

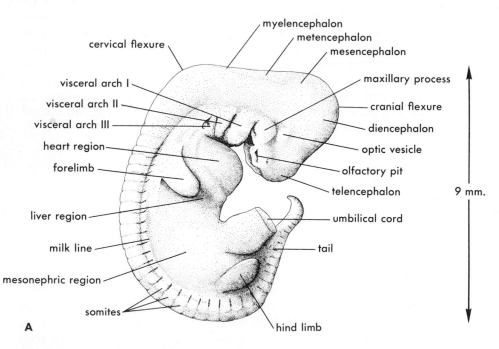

cervical flexure

myelencephalon
metencephalon
mesencephalon

visceral arch I
visceral arch II
visceral arch III

maxillary process
cranial flexure
diencephalon

heart region

optic vesicle

forelimb

olfactory pit
telencephalon

liver region

umbilical cord

milk line

tail

mesonephric region

9 mm.

somites

A

hind limb

Fig. 7.19 Lateral views of 9-mm. pig embryo.

330 THE PIG: *A Diffuse Placentate*

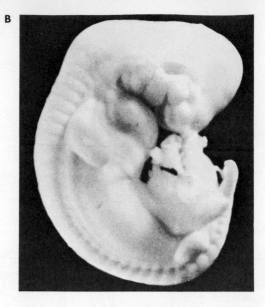

B

Fig. 7.19   (*continued*)

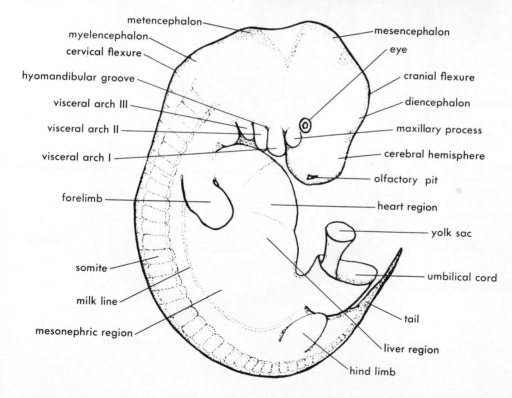

metencephalon

myelencephalon

cervical flexure

hyomandibular groove

visceral arch III

visceral arch II

visceral arch I

forelimb

somite

milk line

mesonephric region

mesencephalon

eye

cranial flexure

diencephalon

maxillary process

cerebral hemisphere

olfactory pit

heart region

yolk sac

umbilical cord

tail

liver region

hind limb

Fig. 7.20   Lateral view of 10-mm. pig embryo. (From R. Rugh, *Laboratory Manual of Vertebrate Embryology*, 5th ed., Burgess, Minneapolis, 1961.)

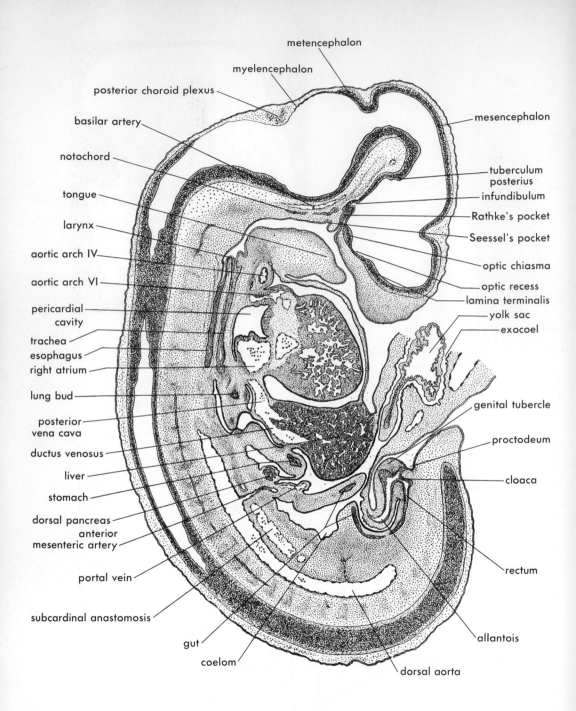

Fig. 7.21   Sagittal section of 10-mm. pig embryo. (From B. M. Patten, *Embryology of the Pig,* 3rd ed., McGraw-Hill, New York, 1948.)

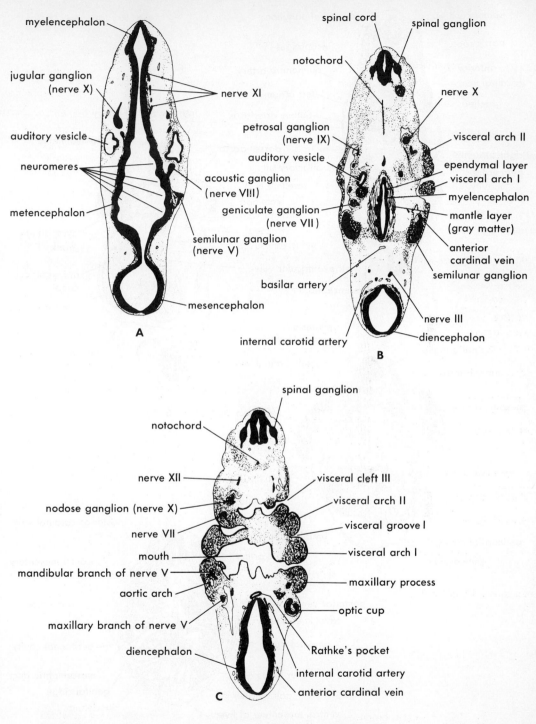

Fig. 7.22 Diagrams of transverse sections of 10-mm. pig embryo.

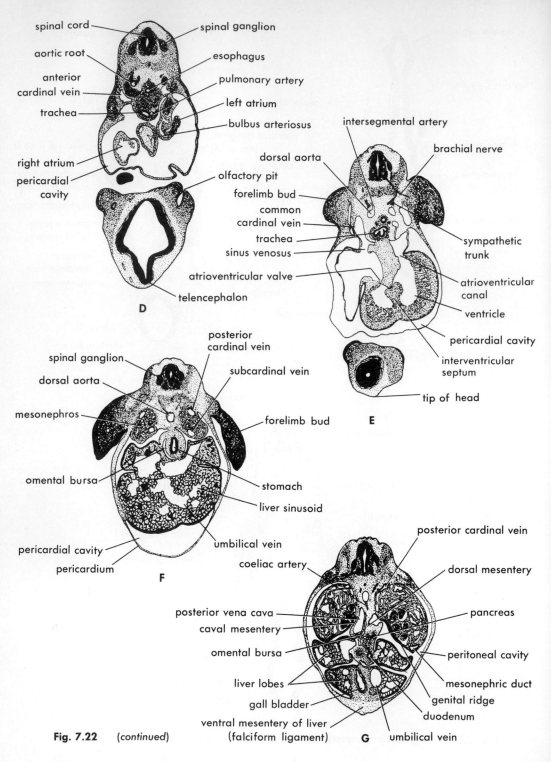

spinal cord — spinal ganglion
aortic root — esophagus
anterior cardinal vein — pulmonary artery
trachea — left atrium
— bulbus arteriosus
right atrium —
pericardial cavity — olfactory pit
— forelimb bud
dorsal aorta

intersegmental artery
brachial nerve

common cardinal vein
trachea
sinus venosus
atrioventricular valve
telencephalon

sympathetic trunk
atrioventricular canal
ventricle
pericardial cavity
interventricular septum
tip of head

D

E

posterior cardinal vein
spinal ganglion — subcardinal vein
dorsal aorta —
mesonephros —
— forelimb bud
omental bursa —
— stomach
— liver sinusoid
pericardial cavity —
pericardium — umbilical vein
coeliac artery

F

posterior cardinal vein
dorsal mesentery
pancreas
posterior vena cava —
caval mesentery —
omental bursa — peritoneal cavity
mesonephric duct
genital ridge
liver lobes — duodenum
gall bladder —
ventral mesentery of liver (falciform ligament) — umbilical vein

G

Fig. 7.22   (continued)

334   THE PIG: *A Diffuse Placentate*

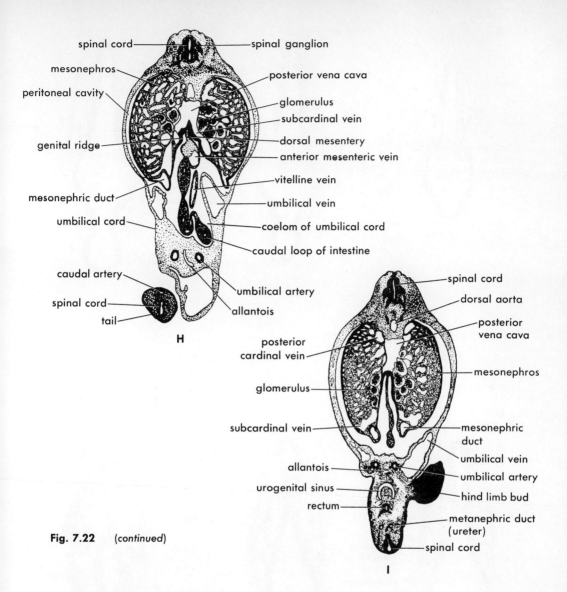

spinal cord
spinal ganglion
mesonephros
posterior vena cava
peritoneal cavity
glomerulus
subcardinal vein
genital ridge
dorsal mesentery
anterior mesenteric vein
vitelline vein
mesonephric duct
umbilical vein
umbilical cord
coelom of umbilical cord
caudal loop of intestine
caudal artery
spinal cord
umbilical artery
tail
allantois

H

posterior
cardinal vein

glomerulus

subcardinal vein

allantois
urogenital sinus
rectum

spinal cord
dorsal aorta
posterior
vena cava

mesonephros

mesonephric
duct
umbilical vein
umbilical artery
hind limb bud
metanephric duct
(ureter)
spinal cord

I

Fig. 7.22   (continued)

Derivatives of the ectoderm

NERVOUS SYSTEM.   The brain of the 10-mm. pig is still quite primitive,
although the telencephalon gives rise to paired *lateral ventricles*, within *cerebral hemispheres*, and the diencephalon to paired optic vesicles (Fig. 7.24).
The *optic recess* marks the point of junction of the telencephalon and diencephalon. Just posterior to it is the *optic chiasma*. The metencephalon is
distinguished from the more posterior myelencephalon by its much thicker
roof. Also, the myelencephalon shows a *choroid plexus* in its roof and lateral
indentations between remnants of neuromeres.

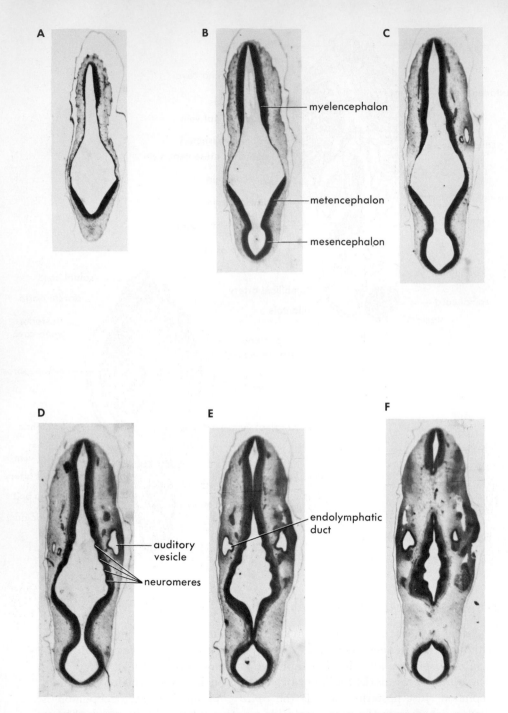

Fig. 7.23 Transverse sections of 10-mm. pig embryo: E, Fig. 7.22A; G, Fig. 7.22B; I, Fig. 7.22C; M, Fig. 7.22D; Q, Fig. 7.22E; U, Fig. 7.22F; X, Fig. 7.22G; B′, Fig. 7.22H; E′, Fig. 7.22I.

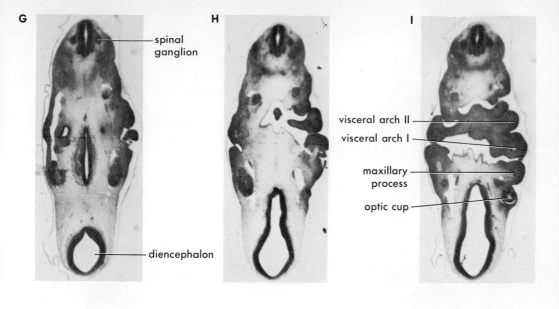

G — spinal ganglion

G — diencephalon

I — visceral arch II
I — visceral arch I
I — maxillary process
I — optic cup

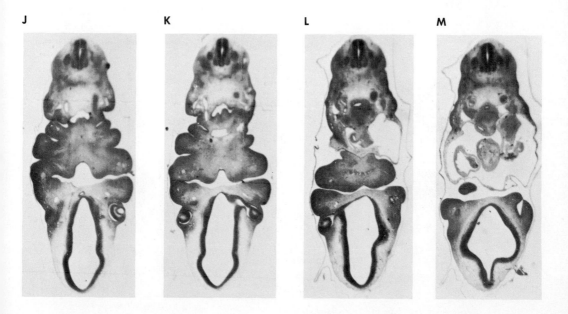

Fig. 7.23   (continued)

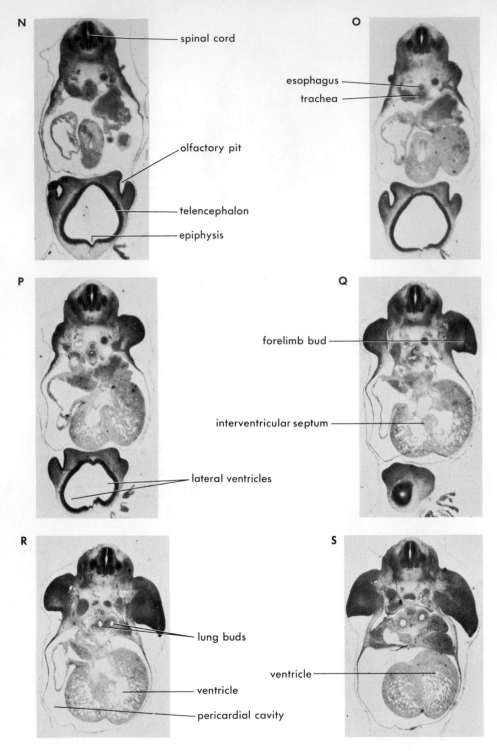

N — spinal cord

O — esophagus — trachea

olfactory pit

telencephalon

epiphysis

P

Q — forelimb bud

interventricular septum

lateral ventricles

R — lung buds

ventricle

pericardial cavity

S — ventricle

Fig. 7.23   (continued)

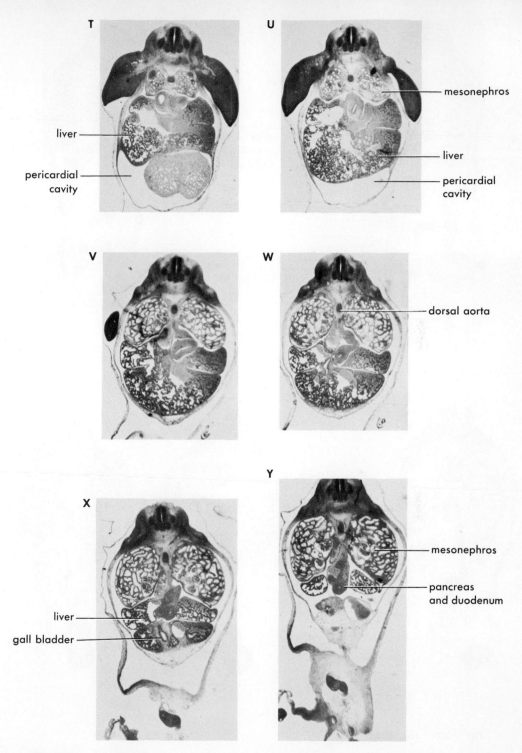

T

U — mesonephros

liver

pericardial cavity

liver

pericardial cavity

V

W — dorsal aorta

X

Y — mesonephros

liver

gall bladder

pancreas and duodenum

Fig. 7.23 (continued)

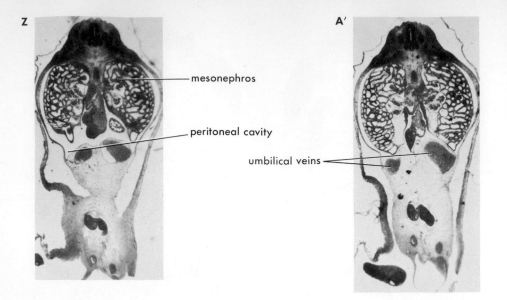

Z

mesonephros

peritoneal cavity

A′

umbilical veins

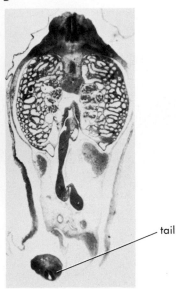

B′

tail

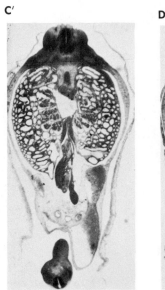

C′

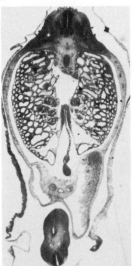

D′

Fig. 7.23   (continued)

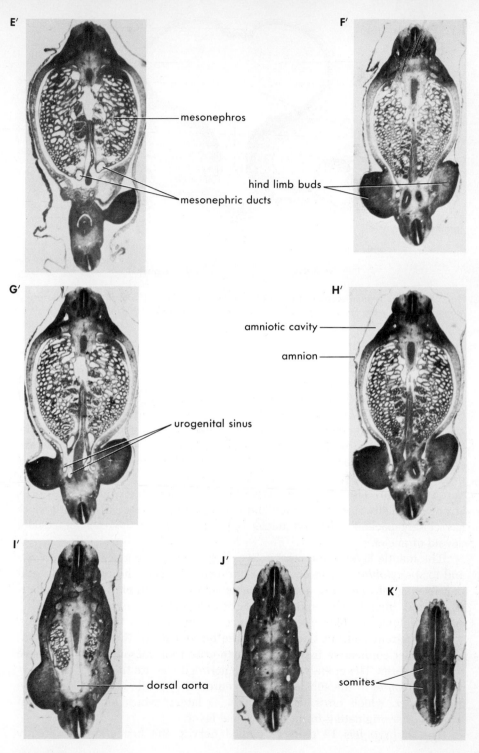

E′

mesonephros

mesonephric ducts

F′

hind limb buds

G′

urogenital sinus

H′

amniotic cavity

amnion

I′

dorsal aorta

J′

K′

somites

Fig. 7.23 (continued)

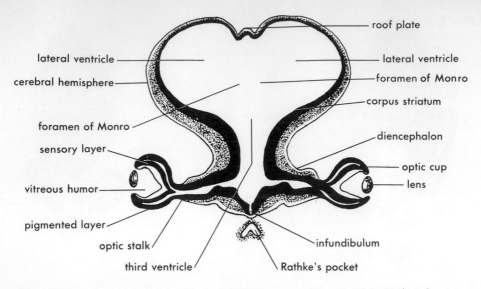

Fig. 7.24 Transverse section of brain of 10-mm. pig embryo. (From R. Rugh, *Laboratory Manual of Vertebrate Embryology*, 5th ed., Burgess, Minneapolis, 1961.)

The brain merges imperceptibly with the *spinal cord*, which has thick lateral walls, a thin roof and floor, and a vertical slit comprising the *neurocoel* (*neural canal*). The transition from a simple, single-layered neural groove to a multi-layered spinal cord occurs with relatively great speed in comparison with differentiations in the brain and other organs. The walls of the spinal cord are bounded on the inner and outer surfaces by limiting membranes and consist of an inner *ependymal layer*, a thick *mantle layer*, and a vacuolated outer *marginal layer*. The ependymal layer contains elongated (ependymal) cells arranged radially from the lumen and many cells in mitosis; the mantle layer has closely packed cells and nuclei; and the marginal layer is practically devoid of nuclei.

The mantle layer is the most active. It gives rise to masses of *neuroblasts* and to *spongioblasts*. The neuroblasts, transient cells in the process of meta-morphosing into *neurons*, are identifiable by means of their large and generally ovoid nuclei. The spongioblasts, forerunners of *neuroglia*, develop extremely long fiberlike processes that sometimes appear to lose connection with the parent cell but that support the nerve cells of the cord and brain. Unlike other connective tissue cells, which arise from mesoderm, these derive from ectoderm. The ependymal cells are neuroglia, as are the long- and short-rayed *astrocytes* in the substance of the cord. The mantle layer makes up the *gray matter*, which cross sections show as lateral wings on either side of *white matter* originating from the marginal layer.

The embryo has 12 pairs of cranial nerves, the first 10 pairs directly associated with the brain and the eleventh and twelfth associated with what would be regarded as the anterior limit of the spinal cord in simpler vertebrates (Fig. 7.25). These nerves, well known in comparative morphology, are listed in Table 7.2.

The neural crests are metamerically distinct as *spinal ganglia,* which begin to send neural outgrowths (*dorsal,* sensory *roots*) both toward the cord and peripherally to the various organs of the body, including the skin (Fig. 7.26). An outgrowth from the ventral neural ectoderm of the cord (*ventral,* motor *root*) joins the peripheral process from each ganglion, forming a spinal

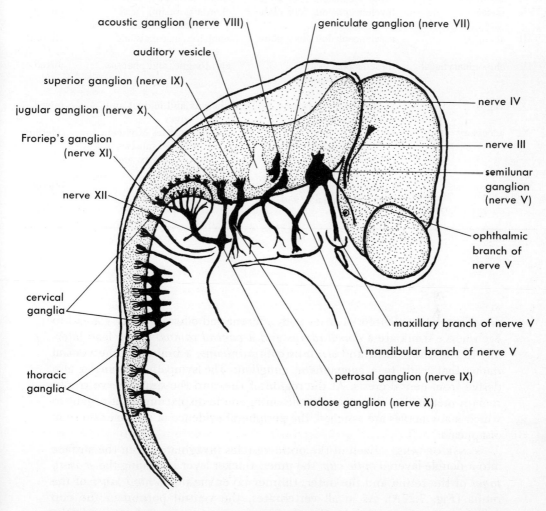

acoustic ganglion (nerve VIII)
geniculate ganglion (nerve VII)
auditory vesicle
superior ganglion (nerve IX)
jugular ganglion (nerve X)
Froriep's ganglion (nerve XI)
nerve XII
cervical ganglia
thoracic ganglia
nerve IV
nerve III
semilunar ganglion (nerve V)
ophthalmic branch of nerve V
maxillary branch of nerve V
mandibular branch of nerve V
petrosal ganglion (nerve IX)
nodose ganglion (nerve X)

Fig. 7.25 Sagittal section showing ganglia and nerves in 10-mm. pig embryo. (From R. Rugh, *Laboratory Manual of Vertebrate Embryology,* 5th ed., Burgess, Minneapolis, 1961.)

Table 7.2   Cranial nerves

NERVE		ORIGIN	DESTINATION	TYPE
I	olfactory	telencephalon	olfactory organ	afferent
II	optic	diencephalon	retina	afferent
III	oculomotor	mesencephalon, floor plate	superior rectus, inferior rectus, median rectus, and inferior oblique eye muscles	efferent
IV	trochlear	mesencephalon, dorsal wall	superior oblique eye muscles	efferent
V	trigeminal	myelencephalon	ophthalmic, maxillary, and mandibular regions	mixed
VI	abducens	myelencephalon, floor plate	lateral rectus eye muscles	efferent
VII	facial	myelencephalon, floor plate	chorda tympani, facial muscles, and taste organs	mixed
VIII	acoustic	myelencephalon, floor plate	semicircular canals and cochlea	afferent
IX	glossopharyngeal	mesencephalon just posterior to auditory vesicle	ear, tongue, and pharynx	mixed
X	vagus	several divisions from myelencephalon	pharynx and midgut and derivatives	mixed
XI	accessory	spinal cord, cervical portion, and possibly myelencephalon, posterior limit	smooth muscles of viscera and striated muscles of pharynx, larynx, and neck region	efferent
XII	hypoglossal	numerous connections with myelencephalon and cord	tongue muscles	efferent

nerve trunk that therefore carries both afferent and efferent tracts. Lateral to each nerve trunk are a *dorsal ramus* and a *ventral ramus*, which lead laterally to the body parts, and a *ramus communicans*, a branch of the ventral ramus that leads to a *sympathetic ganglion*. The sympathetic ganglia also derive from neural crests. At the region of the cord the spinal nerve trunks remain metameric, but owing to the ontogenetic displacement of organs to which many nerves are assigned, the peripheral evidence of metamerism soon disappears.

SENSE ORGANS.   Each of the optic vesicles invaginates from the surface into a double-layered *optic cup*, the inner, thicker layer becoming the *sensory layer* of the retina and the outer, thinner layer the *pigmented layer* of the retina (Fig. 7.27A). As in all vertebrates, the ventral portion of the cup remains open for a while as the *choroid fissure,* an inverted groove in the *optic stalk*. Through this stalk pass the optic nerve from the retina to the brain and blood vessels to and from the retina. The superficial head ectoderm gives rise to the *lens* by the invagination, thickening, and pinching off of cells into the open optic cup. An *auditory (otic) vesicle* appears on each side of the head at the level of the myelencephalon, sunk into the surface and closed off except for a thin tubular *endolymphatic duct* (Fig. 7.27B). The nearby hyomandibular groove becomes the *external auditory meatus* as nerves grow out from the large eighth cranial ganglion to the auditory apparatus. The olfactory pits develop sensory epithelia, which connect with the cerebral hemi-spheres by means of sensory nerves (Fig. 7.27C).

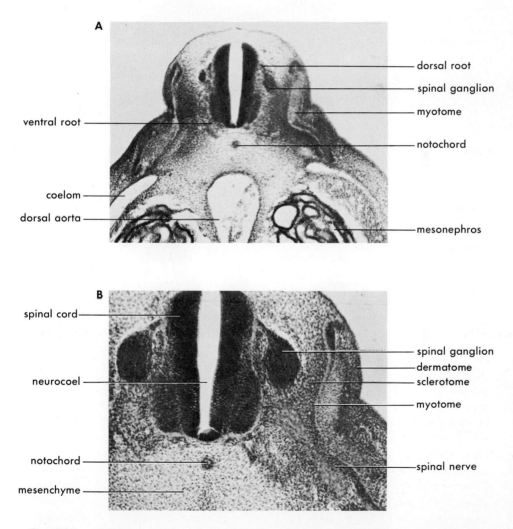

Fig. 7.26   Transverse sections showing spinal cord development in 10-mm. pig embryo (B at high power.)

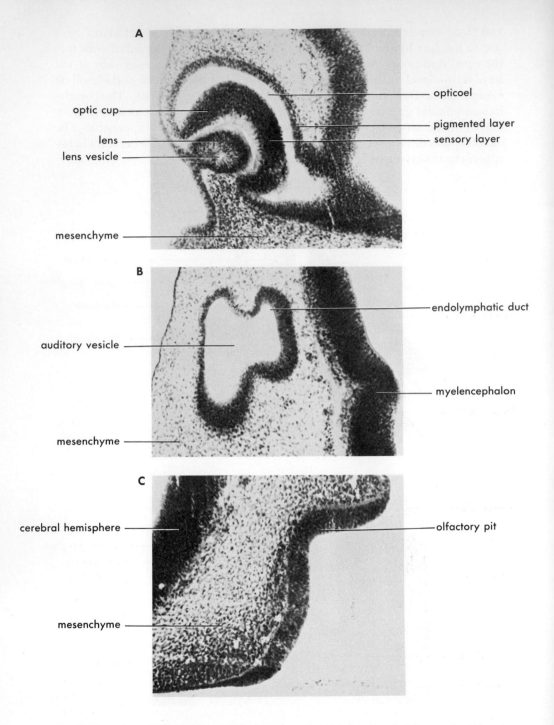

Fig. 7.27 Transverse sections showing sense organ development in 10-mm. pig embryo: A, eye; B, ear; C, olfactory organ.

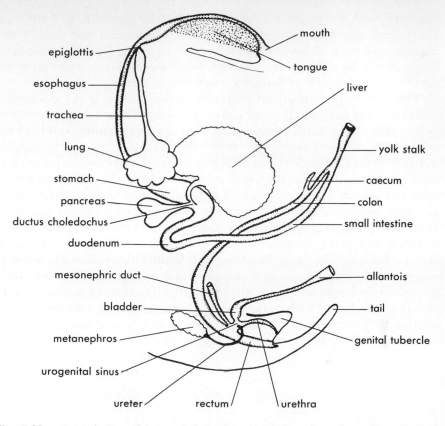

Fig. 7.28 Lateral view of gut and derivatives in 10-mm. pig embryo. (From R. Rugh, *Laboratory Manual of Vertebrate Embryology*, 5th ed., Burgess, Minneapolis, 1961.)

Derivatives of the endoderm

A vestige of Seessel's pocket remains in the mouth at the 10-mm. stage (Figs. 7.21, 7.28). Anteriorly to the mouth opening, the ectodermal Rathke's pocket grows dorsally toward the infundibulum, and posteriorly to the mouth opening, in the pharynx, endodermally lined *visceral pouches* grow out toward the ectodermal visceral grooves (Figs. 7.22, 7.23), although they rarely break through in the pig. The first visceral (hyomandibular) pouch, between the first (mandibular) and second (hyoid) arches, remains dorsally to become the *auditory (Eustachian) tube* and the *tympanic cavity*. Between the first and second pouches the *thyroid gland* arises as a single median ventral diverticulum in the pharyngeal floor (Fig. 7.29). Remnants of the second pouches aid in the formation of the *tonsils* and the tonsillar cavity, and the third and fourth pouches aid in the formation of the *parathyroids, thymus,* and *ultimobranchial bodies* (endocrine). Just behind the last pair of pouches, the laryngotracheal groove closes to become a posteriorly directed tube, the *trachea,* connected with the pharynx by the *larynx* and the *glottis* (Figs. 7.28, 7.30) The paired lung buds give rise to *bronchi* and expand and branch into numerous air sacs, all invested with highly vascular splanchnic mesoderm. Respiration is by diffusion from the air sacs through this vascular layer and the thin layer of endoderm lining the respiratory tract.

The narrow portion of gut posterior to the trachea is the developing esophagus, and beyond the esophagus is the dilated stomach. Just posterior to the stomach is a small constriction, the future *duodenum*, and between this and the yolk stalk is the small intestine, which is beginning to elongate and coil. Branching from the small intestine are the pancreatic outgrowths and the massive, glandular liver, with its related gall bladder. The two ventral pancreatic primordia open into the gut separately from the dorsal primordium. All three rudiments enlarge and merge as they develop saclike processes. Then the first, or ventral, *pancreatic duct* degenerates, leaving the second, or dorsal, duct as the common pancreatic duct. The *cystic duct* connects the liver to the gut. The large intestine, just beyond the yolk stalk, develops a large pouch, the *caecum*, as it elongates and enlarges into a much coiled gut, relatively longer and larger than the large intestines of primates. At its posterior limit, lateral folds in the cloacal lumen, associated with the allantoic junction with the hindgut, divide the cloaca into a ventral urogenital sinus, contiguous with the allantois, and a dorsal *rectum*.

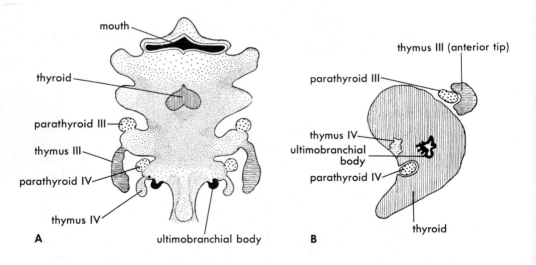

Fig. 7.29 Derivatives of pharynx in 10-mm. pig embryo: A, frontal section; B–E, transverse sections (E at high power). (A, B from B. M. Patten, *Embryology of the Pig*, 3rd ed., McGraw-Hill, New York, 1948.)

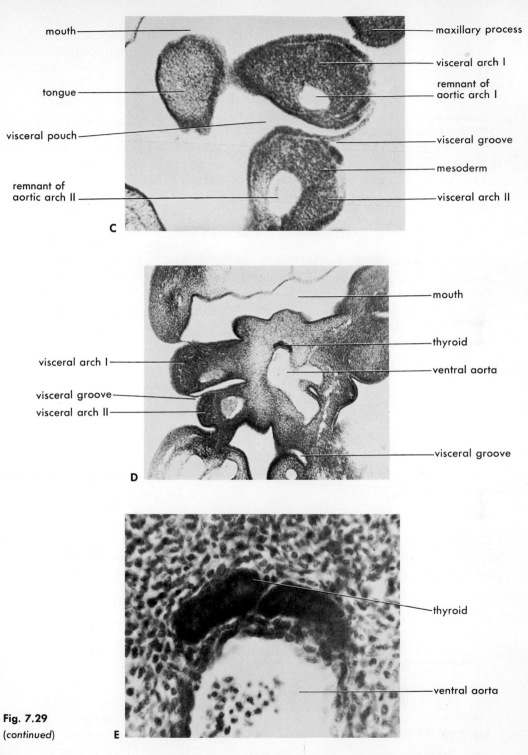

mouth — maxillary process

visceral arch I

remnant of aortic arch I

tongue

visceral pouch

visceral groove

mesoderm

remnant of aortic arch II

visceral arch II

C

mouth

thyroid

visceral arch I

ventral aorta

visceral groove

visceral arch II

visceral groove

D

thyroid

ventral aorta

Fig. 7.29
(continued)

E

10-mm. Embryo **349**

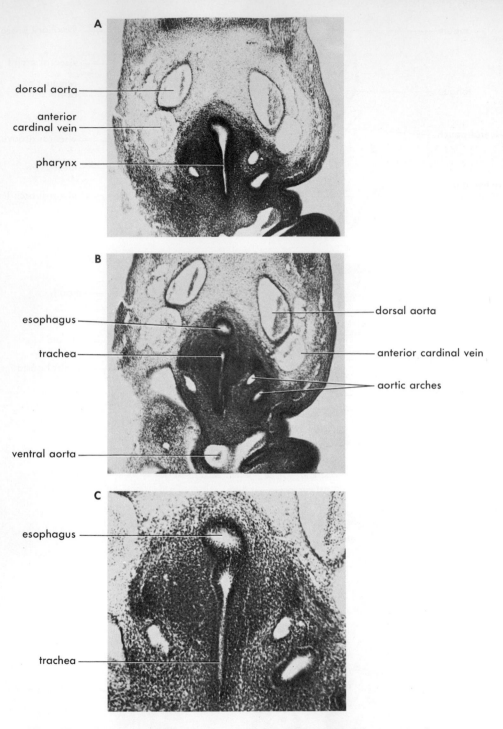

Fig. 7.30 Transverse sections showing derivatives of foregut in 10-mm. pig embryo.

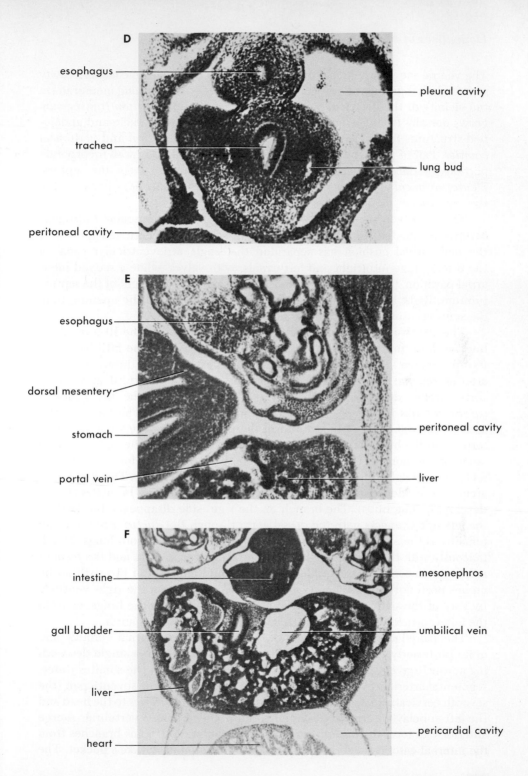

D

esophagus

pleural cavity

trachea

lung bud

peritoneal cavity

E

esophagus

dorsal mesentery

stomach

peritoneal cavity

portal vein

liver

F

intestine

mesonephros

gall bladder

umbilical vein

liver

heart

pericardial cavity

The ventral mesentery breaks at midgut level, so that a single coelomic cavity surrounds that part of the gut. However, it persists as a supporting membrane in the vicinity of the liver and pancreas. The membranous *septum transversum* grows dorsally from the ventral body wall between the thoracic and abdominal structures to divide the coelom transversely into *pleural* and *peritoneal cavities.* Paired *pleuroperitoneal folds* from the dorsal body wall incorporate portions of the dorsal mesentery and grow ventrally to meet the septum. *Pleuroperitoneal canals* may remain temporarily as connections between the two cavities.

The thick ventricular walls of the heart consist of muscular *trabeculae carneae* permeated by blood sinusoids (Fig. 7.31). The continued growth of the endocardial cushion has separated the single atrioventricular canal of the 6-mm. stage into right and left canals, with valves, while a second interatrial partition, the *septum secundum,* has arisen just to the right of the septum primum. Right and left *valves of the sinus venosus* guard the opening from the sinus venosus into the right atrium.

The first two pairs of aortic arches have degenerated by the 10-mm. stage, but the third, fourth, and sixth pairs are still present, and the fifth has made its appearance (at 8 mm.) (Fig. 7.32). The external and internal carotid arteries remain. As the dorsal connections between the third and fourth aortic arches disappear, their ventral connections become the *common carotid arteries* joining the external and internal carotids. The fourth aortic arch on the right side reduces to form the *innominate artery* while its counterpart on the left side enlarges tremendously to become the *systemic arch* (arch of the aorta). The ventral connection between the fourth and sixth arches on the right side gives rise to the right *subclavian artery.* The fifth pair of arches has no derivatives, but the sixth develops pulmonary branches (to the developing lung buds). The branch on the right side disappears, but that on the left side connects with the dorsal aorta through the *ductus arteriosus* and remains as the enlarged *pulmonary artery,* which supplies both lungs. Simultaneously with the partitioning of the heart, the ventral aorta and the *truncus arteriosus* become bifurcated lengthwise, from the origin of the sixth aortic arches posteriorly to the heart, so that blood passes from the right ventricle by way of the sixth aortic arch and pulmonary artery to the lungs, or from the left ventricle via the left fourth aortic arch to the dorsal aorta.

The paired dorsal aortae extend anteriorly as the internal carotids and unite posteriorly, from the level of the eighth somite, into a single descending aorta. It gives off numerous paired branches between the somites (intersegmental arteries) to various organs and the body wall. The seventh pair (the seventh cervical intersegmentals) gives rise to *vertebral arteries* to the head and the left subclavian artery to the left forelimb. The paired vertebrals merge anteriorly to form the *basilar artery* beneath the brain. It joins branches from the internal carotids to form the *circle of Willis* around Rathke's pocket. The

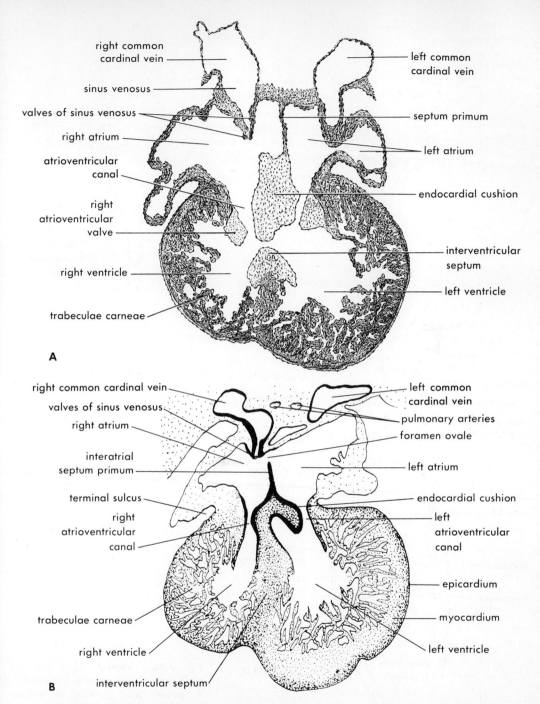

Fig. 7.31 Frontal sections through heart of pig embryo: A, at 9.4 mm.; B, at 10 mm. (A from B. M. Patten, *Embryology of the Pig,* 3rd ed., McGraw-Hill, New York, 1948; B from R. Rugh, *Laboratory Manual of Vertebrate Embryology,* 5th ed., Burgess, Minneapolis, 1961.)

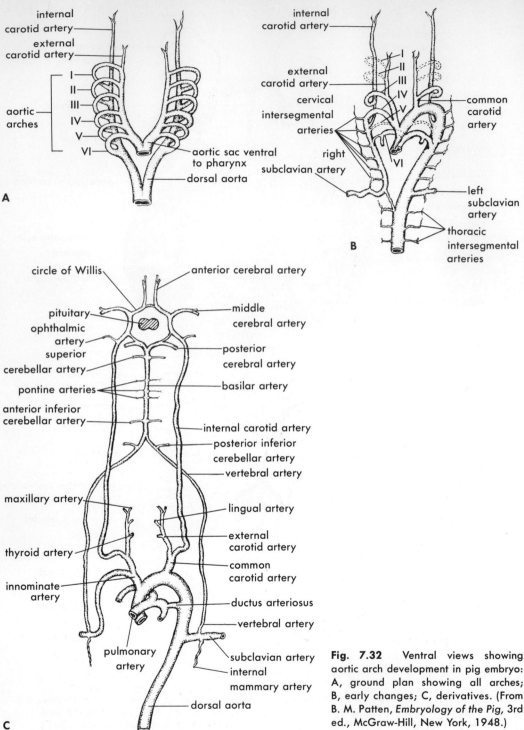

Fig. 7.32 Ventral views showing aortic arch development in pig embryo: A, ground plan showing all arches; B, early changes; C, derivatives. (From B. M. Patten, *Embryology of the Pig*, 3rd ed., McGraw-Hill, New York, 1948.)

354 THE PIG: *A Diffuse Placentate*

thoracic intersegmentals fuse to form the *internal mammary arteries*. Both the vertebrals and the mammaries establish connections with the subclavians. Still farther posteriorly paired intersegmentals supply the dorsal body muscles. Branching ventrally from the descending aorta are the paired *coeliac*, vitelline, and umbilical arteries (Figs. 7.33, 7.34). The coeliacs pass by way of the dorsal mesentery to the stomach region. As the umbilical cord constricts, the two vitelline arteries fuse in the mid-line into a single vessel. The yolk sac then degenerates, and this large artery becomes the *anterior (superior) mesenteric artery* to the small intestine. The descending aorta also gives off many branches (*renal arteries*) to the developing glomeruli of the mesonephros. The umbilical arteries drain most of the remaining blood from the aorta and reduce its size posteriorly, leaving a tapering *caudal artery*.

The anterior cardinal veins receive blood from various venous sinuses of the cephalic region to become the *internal jugular veins*. Just before they empty into the common cardinal veins, and thence into the heart, they meet the *intersegmental veins* from the cervical region and the *external jugular veins* from the head. The posterior cardinal veins, large in the early embryo, begin to degenerate and lose their position dorsal to the paired mesonephroi. Paired *subcardinal veins* arise ventromesially to the mesonephroi, establish connections with the anterior portions of the degenerating posterior cardinals, and take over their functions. As each mesonephros enlarges, the two parallel subcardinals meet and join (at the 9.4-mm. stage) to form a large *subcardinal anastomosis*, which receives the blood from both mesonephroi. This midventral subcardinal anastomosis becomes the mesenteric part of the *posterior (inferior) vena cava*.

The posterior vena cava develops from numerous small vessels merging in the vicinity of the highly vascular liver and the nearby mesonephroi (Fig. 7.34). It leads from the subcardinal anastomosis through the right subcardinal vein, the dorsal mesentery, and the liver to the sinus venosus and the right atrium of the heart.

The *pulmonary veins* arise along with the lung buds and merge to form a single large vein entering the left atrium. The paired vitelline veins, which drain blood from the yolk sac into the vascular network of the liver, degenerate peripherally along with the yolk sac but fuse within the body to form the coiled *portal vein*, which joins the posterior vena cava (Fig. 7.34). The coiling of the portal vein is due to the dropping out of segments of each of the original vitellines in the process of fusion into one large vein. The umbilical veins, which pass from the umbilical cord through the body wall and directly into the sinus venosus, enlarge peripherally as the placenta grows but must alter their positions because of the development of the liver. Their new route passes from the umbilical cord through the body wall to the liver capillaries and thence to the sinus venosus. Outside the embryonic body they fuse into one large umbilical vein (Figs. 7.33B, 7.34). Inside the body the right umbilical vein degenerates, and the left umbilical vein enlarges. Within the liver it becomes the substantial *ductus venosus*, which joins the *hepatic veins*. From

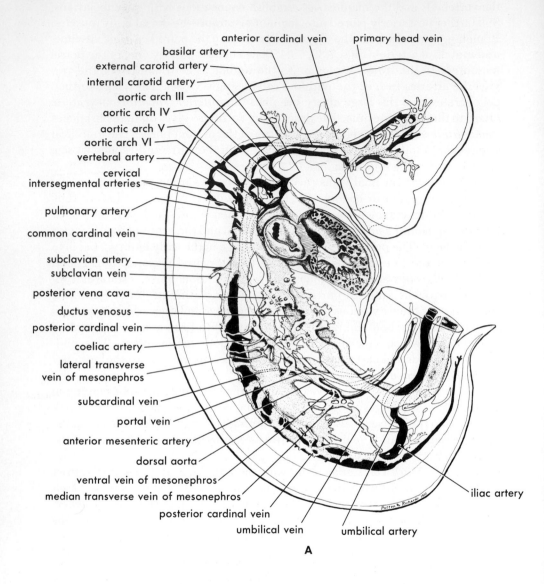

anterior cardinal vein — primary head vein

basilar artery

external carotid artery

internal carotid artery

aortic arch III

aortic arch IV

aortic arch V

aortic arch VI

vertebral artery

cervical intersegmental arteries

pulmonary artery

common cardinal vein

subclavian artery

subclavian vein

posterior vena cava

ductus venosus

posterior cardinal vein

coeliac artery

lateral transverse vein of mesonephros

subcardinal vein

portal vein

anterior mesenteric artery

dorsal aorta

ventral vein of mesonephros

median transverse vein of mesonephros

posterior cardinal vein

umbilical vein   umbilical artery

iliac artery

A

Fig. 7.33 Sagittal sections showing vascular system development in pig embryo: A, at 9.4 mm.; B, at 9.5 to 10 mm., with special emphasis on arterial system. (A from B. M. Patten, *Embryology of the Pig,* 3rd ed., McGraw-Hill, New York, 1948; B from O. E. Nelsen, *Comparative Embryology of the Vertebrates,* McGraw-Hill, New York, 1953.)

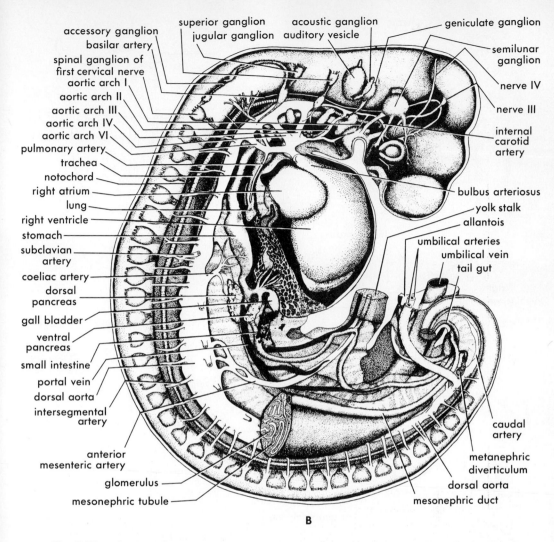

accessory ganglion
basilar artery
spinal ganglion of
first cervical nerve
aortic arch I
aortic arch II
aortic arch III
aortic arch IV
aortic arch VI
pulmonary artery
trachea
notochord
right atrium
lung
right ventricle
stomach
subclavian
artery
coeliac artery
dorsal
pancreas
gall bladder
ventral
pancreas
small intestine
portal vein
dorsal aorta
intersegmental
artery

anterior
mesenteric artery
glomerulus
mesonephric tubule

superior ganglion
jugular ganglion

acoustic ganglion
auditory vesicle

geniculate ganglion

semilunar
ganglion

nerve IV

nerve III

internal
carotid
artery

bulbus arteriosus
yolk stalk
allantois

umbilical arteries
umbilical vein
tail gut

caudal
artery

metanephric
diverticulum
dorsal aorta
mesonephric duct

B

Fig. 7.33   (*continued*)

this junction to the heart, blood from the embryonic body (systemic), the placenta (allantoic), and the yolk sac (portal) mingles in the posterior vena cava. The liver is thus an enlarging reservoir of venous blood from the posterior body parts mixed with nutrient and oxygenated blood from the extraembryonic regions. It does not, however, contain blood from the anterior cardinals or the remnants of the posterior cardinals.

The mesonephros is a bulky and compact organ of tortuous tubules extending from about the fourteenth to the thirty-second somite (Figs. 7.35, 7.36). Although it arises from the continuous nephrogenic cord (nephrotome) joining the segmented somites with the lateral plate mesoderm, its tubules are con-

10-mm. Embryo   **357**

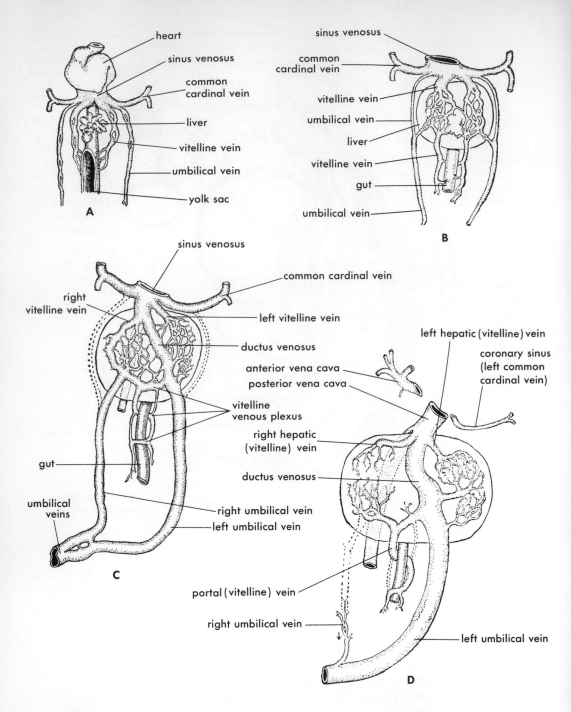

Fig. 7.34   Ventral views showing development of hepatic portal circulation in pig embryo: A, at 3 to 4 mm.; B, at 6 mm.; C, at 8 to 9 mm.; D, at 20 mm. (From B. M. Patten, *Embryology of the Pig,* 3rd ed., McGraw-Hill, New York, 1948.)

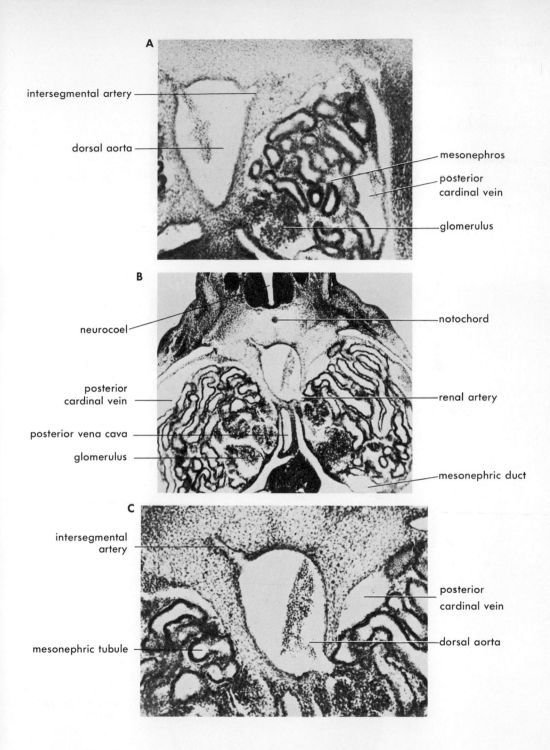

Fig. 7.35 Transverse sections showing kidney development in 10-mm. pig embryo.

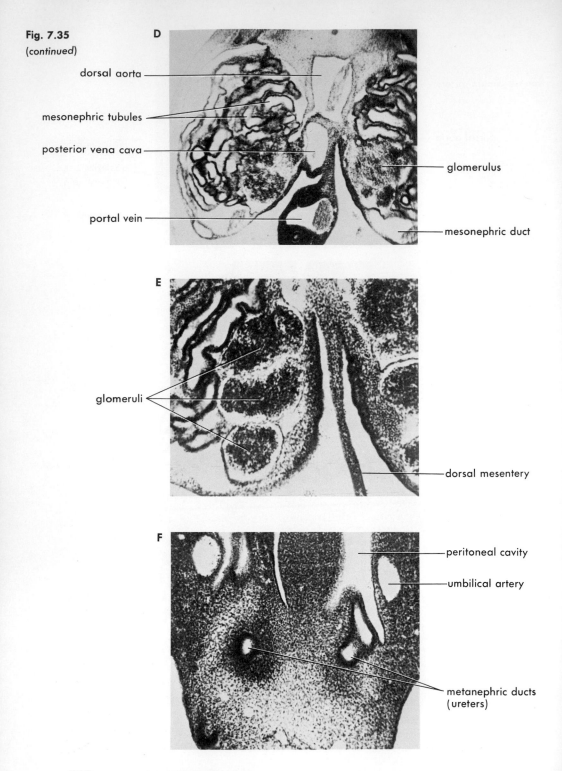

Fig. 7.35
(continued)

D

dorsal aorta

mesonephric tubules

posterior vena cava

glomerulus

portal vein

mesonephric duct

E

glomeruli

dorsal mesentery

F

peritoneal cavity

umbilical artery

metanephric ducts
(ureters)

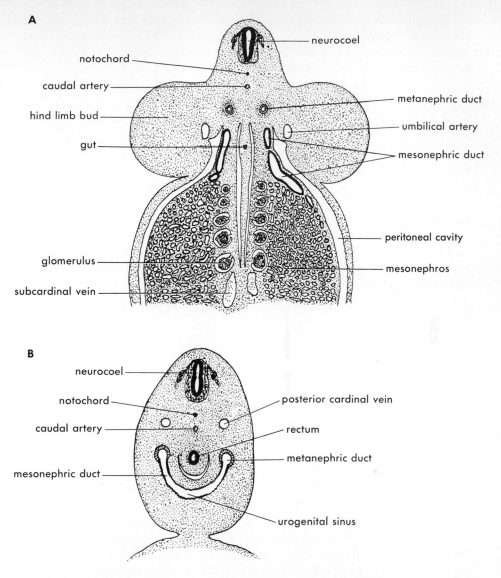

Fig. 7.36   Diagrams of transverse sections showing development of kidney and urogenital ducts in 10-mm. pig embryo. (From R. Rugh, *Laboratory Manual of Vertebrate Embryology,* 5th ed., Burgess, Minneapolis, 1961.)

siderably more numerous than the somites. Each tubule enmeshes with a knot of blood capillaries (a *glomerulus*) from which it drains nitrogenous wastes into a mesonephric duct and thence into the cloaca. Just before entering the cloaca, the mesonephric duct gives off an anterodorsally directed diverticulum that terminates in a congested mass of nephrotome mesoderm. The diverticulum forms the duct of the *metanephric* kidney, while the mesodermal mass develops into its tubules. The beginning of the metanephric diverticulum is sometimes apparent as early as the 5-mm. stage. The metanephric duct bulges considerably at its distal end to become the renal *pelvis*. Its tubular portion becomes the long, slender *ureter*.

▪ Later Embryo

Since most of the major organs are present at the 10-mm. stage, later stages show only their growth and differentiation. By the 18-mm. stage the body has a much straighter form than at the 10-mm. stage, although it is still markedly curved (Figs. 7.37–7.39). The head is larger in relation to the other body parts, the facial structures are defined, and the sense organs are prominent. The visceral grooves have disappeared. The limbs are also much larger than before, with indications of feet, whereas the umbilical cord is reduced in size. The genital tubercle has become a phallus. At the 35-mm. stage the body is still straighter, and its proportions approach those of the newborn. The neck is evident, the snout is enlarging, and the umbilical cord and tail continue to shrink.

Derivatives of the ectoderm

NERVOUS SYSTEM.   As the development of the mammalian nervous system, particularly the *cerebellum,* continues after birth, dissection of the late fetus is most helpful. However, serial sections of the 18- or 25-mm. embryo illustrate well some of the developmental changes.

The nervous system correlates and integrates the functioning of all other systems. Its unique cells appear first (at about 14 days) as neural ectoderm, which forms neuroblasts that metamorphose into *proneurons* and finally into permanent neurons. These cells develop throughout the body continuously from the neurula stage until 2 or 3 weeks after birth. They are specialized to *receive* electrochemical changes or impulses in their numerous short, thin *dendrites* and to *transmit* these changes through the cell body and along single fibers (*axons*) of various lengths to all parts of the body. Frequently the neurons are in chains, so that an impulse is carried from the terminal process of one axon to the receiving dendrites of the next neuron. As impulses always move in the same direction in a neuron, there are tracts for conveying impulses outward, inward, and in between (efferent, afferent, and association neurons).

Gross dissection shows that a nerve is a bundle of axons, sheaths, and connective tissue, the central bodies and nuclei of which are in ganglia, spinal cord, or brain (Fig. 7.40). The spinal cord, the center of automation, short-circuits many impulses to relieve the brain of disturbing interruptions and thus produces *reflexes,* with stimuli along nerve pathways known as *reflex arcs.* Paths within the cord and brain that conduct impulses to remote organs are

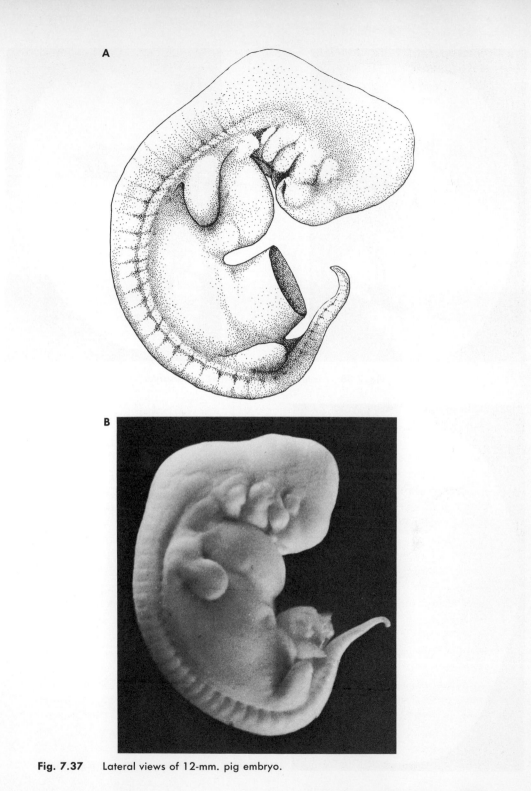

Fig. 7.37 Lateral views of 12-mm. pig embryo.

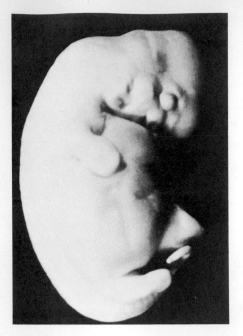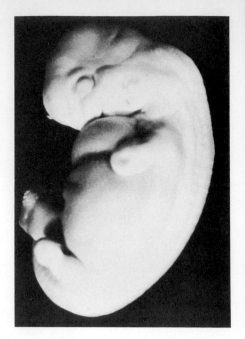

Fig. 7.38   Lateral views of 15-mm. pig embryo.

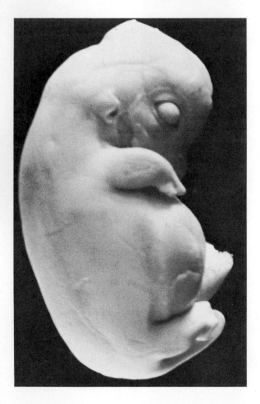

Fig. 7.39   Lateral view of 20-mm. pig embryo.

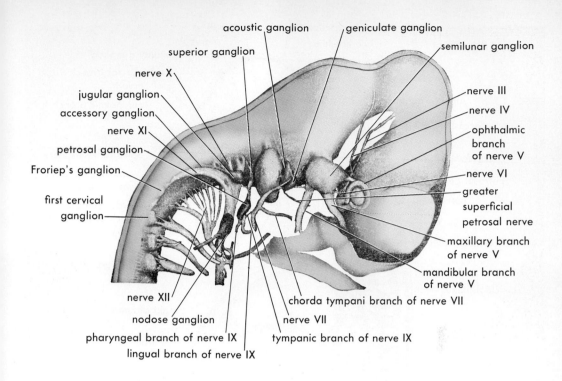

acoustic ganglion

geniculate ganglion

superior ganglion

semilunar ganglion

nerve X

jugular ganglion

nerve III

accessory ganglion

nerve IV

nerve XI

ophthalmic
branch
of nerve V

petrosal ganglion

Froriep's ganglion

nerve VI

first cervical
ganglion

greater
superficial
petrosal nerve

maxillary branch
of nerve V

mandibular branch
of nerve V

nerve XII

chorda tympani branch of nerve VII

nodose ganglion

nerve VII

pharyngeal branch of nerve IX

tympanic branch of nerve IX

lingual branch of nerve IX

Fig. 7.40   Lateral view of brain and cranial nerves in 12-mm. pig embryo. (From B. M. Patten, *Embryology of the Pig*, 3rd ed., McGraw-Hill, New York, 1948. Adapted from Lewis.)

known as white matter because of the fatty myelin sheath covering the axons. The major portion of the white matter conveys motor impulses from the brain to the periphery via the spinal nerves; however, the axons of the mid-dorsal white matter are largely sensory in function. More centrally situated is the gray matter, composed of association neurons and cell bodies of motor neurons, which extend into the spinal nerves. The major sense organs are in the circuit as, primarily, receptors initiating impulses that bring about reflex action or deliberate (conscious) action.

Telencephalon.   The neural growth of the telencephalon occurs primarily in its lateral walls, which expand to such an extent that they overlie both the diencephalon and the mesencephalon and become convoluted (Fig. 7.41A). The ventral portion contains the *olfactory tract* and *bulb* and the related *ol-factory lobe.* The bulbous dorsal portions are the cerebral hemispheres, where consciousness and voluntary and inhibitory controls are localized. The cerebral hemispheres of mammals have numerous *gyri* (folds) and *sulci* (grooves), which are associated with the various centers of conscious action.

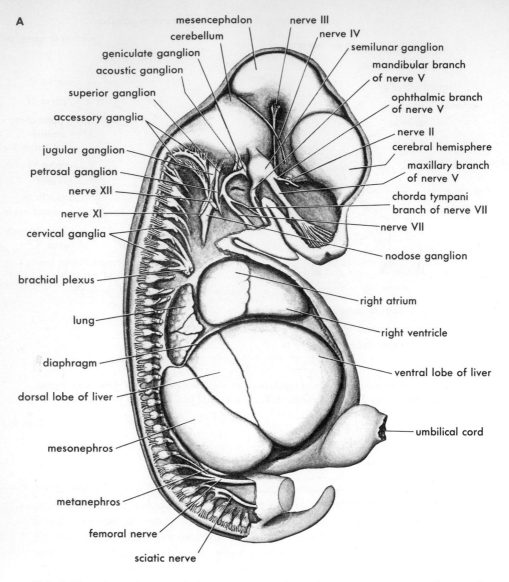

A

mesencephalon
cerebellum
geniculate ganglion
acoustic ganglion
superior ganglion
accessory ganglia
jugular ganglion
petrosal ganglion
nerve XII
nerve XI
cervical ganglia
brachial plexus
lung
diaphragm
dorsal lobe of liver
mesonephros
metanephros
femoral nerve
sciatic nerve

nerve III
nerve IV
semilunar ganglion
mandibular branch
of nerve V
ophthalmic branch
of nerve V
nerve II
cerebral hemisphere
maxillary branch
of nerve V
chorda tympani
branch of nerve VII
nerve VII
nodose ganglion
right atrium
right ventricle
ventral lobe of liver
umbilical cord

Fig. 7.41   Sagittal sections of 18-mm. pig embryo. (From L. B. Arey, *Developmental Anatomy*, 6th ed., Saunders, Philadelphia, 1954.)

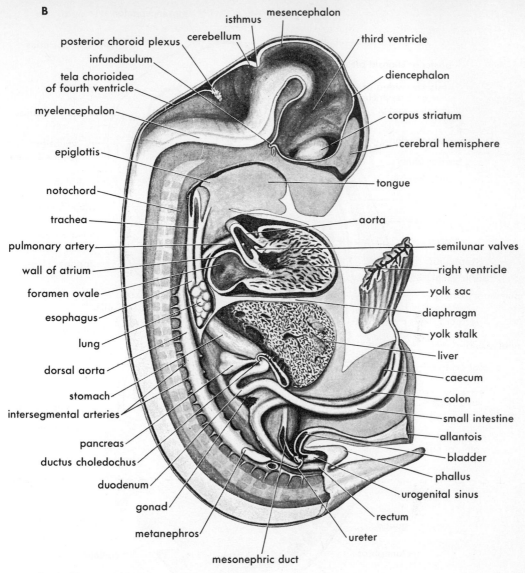

B

posterior choroid plexus
isthmus
cerebellum
mesencephalon
infundibulum
tela chorioidea
of fourth ventricle
myelencephalon
epiglottis
notochord
trachea
pulmonary artery
wall of atrium
foramen ovale
esophagus
lung
dorsal aorta
stomach
intersegmental arteries
pancreas
ductus choledochus
duodenum
gonad
metanephros
mesonephric duct

third ventricle
diencephalon
corpus striatum
cerebral hemisphere
tongue
aorta
semilunar valves
right ventricle
yolk sac
diaphragm
yolk stalk
liver
caecum
colon
small intestine
allantois
bladder
phallus
urogenital sinus
rectum
ureter

Fig. 7.41 (*continued*)

The paired lateral ventricles within the cerebral hemispheres gradually constrict as their walls thicken. They remain as the first and second ventricles, each connected by a *foramen of Monro* with a median telencephalic lumen and thence with the diocoel, or *third ventricle* (Figs. 7.41B, 7.42, 7.43). The third ventricle joins the *fourth ventricle* located in the metencephalon and myelencephalon. A cerebrospinal fluid, derived from the vascular *anterior choroid plexus* appearing in the roof of the third ventricle at the 24-mm. stage and the posterior choroid plexus arising earlier in the roof of the fourth

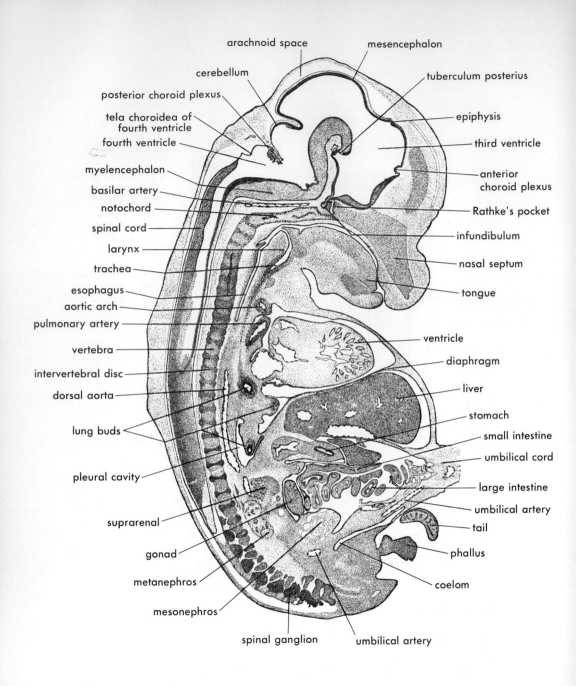

Fig. 7.42   Sagittal section of 24-mm. pig embryo. (From B. M. Patten, *Embryology of the Pig,* 3rd ed., McGraw-Hill, New York, 1948. Adapted from Minot.)

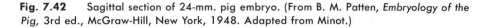

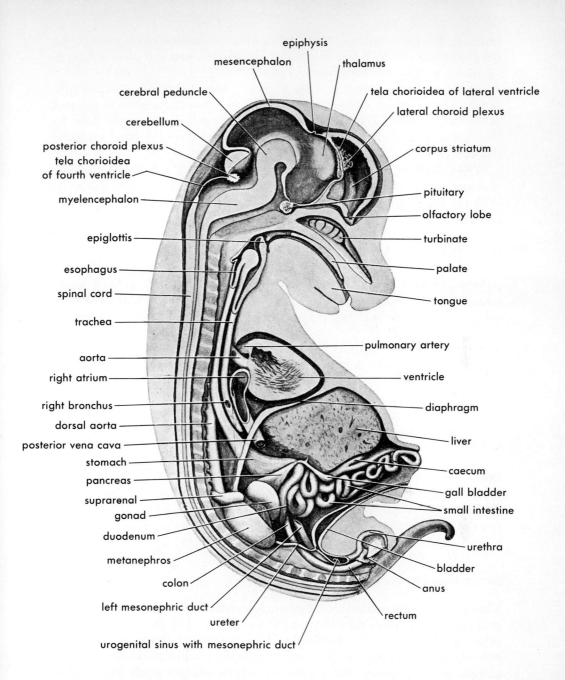

epiphysis

mesencephalon

thalamus

cerebral peduncle

tela chorioidea of lateral ventricle

lateral choroid plexus

cerebellum

posterior choroid plexus
tela chorioidea
of fourth ventricle

corpus striatum

myelencephalon

pituitary

olfactory lobe

epiglottis

turbinate

esophagus

palate

spinal cord

tongue

trachea

pulmonary artery

aorta

ventricle

right atrium

right bronchus

diaphragm

dorsal aorta

posterior vena cava

liver

stomach

caecum

pancreas

gall bladder

suprarenal

small intestine

gonad

duodenum

urethra

metanephros

bladder

colon

anus

left mesonephric duct

rectum

ureter

urogenital sinus with mesonephric duct

Fig. 7.43 Sagittal section of 35-mm. pig embryo. (From L. B. Arey, *Developmental Anatomy*, 6th ed., Saunders, Philadelphia, 1954.)

Later Embryo **369**

ventricle, fills the ventricles. The anterior choroid plexus spreads through the third ventricle and both foramina of Monro into the first and second (lateral) ventricles, to form the *lateral choroid plexi*.

Diencephalon. Posterior to the anterior choroid plexus is the *epiphysis*, or pineal body, which exists as a single median dorsal evagination in the roof of the diencephalon. The infundibulum is a single evagination in the floor. By the 35-mm. stage it merges with Rathke's pocket to form the *pituitary gland* (*hypophysis*) (Fig. 7.43).

The dorsolateral walls of the diencephalon thicken to become the *thalami*, passages of nerve fibers between the posterior and anterior parts of the brain. With this thickening the central canal shrinks, and at one spot the sides touch and fuse to form the *intermediate mass*.

Mesencephalon. The *colliculi* (*corpora quadrigemina*) arise as moderate thickenings in the dorsolateral walls of the mesencephalon. The two anterior bodies (*superior colliculi*) are visual centers, whereas the two posterior bodies (*inferior colliculi*) are auditory reflex centers. Nerve tracts running longitudinally in the ventrolateral walls are the *cerebral peduncles*, and the remnant of the central canal (compressed by lateral wall growth) is the *aqueduct of Sylvius* (Fig. 7.43).

Metencephalon. Through extensive expansion the dorsolateral walls of the metencephalon develop into the cerebellum (Figs. 7.41–7.43). This organ differentiates slowly but eventually has two lateral lobes and one median lobe, all much convoluted. Its floor is the *pons*. Since all axons to the fore part of the brain pass through the metencephalon, the pons is a true "bundle of nerves." The lumen, which is not so compressed as in the brain areas farther forward, is the anterior portion of the fourth ventricle.

Myelencephalon. The myelencephalon, the most posterior portion of the brain, gives rise to the *medulla oblongata*, which contains the enlarged posterior part of the fourth ventricle, partially occluded dorsally by the posterior choroid plexus. The roof and floor are thin as in the adjacent spinal cord, but the lateral walls are very thick and separated into a dorsal (*alar*) plate and a ventral (*basal*) plate by a longitudinal *sulcus limitans*.

Derivatives of the endoderm

The oral cavity enlarges so that the junction of stomodeal ectoderm and pharyngeal endoderm moves posteriorly to about the level of the second visceral pouches. Meanwhile, the pharynx becomes dorsoventrally compressed. Just behind the visceral pouches the opening into the trachea marks the posterior margin of the pharynx. The esophagus, which remains small and tubular, extends from this point to the point of stomach enlargement. The small intestine is maximally coiled at the 35-mm. stage and separated from the large intestine by the *ileocaecal valve*. The pancreas and gall bladder are also well developed (Fig. 7.44).

In transverse sections the thickness of its wall easily distinguishes the

stomach from the thinner-walled esophagus and intestines. Through elongation and muscular expansion, the stomach rotates to the left side of the
embryo with its concave surface facing the upper right side. The dorsal
mesentery (*mesogastrium*) is carried to the left by this movement but is
retained. The pouch between the stomach, in its new position, and the dorsal
mesogastrium is the *omental bursa*. It connects with the embryonic coelom
(now the peritoneal cavity) through the *epiploic foramen*, or *foramen of
Winslow*.

The part of the allantois nearest the embryo dilates to become the urinary
bladder. The mesonephric ducts maintain their connection with the urogenital sinus and remain as the *urethra;* the metanephric ducts, which have
independent connections with the urogenital sinus and thence with the
bladder, become the *ureters*. All these changes occur by the 35-mm. stage,
when the cloacal membrane ruptures, opening the urogenital sinus and the
rectum to the outside. The rectal opening is the *anus*. By the 85-mm. stage
the final relations of the excretory organs to the genital organs and tracts are
established.

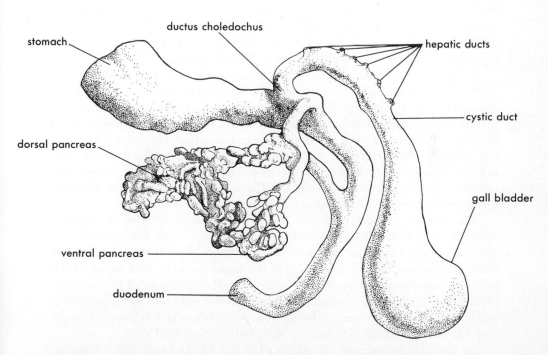

Fig. 7.44   Pancreas and hepatic duct system in 20-mm. pig embryo. (From B. M. Patten,
Embryology of the Pig, 3rd ed., McGraw-Hill, New York, 1948. Adapted from Thyng.)

The embryonic coelom extends from beneath the pharynx almost to the limits of the hindgut. As the septum transversum and the pleuroperitoneal folds join to form the *diaphragm* separating the thoracic and abdominal organs, paired *pleuropericardial folds,* continuous with the paired pleuroperitoneal folds, arise from the dorsal wall of the pleural cavity behind the heart (near the common cardinal veins). The pleuropericardial folds fuse to separate the heart, in the pericardial cavity, from the lungs, in the pleural cavity (Fig. 7.41). When the division of the embryonic coelom is complete, therefore, pleural, pericardial, and peritoneal cavities exist. The embryonic coelom, with a lining entirely of mesodermal origin, thus divides to enclose in three separate chambers the major derivatives of the endoderm, which have endodermal linings only and which would be functionless without their mesodermally derived blood vessels and muscles.

The embryonic circulation changes with each stage of development, as various organ centers differentiate, making certain structural and functional adjustments so that at birth the fetus may relinquish its parasitic dependence on its mother and become functionally independent. A review of the developmental changes through which the circulatory system of the embryo must go includes: tubular to multichambered heart; metameric and paired aortic arches to three major remnants; paired dorsal aortae to a single large systemic arch and dorsal aorta; bilaterally symmetrical venous system to a single portal vein; and very complicated modifications in the venous circulation to the liver resulting in its becoming the largest vascular reservoir of the body. In addition, separation of the arterial and the venous blood occurs at birth.

Following the 10-mm. stage, development proceeds as follows (Figs. 7.45, 7.46). The *posterior (inferior) mesenteric artery* arises posteriorly to the anterior mesenteric artery and supplies the large intestine. As the mesonephric and metanephric kidneys develop and function, they acquire renal arteries, which branch metamerically from the dorsal aorta. These branches later fuse, forming a large renal artery for each metanephric kidney. The *external iliac arteries* develop as branches of the umbilical arteries. The *internal iliac arteries* are remnants of the umbilicals. The aortic origin of the umbilicals remains as the *common iliac artery.*

The anterior cardinal veins give rise to the precaval (*anterior,* or superior, *vena cava*) system. The *subclavian veins,* together with the external and internal jugular veins and the cardinals, transport blood from anterior body parts. Because of the posterior shift of the heart with the elongation of the body, the subclavians drain into the anterior cardinals instead of the posterior cardinals as earlier. The *innominate vein* joins the right and left subclavians, and between it and the heart is the anterior vena cava, which is also continuous with the common cardinals and the right anterior cardinal vein.

As the early pulmonary circulation does not fill the heart, the left atrium might collapse or fail to develop properly if an opening from the right atrium

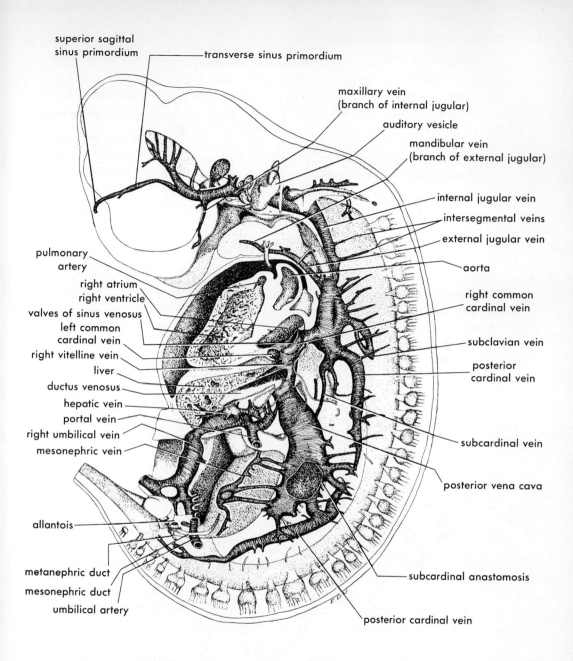

Fig. 7.45 Sagittal section of 12-mm. pig embryo showing venous system. (From O. E. Nelsen, *Comparative Embryology of the Vertebrates*, McGraw-Hill, New York, 1953. Adapted from Minot.)

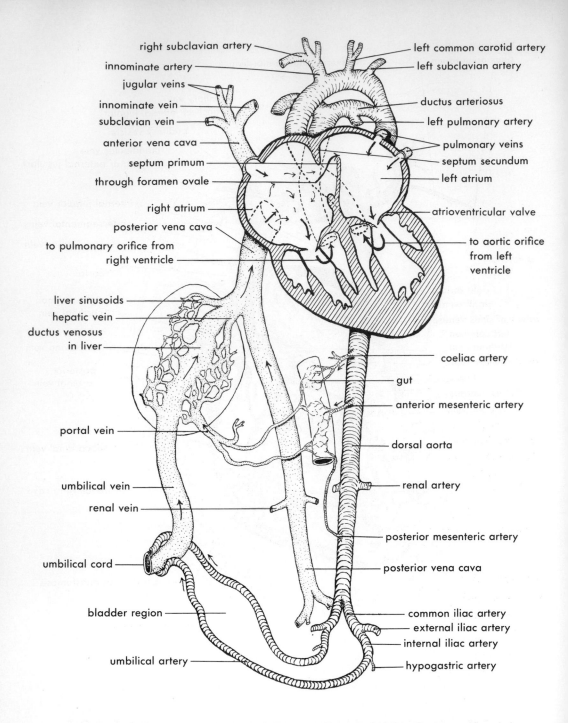

Fig. 7.46 Vascular system of pig embryo just before birth. (From B. M. Patten, *Embryology of the Pig*, 3rd ed., McGraw-Hill, New York, 1948.)

did not exist to permit a continuous flow of blood between the chambers. The foramen primum closes, but it is replaced by the *foramen secundum*, a rupture in the septum secundum that becomes known as the *foramen ovale*.

Portions of the interatrial septa form a valve controlling the flow of blood forward between the atria and preventing the flow of blood backward. Blood from the vena cava passes into the right atrium, through the foramen ovale, and into the left atrium. As it fills the left atrium, it closes the flap of the septum primum over the foramen ovale and is forced into the left ventricle. The ductus arteriosus, between the pulmonary artery and the dorsal aorta, allows the right ventricle to function to some degree.

In the late fetal heart blood from the posterior vena cava mixes with that from the anterior vena cava in the right atrium. The pulmonary vein carries blood to the left atrium, where it mixes with blood that passes through the foramen ovale from the right atrium. Thus the two atria are under approximately equal distention. Most of the blood from the right ventricle goes directly to the lungs, but some passes by way of the ductus arteriosus to the dorsal aorta. Thus venous and arterial blood mingle in the ductus arteriosus, as well as in the liver, where blood from the umbilical vein and blood from the portal vein mix. As long as the organism is dependent upon maternal sources for nutrition, oxygen, and excretion, even mixed blood is highly beneficial to its growing tissues. However, the moment it dissociates itself from its mother, a separation of the "pure" and "impure" blood is essential. At birth a gradual increase in the carbon dioxide level in the blood stimulates the respiratory center of the brain to bring about the first inspiration of air, and the circulatory system assumes the respiratory and, to some extent, the nutritive and excretory functions of the placenta, which is cut off. The foramen ovale then closes, so that the heart has four distinct chambers, and at about 4 weeks after birth the ductus arteriosus closes.

The newborn mammal carries numerous vestiges of its ancestors but also may retain evidence of its embryonic development. These anomalies may be relatively harmless and often go undiscovered; examples are the round ligament of the liver, a fibrous cord where the umbilical vein once functioned; the ligamentum arteriosus, a cordlike remnant of the ductus arteriosus; and the persistent foramen ovale.

Although the mesonephros is the permanent functional kidney in the amphibia, it functions only during the embryonic stages in mammals. Its size is relatively tremendous in the 60-mm. pig embryo. As the diverticulum from each of the mesonephric ducts becomes a metanephric duct, and the mass of mesoderm in which it terminates gives rise to tubules that constitute the metanephros, or functional kidney, the mesonephric structures, except for the two major ducts and a few tubules, begin to degenerate. The portions of the mesonephros that remain assume reproductive functions in the male.

The collecting tubules that empty into the pelvis of the metanephros arise as fingerlike projections from the dilated end of the metanephric duct. Several uriniferous tubules develop near the end of each collecting tubule, and each

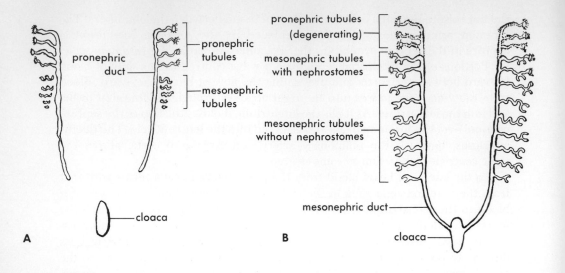

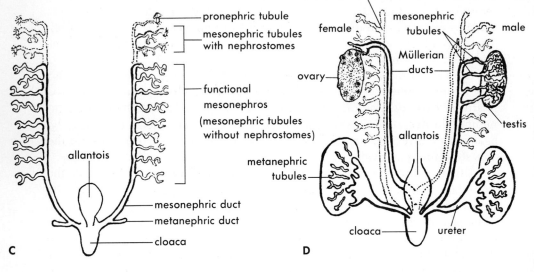

Fig. 7.47 Diagrams showing relations of pronephros, mesonephros, and metanephros in pig embryo. (From B. M. Patten, *Embryology of the Pig,* 3rd ed., McGraw-Hill, New York, 1948.)

of these is associated with a glomerulus. Blood from renal arteries direct from the dorsal aorta enters the glomeruli and discharges excretory wastes from the embryonic body into the uriniferous tubules and thence the collecting tubules. It returns through subcardinal veins to the heart. The metanephros begins operating at the 35-mm. stage (Fig. 7.47).

Chromaffin cells originating in the neural crests leave their positions close to the sympathetic ganglia and aggregate near the anterior limit of the metanephros to become the medulla of the *suprarenal gland*. The cortex of the suprarenal (its outer cortical layer) develops from splanchnic mesoderm.

THE HUMAN:

A Discoid Placentate

8

■ Introduction

The established essentials in human embryonic development differ little from those in the development of other mammalian embryos. There is some deviation in the late stages, but throughout the value of comparative studies is apparent.

■ Reproductive Systems

Male

SPERMATOGENESIS.   Seven weeks after fertilization of the *ovum*, the *testes* begin to form. At 14 weeks a few scattered *spermatogonia* appear within the testis cords. By the time of birth the testes are well formed, but their development is retarded by the maternal hormones to which they have been subject. They therefore differentiate slowly, and not until almost puberty do their germinal epithelial strands become hollow tubules. Two major types of cells are present in the *seminiferous tubules:* the supporting and nursing *Sertoli cells* and the *germ* (sex) *cells* in various stages of maturation from spermatogonia to mature *spermatozoa.*

Spermatogenesis begins at puberty and persists continuously to old age, sometimes until the end of a long life. The maturation process, from spermatogonium to spermatozoa, presumably takes about 16 days. The spermatogonium grows into a *primary spermatocyte,* a relatively large cell with abundant *mitochondria* and a *Golgi apparatus* that aids in the formation of the *acrosome.* Two divisions occur, one giving rise to two *secondary spermatocytes* and the next to four *spermatids.* The spermatids then go through a metamorphosis or transformation (*spermiogenesis*) into as many mature and functional spermatozoa, without divisions. The reductional division (*meiosis*) that provides chromosomal *haploid* cells is believed to occur when the primary spermatocytes divide into secondary spermatocytes. The next division

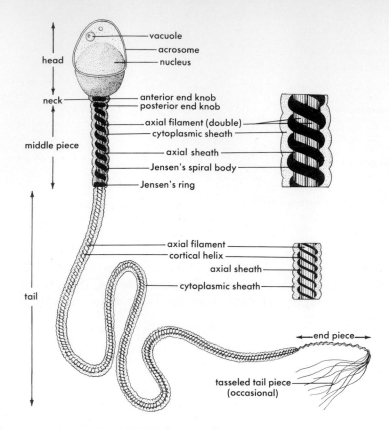

Fig. 8.1   Human spermatozoon. (From J. T. Velardo, ed., *Endocrinology of Reproduction*, Oxford Univ. Press, New York, 1958. Adapted from Wabnitz.)

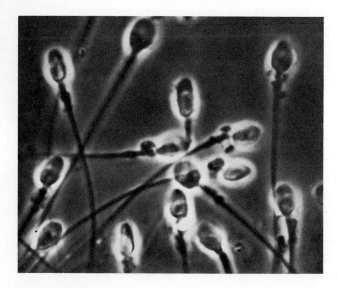

Fig. 8.2   Human spermatozoa under dark-field illumination. (From L. B. Shettles.)

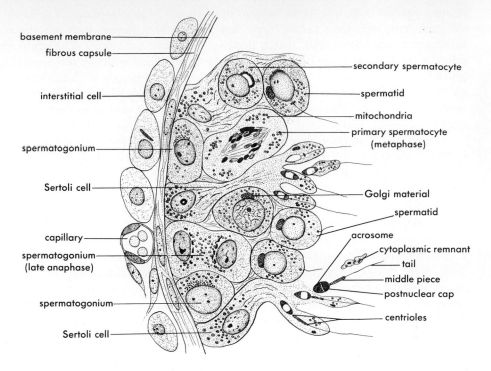

Fig. 8.3 Section of portion of human seminiferous tubule, showing spermatozoa in all stages of maturation. (Adapted from W. J. Hamilton, J. D. Boyd, and H. W. Mossman, *Human Embryology*, 2nd ed., Williams & Wilkins, Baltimore, 1952. After Stieve.)

would then be equational (*mitosis*), each spermatid receiving as many chromosomes as the parent secondary spermatocyte and thus being haploid.

The human spermatozoon (Figs. 8.1, 8.2) is so small that enough to generate the next entire population of almost any continent could be placed upon the blunt end of a pin. Its head is oval or pear-shaped, depending upon the angle of view, and contains the homogeneous genetic contribution of the male to his progeny. An acrosomal cap covers the top of the head and may provide a perforating tip. The middle piece or neck contains a granule (*centrosome*) that may aid in providing the mitotic mechanism for the first cleavages. The tail has an elaborate connecting piece that contains mitochondria and an axial filament that extends its length. At the tip end of the tail the naked axial filament protrudes as an end piece.

Each testis is made up of hundreds of coiled seminiferous tubules, all enclosed in a connective tissue *tunica albuginea*. Each tubule has an outer fibrous coating, the *basement membrane*, against which lie the Sertoli cells and the undifferentiated spermatogonia. As maturation of a particular spermatogonium proceeds, its division products move toward the central lumen of the tubule (Fig. 8.3). The most mature spermatozoa lie with their heads pointed peripherally, usually embedded in or close to the cytoplasm of a Sertoli cell, and with their tails loosely dispersed in the lumen. Between the tubules are *interstitial cells,* which produce male sex hormones. The seminiferous tubules are looped but have straight connections with the *rete testis,* a network of cords at the hilus of the testis that is continuous with the *vasa efferentia* of the *epididymis* and thence with the thick-walled *vas (ductus) deferens* (Fig. 8.4). The vas deferens joins the *seminal vesicle* to form the ejaculatory duct, which opens into the prostatic part of the *urethra.*

EMBRYOLOGICAL ORIGIN OF THE TESTIS. The reproductive and excretory (urinary) systems have closely related origins. The *pronephros* is functionless in the human and degenerates at 4 weeks, leaving only its duct (Fig. 8.5A,B). The *mesonephros* is fully developed by 7 weeks, when the related gonad differentiation begins (Figs. 8.5B, 8.6A,B,C,D). The anterior mesonephric tubules degenerate while others form posteriorly to enlarge greatly the mesonephros, which bulges into the body cavity, giving rise to the *urogenital ridge.* The *metanephros* develops meanwhile and begins to assume all excretory functions (Figs. 8.5B,C, 8.6B,C,D,E). The *genital ridge* is a thickening on the median aspect of the urogenital ridge, and its superficial cells are the *germinal epithelium.* These proliferate inward to form an inner epithelial mass (Fig. 8.7) that becomes the undifferentiated gonad. Primordial germ cells are apparent as early as 7 weeks.

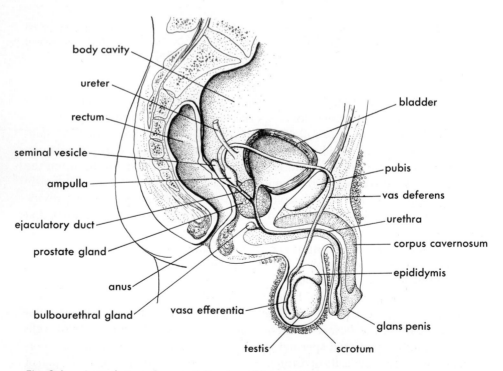

Fig. 8.4 Lateral view of urogenital system of human male.

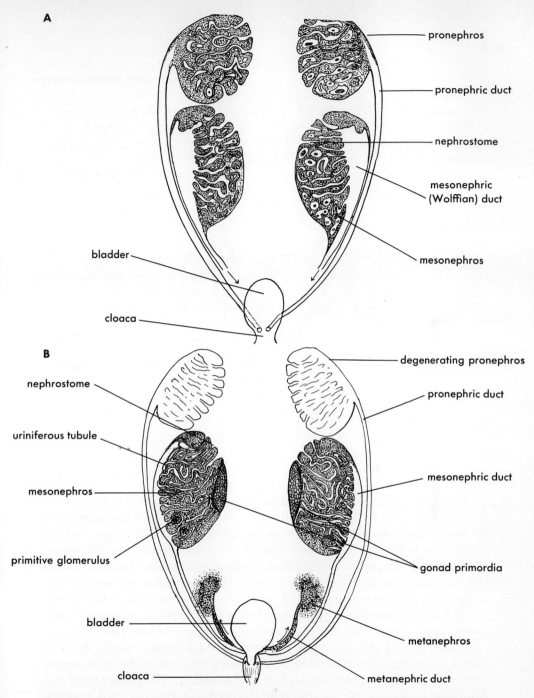

A

pronephros

pronephric duct

nephrostome

mesonephric (Wolffian) duct

mesonephros

bladder

cloaca

B

degenerating pronephros

pronephric duct

nephrostome

uriniferous tubule

mesonephric duct

mesonephros

primitive glomerulus

gonad primordia

bladder

metanephros

cloaca

metanephric duct

Fig. 8.5 Frontal views showing kidney development in human embryo: A, primitive kidneys; B, temporary embryonic kidneys; C, final excretory system, with that of female on left and that of male on right.

C

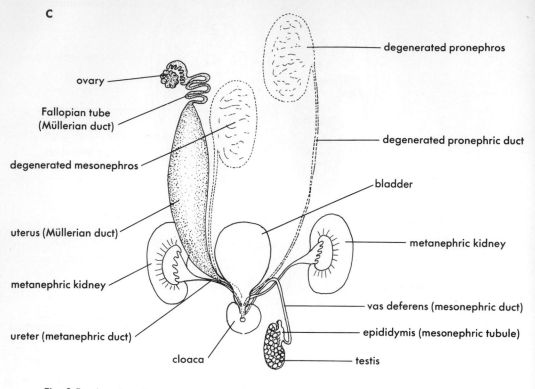

ovary

Fallopian tube
(Müllerian duct)

degenerated mesonephros

uterus (Müllerian duct)

metanephric kidney

ureter (metanephric duct)

cloaca

degenerated pronephros

degenerated pronephric duct

bladder

metanephric kidney

vas deferens (mesonephric duct)

epididymis (mesonephric tubule)

testis

Fig. 8.5   (*continued*)

The testes differentiate earlier than the *ovaries,* with the development of cords of germ cells in the inner epithelial mass at 8 weeks and the appearance of the fibrous tunica albuginea between the germinal epithelium and the cords. The testis cords converge toward the *mesorchium,* the mesenteric attachment of the gonad. At 9 weeks interstitial cells appear, and at 5 months they are more abundant than the germ cells. However, many of them atrophy, so that only clusters remain at birth, and they do not multiply until puberty.

The mesonephric duct and some of its related tubules become the male genital tract (Figs. 8.5C, 8.8). Anterior mesonephric tubules form the *vasa efferentia,* joining the rete testis to the *ductus epididymis,* which develops from the anterior part of the mesonephric duct. The rest of the mesonephric duct becomes the vas deferens leading to the urethra. The *prostate* and *bulbourethral (Cowper's) glands* arise from the urethra during the third month to provide seminal fluid for the spermatozoa. Seminal vesicles develop during the fourth month, from the vas deferens.

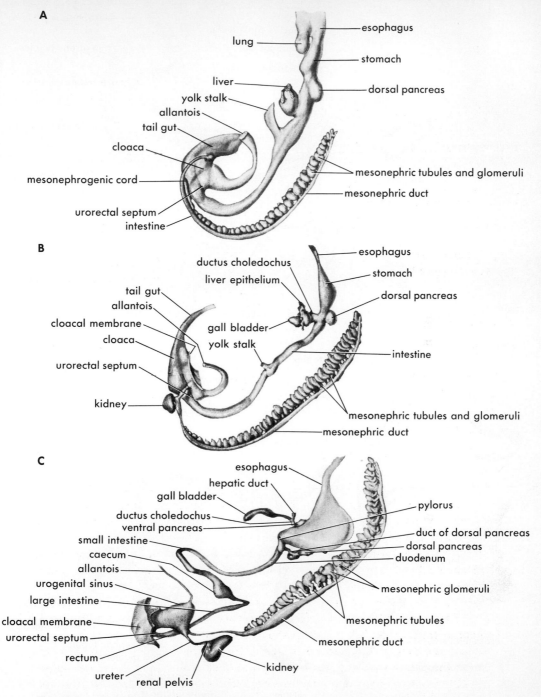

Fig. 8.6 Kidney development in human embryo: A, at 4 mm.; B, at 5.5 mm.; C, at 8 mm.; D, at 14.6 mm.; E, at 23 mm. (From J. Shikinami, *Carnegie Inst. Wash. Publ.* No. 363, *Contribs. Embryology* No. 93 (1926).)

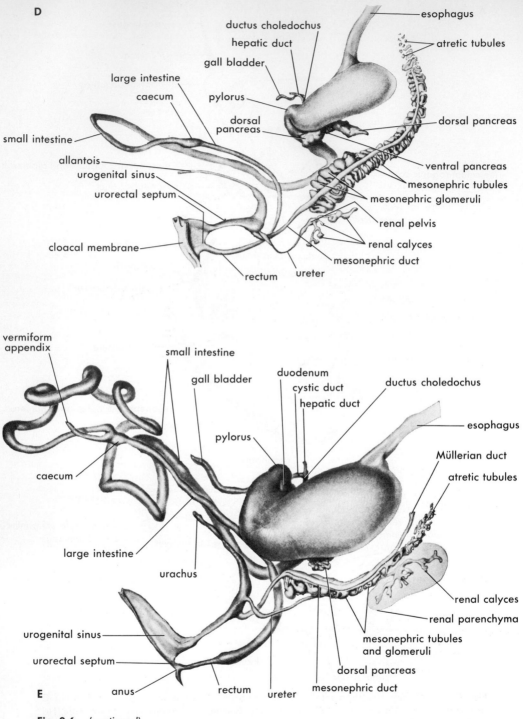

D

esophagus

ductus choledochus

hepatic duct

atretic tubules

gall bladder

large intestine

caecum

pylorus

dorsal pancreas

small intestine

dorsal pancreas

allantois

ventral pancreas

urogenital sinus

mesonephric tubules

urorectal septum

mesonephric glomeruli

renal pelvis

renal calyces

cloacal membrane

mesonephric duct

rectum

ureter

vermiform appendix

small intestine

gall bladder

duodenum

cystic duct

ductus choledochus

hepatic duct

esophagus

pylorus

Müllerian duct

atretic tubules

caecum

large intestine

renal calyces

urachus

renal parenchyma

urogenital sinus

mesonephric tubules and glomeruli

urorectal septum

dorsal pancreas

E

anus

rectum

ureter

mesonephric duct

Fig. 8.6 (*continued*)

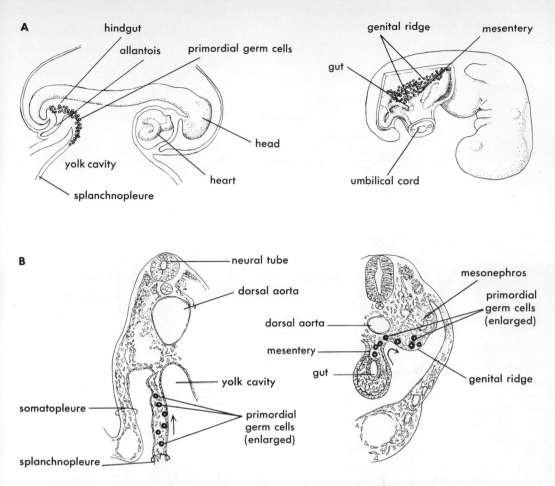

Fig. 8.7 Migration of primordial germ cells in human embryo: A, lateral view and transverse section at 3 mm.; B, lateral view and transverse section at 4.2 mm. (Adapted from J. T. Velardo, ed., *Endocrinology of Reproduction*, Oxford Univ. Press, New York, 1958.)

Müllerian ducts are present in both male and female embryos, but they degenerate in the male at 3 months, leaving only the *testis appendix* anteriorly and the *prostatic utricle* near the *urogenital sinus*.

Adjacent to the *proctodeum* an ectodermal depression forms the *genital tubercle* at about 6 weeks. In the seventh week this develops into the *phallus*, which becomes the *penis* of the male (the *clitoris* of the female) (Fig. 8.8). Paired *genital folds* close over to form the penile urethra of the male (*labia minora* of the female), and lateral *genital swellings* become the *scrotum* of the male (*labia majora* of the female). The external genitalia are considered unreliable in determining sex until the embryo reaches a crown-rump length of 50 mm. (about 2½ months), and those of the male seem the more retarded in development.

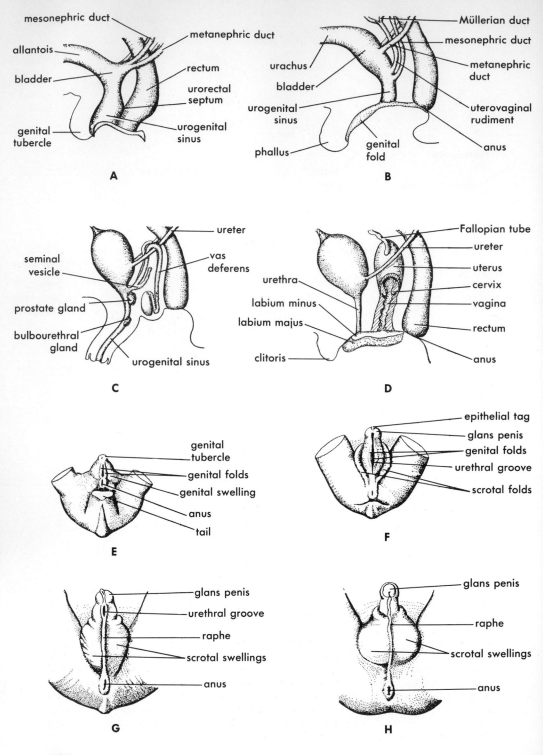

A

mesonephric duct
metanephric duct
allantois
rectum
bladder
urorectal septum
urogenital sinus
genital tubercle
urogenital sinus

B

Müllerian duct
mesonephric duct
metanephric duct
urachus
bladder
urogenital sinus
uterovaginal rudiment
phallus
genital fold
anus

C

ureter
seminal vesicle
vas deferens
prostate gland
bulbourethral gland
urogenital sinus

D

Fallopian tube
ureter
uterus
urethra
cervix
labium minus
vagina
labium majus
rectum
clitoris
anus

E

genital tubercle
genital folds
genital swelling
anus
tail

F

epithelial tag
glans penis
genital folds
urethral groove
scrotal folds

G

glans penis
urethral groove
raphe
scrotal swellings
anus

H

glans penis
raphe
scrotal swellings
anus

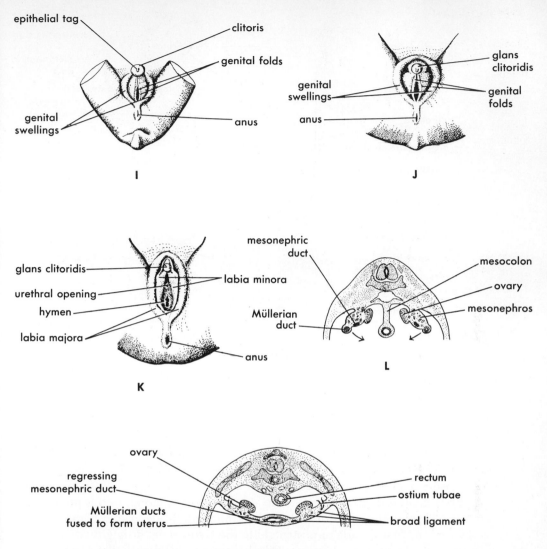

Fig. 8.8 Differentiation of caudal urogenital structures in human embryo: A, at 6 weeks, with rectal area being separated from urogenital sinus by urorectal septum; B, at 8 weeks, with rectal and urogenital areas completely separated, mesonephric ducts present, meta-nephric ducts moved forward into area of developing bladder, and Müllerian ducts fused at caudal ends to form uterovaginal rudiment; C, male at 5 months, with urogenital sinus completely enclosed within developing penis, where it forms part of urethra, and testis beginning to pass into developing scrotal sac; D, female at 5 months; E–K, development of external genitalia; E, indifferent condition at 7 weeks; F, male at 10 weeks; G, male at 3 months; H, male at end of fetal life; I, female at 10 weeks; J, female at 3 months; K, female at end of fetal life; L, M, development of broad ligament and separation of rectouterine pouch above from vesicouterine pouch below. (From O. E. Nelsen, *Comparative Embryology of the Vertebrates*, McGraw-Hill, New York, 1953.)

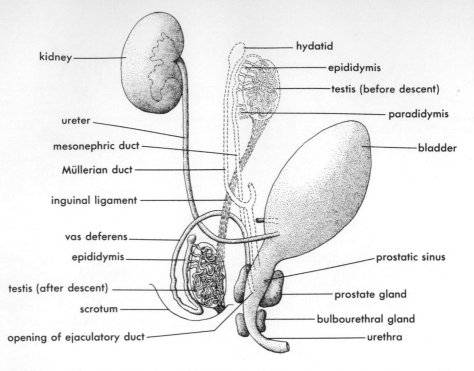

kidney

hydatid

epididymis

testis (before descent)

paradidymis

ureter

mesonephric duct

Müllerian duct

inguinal ligament

bladder

vas deferens

epididymis

prostatic sinus

testis (after descent)

prostate gland

scrotum

bulbourethral gland

opening of ejaculatory duct

urethra

Fig. 8.9　Lateral view showing position changes in fetal urogenital system of human male. (Adapted from Hertwig.)

As the mesonephros regresses, its *diaphragmatic ligament* becomes the *suspensory ligament* of the testis, and its *inguinal ligament* extends into the scrotal swelling. Between the seventh and ninth months the internal testis follows the associated pouchlike *processus vaginalis* through the *inguinal canal* into a pocket of the scrotum, aided and guided by the contraction of the *gubernaculum testis* (Fig. 8.9). The survival of the spermatozoa is probably more likely within the external scrotum than within the heated body.

During the first decade of postnatal life the testes show little growth, but during adolescence (11 to 15 years) they become ovoid, slightly flattened organs, each 4 to 5 cm. long, 2.5 to 3 cm. wide, and 10 to 45 grams in weight. The seminiferous tubules may measure up to 70 cm. in length, and their walls may produce at any one time some 300,000,000 mature sperm, only one of which usually functions in fertilization. The volume of sperm and seminal fluid together varies from 2 to 10 cc., but it is estimated that a concentration of 60,000,000 active sperm per cubic centimeter is required for successful fertilization of a single mature egg.

Secondary sex characters responding to hormones from the testes in the postnatal human male, and the age at which they usually appear, include these: long downy pubic hairs (10 to 11 years); coarse definitive pubic hairs and long down on the sides of the face (12 to 13 years); axillary hair and a lowering of the voice (14 to 15 years); pubic hairs extending to the umbilicus, adult genitalia with sperm present, acne (frequently) (15 to 16 years); adult-like facial hair resembling a down beard, adult scalp line (16 to 17 years); and the arrest of skeletal growth (21 years).

Female

OÖGENESIS. The time of origin of the ova is in dispute, but the most common theory is that they arise from the germinal epithelium of the ovary during fetal life and are all present at birth. At 8 weeks the germinal epithelium proliferates cells inward to form clusters, the *primary follicles*. In the center of each cluster is an *oögonium*, a cell destined to become an ovum, and surrounding it are nurse or *follicle cells*. The wall of the oögonium, encompassing its mitochondria, fat, and Golgi apparatus, is the *vitelline membrane*, so called because of the abundant *yolk* developing inside it, and between it and the follicle cells is another membrane, the *zona pellucida*, probably of follicular origin. The oögonium enlarges to become a *primary oöcyte*, its layer of follicle cells thickening simultaneously (Fig. 8.10).

Because of their proliferation and granular consistency, the follicle cells collectively are known as the *membrana (zona) granulosa*. As the oöcyte develops, minute spaces appear in the membrana granulosa and coalesce to form an *antrum*, filled with *liquor folliculi*. The oöcyte and its surrounding follicle cells are suspended within the antrum by a clump of granulosa cells, which, together with the cells around the oöcyte, constitute the *cumulus oöphorus (discus proligerus)* (Figs. 8.10–8.12). The large follicle resulting from these changes is the *Graafian follicle*. The *membrana propria* (basement membrane), the *theca interna* (compressed stromal cells), and a spongy, fibrous *theca externa* surround the membrana granulosa (Fig. 8.11). The theca interna liberates an estrogenic hormone into the follicular fluid.

The Graafian follicles develop throughout the ovary but eventually always project from the surface. At *ovulation* a follicle ruptures (Fig. 8.13), and the oöcyte and its follicle cells (now called the *corona radiata*) are expelled together. Prior to ovulation, however, the nucleus of the growing oöcyte undergoes its first maturation division. This division is probably reductional; that is, the chromosome pairs split so that each resultant nucleus receives but half the original chromosomal complex. The discarded nucleus is the *first polar body*. As the second maturation spindle forms, preparatory to elimination of the *second polar body*, ovulation generally occurs. Fertilization is then possible. Maturation is not complete until after fertilization.

Although primary follicles appear in the late fetal ovary, and each ovary of a newborn female may contain as many as 300,000 oögonia, shortly after birth the development of the oögonia ceases. Puberty (11+ years) reactivates the maturation process, and for the succeeding 35 years or so it continues. The degeneration of oögonia reduces the number in each ovary to about 15,000 at puberty, and on an average only 200 in each ovary ever ripen. The

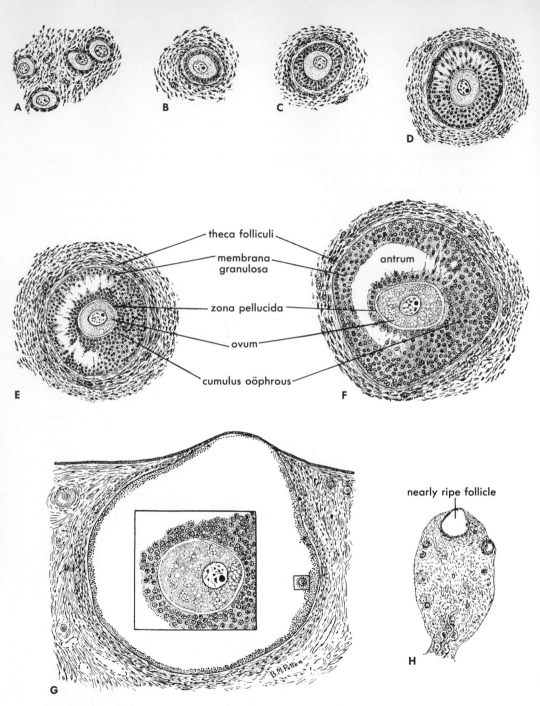

Fig. 8.10 Development of human ovum and ovarian follicle. In G follicle is × 15, and inset detail is × 150; in H ovary is natural size. (From B. M. Patten, *Human Embryology,* 2nd ed., McGraw-Hill, New York, 1953.)

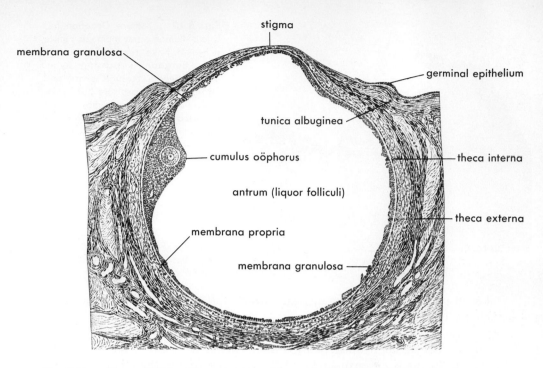

Fig. 8.11 Human follicle with ovum approaching maturity. (From L. B. Arey, *Developmental Anatomy,* 6th ed., Saunders, Philadelphia, 1954. Adapted from Bumm.)

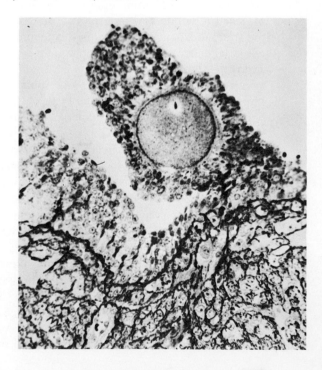

Fig. 8.12 Separation of cumulus oöphorus from human follicle at ovulation, with chromosomes of second maturation metaphase apparent as dark spot on ovum. (From L. B. Shettles, *Ovum Humanum,* Hafner, New York, 1960.)

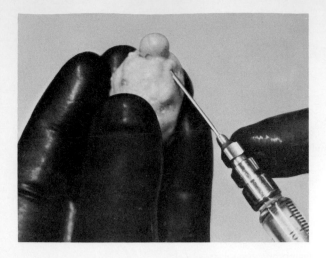

Fig. 8.13 Mature Graafian follicle of human a few moments before it would have ruptured at ovulation. Surgeon is passing hypodermic needle through ovary and into follicle to aspirate for ovum (after artificial fertilization under microscope, it will develop for several days). (From L. B. Shettles.)

loss of potential ova results in many *atretic follicles* in the ovary, and after menopause no follicles at all.

The oögonium measures approximately 0.02 mm. in diameter, and the primary oöcyte approximately 0.135 mm. The diameter of the oöcyte and the zona pellucida is approximately 0.176 mm., and that of the Graäfian follicle at the time of rupture approximately 10 mm. The maximum diameter of the oöcyte itself, 0.135 mm., compares with that in such other divergent mammals as the whale and mouse. The oöcyte is about 90,000 times the size of the spermatozoon. It represents the accumulated yolk and cytoplasm of four potential cells, as the original oögonium becomes one large and mature ovum and three discarded nuclei, the polar bodies.

EMBRYOLOGICAL ORIGIN OF THE OVARY. The ovary develops from the same germinal epithelium as the testis (Fig. 8.7), and which organ forms depends upon which of two types of spermatozoa fertilizes the egg. In combination with identical eggs, one type produces a male, and the other a female.

Cells arising from the genital ridges during the eighth week form the primary follicles of the developing ovary. Shortly an inner *medulla* and an outer primary *cortex*, just beneath the germinal epithelium, appear, to be followed by a superimposed secondary cortex. At 3 to 4 months connective tissue septa divide the cortical substance into small clusters containing the follicles, and at 6 months a loose tunica albuginea encloses the whole mass. The ovary remains in this state until puberty.

Also at 8 weeks the external genital tubercle becomes recognizable as the clitoris (Fig. 8.8), and the genital folds and swellings as the labial swellings. The primitive Müllerian ducts give rise to the *Fallopian tubes, uterus,* and portions of the *vagina* (Figs. 8.5C, 8.8, 8.14, 8.15). Anteriorly each duct forms the ciliated *ostium tubae* (or *infundibulum*) of the Fallopian tube, the ostium part developing in all likelihood from fused mesonephric tubules. Posteriorly

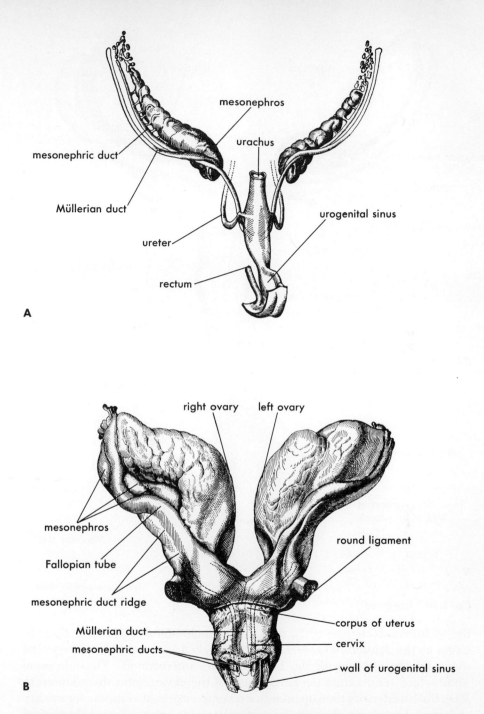

Fig. 8.14 Ventral views showing development of urogenital system of human female: A, at 23 mm.; B, at 36 mm.; C, D, at 48 mm.; E, at 139 mm.; F, at 227 mm. (From R. H. Hunter, *Carnegie Inst. Wash. Publ.* No. 414, *Contribs. Embryology* No. 129 (1930).)

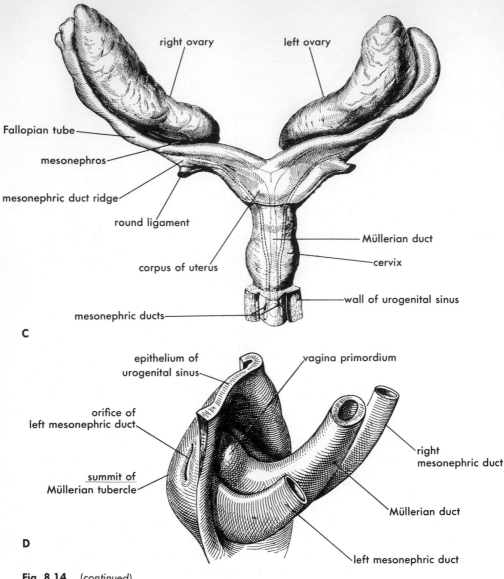

right ovary   left ovary

Fallopian tube

mesonephros

mesonephric duct ridge

round ligament

corpus of uterus

mesonephric ducts

Müllerian duct

cervix

wall of urogenital sinus

C

epithelium of
urogenital sinus

orifice of
left mesonephric duct

summit of
Müllerian tubercle

vagina primordium

right
mesonephric duct

Müllerian duct

left mesonephric duct

D

Fig. 8.14 (*continued*)

the Müllerian ducts fuse by 70 days into a single uterovaginal canal that en-larges as the *Müllerian tubercle*, a blind pocket adjacent to the urogenital sinus. By the fifth month the two chambers interconnect. The urogenital sinus, which results from the partitioning of the cloaca, joins the *allantois* to form the bladder and then opens into a common external vestibule for urinary and genital products, through the urethral meatus anteriorly and the vaginal orifice posteriorly (Fig. 8.16). A perforate membrane, the *hymen* (Figs. 8.8, 8.14F), covers the latter opening at about 6 months. The hymen is probably

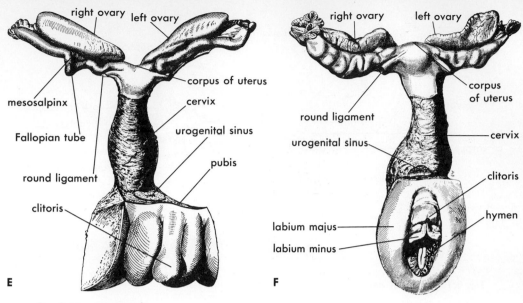

Fig. 8.14 (continued)

a remnant of the epithelium of the Müllerian tubercle and the urogenital sinus.

At about 5 months the uterus and vagina are partially separated and can be distinguished by the muscles in the uterine wall. During the later stages of fetal life the uterine wall also becomes glandular. The uterus tapers from the posterior *cervix* to the anterior *fundus,* where the *horns* join. The fundus remains small until hormone stimulation at puberty.

As the mesonephric duct and tubules degenerate, their anterior remnants form the *epoöphoron,* sometimes associated with the *rete ovarii,* while their posterior remnants form the *paroöphoron* and *Gartner's duct.* All of these derivatives of the mesonephros are found in the *broad ligament.* The enclosing peritoneum of the mesonephros, which also surrounds the Müllerian duct, becomes the *mesosalpinx* of the uterus.

Like the testis, the ovary shifts during the seventh month from its dorsal origin to a more caudal location within the pelvis (Fig. 8.17). The diaphragmatic ligament of the mesonephros becomes the suspensory ligament of the ovary, and the inguinal ligament of the mesonephros becomes the *round ligament.*

At puberty (about 11 years) follicles begin to mature within the ovaries, the body contours alter, the breasts develop, pubic and axillary hair appears, and *menstruation* becomes a cyclic event.

Each of the mature ovaries measures about $4 \times 2 \times 1$ cm. and weighs from 2 to 4 grams. It is dull pink in color and nodular and is suspended by a mesentery, the *mesovarium.* The ovaries have a dual purpose, producing both the ova necessary for survival of the species and the sex hormones necessary for the development, growth, and function of the mammary glands and asso-

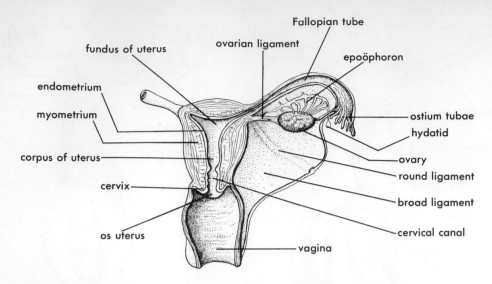

Fig. 8.15   Dorsal view of reproductive system of human female.

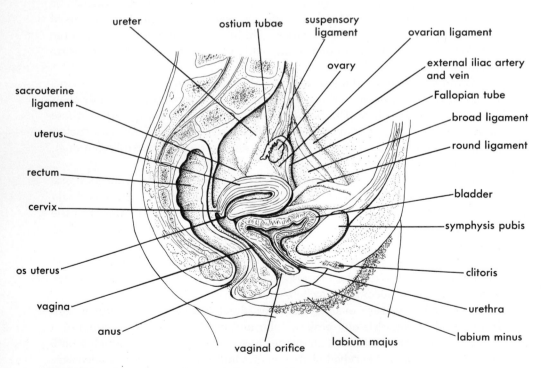

Fig. 8.16   Lateral view of urogenital system of human female.

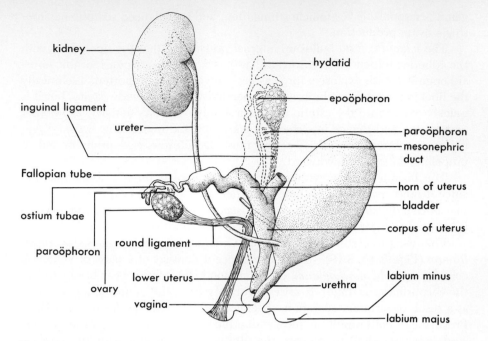

Fig. 8.17 Lateral view showing position changes in fetal urogenital system of human female. (Adapted from Hertwig.)

ciated secondary sexual structures and characters. The secondary sexual structures provide for the reception and conveyance of spermatozoa to the uterus and tubes, where fertilization may occur; for a proper environment for the *implantation* and growth of the embryo; and for assistance in the expulsion of the fully matured fetus from the maternal body.

■ Ovulation and Menstruation

Ovulation is the discharge of the mature (ripe) ovum from its Graafian follicle in the ovary. It normally occurs at regular intervals of 28 to 30 days throughout the reproductive period of the female, which extends from about ages 11 to 45, and generally takes place 14 ± 2 days after the onset of menstruation, although the range in normal women is 8 to 20 days. The human is unlike nonprimate mammals in that ovulation does not occur at menstruation but rather about midway between menstrual periods.

Usually only one ovum matures each month, the two ovaries alternating in production. Occasionally, however, two or more ova ripen simultaneously. If they are fertilized, twins or other multiple births result. More rarely a single ovum divides completely at the two-cell stage to produce identical twins. Follicle-stimulating hormone (FSH, also called Prolan A) from the pituitary gland is responsible for follicle stimulation, and its balanced secretion assures single ovum production.

The *follicular fluid* builds up internal pressure so that the ripe ovum, with the adhering follicle cells (corona radiata), is expelled with considerable force, although not with explosive force as early investigators reported. Technically the liberated ovum may be briefly suspended within the body cavity, but it is quickly drawn into the ostium tubae (probably by ciliary activity, as in other vertebrates) and thence into the Fallopian tube and uterus (Fig. 8.18). Wave-like contractions (peristalsis) of the muscular uterine wall probably aid in propelling the ovum downward.

The liberated ovum within the upper Fallopian tube is still immature, since it must await penetration by a spermatozoon to complete its second maturation division, which liberates a second polar body. The human ovum is believed to have a life span under such conditions of about 2+ hours.

Following ovulation, the collapsed Graafian follicle becomes the *corpus luteum* (Figs. 8.18, 8.19), so called because it consists of a mass of yellowish cells (a *corpus hemorrhagicum,* due to a blood clot, may appear briefly before the corpus luteum stage). It arises, probably from the membrana granulosa, as a result of pituitary secretion, specifically the luteinizing hormone (LH, or Prolan B). Its cells rapidly acquire endocrine functions, secreting progesterone (and some estradiol) to prepare the uterine mucosal lining for the implantation of the fertilized ovum. Other functions are to prevent further ovulations during pregnancy and to activate the mammary glands. If pregnancy does not follow, the corpus luteum reaches maximum size in 10 days and then recedes, disappearing about the time of the next menstruation. Menstruation is a discharge of uterine blood and superficial mucosa indicating failure in fertilization and implantation of the ripe ovum. The scar tissue replacing the corpus luteum is known as the *corpus albicans* because of the paucity of blood. If pregnancy does follow, the corpus luteum grows until about the fifth month, reaching a diameter of 3 cm., and then slowly regresses.

During a single 28-day ovulatory or *menstrual cycle,* these four phases occur: proliferative, secretory, menstrual, and reparative. Each phase progresses into its successor, with changes in the pituitary gland, the ovary (Fig. 8.19), and the uterine mucosa (Fig. 8.20). Whereas cyclic and hormonal changes in the vaginal epithelium accompany the maturation of ova in other primates and lower mammals, such a relationship does not exist in the human. Further, in lower mammals the female accepts the male only during estrus.

The anterior pituitary gland controls the ovulatory cycle. Its three gonadotropic hormones, FSH, LH, and LTH, act on the ovary but not directly on the uterus or vagina (Fig. 8.21). FSH is responsible for the stimulation and the growth of the Graafian follicles and also for the production of estradiol by the theca interna. LH controls the luteinizing of the Graafian follicle following ovulation. LTH (luteotropic hormone) is related to the production of the endocrine secretion by the corpus luteum. Either FSH or LH or both may cause ovulation; normally they are synergistic.

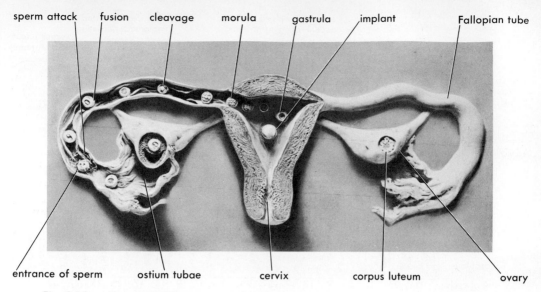

Fig. 8.18   Transport of human ovum from ovary to implantation site in the uterus. (From *Birth Atlas,* Maternity Center Association, New York.)

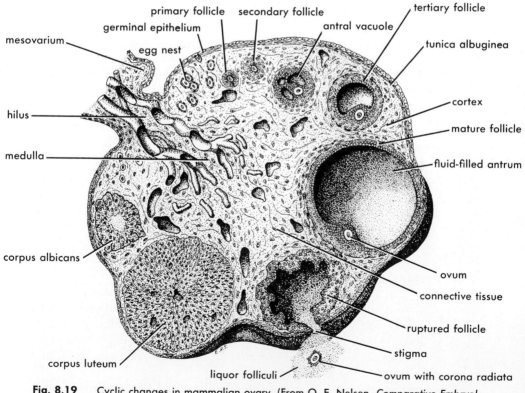

Fig. 8.19   Cyclic changes in mammalian ovary. (From O. E. Nelsen, *Comparative Embryology of the Vertebrates,* McGraw-Hill, New York, 1953.)

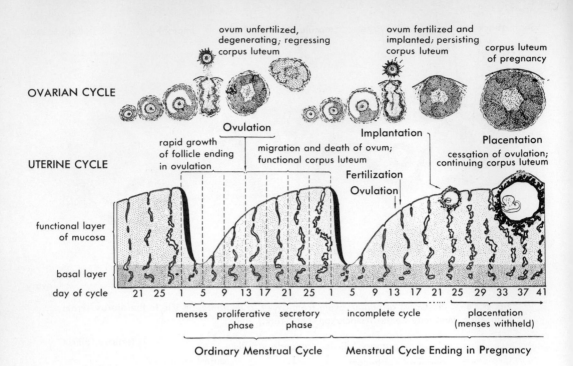

OVARIAN CYCLE

ovum unfertilized, degenerating; regressing corpus luteum

ovum fertilized and implanted; persisting corpus luteum

corpus luteum of pregnancy

Ovulation

Implantation

Placentation

UTERINE CYCLE

rapid growth of follicle ending in ovulation

migration and death of ovum; functional corpus luteum

cessation of ovulation; continuing corpus luteum

Fertilization

Ovulation

functional layer of mucosa

basal layer

day of cycle   21 25   1   5   9   13 17   21 25   1   5   9   13 17 21 25 29 33 37 41

menses proliferative secretory   incomplete cycle   placentation
        phase   phase   (menses withheld)

Ordinary Menstrual Cycle   Menstrual Cycle Ending in Pregnancy

Fig. 8.20 Relationship of ovarian changes and uterine mucosal changes, as represented graphically, in human during ordinary menstrual cycle and subsequent cycle in which pregnancy occurs. (From B. M. Patten, *Human Embryology*, 2nd ed., McGraw-Hill, New York, 1953. Adapted from Schröder.)

▪ Coitus and Sperm Transport

Semen, or seminal fluid, is a mixture of spermatozoa and secretions from the seminal vesicles, the prostate gland, the bulbourethral gland, and other glands of the urethra. The spermatozoa, which are inactive while in the seminiferous tubules, accumulate and complete their maturation in the epididymis. Ciliary and muscular pulsations propel them through the vas deferens, the ejaculatory duct, and the urethra, and en route they mix with the fluids from the male urogenital tract and become active. The bulbourethral and urethral secretions serve as a lubricating fluid for the intromission of the glans penis into the vaginal vestibule during *coitus* (copulation). A single ejaculation of semen at the climax of coitus has a volume of 2 to 10 cc. and normally contains as many as 300,000,000 mature, functional spermatozoa. The deposition of semen in the vagina is called *insemination.* It occurs in reptiles, birds, and mammals but not in the lower vertebrates.

The spermatozoa are further activated by the usual alkaline environment of the vagina; an acid environment is fatal to them. They pass through the

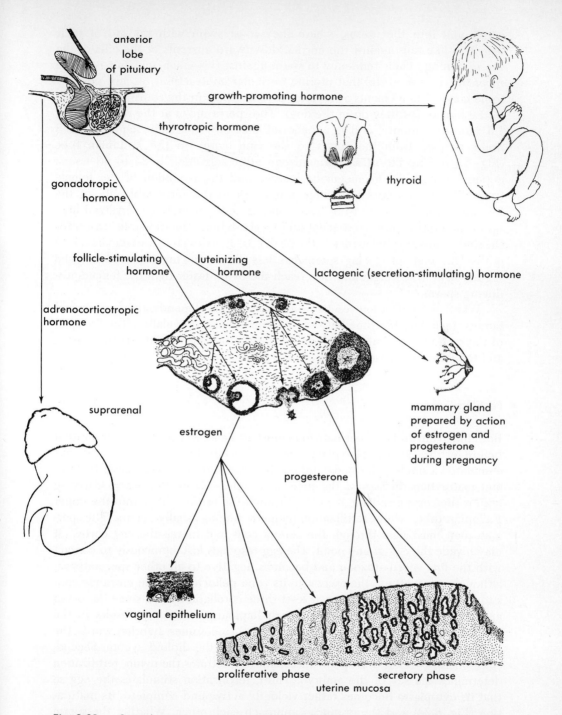

anterior
lobe
of pituitary

growth-promoting hormone

thyrotropic hormone

thyroid

gonadotropic
hormone

follicle-stimulating
hormone

luteinizing
hormone

lactogenic (secretion-stimulating) hormone

adrenocorticotropic
hormone

suprarenal

estrogen

mammary gland
prepared by action
of estrogen and
progesterone
during pregnancy

progesterone

vaginal epithelium

proliferative phase

secretory phase

uterine mucosa

Fig. 8.21 Some hormones arising in anterior lobe of human pituitary gland, with particular emphasis on those involved in regulating cyclic activities of female reproductive organs. (From B. M. Patten, *Human Embryology*, 2nd ed., McGraw-Hill, New York, 1953.)

cervix and into the uterus, where they must swim with the aid of their flagellum-like tails against the normal downward currents of the cilia of the uterine lining. Their tendency to swim against this ciliary current is called *rheotaxis*. It is doubtful that uterine muscular contractions, except possibly some cervical movements at orgasm, play any part in the transport of sperm in the human (as they do in the dog). The sperm move at the rate of about 1.5 mm. per minute, and it is believed that they normally require 2 to 3 hours to pass from the cervix to the ripe ovum, in the Fallopian tube (Fig. 8.18). The life of a spermatozoon after activation is 24 to 48 hours, depending both on its metabolic reserve and the condition of the female tract. Motility outlasts fertilizing power. Since the fertilizable life of the human ovum is thought to be only about 2 hours, it must be fertilized high up in the uterus, prior to descent and implantation. One possible reason for the slight statistical imbalance in the birth rate of males (106) and females (100) is that the male-producing sperm has less chromatin material and may be slightly lighter in weight and thus reach the ovum faster than the female-producing sperm.

Whether fertilization results from insemination depends, then, on several factors, including the time between insemination and ovulation, the life span of the ovum, the number of sperm in the uterus, the viability of the sperm, and the time for sperm transport to the ovum.

■ Fertilization

Both the ovum and the spermatozoon must attain a certain stage of maturation before fertilization can take place (Figs. 8.22, 8.23). The secondary oöcyte has eliminated a single polar body and reached the mitotic metaphase of the second maturation division at the time of its release from the ovary. Carrying with it the corona radiata, it moves through the ostium tubae into the upper Fallopian tube, where fertilization (gametic union) usually occurs. The spermatozoon must pass through the corona cells and pierce the egg cortex. It may invade the egg at any point. The egg responds instantaneously to contact with the first spermatozoon and becomes negative to all other spermatozoa, although many attach themselves to its zona pellucida. Sperm entrance constitutes fertilization. There are at least three corollaries. First, since the ovum and the spermatozoon nuclei are each haploid, fertilization results in the restoration of the normal diploid number of chromosomes. In other words, the male and female haploid pronuclei fuse to form the diploid zygote. Second, since one of two kinds of sperm successfully penetrates the ovum, fertilization determines the sex of the embryo. Third, fertilization stimulates the egg so that its cytoplasm becomes rather violently active and completes its maturation (Fig. 8.24) and the pronuclei approach each other. Whether the sperm entrance point is in any way related to the future embryonic axes in the human (as it is in the amphibia) is not known.

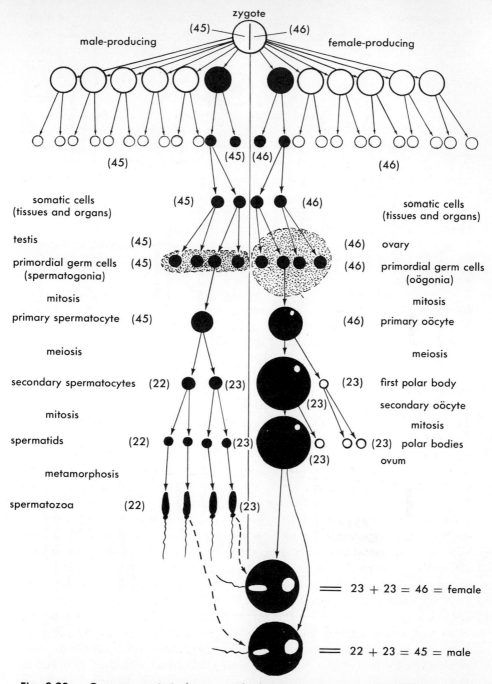

Fig. 8.22 Gametogenesis in human, with chromosome numbers in parentheses. First maturation (meiotic) division is shown as reductional, and second as equational, although order may be reversed. Further, chromosome 23 may be present in all spermatozoa and merely be reduced in size in half of them.

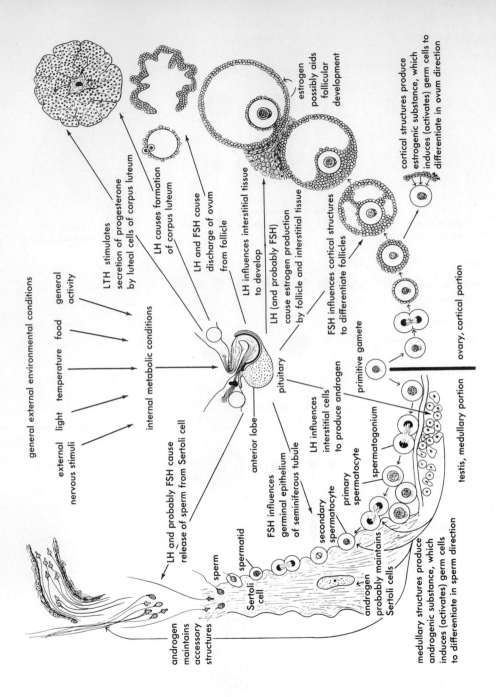

Fig. 8.23 Effects of anterior lobe of pituitary gland upon developing gametes in human. (From O. E. Nelsen, *Comparative Embryology of the Vertebrates*, McGraw-Hill, New York, 1953.)

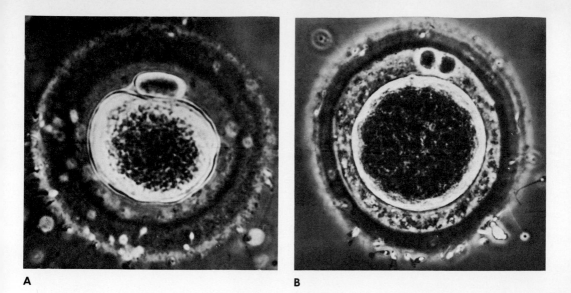

Fig. 8.24   Polar body formation in fertilized human egg: A, first polar body; B, first and second polar bodies. (From L. B. Shettles, *Ovum Humanum*, Hafner, New York, 1960.)

The male pronucleus, occasionally seen in eggs recovered from the upper uterus, consists of the swollen head (nucleus) of the spermatozoon. The middle piece and tail of the spermatozoon are difficult to identify, but it is likely that the centrosome of the middle piece is the activating center of the first cleavage (mitotic) spindle. It is believed that the head of the sperm rotates 180° so that the centrosome precedes it toward the egg pronucleus.

After union of the pronuclei, chromosomes appear, split lengthwise, and arrange themselves on the mitotic spindle in anticipation of the first cell division. The great disparity in size and consistency of the spermatozoon and ovum are not reflected in the genetically important chromosomes of the nucleus. Each cell has its full haploid complement of chromosomes, and each chromosome must find its pair mate in the other nucleus.

The spermatozoon contributes nothing to the nutrition of the early fertilized egg and probably has little to do with the type of cleavage that ensues. It stimulates the dormant ovum to activity, contributes its hereditary influence, and then is absorbed as the zygotic nucleus readies the stored yolk and cytoplasm of the ovum for the early cleavages.

■ Cleavage

It is possible to remove a ripe ovum from a Graafian follicle protruding from the surface of the ovary and to fertilize it under the microscope and then observe its first divisions (Fig. 8.25). The early cleavages are total and nearly equal,

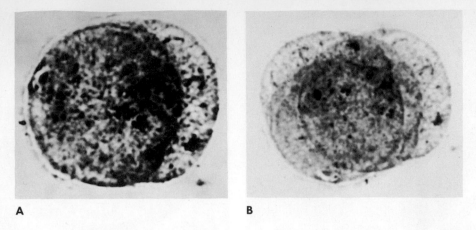

Fig. 8.25 Cleavage in human egg: A, two-cell stage; B, four-cell stage. (From L. B. Shettles, *Ovum Humanum*, Hafner, New York, 1960.)

conditions expected in normal isolecithal eggs. The first three cleavages are believed to occur in the uterus at about 36, 60, and 72 hours after fertilization; the first cleavage is long delayed and the interval between cleavages shortens with each successive division. There is no explanation for the late timing of the first cleavage except that the maturation of the egg must be accomplished, the spermatozoon head must be transformed into a pronucleus, some degree of zygogenesis (fusion of pronuclei) must take place, the cytoplasm of the ovum must undergo some changes, and the apparatus for the cleavage must be set up. Once cleavage begins, it accelerates as the resulting cells become smaller and smaller.

■ Blastocyst and Germ Layers

The first four cleavages produce 2, 4, 8, and then 16 similar cells. The 16 cells cluster together in a ball, the *morula* (Fig. 8.26), inside the zona pellucida. Nutriment and oxygenated fluid from the maternal uterus may pass through the zona pellucida to these cells, but for several additional cleavages they are more or less independent of their environment.

Fluid does accumulate among the morula cells, however, and at the 32-cell stage a somewhat eccentrically placed cavity (*blastocoel*) filled with the fluid develops. The human blastocoel is associated with a *yolk cavity* totally devoid of yolk. In this respect it differs from the blastocoel of the reptile or bird, and for this reason it is itself often referred to as the yolk cavity.

When the blastocoel appears, a *blastula*, normally called a *blastocyst* or *blastodermic vesicle*, exists (Fig. 8.27). Cells on one side of the blastula are a

Fig. 8.26 Late human morula, with forming blastocoel. (From L. B. Shettles, *Ovum Humanum,* Hafner, New York, 1960.)

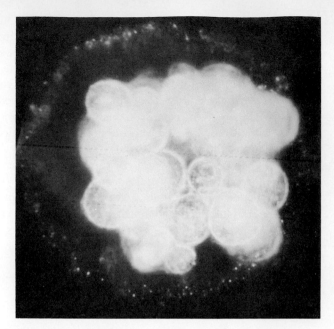

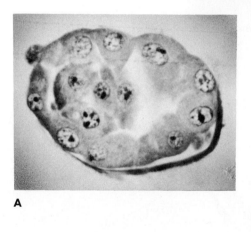

A

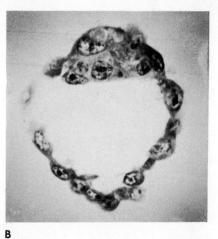

B

Fig. 8.27 Human blastula: A, formation of inner cell mass and blastocoel; B, formation of embryonic disc. (From A. T. Hertig, J. Rock, E. C. Adams, and W. J. Mulligan, *Carnegie Inst. Wash. Publ.* No. 603, *Contribs. Embryology* No. 240 (1954).)

bit more sluggish in division than the others. These constitute the *inner cell mass* of the embryo proper. The other cells, which are smaller as a result of more rapid division, constitute the accessory or *trophoblast* cells. As the pressure of the fluid increases, the trophoblast cells flatten against the zona pellucida, and the cells of the inner mass gather in one area to form the *embryonic disc,* or *blastoderm* (Fig. 8.27B). The embryo develops from the embryonic disc, and the accessory structures from the trophoblast.

The zona pellucida sloughs off and disappears, so that the outer trophoblast cells are in direct contact with the uterine epithelium. The trophoblast cells divide rapidly and invade the maternal tissues in the process of implantation (Figs. 8.28–8.35), which is probably accomplished by means of an erosion involving some enzyme action. Certainly the uterine epithelium is sensitized toward the blastocyst, and the trophoblast appears to aggressively penetrate the maternal tissues.

Cells on the inner side of the inner cell mass, toward the blastocoel, form layers identified as primitive *endoderm* (Fig 8.30A), in contrast with the other (outer) cells of the inner cell mass, which are primitive *ectoderm*. The primitive ectoderm is the source of embryonic ectoderm, mesoderm, and more endoderm. Between 7½ and 8 days a cavity appears between the outermost layer of ectoderm and the thin covering trophoblast. This is the beginning of the *amniotic cavity* (Fig. 8.32).

The endoderm spreads rapidly to line the trophoblast and form a *yolk sac*

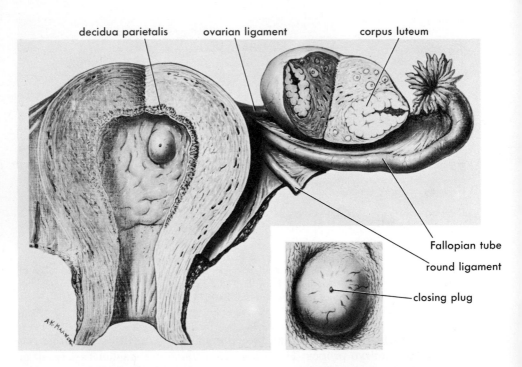

Fig. 8.28 Dorsal half of pregnant human uterus with left Fallopian tube and ovary. (From W. J. Hamilton, J. D. Boyd, and H. W. Mossman, *Human Embryology*, 2nd ed., Williams & Wilkins, Baltimore, 1952. Adapted from Teacher and Ramsey.)

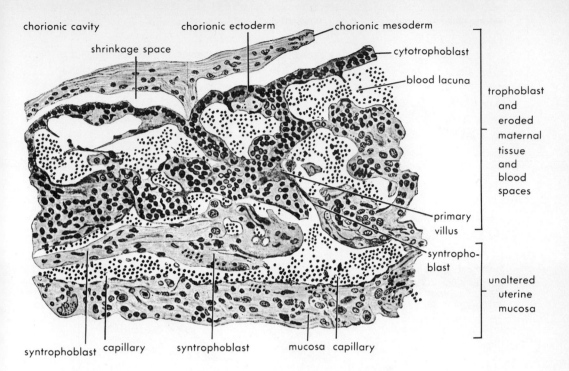

Fig. 8.29   Invasion of uterine mucosa in human by implanting embryo. (From L. B. Arey, *Developmental Anatomy*, 4th ed., Saunders, Philadelphia, 1940. Adapted from Peters.)

(without yolk) (Fig. 8.33). The endoderm cells of the yolk sac are cuboid near the ectoderm cells of the inner cell mass and flat and mesothelium-like elsewhere. Some of the cuboid cells become columnar to indicate the impending formation of the *prechordal plate* and the determination of the anteroposterior axis of the embryo. As the yolk cavity is thus reduced, the amniotic cavity enlarges. For a time, however, the yolk sac endoderm obtains nutrition for the embryo by diffusion from the maternal tissues. Primitive extraembryonic mesoderm rapidly masses between the yolk sac endoderm and the trophoblast (Fig. 8.32), and there is evidence that at least some of it comes from the trophoblast cells. The mesoderm shortly acquires *lacunae* (small spaces), which coalesce to form the *exocoel* (extraembryonic coelom) except between part of the amniotic cavity and the trophoblast. The exocoel splits the mesoderm into two layers, an outer *somatic* one lining the trophoblast and an inner *splanchnic* one covering the yolk sac. The somatic mesoderm and the trophoblast constitute the *somatopleure,* and the splanchnic mesoderm and the endoderm constitute the *splanchnopleure.* The embryo is suspended from the inner aspect of the chorionic vesicle by the mesoderm not invaded by the exocoel (Figs. 8.33, 8.34).

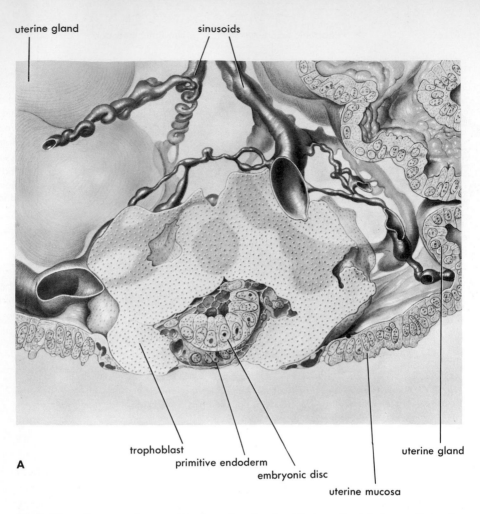

A

Fig. 8.30   Human embryo and implantation site: A, at 8 days; B, at 9 days, with tropho-blast and uterine mucosa fused and trophoblastic lacunae communicating with maternal sinusoids. (From A. T. Hertig and J. Rock, *Carnegie Inst. Wash. Publ.* No. 583, *Contribs. Embryology* No. 221 (1949).)

▪ Primitive Streak and Notochord

The embryonic disc, between the amniotic and yolk sac cavities, is composed of endoderm toward the yolk sac and ectoderm toward the amniotic cavity. Cells within the ectoderm of the disc rapidly proliferate toward its posterior edge, causing a bulge into the amniotic cavity, the beginning of the *primitive streak*. Cells from the streak move outward between the ectoderm and endoderm to constitute the *intraembryonic mesoderm*. The embryonic disc is now triplo-blastic, having all three primary germ layers. It expands into a pear-shaped mass, with mesoderm emanating from its primitive streak in almost all direc-

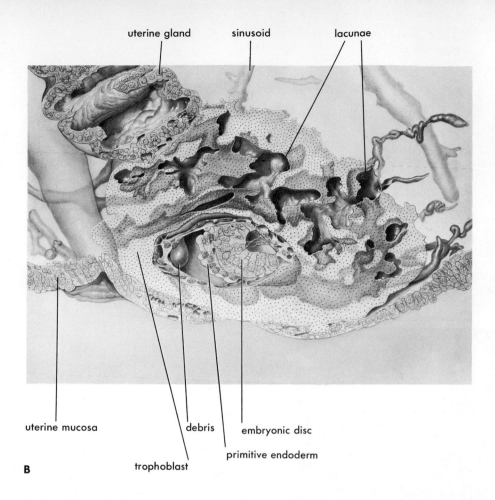

uterine gland   sinusoid   lacunae

uterine mucosa   debris
                              embryonic disc
                        primitive endoderm
B   trophoblast

tions. Although the streak remains in the posterior portion of the disc, this out-
flow of mesoderm may be in part responsible for the elongation and expansion
of the disc.

A *primitive groove* extends the length of the primitive streak, ending
anteriorly in a *primitive pit* (Figs. 8.36–8.38). Just anterior to the primitive pit
is the ectodermal *Hensen's node* (*primitive knot*), homologous to that in the
chick embryo. Hensen's node adds mesoderm to that derived from the primitive streak. Anteriorly from the primitive pit to the prechordal plate, cells bud
off between the ectoderm and endoderm to form the *head process*, the
precursor of the *notochord*. The primitive streak shrinks after the head process
appears, and, as it shrinks, Hensen's node moves posteriorly so that the early
embryonic axis lengthens. Curiously, the primitive pit invagination continues
into the notochordal mass to form an elongated cavity, the *notochordal canal.*
The notochordal canal sends tributaries through the underlying endoderm
into the yolk sac so that, by way of the primitive pit, the amniotic and yolk
cavities are for a time connected. The notochordal cells then coalesce

Primitive Streak and Notochord   **413**

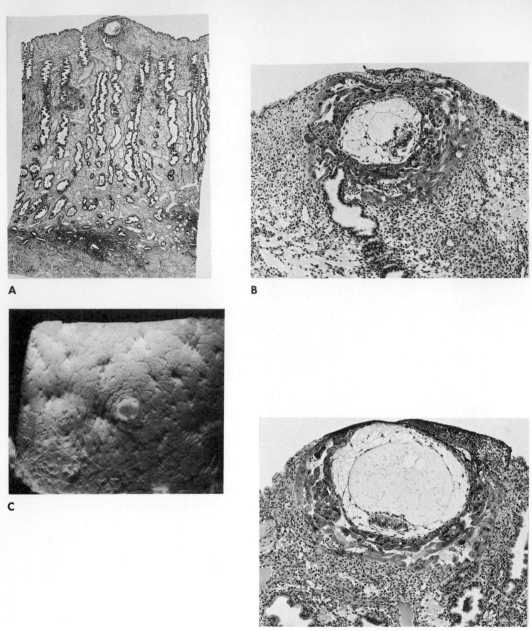

Fig. 8.31   Human embryo and implantation site: A, at 11 days, showing mucosal edema, with tortuous secretory glands and congested sinusoids; B, high-power view of A; C, at 12 days, showing mouths of glands; D, specimen of C, showing mucosal reaction around implanting ovum. (From A. T. Hertig and J. Rock, *Carnegie Inst. Wash. Publ.* No. 525, *Contribs. Embryology* No. 184 (1941).)

414   THE HUMAN: *A Discoid Placentate*

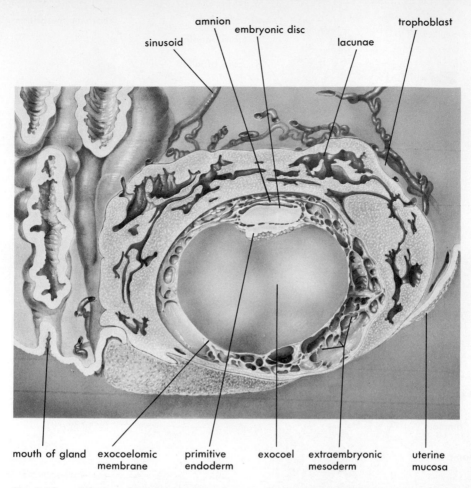

sinusoid   amnion   embryonic disc   lacunae   trophoblast

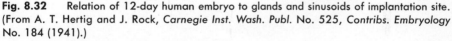

mouth of gland   exocoelomic membrane   primitive endoderm   exocoel   extraembryonic mesoderm   uterine mucosa

Fig. 8.32 Relation of 12-day human embryo to glands and sinusoids of implantation site. (From A. T. Hertig and J. Rock, *Carnegie Inst. Wash. Publ.* No. 525, *Contribs. Embryology* No. 184 (1941).)

into a *notochordal plate* in the roof of the yolk sac. This notochordal plate appears to become an integral part of the endodermal roof of the yolk sac in a lengthwise direction from the prechordal plate to the primitive pit. The notochord is shortly pinched off dorsally from the endoderm, and at 18 days after fertilization (1.5-mm. stage) it is the major axial element of the embryo, with a thickened *neural (medullary) plate* and *neural groove* forming in the ectoderm above it.

Although some embryonic mesoderm is anterior to the primitive streak, most of it arises from the streak and ultimately merges with the extraembryonic mesoderm between the amniotic ectoderm and yolk sac endoderm. As the streak recedes posteriorly, it leaves mesoderm on either side of the extending notochord. The only regions remaining free of this embryonic

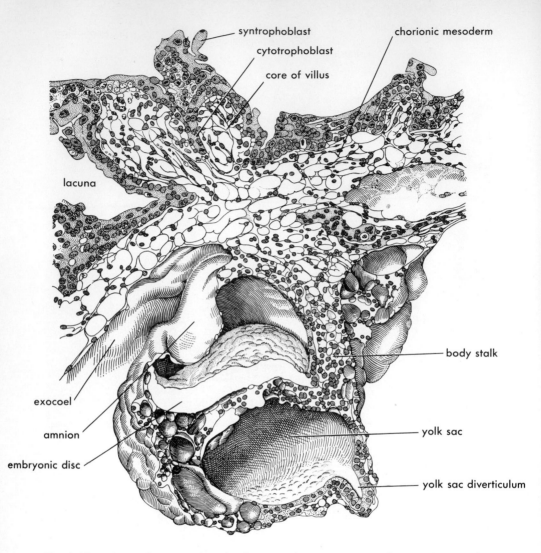

Fig. 8.33 Sagittal section of 13-day human embryo. (From J. Krafka, Jr., *Carnegie Inst. Wash. Publ.* No. 525, *Contribs. Embryology* No. 186 (1941).)

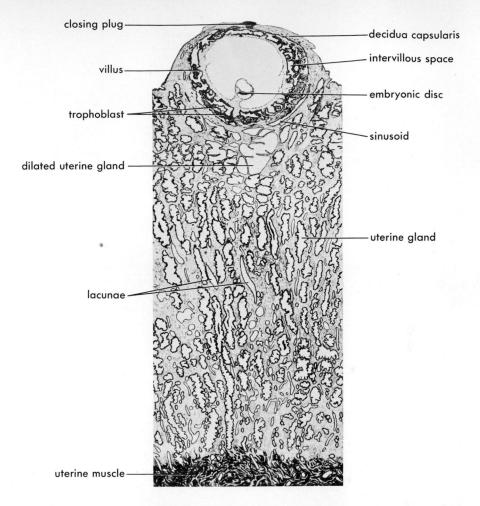

closing plug

decidua capsularis

intervillous space

villus

embryonic disc

trophoblast

sinusoid

dilated uterine gland

uterine gland

lacunae

uterine muscle

Fig. 8.34 Sagittal section of 15-day human embryo, showing relationship between chorionic vesicle and uterine mucosa. (From W. J. Hamilton, J. D. Boyd, and H. W. Mossman, *Human Embryology*, 2nd ed., Williams & Wilkins, Baltimore, 1952.)

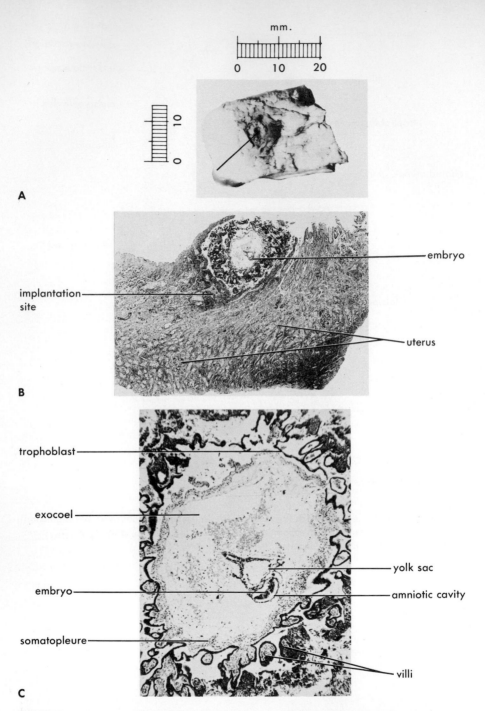

Fig. 8.35 Human embryo and implantation site at 17 days: A, implantation site; B, ovum in uterine mucosa; C, high-power view of B. (From F. Thomas and E. Van Campenhout, *Ann. méd. légale (Bruxelles)*, **4**, 1 (1953).)

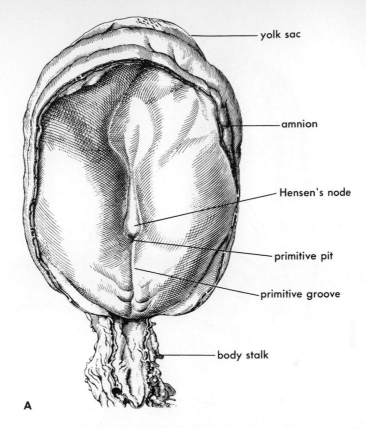

yolk sac

amnion

Hensen's node

primitive pit

primitive groove

body stalk

A

Fig. 8.36 Human embryo at 17 days: A, dorsal view; B, sagittal section. (From W. C. George, *Carnegie Inst. Wash. Publ.* No. 541, *Contribs. Embryology* No. 187 (1942).)

mesoderm are the streak itself and the node from which it derives. The mesoderm immediately lateral to the notochord and continuous lengthwise is thicker than the adjoining *nephrotome* (*intermediate cell mass*) mesoderm and the most laterally situated *lateral plate* mesoderm. At 18 days it anticipates the *somites* (Fig. 8.38). As in other vertebrates, the first somites to appear are the most anterior (but never anterior to the anterior tip of the notochord), and development proceeds posteriorly. A total of about 44 pairs of somites eventually forms.

The lateral plate splits into somatic and splanchnic layers. As in the embryos studied earlier, the nephrotome between these layers and the somites gives rise to much of the excretory system. Some mesenchyme anterior to the prechordal plate and ventral to the notochord becomes *cardiac mesoderm.* An extension of the exocoel within the embryonic lateral plate forms the intracoel, or true *coelom* of the embryo. This is continuous with the *pericardial cavity* (Fig. 8.38C–E) in the cardiac mesoderm.

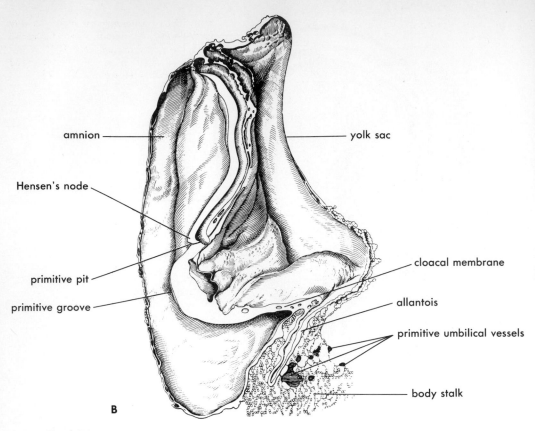

amnion

yolk sac

Hensen's node

cloacal membrane

primitive pit

allantois

primitive groove

primitive umbilical vessels

body stalk

B

Fig. 8.36 (continued)

■ **Placentation and Embryonic Membranes**

Normally the uterine mucosa (*endometrium*) undergoes a 28-day cycle of changes, all related to the maturation, ovulation, implantation, and placentation of the ovum (Fig. 8.20). This is conveniently called a menstrual cycle because menstruation, one of its phases, is quite definitive. The four phases of the cycle are as follows:

Menstruation (days 1 to 5), which results from failure of the previously ovulated ovum to be fertilized and implanted. It is the desquamation of the mucosa along with glands and blood vessels that were prepared to receive the fertilized ovum. Both the compact and spongy layers may be lost.

Repair (days 5 to 6), a short period of epithelial regeneration to replace the lost mucosa.

Proliferation (days 7 to 15), during which repair is completed. Under the influence of the follicle-stimulating hormone from the pituitary gland, the next ovum matures, and the uterine mucosa returns to normal. Ovulation terminates this phase.

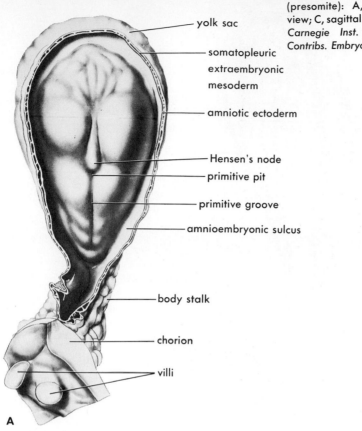

yolk sac

somatopleuric extraembryonic mesoderm

amniotic ectoderm

Hensen's node

primitive pit

primitive groove

amnioembryonic sulcus

body stalk

chorion

villi

Fig. 8.37 Human embryo at 18 days (presomite): A, dorsal view; B, ventral view; C, sagittal section. (From C. H. Heuser, Carnegie Inst. Wash. Publ. No. 433, Contribs. Embryology No. 138 (1932).)

A

Secretion (days 16 to 28). The corpus luteum from the region of the ovulated ovum secretes progesterone to bring about changes in the uterine mucosa favorable to ovum implantation. The uterine glands swell and secrete a glycogen-rich mucoid, and the superficial, compact, deeper spongy, and deepest basal layers of the uterus become distinguishable. The result is a considerable thickening of the uterine wall, due in part to edema and vascular congestion.

In the event that no fertilized egg is available for implantation, the cycle is repeated.

Ovulation, as previously stated, may take place at any time from 8 to 20 days after the beginning of the cycle, although it most frequently occurs about 14 days after the onset of menstruation. Thus ovulation in the human does not occur during *estrus* (heat) or menstruation, as it does in lower mammals, but rather during the proliferative or secretory phase of the cycle.

After its fertilization in the upper Fallopian tube, the ovum is carried down into the uterine lumen, requiring about 3 days to complete the passage and undergoing the first several cleavages en route. By the time it reaches the

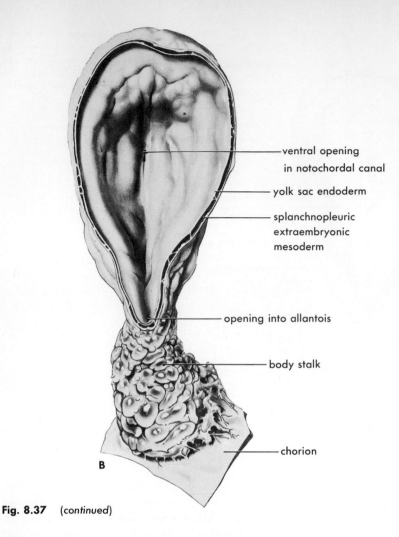

ventral opening
in notochordal canal

yolk sac endoderm

splanchnopleuric
extraembryonic
mesoderm

opening into allantois

body stalk

chorion

B

Fig. 8.37 (continued)

implantation site, it is a morula, or possibly a blastocyst, and has lost the corona radiata cells acquired in the ovary. The zona pellucida generally remains until just before implantation.

Implantation is presumed to begin about 7 days after fertilization, or during the secretory phase of the cycle. It prevents menstruation, and so if menstruation does not occur, pregnancy is suspected. On the ninth or tenth day following fertilization of the egg (or 24 days after the onset of menstruation), the blastocyst is entrapped in a mucosal crypt in the dorsal wall of the uterus. (Although implantation is possible at almost any point from the ovary to the cervix, an ovarian, abdominal, ampullary, tubal, or cervical implantation is abnormal, and an ovum implanted anywhere except along the dorsal wall of the uterus generally dies or becomes anomalous.)

The trophoblast contacts and then, with the aid of enzymes, eats into the

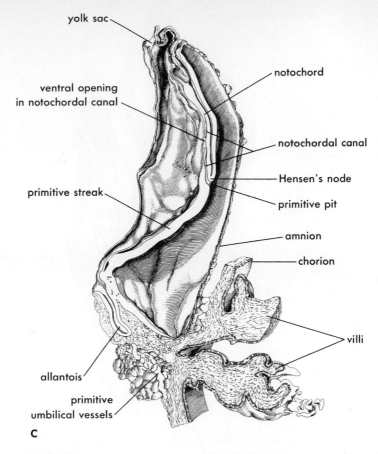

yolk sac

notochord

ventral opening
in notochordal canal

notochordal canal

Hensen's node

primitive streak

primitive pit

amnion

chorion

villi

allantois

primitive
umbilical vessels

C

Fig. 8.37 (continued)

uterine columnar epithelium, which is receptive to its attack. The enzymatic action brings about dissolution of the mucosa, so that cellular detritus (histotroph) and blood surround the trophoblast. This material is nutritive for this early stage, when the only means of acquiring food is by direct absorption. Immediately the blastocyst begins to enlarge, and the enlargement results in a further destruction of maternal tissue. The blastocyst usually sinks below the surface, although occasionally it projects slightly through the compact layer of the mucosa, and the epithelium closes over it and forms a fibrin-blood clot. At about 9 days the trophoblast differentiates into a thin inner *cytotrophoblast* (cellular) and an outer *syntrophoblast* (syncytial) that becomes quite thick (Figs. 8.29, 8.33, 8.39). The trophoblast then produces amoebalike projections that invade the mucosa. This invasion is hemotrophic, because it involves particularly the blood sinuses. The embryo thus establishes a parasitic relationship with its host, the uterus.

Implantation in the human therefore involves loss of the zona pellucida; contact of the embryonic trophoblast with the uterine epithelium; digestion

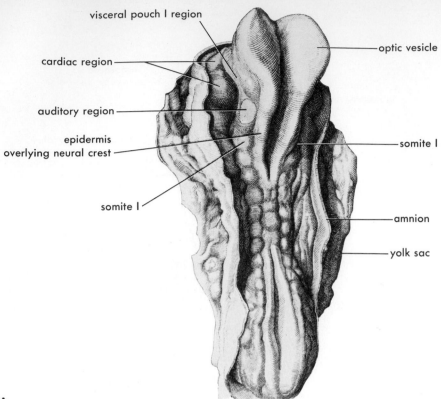

visceral pouch I region

optic vesicle

cardiac region

auditory region

epidermis
overlying neural crest

somite I

somite I

amnion

yolk sac

A

Fig. 8.38   Human embryo at 19 days (7 somites): A, dorsal view; B, dorsal view with ectoderm and part of mesoderm removed to show blood vessels and somites; C, sagittal section; D, ventral view of heart region; E, sagittal section showing vascular system. (From F. Payne, *Carnegie Inst. Wash. Publ.* No. 361, *Contribs. Embryology* No. 81 (1925).)

of the uterine mucosa in preparation for the invasion of the blastocyst; edema and capillary destruction in the environs of the blastocyst; engulfing of the blastocyst by the mucosa; distinction of the inner cellular and outer syncytial trophoblast; expansion of the syntrophoblast; and differentiation of the uterine mucosal layers. There is never any direct connection between the embryonic and maternal circulations.

The so-called embryonic membranes of the human embryo, like those of other vertebrates studied, arise from embryonic structures but are themselves extraembryonic (Fig. 8.40). The yolk sac comes from the gut and is lined with endoderm; the *allantois* comes from the primitive bladder and is also lined with endoderm; and the *amnion* and *chorion* come from the somatopleure and therefore have ectodermal layers. A requisite of all these membranes is some mesoderm, within which develop *blood islands*, then blood vessels, and finally blood for the use of the embryo from which the membranes

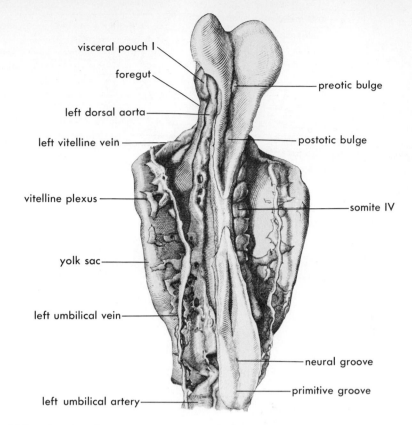

visceral pouch I

foregut

left dorsal aorta

left vitelline vein

vitelline plexus

yolk sac

left umbilical vein

left umbilical artery

preotic bulge

postotic bulge

somite IV

neural groove

primitive groove

B

Fig. 8.38 (*continued*)

derive. Although the yolk sac and the allantois are poorly developed in the human as compared with the chick, their blood vessels are nevertheless very important to the survival and growth of the embryo.

Simultaneously with implantation the embryo develops its membranes, which have the same basic origins and structures as those of other vertebrates but which do not have the same functions. Since the human ovum contains essentially no yolk, the yolk sac, sometimes called the *umbilical vessel*, is underdeveloped. However, it originates with the embryonic gut, and its roof is incorporated as the roof of most of the gut. In its splanchnic mesoderm the first blood islands and subsequently the first blood vessels (vitelline) appear. It is at first larger than the amniotic cavity but is restricted and smaller by 15 days. As the foregut and hindgut regions form floors and close off, the midgut retains a small, tubular *yolk stalk*. This is included in the *body stalk*, or primitive umbilical cord, but is separated from the gut by the fifth week and degenerates. The yolk sac is never more than 5 mm. long at 8 weeks. It may persist to delivery but without continued function.

The amniotic cavity appears very early (7½ to 8 days) as a space within the inner cell mass. The embryonic disc is its floor, and continuous from it is

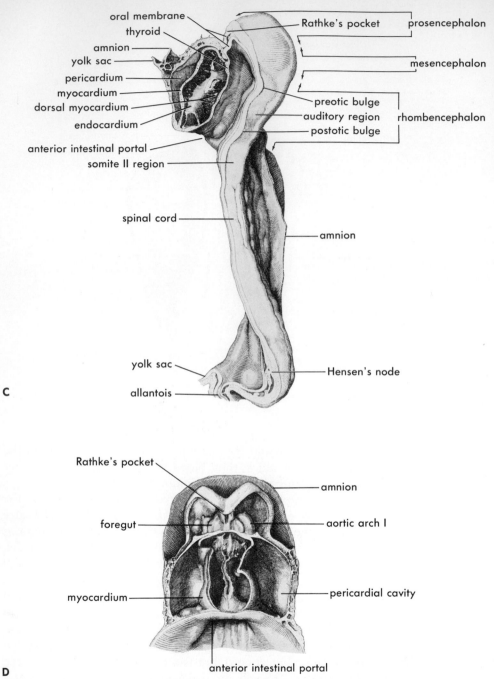

oral membrane
thyroid
amnion
yolk sac
pericardium
myocardium
dorsal myocardium
endocardium
anterior intestinal portal
somite II region
spinal cord
yolk sac
allantois

Rathke's pocket
prosencephalon
mesencephalon
preotic bulge
auditory region
postotic bulge
rhombencephalon
amnion
Hensen's node

C

Rathke's pocket
foregut
myocardium

amnion
aortic arch I
pericardial cavity
anterior intestinal portal

D

Fig. 8.38 (continued)

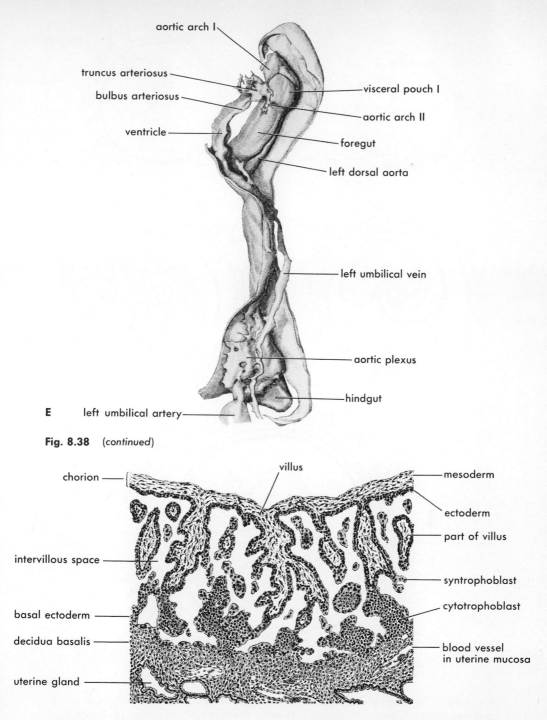

aortic arch I

truncus arteriosus

bulbus arteriosus

ventricle

visceral pouch I

aortic arch II

foregut

left dorsal aorta

left umbilical vein

aortic plexus

hindgut

E   left umbilical artery

Fig. 8.38 (continued)

chorion

villus

mesoderm

ectoderm

part of villus

intervillous space

syntrophoblast

cytotrophoblast

basal ectoderm

decidua basalis

blood vessel in uterine mucosa

uterine gland

Fig. 8.39 Section of human placenta at 3 weeks. (From L. B. Arey, *Developmental Anatomy,* 4th ed., Saunders, Philadelphia, 1940.)

Placentation and Embryonic Membranes **427**

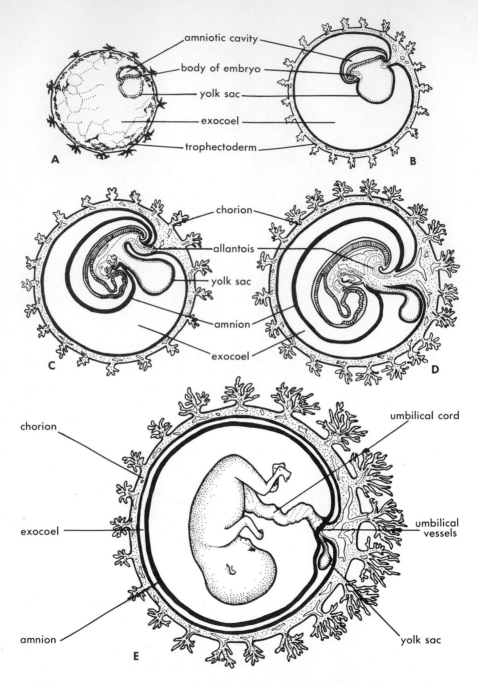

Fig. 8.40   Development of human embryonic membranes: A–E, interrelations of embryo and membranes; F, section of placenta, showing structure and circulation. (A–E from B. M. Patten, *Human Embryology*, 2nd ed., McGraw-Hill, New York, 1953; F from Carnegie Institution of Washington.)

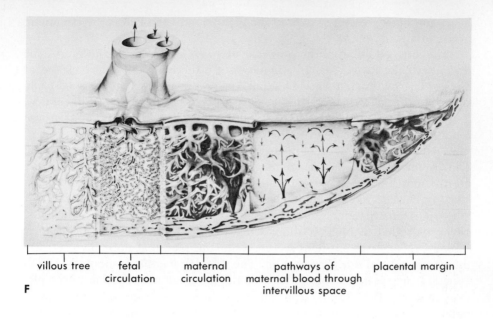

| villous tree | fetal circulation | maternal circulation | pathways of maternal blood through intervillous space | placental margin |

F

Fig. 8.40   (continued)

the ectoderm of the amnion, the amniotic membrane. As always, the amnion is somatopleure (ectoderm and mesoderm). The amniotic cavity enlarges rapidly and by the eighth week fills the chorionic sac and reduces the exocoel. As in the chick, the amnion fuses with the chorion to obliterate eventually the exocoel. An amniotic fluid accumulates in the sac, acting as a protective cushion for the young embryo. At birth it amounts to more than a liter of fluid and aids in cervical dilation.

The chorion arises from the ectodermal trophoblast of the blastocyst but shortly acquires somatic mesoderm. It is the reciprocal structure to the amnion. During early implantation solid fingerlike projections (*primary villi*) grow out from the trophoblast and invade the uterine mucosa to absorb histotroph nutrition, but later true chorionic villi (*secondary villi*), containing blood vessels, appear.

The chorionic villi begin to form at about 14 days. Each villus has a core of mesenchyme inside a thin layer of ectoderm, composed of both syntrophoblast and cytotrophoblast. The chorionic mesenchyme and its vascular derivatives in the human are believed to come originally from the cytotrophoblast. By 21 days the villi are well organized, providing the embryo with an efficient means of obtaining nutrition from the mother. The circulatory system develops from blood islands in the mesenchyme of the chorionic villi, the embryo, and the yolk sac. Each villus ultimately contains, besides its mesenchymal connective tissue center, free phagocytic (Hofbauer) cells and two arterioles and two venules, which are extensions of the umbilical (allantoic) vessels. The vessels soon connect through the body stalk with the embryonic

Placentation and Embryonic Membranes   **429**

heart and blood vascular system. The formation of the villi is the beginning of the human *placenta*.

The mucosal lining of the pregnant uterus is known as the *decidua* since it sloughs off at birth. A *deciduate placenta* is therefore one that includes, at birth, some maternal tissue. This portion of the uterine lining is basically similar to that of any nonfertile menstrual cycle but somewhat exaggerated. As soon as chorionic villi begin to form, three distinct areas of the uterus are recognizable, all in relation to the embryo. The *decidua parietalis* (or *vera*) lines all the uterus except the region immediately around the embryo. The *decidua basalis* lies under the embryo, between the chorion and the uterine muscles. The *decidua capsularis* covers the implanted embryo, lying between the chorion and the lumen of the uterus.

The decidua parietalis, a superficial layer, attains its maximum thickness, never more than ½ inch, at about 4 months and then regresses. It does not extend to the cervix but does secrete a mucous plug that normally obstructs the cervical canal during gestation. The decidua basalis, composed of both compact and spongy layers, persists as the maternal contribution to the placenta and is believed to control somehow the hemorrhages of early implantation. The decidua capsularis, a compact layer, is continuous at its margins with the decidua parietalis. As the embryo expands, the decidua capsularis meets the decidua parietalis across the uterine lumen. The decidua capsularis eventually degenerates and disappears, so that the chorionic membrane comes into direct contact with the decidua parietalis of the opposite side of the uterus.

The chorionic villi first cover the entire surface of the chorion. As the embryo expands within its membranes, those villi in the direction of the decidua capsularis are compressed out of existence so that by 2 months the surface on one side of the chorion is bare (*chorion laeve*). The villi toward the decidua basalis become bushlike (*chorion frondosum*) and form the most important part of the *fetal* placenta (the term *fetus* being used for the human embryo after the second month).

The embryonic and maternal circulatory systems remain independent throughout pregnancy. The chorionic villi are bathed in blood that escapes from the maternal vessels into sinuses, and derive from it both nutriment and oxygen, but no corpuscle enters or leaves the embryonic circulation, which is entirely closed. The trophoblast is the separating membrane. However, the placenta as a whole may be regarded as shielding the embryo from bacterial infections. It may also contain enzymes that aid in the digestive process. As the embryo and its membranes enlarge, the outer walls of the membranes and the placenta become thinner and hence better adapted for the diffusion of material from the uterine blood sinuses. The thousands of small and separate villi present at 4 to 8 weeks give way to villous trees in the middle months of pregnancy and finally to some 15 to 20 cotyledons, each incorporating many branching villi and covered by a thin layer of decidua basalis or decidua parietalis. Like lung alveoli, the villi must have large surfaces for the exchange of metabolic products, and estimates of the total absorbing surface of all the chorionic villi range as high as 100 square feet (still less than the surface of the lung alveoli in the newborn).

By the fifth month the placenta is disc-shaped, about 20 cm. in diameter, and 1½ cm. in thickness (Fig. 8.40F). Although the diameter does not increase appreciably thereafter, the thickness more than doubles by full term. At delivery the placenta may be 7 or 8 inches in diameter and may weigh over 1 pound. Since the vascular supply for the chorionic villi comes from the allantoic vessels, the human placenta is said to be *chorioallantoic*. It is also described as discoid (disc-shaped), deciduate (tearing tissue away from the uterus), and villous (having fingerlike processes interdigitating with the uterine mucosa). It assumes functions that in the chick belong to the yolk sac.

The allantois is apparent at 3 weeks as a slender endodermal tube caudal to the origin of the yolk sac and extending into the mesoderm of the body stalk. As the body stalk becomes the umbilical cord, the allantois stops growing and recedes, so that at 4 months no traces of it remain. During its development, however, allantoic vessels form and reach into the chorion to vascularize all its villi. Therefore, even though the allantois itself is vestigial and degenerates, the accompanying vascular elements provide the means of exchange of nutritive and respiratory products and their wastes through the placenta.

The primitive *umbilicus* represents the junction of the embryonic and extraembryonic regions, particularly as the gut closes off anteriorly and posteriorly. It separates the coelom from the exocoel and is the connecting link between the embryo and the placenta. Before the fifth week, the amnion expands around both the body stalk and the yolk stalk to form the umbilical cord. In its early stages the umbilical cord contains some of the exocoel, the yolk stalk, the allantois, an umbilical (allantoic) vein, and two umbilical (allantoic) arteries. Later it loses the yolk stalk and the allantois. It also contains a viscous supporting connective tissue known as *Wharton's jelly*. At birth the cord may measure 1½ yards in length and ½ inch in diameter. It is usually twisted.

With the growth of the embryo (or fetus) and the extraembryonic structures, the uterus expands until at 4 months it projects over the pelvis, and just before birth it may extend to the sternum (Fig. 8.41). The muscular layers of the uterus may increase in bulk 25 times, and the individual smooth muscle fibers may stretch to 60 times their relaxed length. The body of the fetus is normally directed downward (Fig. 8.42A) in anticipation of delivery at about 266 days after fertilization (or 10 lunar months from the onset of the last menstruation). *Parturition* begins with periodic contractions of the uterine muscles, which dilate the cervix and rupture the flexible amnion, liberating the amniotic fluid and the contained fetus. The fluid and the fetus are forced through the cervix and the vagina (Fig. 8.42B–D), and the membranes, along with the placenta, are retained. The final uterine contractions force any remaining placental blood through the umbilical cord into the embryo. The umbilical cord is then tied and cut, and the consequent accumulation of car-

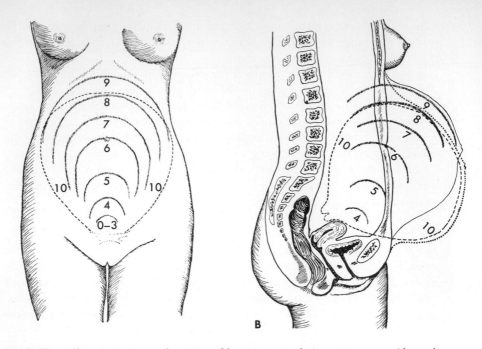

Fig. 8.41   Changes in size and position of human uterus during pregnancy, with numbers indicating age of embryo in lunar months: A, ventral view; B, sagittal section. (From B. M. Patten, *Human Embryology*, 2nd ed., McGraw-Hill, New York, 1953. A, adapted from Broman; B, adapted from Eufinger.)

bon dioxide in the circulation of the newborn stimulates the respiratory center of its brain so that it inhales its first air. In the meantime, irregular uterine contractions lead to the expulsion of the placenta, the decidua, and the membranes as the *afterbirth*. Hemorrhage is sometimes extensive but is usually limited by the rapid contraction of the uterus.

■ Survey of Growth

The period from fertilization of the ovum to delivery of the normal human fetus is believed to average 266 days. If conception occurs on the fourteenth day of the menstrual cycle, delivery may then be expected 280 days from the onset of the last menstruation. An isolated coitus resulting in pregnancy provides accurate information concerning the length of the gestation period.

The embryonic period is the period of most rapid growth in the life of an organism. The human embryo increases its size over three million times as it evolves from the fertilized ovum to the newborn (Figs. 8.43, 8.44). Its development may be conveniently divided into three stages. First is the period from the fertilization of the ovum to the end of the second week, when the embryo is successfully implanted and begins to acquire nutrition. Second is the period from the third week through the eighth week, during which all the major organ primordia appear and the embryo assumes quite human features. Third is the period of the fetus, from the third month through the tenth month, during which the organ systems are refined and the parasitic organism gradually becomes able to survive independently of its host environment. If the term fetus were restricted to the period at which independent existence is possible, it would be applicable only after 4 or 5 months.

The age of the embryo can be estimated from the normal crown-rump length and the total body weight. The values given in Table 8.1 derive from various sources and are probably average.

It is evident that the fetus gains weight more rapidly than length. During the last 2 months of pregnancy weight almost doubles while crown-rump length increases only 25%. The exact age of the human embryo is rather difficult to determine, but data are being accumulated so that the ages of embryos at more than 18 days postconception can be gauged by the number of paired somites.

Table 8.1   Relation of age to crown-rump length and weight

AGE	LENGTH, MM.	WEIGHT, GRAMS
20 days	2.3	
21 days	2.3+	
22 days	2.5–3.0	
3–4 weeks	3.5–4.0	
4 weeks	4–5	0.02
5 weeks	7–8	
6 weeks	12–13	
7 weeks	17–20	
8 weeks	27–30	1.0
9 weeks	39–41	
10 weeks	50–55	
11 weeks	64–66	
12 weeks	75–80	14–20
13 weeks	91–93	
14 weeks	105–107	
15 weeks	119–121	
16 weeks	132–134	
17 weeks	147±	105–120
18 weeks	160±	
19 weeks	173±	
20 weeks	185±	
21 weeks	197±	200–310
22 weeks	208±	
23 weeks	219±	
24 weeks	236±	635–650
28 weeks	270±	
32 weeks	310±	1080–1225
36 weeks	346±	1670–1700
38 weeks	362±	2240–2400

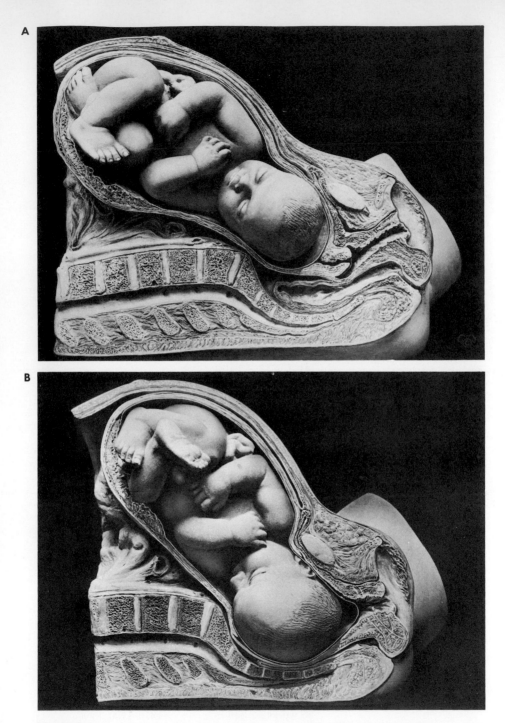

Fig. 8.42   Lateral views of human parturition. (From *Birth Atlas*, Maternity Center Association, New York.)

C

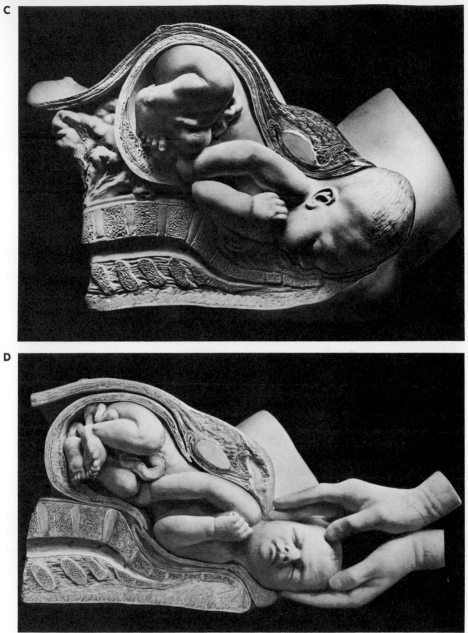

D

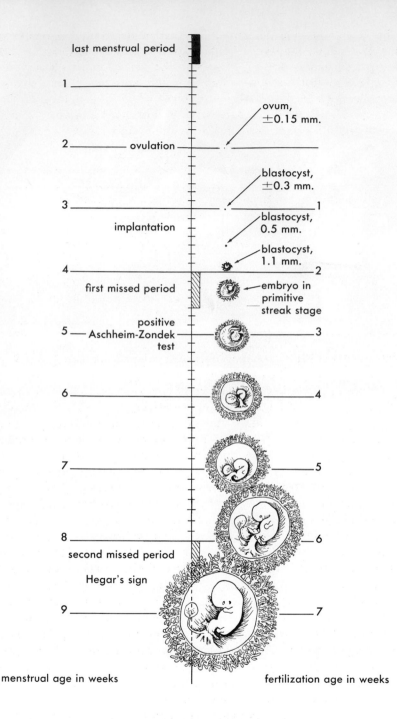

last menstrual period

1

2 — ovulation

ovum, ±0.15 mm.

blastocyst, ±0.3 mm.

3 — 1

implantation

blastocyst, 0.5 mm.

blastocyst, 1.1 mm.

4 — 2

first missed period

embryo in primitive streak stage

5 — positive Aschheim-Zondek test — 3

6 — 4

7 — 5

8 — 6

second missed period

Hegar's sign

9 — 7

menstrual age in weeks

fertilization age in weeks

Fig. 8.43 Relation of size of human embryo and membranes to age. (From B. M. Patten, *Human Embryology*, 2nd ed., McGraw-Hill, New York, 1953.)

The first embryonic differentiation, that of the central nervous system, begins shortly after the start of implantation at 7 days. At about 18 days the earliest paired somites appear. Therefore, the 18-day embryo is very actively deriving its central nervous system and its basic muscular and skeletal systems. Between 18 and 32 days most, if not all, of the somites form. The 44 pairs are as follows: occipital, 4; cervical, 8; thoracic, 12; lumbar, 5; sacral, 5; and coccygeal, 10. Their relation to the age of the embryo is shown in Table 8.2.

Table 8.2   Relation of age to number of somite pairs

AGE, DAYS	SOMITES	AGE, DAYS	SOMITES
18	1–3	26	27–28
19	4–7	27	29–30
20	8–11	28	30–31
21	12–14	29	32–33
22	15–17	30	34–35
23	18–20	31	36–37
24	21–23	32	38–39
25	24–26		

During the second month the length of the embryo increases sixfold, paired arms and legs appear, the cervical flexure bends the anterior tip of the head down onto the cardiac region, both *auditory* and *optic vesicles* are prominent, the *olfactory placodes* begin to form, the *visceral grooves* are evident, and, toward the end of the month, the eyes, ears, fingers, and toes give the embryo a human look. The head is out of all proportion to the rest of the body, largely owing to the rapid and early growth of the *prosencephalon*.

During the third month the embryo doubles its length, and all its major organs are actively differentiating. Differentiation continues, and the process is not complete in some organs (for example, the *cerebellum*) until after birth.

Except for details due to anatomical variations between the adult human and the adult mouse or the adult pig, the later embryonic development of all these mammals is basically the same. However, because of these structural variations, the derivatives of the germ layers in the human are enumerated here.

DERIVATIVES OF THE ECTODERM. The *epidermis* and its derivatives, such as hair, nails, and lining of the sweat, sebaceous, and mammary glands; the epithelium of the mouth, lower anal canal, and terminal portions of the urogenital system; the *anterior pituitary gland* (*Rathke's pocket*); the *lens* of the eye, epithelial covering of the *cornea*, and epithelial covering of the *tympanic membrane*; the entire nervous system (except the *microglia*, which are mesodermal connective tissue cells); parts of the *suprarenal glands*; the muscles of the *iris*; one layer of the amnion and chorion.

DERIVATIVES OF THE ENDODERM. The epithelial lining of the entire *gut* except for the mouth and *anus*; the derivatives of the gut, such as the *pharynx, thymus, thyroid, parathyroid, larynx, trachea, bronchi, lung alveoli,*

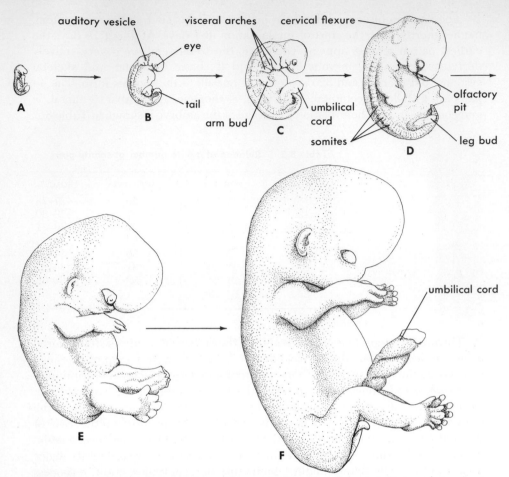

Fig. 8.44 Changes in proportions of human body parts with age: A–H, in embryo; A, at 3 weeks (2.3 mm.); B, at 4 weeks (4–5 mm.); C, at 5 weeks (7–8 mm.); D, at 6 weeks (12–13 mm.); E, at 7 weeks (17–20 mm.); F, G, at 8 weeks (27–30 mm.); H, at 4 months; I, in newborn; J, at 2 years; K, at 6 years; L, at 12 years; M, at 25 years. (G–M from B. M. Patten, *Human Embryology*, 2nd ed., McGraw-Hill, New York, 1953. Adapted from Scammon.)

esophagus, stomach, liver, pancreas, intestines, bladder, most of the urethra, part of the vagina, and the lining of the allantois and yolk sac.

DERIVATIVES OF THE MESODERM. The lining of the coelom and its derivatives (exocoel, pericardium, *peritoneum, pleura*); the germinal epithelium; most of the excretory system and parts of the suprarenal glands; all of the 44 somites and the cartilage, bone, and connective tissue of the skeleton; the entire blood vascular system, including the blood; the *lymphatic system* and *spleen;* the connective tissues of the various types scattered throughout the body; one layer of the somatopleure and splanchnopleure, amnion, chorion, allantois, and yolk sac.

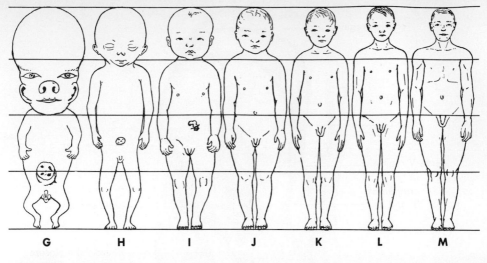

G H I J K L M

Fig. 8.44 (*continued*)

▪ Organogenesis

It is not the purpose of this text to provide a detailed description of the human embryo from conception to birth. There are excellent books on this subject. It is rather the aim of this text to provide the student with sufficient information on human development to serve as a basis for further study. What follows is therefore a succinct survey of the major events up to the fourteenth week after fertilization, with mere reference to the events of the succeeding 6 months to birth. The result is a panorama of primordia revealing the major differentiating centers at specific times. The treatment proceeds from the derivatives of the ectoderm to those of the endoderm and finally to those of the mesoderm, in so far as possible. Lengths are crown-rump measurements.

1 week (0.3 mm.)

Fertilization usually occurs in the upper Fallopian tube, and cleavage progresses to the gastrula stage during the first week, with implantation at the end of this period. The embryo is a two-layered disc with an amniotic cavity.

2 weeks (1.5 mm.)

The embryo consists only of a flat disc, in the center of which are the primitive streak, neural plate, and early groove. A head process and notochordal plate may be indicated. No endodermal derivatives are present as yet. Blood islands are arising in the extraembryonic chorion and yolk sac. The exocoel is well established, and the coelom is forming. The allantois and the rudiments of the heart are apparent.

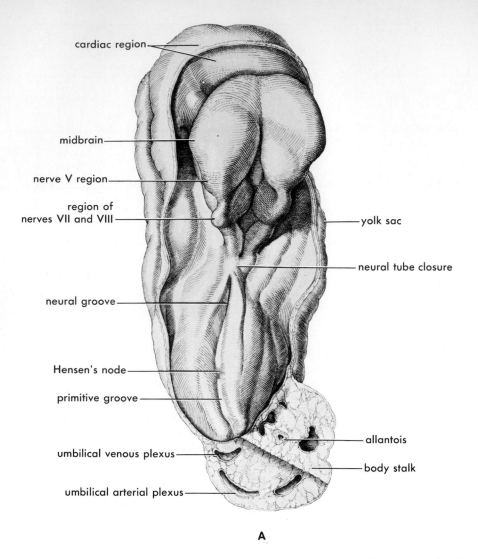

cardiac region

midbrain

nerve V region

region of
nerves VII and VIII

yolk sac

neural tube closure

neural groove

Hensen's node

primitive groove

allantois

umbilical venous plexus

body stalk

umbilical arterial plexus

A

Fig. 8.45 Human embryo at 8-somite stage: A, dorsal view; B, sagittal section; C, dorsal view of vascular system; D, lateral view of vascular system. (From C. M. West, *Carnegie Inst. Wash. Publ.* No. 407, Contribs. Embryology No. 119 (1930).)

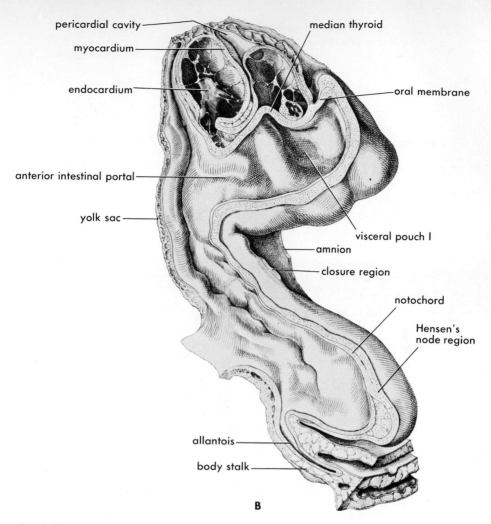

pericardial cavity

myocardium

endocardium

anterior intestinal portal

yolk sac

median thyroid

oral membrane

visceral pouch I

amnion

closure region

notochord

Hensen's node region

allantois

body stalk

B

Fig. 8.45 (continued)

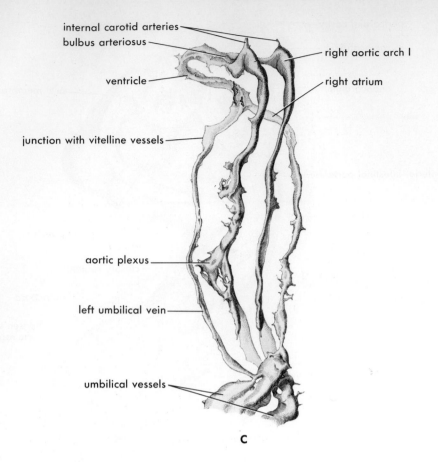

internal carotid arteries

bulbus arteriosus

right aortic arch I

ventricle

right atrium

junction with vitelline vessels

aortic plexus

left umbilical vein

umbilical vessels

C

Fig. 8.45 (continued)

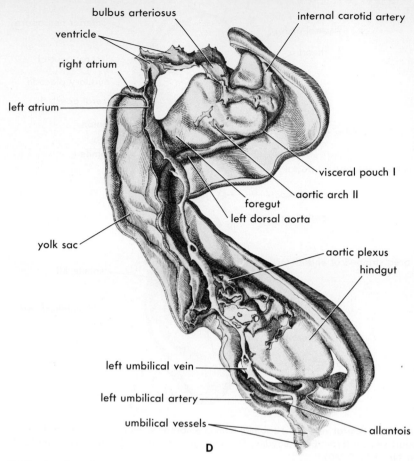

bulbus arteriosus

ventricle

right atrium

left atrium

internal carotid artery

visceral pouch I

aortic arch II

foregut

left dorsal aorta

yolk sac

aortic plexus

hindgut

left umbilical vein

left umbilical artery

umbilical vessels

allantois

D

Fig. 8.45 (continued)

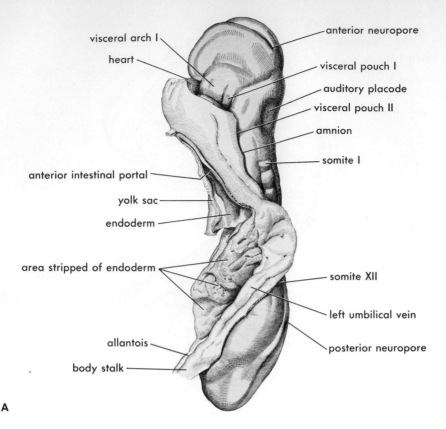

visceral arch I

heart

anterior neuropore

visceral pouch I

auditory placode

visceral pouch II

amnion

somite I

anterior intestinal portal

yolk sac

endoderm

area stripped of endoderm

somite XII

left umbilical vein

posterior neuropore

allantois

body stalk

A

Fig. 8.46 Lateral views of 12-somite human embryo: A, entire organism; B, head region; C, heart region. (From E. H. Boyden, *Carnegie Inst. Wash. Publ.* No. 518, *Contribs. Embryology* No. 175 (1940).)

3 weeks (2.3 mm.)

The neural groove is complete and beginning to close at the center, and the *neural crests* are continuous bands on either side of the forming *neural tube* (Figs. 8.45, 8.46). The optic vesicles, *auditory placodes,* and *ganglia* are present. The *stomodeum* is an ectodermal pit, and the *oral membrane* may rupture to form the mouth. An undercutting at the extremities starts the separation of the body from the yolk sac (Figs. 8.47, 8.48A,B), producing the *foregut* and *hindgut* and yolk stalk; the *pharynx* is dorsoventrally compressed and gives rise to *visceral pouches* between externally evident *visceral arches;* a thyroid pocket forms in the pharyngeal floor; and lung (*laryngotracheal groove*) and liver diverticula appear. Fourteen pairs of somites, the anterior ones with *sclerotomes* and *myotomes,* are apparent. The notochord is cellular. Blood vessels containing corpuscles arise in both the embryo and the extra-embryonic membranes and connect with an S-shaped heart, in which pulsations begin (Figs. 8.49, 8.50A,B). The pronephros forms, and its ducts grow

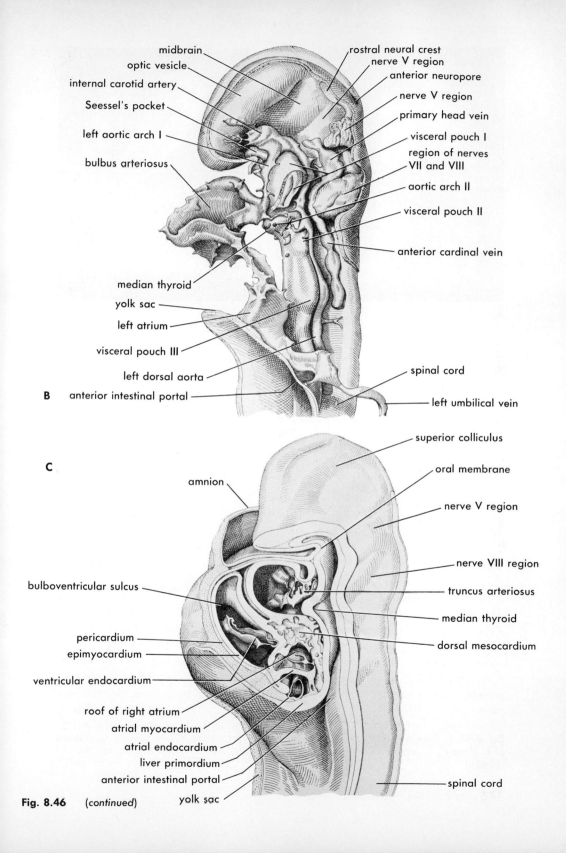

midbrain

optic vesicle

internal carotid artery

Seessel's pocket

left aortic arch I

bulbus arteriosus

rostral neural crest

nerve V region

anterior neuropore

nerve V region

primary head vein

visceral pouch I

region of nerves VII and VIII

aortic arch II

visceral pouch II

anterior cardinal vein

median thyroid

yolk sac

left atrium

visceral pouch III

left dorsal aorta

B   anterior intestinal portal

spinal cord

left umbilical vein

C

amnion

superior colliculus

oral membrane

nerve V region

nerve VIII region

bulboventricular sulcus

truncus arteriosus

median thyroid

dorsal mesocardium

pericardium

epimyocardium

ventricular endocardium

roof of right atrium

atrial myocardium

atrial endocardium

liver primordium

anterior intestinal portal

yolk sac

spinal cord

Fig. 8.46   (continued)

A

B

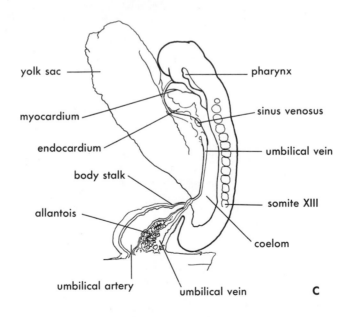

yolk sac ——————

pharynx

myocardium ——————

sinus venosus

endocardium ——————

umbilical vein

body stalk ——————

somite XIII

allantois ——————

coelom

umbilical artery ——————

umbilical vein

C

Fig. 8.47   Human embryo at 13-somite stage: A, dorsal view; B, lateral view; C, diagram of B. (From G. L. Streeter, *Carnegie Inst. Wash. Publ.* No. 541, *Contribs. Embryology* No. 197 (1942).)

446   THE HUMAN: *A Discoid Placentate*

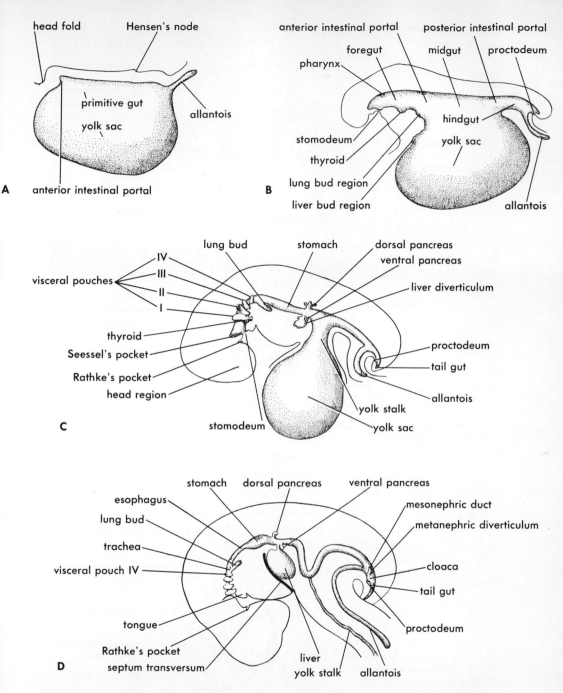

Fig. 8.48 Lateral views showing digestive tract development in human embryo: A, at about 16 days; B, at about 18 days; C, at about 25 days; D, at about 4½ weeks; E, at 5 to 6 weeks; F, at about 8 weeks; G, at about 9½ weeks. (From O. E. Nelsen, *Comparative Embryology of the Vertebrates*, McGraw-Hill, New York, 1953.)

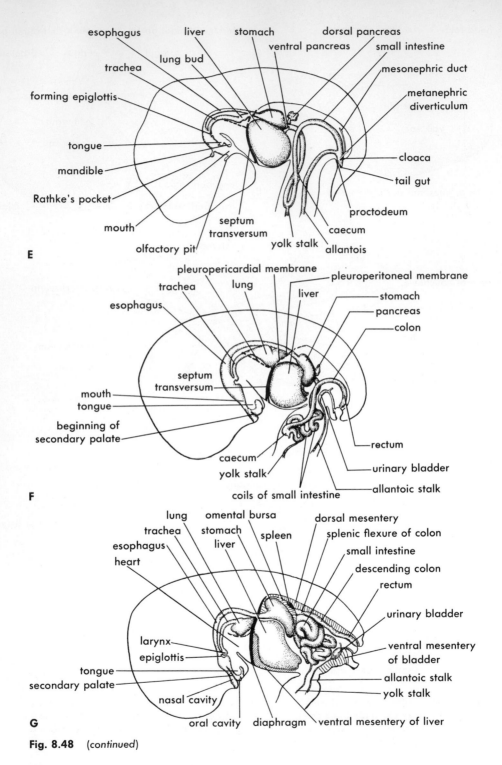

Fig. 8.48 (continued)

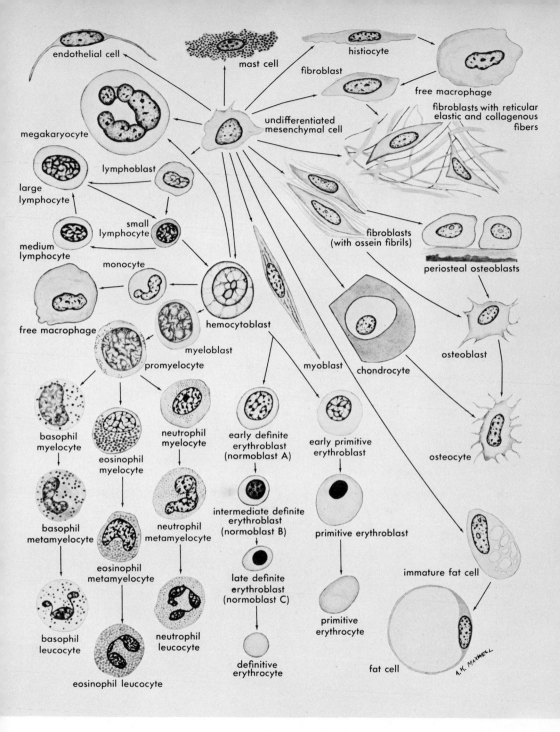

Fig. 8.49 Differentiation of various cells from mesenchymal cell in human. (From W. J. Hamilton, J. D. Boyd, and H. W. Mossman, *Human Embryology*, 2nd ed., Williams & Wilkins, Baltimore, 1952.)

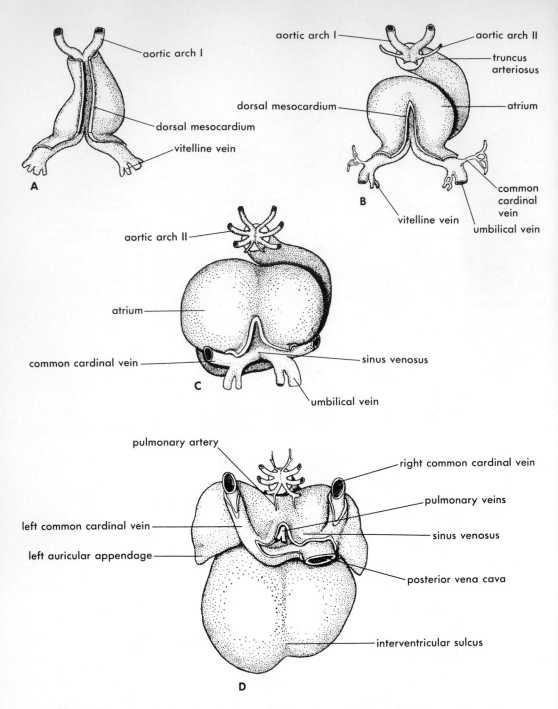

Fig. 8.50 Dorsal views showing heart development in human embryo: A, at 2½ weeks; B, at 3 weeks; C, at 3½ weeks; D, at 5 weeks; E, at 8 weeks; F, at 11 weeks. (From B. M. Patten, *Human Embryology*, 2nd ed., McGraw-Hill, New York, 1953.)

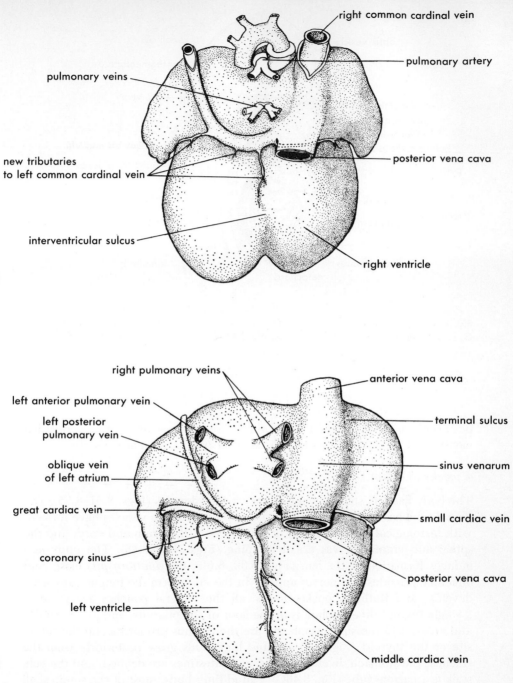

E

right common cardinal vein

pulmonary artery

pulmonary veins

posterior vena cava

new tributaries
to left common cardinal vein

interventricular sulcus

right ventricle

F

right pulmonary veins

anterior vena cava

left anterior pulmonary vein

terminal sulcus

left posterior
pulmonary vein

sinus venarum

oblique vein
of left atrium

great cardiac vein

small cardiac vein

coronary sinus

posterior vena cava

left ventricle

middle cardiac vein

Organogenesis **451**

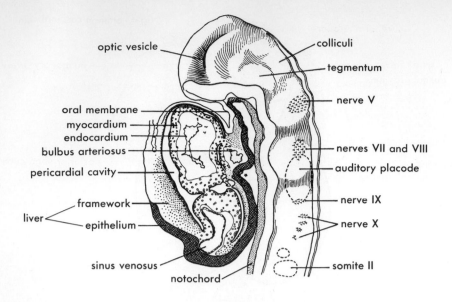

optic vesicle

colliculi

tegmentum

nerve V

oral membrane

myocardium

endocardium

bulbus arteriosus

pericardial cavity

nerves VII and VIII

auditory placode

framework

liver

epithelium

nerve IX

nerve X

sinus venosus

notochord

somite II

Fig. 8.51   Lateral view of head and heart regions of 16-somite human embryo. (From G. L. Streeter, *Carnegie Inst. Wash. Publ.* No. 541, *Contribs. Embryology* No. 197 (1942).)

posteriorly to the cloaca. Part of the coelom closes off as the pericardial cavity; and the mesenteries and the *septum transversum* are evident.

4 weeks (5.0 mm.)

The body has a C shape, owing to the various flexures (Figs. 8.51–8.55). The neural tube has entirely closed; the three primary brain vesicles have formed, with histological differentiation of the layers of the brain and cord; and the spinal and cranial nerves are developing (Figs. 8.56–8.58). The *optic cup* induces formation of the lens (Figs. 8.59, 8.60), the *auditory pits* close, and olfactory placodes and nerves appear. In the endoderm the tongue primordia develop, and Rathke's pocket forms; all the visceral pouches are present; a single thyroid diverticulum is in the floor of the pharynx, and just behind it and anterior to the short esophagus are the thymus primordia and the future site of the thyroid (Fig. 8.61); paired lung buds grow posteriorly from the trachea; the stomach, liver, pancreas, and intestines are defined; and the yolk stalk is a narrow tube (Fig. 8.48C). Paired limb buds, most of the somites, all the visceral arches, and *maxillary processes* are apparent. Primitive vertebral organization is evident around the notochord. Abundant blood is forming in

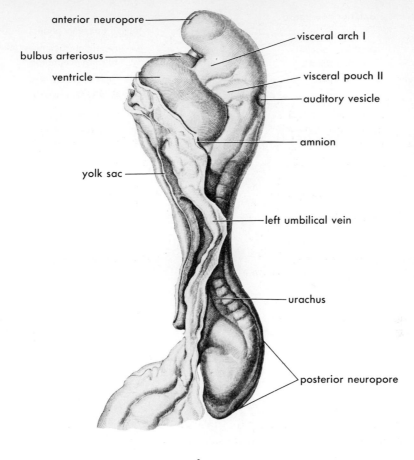

anterior neuropore

bulbus arteriosus

ventricle

yolk sac

visceral arch I

visceral pouch II

auditory vesicle

amnion

left umbilical vein

urachus

posterior neuropore

A

Fig. 8.52 Human embryo at 17-somite stage: A, lateral view; B, sagittal section; C, lateral view of vascular system. (From W. J. Atwell, *Carnegie Inst. Wash. Publ.* No. 407, *Contribs. Embryology* No. 118 (1930).)

the yolk sac splanchnopleure and circulating through the body vessels (Figs. 8.62–8.64); and the heart is tubular but shows a *sinus venosus, ventricle, atrium,* and *bulbus arteriosus* (8.50C). The pronephros is degenerating as the mesonephros is developing, and the metanephros arises as a diverticulum from the cloaca (Figs. 8.5A, 8.6A).

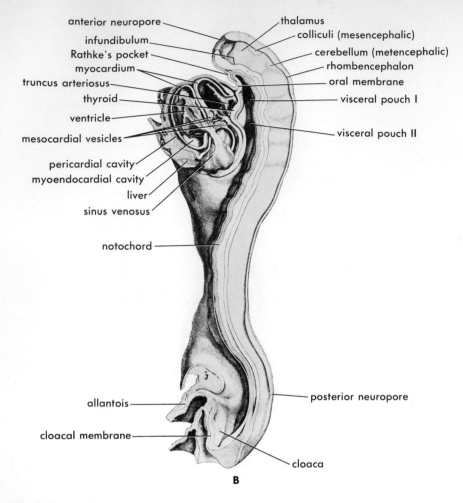

anterior neuropore

infundibulum

Rathke's pocket

myocardium

truncus arteriosus

thyroid

ventricle

mesocardial vesicles

pericardial cavity

myoendocardial cavity

liver

sinus venosus

notochord

allantois

cloacal membrane

thalamus

colliculi (mesencephalic)

cerebellum (metencephalic)

rhombencephalon

oral membrane

visceral pouch I

visceral pouch II

posterior neuropore

cloaca

B

Fig. 8.52 (continued)

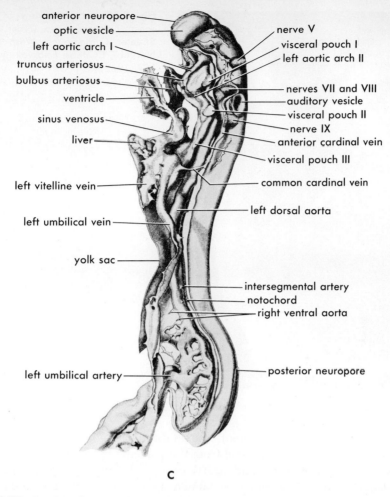

anterior neuropore
optic vesicle
left aortic arch I
truncus arteriosus
bulbus arteriosus
ventricle
sinus venosus
liver
left vitelline vein
left umbilical vein
yolk sac
left umbilical artery

nerve V
visceral pouch I
left aortic arch II
nerves VII and VIII
auditory vesicle
visceral pouch II
nerve IX
anterior cardinal vein
visceral pouch III
common cardinal vein
left dorsal aorta
intersegmental artery
notochord
right ventral aorta
posterior neuropore

C

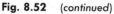

Fig. 8.52 (continued)

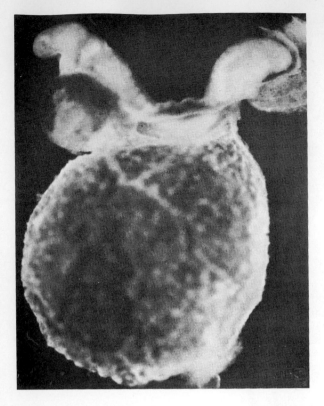

Fig. 8.53 Lateral view of 19-somite human embryo. (From G. L. Streeter, Carnegie Inst. Wash. Publ. No. 541, Contribs. Embryology No. 197 (1942).)

5 weeks (8 mm.)

The *olfactory pits* are prominent, the embryo has a temporary tail, the umbilical cord is the main channel from the placenta to the embryo, and the viscera (mesonephroi, liver, and heart) cause a bulging of the body (Fig. 8.65A–D). The face is assuming a human appearance with jaws indicated (Figs. 8.66, 8.67). The ectoderm is a double-layered epidermis; five brain vesicles are present, with obvious cephalization; the eye has a lens and *choroid fissure,* and *vitreous humor* is forming; and *endolymphatic ducts* are evident. Rathke's pocket moves toward the *infundibulum;* derivatives of the visceral pouches form; the thyroid loses its connection with the pharynx and becomes bilobed; bronchial buds develop; the *gall bladder* and the *ductus choledochus* arise, and a *cystic duct* forms between them while a *hepatic duct* forms between the liver and the ductus (Fig. 8.6B,C); the yolk stalk separates from the gut; and the intestines elongate (Figs. 8.48D, 8.68). The trunk and appendage muscles develop (Fig. 8.69), and bone-forming centers arise. The circulatory system is extensive within the body; the heart begins its final divisions (Fig. 8.50D); and the spleen primordium appears. The mesonephros is complete (Figs. 8.5B, 8.6B,C); genital ridges form; and *ureters* develop. Membranes begin to divide the coelom into pericardial, peritoneal, and pleural cavities (Fig. 8.48D).

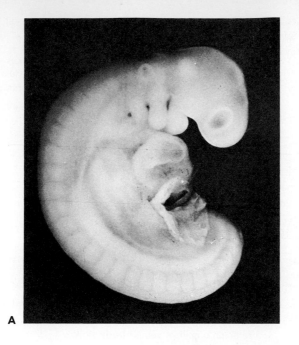

A

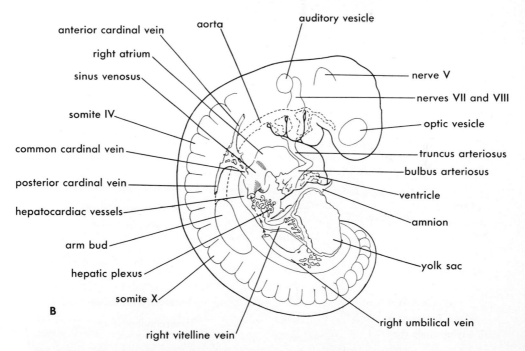

anterior cardinal vein

right atrium

sinus venosus

somite IV

common cardinal vein

posterior cardinal vein

hepatocardiac vessels

arm bud

hepatic plexus

somite X

B

right vitelline vein

aorta

auditory vesicle

nerve V

nerves VII and VIII

optic vesicle

truncus arteriosus

bulbus arteriosus

ventricle

amnion

yolk sac

right umbilical vein

Fig. 8.54   Human embryo at 28-somite stage: A, lateral view; B, C, diagrams of A, showing heart and vascular system. (From G. L. Streeter, *Carnegie Inst. Wash. Publ.* No. 541, *Contribs. Embryology* No. 197 (1942).)

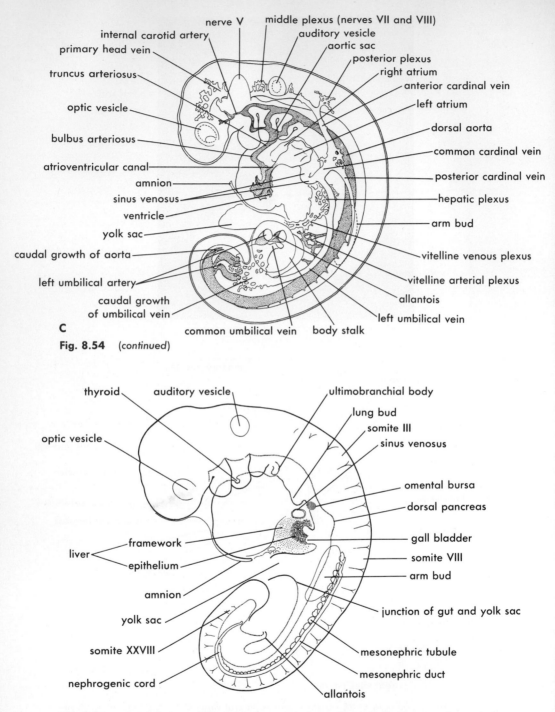

C

Fig. 8.54 (*continued*)

Labels for Fig. 8.54 C:
nerve V
middle plexus (nerves VII and VIII)
internal carotid artery
auditory vesicle
primary head vein
aortic sac
truncus arteriosus
posterior plexus
right atrium
optic vesicle
anterior cardinal vein
bulbus arteriosus
left atrium
dorsal aorta
atrioventricular canal
common cardinal vein
amnion
posterior cardinal vein
sinus venosus
hepatic plexus
ventricle
arm bud
yolk sac
caudal growth of aorta
vitelline venous plexus
left umbilical artery
vitelline arterial plexus
caudal growth of umbilical vein
allantois
left umbilical vein
common umbilical vein
body stalk

Labels for Fig. 8.55:
thyroid
auditory vesicle
ultimobranchial body
lung bud
somite III
sinus venosus
optic vesicle
omental bursa
dorsal pancreas
framework
gall bladder
liver
somite VIII
epithelium
arm bud
amnion
junction of gut and yolk sac
yolk sac
somite XXVIII
mesonephric tubule
nephrogenic cord
mesonephric duct
allantois

Fig. 8.55 Lateral view of 29-somite human embryo. (From G. L. Streeter, *Carnegie Inst. Wash. Publ.* No. 541, *Contribs. Embryology* No. 197 (1942).)

6 weeks (13 mm.)

The head is relatively enormous but bent onto the chest by the *cervical flexure;* and the limbs, digits, and *milk line* are evident (Figs. 8.65E–J, 8.70). The *diencephalon* is excessively large (Fig. 8.57D). The region of the *anterior neuropore* becomes the *epiphysis;* the cranial ganglia are prominent (Fig. 8.71), and *sympathetic ganglia* form; the optic cup is double-layered and contains a thick lens; and all the ear parts are differentiating. The oral glands develop; the thyroid is solid and bilobed; the lung buds and bronchi branch; the larynx is briefly obstructed; the stomach and intestine rotate; and liver lobes form (Fig. 8.48E). Elongated muscles arise from the fusion of myotomes. Chondrification occurs in the mesenchyme, principally in the head; the bilateral jaw parts are fusing; and cartilage primordia are apparent (Fig. 8.72). The liver becomes a hematopoietic center; and the heart is the four-chambered organ of the adult with the left umbilical vein and *ductus venosus* assuming leading roles in circulation (Figs. 8.64B,C,G, 8.73). Undifferentiated gonad primordia are prominent (Fig. 8.74), and Müllerian ducts are distinguishable. The heart and lungs are separated by completed membranes, and the *dorsal mesentery* is extended along the gut.

7 weeks (20 mm.)

Externally the embryo shows a beginning distinction between the head and neck although the head continues to be large because of the growth of the *cerebral hemispheres* (Figs. 8.57E, 8.65K–Q). The back is straighter than before, the tail is regressing, the digits are complete, and the milk line is developing. The ancestral visceral arches are gone, but the abdominal bulge remains because of the size of the liver and the cardiac region. The pituitary arises as Rathke's pocket and the infundibulum make contact, and the brain shows many sites of active differentiation (Fig. 8.75). The eye is well developed, with the choroid fissure closed and eyelids forming; and olfactory connections with the mouth appear (Fig. 8.76). The *suprarenal medulla* begins to penetrate the *cortex.* The endodermally derived cover of the tongue is complete since the three mesodermal tongue primordia are fused; the thymus, parathyroids, thyroid, and *ultimobranchial* bodies are all differentiating; the lungs and bronchi are developing well (Fig. 8.77); the stomach has a shape as in the adult; the *duodenum* is stenosed; the pancreatic rudiments are fused; the gut projects into the umbilical cord; the urogenital cavities are separated; and the *proctodeum* ruptures through the *cloacal membrane.* All the body muscles are organizing well; chondrification is extensive; and the jaws, vertebrae, and ribs are ossifying (Fig. 8.78). The arterial system sends branches throughout the body (Fig. 8.79); the venous system shifts so that the *posterior vena cava* comes into prominence (Fig. 8.64D,H); cardiac valves develop; and the spleen primordium enlarges. The mesonephros is most active, but the metanephros is differentiating rapidly, with some secreting tubules apparent (Fig. 8.6D).

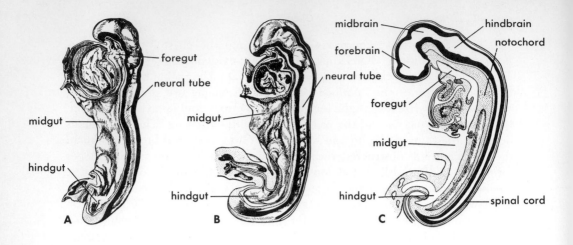

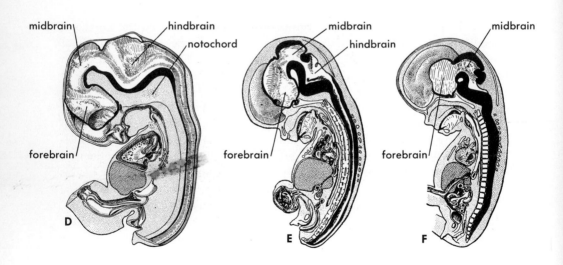

Fig. 8.56 Sagittal sections showing development of human central nervous system: A, at 20 days; B, at about 22 days; C, at 4 weeks; D, at 7 weeks; E, at 8 weeks; F, at 10 weeks; G, at 12 weeks; H, at 20 weeks; I, at 24 weeks; J, at 34 weeks; K, in newborn; L, at 6 years; M, in adult. (From J. P. Schaeffer, ed., *Morris' Human Anatomy*, 11th ed., McGraw-Hill, 1953. Adapted from Lewis.)

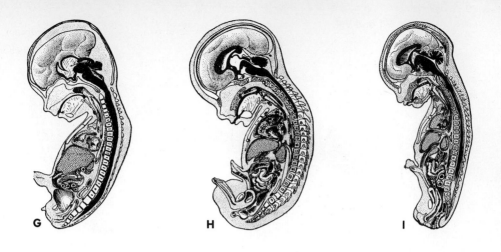

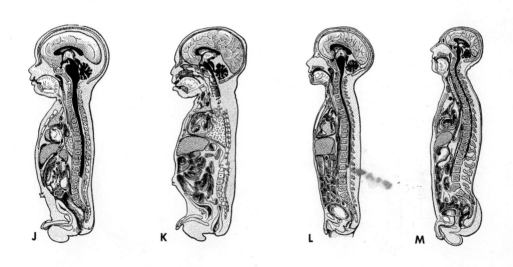

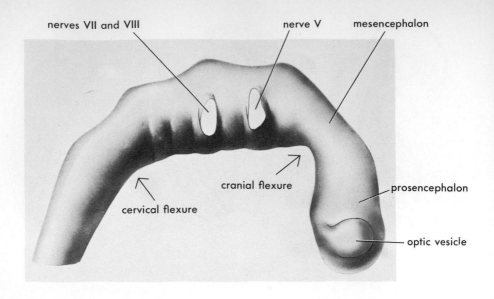

A

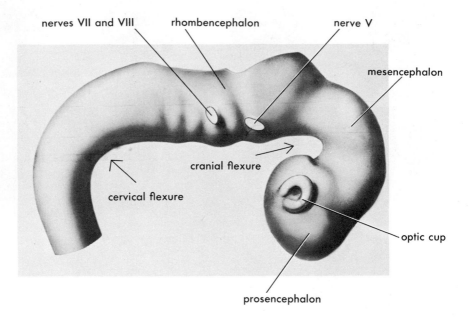

B

Fig. 8.57 Lateral views showing brain development in human embryo: A, at 3½ mm.; B, at 5 mm.; C, at 9 mm.; D, at 11 mm.; E, at 15 mm.; F, at 27 mm.; G, at 53 mm. (From W. J. Hamilton, J. D. Boyd, and H. W. Mossman, *Human Embryology*, 2nd ed., Williams & Wilkins, Baltimore, 1952. Adapted from Hochstetter.)

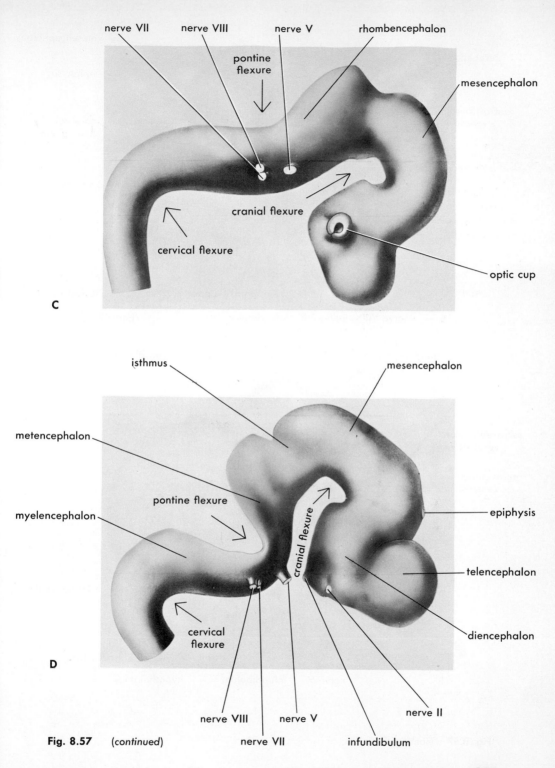

nerve VII   nerve VIII   nerve V   rhombencephalon

pontine
flexure

mesencephalon

cranial flexure

cervical flexure

optic cup

C

isthmus   mesencephalon

metencephalon

pontine flexure

cranial flexure

epiphysis

myelencephalon

telencephalon

diencephalon

cervical
flexure

D

nerve VIII   nerve V

nerve II

nerve VII

infundibulum

Fig. 8.57 (continued)

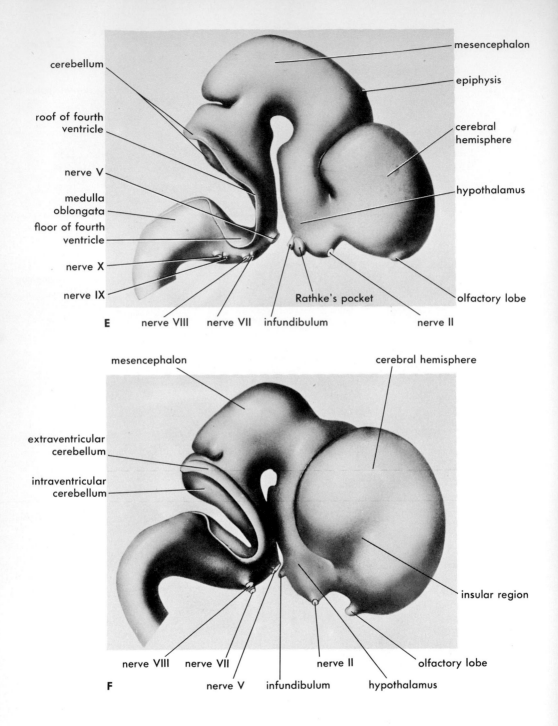

E

cerebellum
roof of fourth ventricle
nerve V
medulla oblongata
floor of fourth ventricle
nerve X
nerve IX
nerve VIII
nerve VII
infundibulum
Rathke's pocket

mesencephalon
epiphysis
cerebral hemisphere
hypothalamus
olfactory lobe
nerve II

F

mesencephalon
extraventricular cerebellum
intraventricular cerebellum
nerve VIII
nerve VII
nerve V
infundibulum

cerebral hemisphere
insular region
olfactory lobe
hypothalamus
nerve II

Fig. 8.57 (continued)

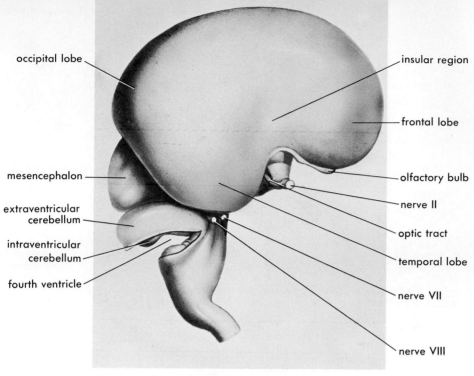

occipital lobe

insular region

frontal lobe

mesencephalon

extraventricular cerebellum

intraventricular cerebellum

fourth ventricle

olfactory bulb

nerve II

optic tract

temporal lobe

nerve VII

nerve VIII

G

Fig. 8.57 (*continued*)

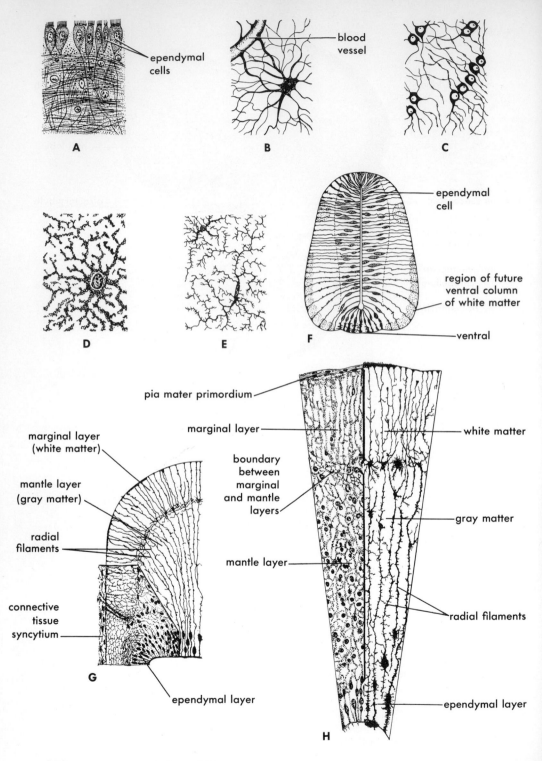

A

ependymal cells

B

blood vessel

C

D

E

F

ependymal cell

region of future ventral column of white matter

ventral

G

pia mater primordium

marginal layer

boundary between marginal and mantle layers

mantle layer

marginal layer (white matter)

mantle layer (gray matter)

radial filaments

connective tissue syncytium

ependymal layer

H

white matter

gray matter

radial filaments

ependymal layer

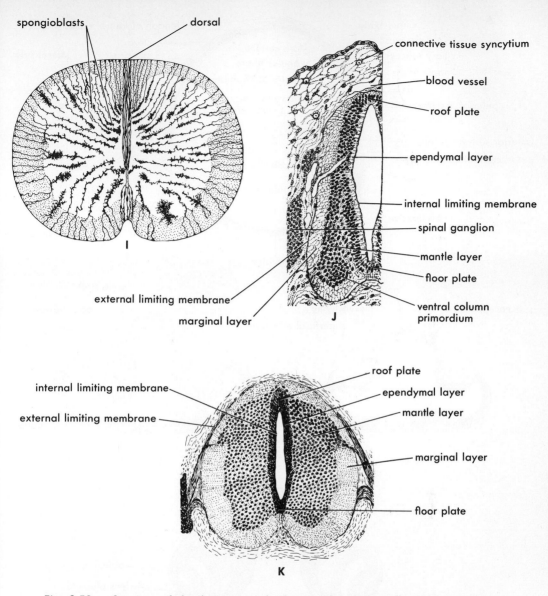

Fig. 8.58 Structure of developing neural tube: A, ciliated neuroglia from ependymal layer of fourth ventricle of cat; B, fibrous astrocyte; C, oligodendroglia; D, protoplasmic astrocyte; E, microglia; F, transverse section of neural tube of 3-day chick, showing spongioblasts; G, transverse section of part of spinal cord of 15-mm. pig; H, transverse section of part of spinal cord of 55-mm. pig; I, transverse section of spinal cord of newborn mouse, showing spongioblasts moving peripherally from the central canal and transforming into astrocytes; J, transverse section of part of spinal cord of 9-mm. pig; K, transverse section of spinal cord of 20-mm. opossum. (From O. E. Nelsen, *Comparative Embryology of the Vertebrates*, McGraw-Hill, New York, 1953. A adapted from Maximow and Bloom after Rubaschkin; B, C, D, E adapted from Ransom after Rio Hortega; F adapted from Maximow and Bloom after Cajal; G, H, J adapted from Hardesty.)

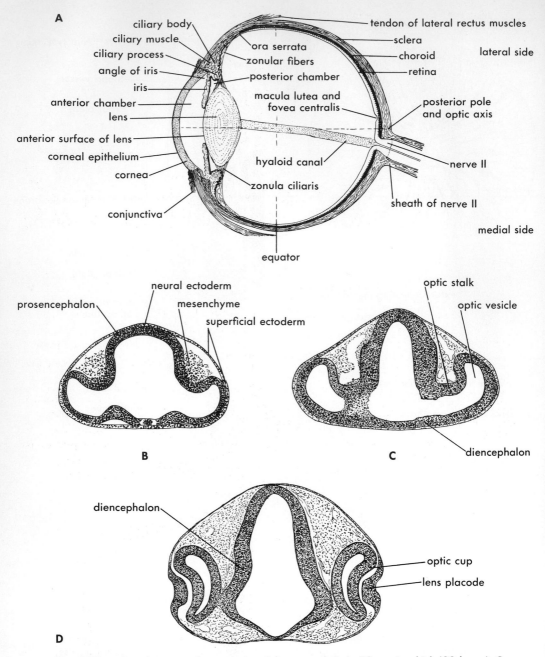

Fig. 8.59 Development of eye: A, in adult mammal; B, in 12-somite chick (38 hours); C, in 16-somite chick (45 to 49 hours); D, in 22-somite chick (50 hours); E, in 55-hour chick; F, ventral view of E; G, in 72- to 75-hour chick (40 somites); H, in 96- to 100-hour chick; I, in 8- to 9-day chick; J, in 18-mm. pig (sagittal section); K, retina. (From O. E. Nelsen, *Comparative Embryology of the Vertebrates*, McGraw-Hill, New York, 1953. A adapted from Morris.)

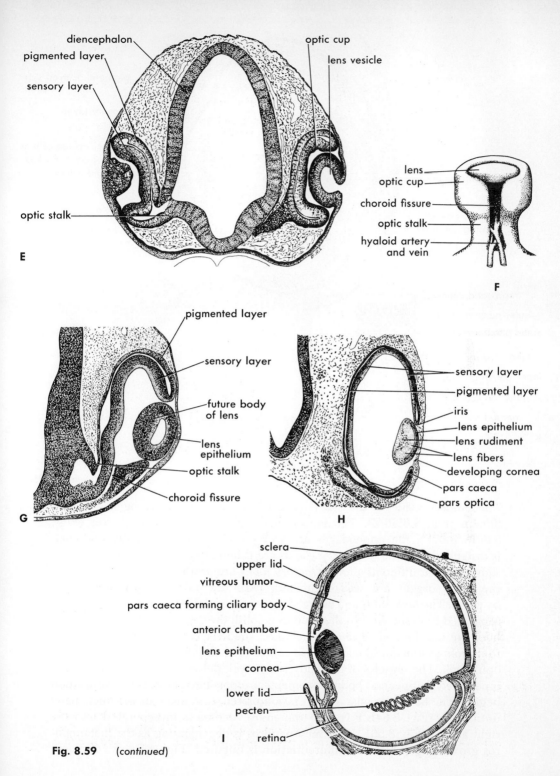

Fig. 8.59 (*continued*)

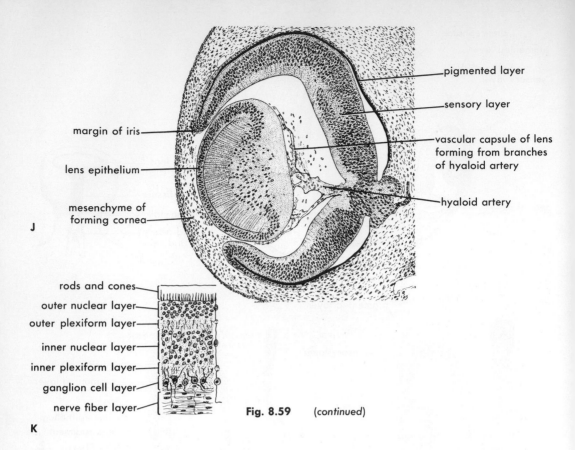

pigmented layer

sensory layer

margin of iris

vascular capsule of lens forming from branches of hyaloid artery

lens epithelium

hyaloid artery

mesenchyme of forming cornea

J

rods and cones
outer nuclear layer
outer plexiform layer
inner nuclear layer
inner plexiform layer
ganglion cell layer
nerve fiber layer

Fig. 8.59   (*continued*)

K

8 weeks (30 mm.)

The embryo achieves the status of a fetus and is easily recognizable as a human (Fig. 8.65R–Z). The face is flat with widely separated eyes (Figs. 8.66F, 8.67F), the appendages are well formed with digits, the abdomen is distended, and the mammary glands are differentiating. The cerebral cortex shows cellular differentiation; *olfactory lobes* are prominent (Fig. 8.57F); and the sense organs are well organized, with the *nares* temporarily closed by plugs. The *taste buds* and oral glands are formed; Rathke's pocket becomes separated from the mouth; the thymus is solid; the thyroid is cellular; the lung buds are multibranched into bronchioles; the liver is excessively large owing to its role as a major hematopoietic center (Fig. 8.48F); and the gut is developing villi. The muscles of the body are so well differentiated, organized, and innervated that general body movements are possible; and skeletal ossification begins. The blood vascular system is completed, to remain almost unchanged until birth (Fig. 8.64E,F,I); and the sinus venosus is incorporated into the right atrium (Fig. 8.50E). The mesonephros is degenerating as the metanephros grows (Fig. 8.6E); sex differentiation is initiated (Figs. 8.8B, 8.14A); and

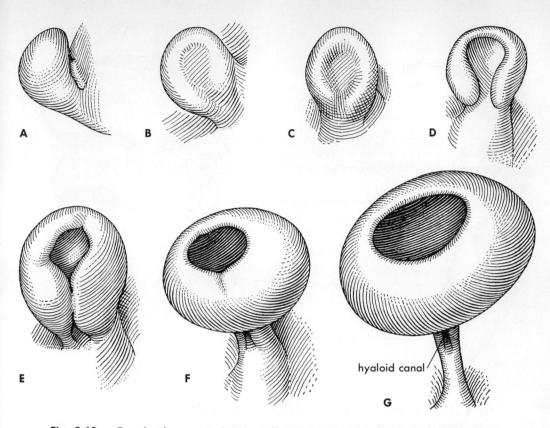

Fig. 8.60 Eye development in human embryo between 27 and 37 days. (From G. L. Streeter, *Carnegie Inst. Wash. Publ.* No. 592, *Contribs. Embryology* No. 230 (1951).)

the Müllerian ducts join the cloaca. The pericardial cavity is enlarged; and the *diaphragm* is forming.

9 weeks (41 mm.)

The head is no longer bent on the chest, the back is straight, and the abdomen is less prominent than at 8 weeks (Fig. 8.65A'–G'). Nails and hair follicles are forming; the epidermis is multilayered; the spinal cord is histologically differentiated; and the eye has an *iris*, a *ciliary body*, and eyelids. The *enamel organs* and *dental papillae* arise in the oral cavity; the thymus is cellular and enlarging; the ultimobranchial bodies degenerate; the gut withdraws into the body from the umbilical cord; and the pancreas shows cellular differentiation. All skeletal and muscular organizations are advanced except the *perineal* muscles, which begin to form; and chondrification and ossification are active (Fig. 8.80), with nasal cartilages partitioning the nares. The metanephric kidney is functional and secreting (Fig. 8.5C); useless genital ducts degenerate; and the bladder and vagina of the female are developing.

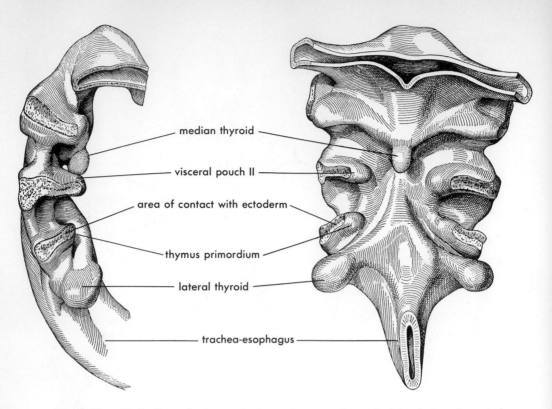

median thyroid

visceral pouch II

area of contact with ectoderm

thymus primordium

lateral thyroid

trachea-esophagus

Fig. 8.61   Derivatives of pharynx in 4-mm. human embryo: A, lateral view; B, ventral view. (From G. L. Weller, Jr., *Carnegie Inst. Wash. Publ.* No. 443, *Contribs. Embryology* No. 141 (1933).)

10 weeks (55 mm.)

The head is still out of proportion to the rest of the body; the face is more human than before; and sex may be determined externally. The epidermis is completed; the brain is essentially that of the newborn, except for refinements (Figs. 8.56F, 8.57G); *neuroglia* are abundant; the *retina* is multilayered; and the nasal structures are completed. The *palate* fuses, and tooth formation is indicated; the thymus appears lymphoid for the first time; the thyroid is completed; the lungs are almost completed (Fig. 8.48G); the gall bladder secretes bile; the *islands of Langerhans* are formed; and the gut could be functional. The smooth musculature of the entire gut, from mouth to anus, is extensively organized; the notochord is resorbing; and ossification extends to the small bones. Hematopoiesis is evident in the bone marrow; and the blood vessels acquire additional coats. The gonads are actively differentiating (Fig. 8.14C, D), and secondary sexual characters are emphasized (Fig. 8.8F, I). The *omentum* and mesenteries become important.

472   THE HUMAN: *A Discoid Placentate*

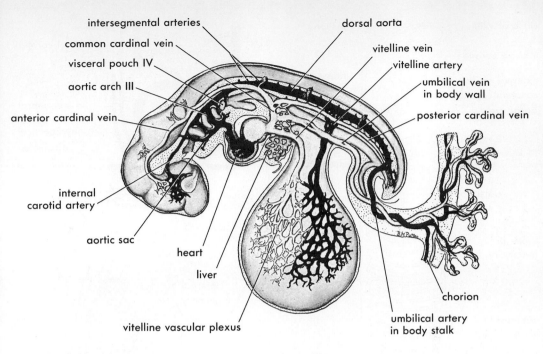

Fig. 8.62   Lateral view of vascular system of 4-week human embryo. (From L. B. Arey, *Developmental Anatomy*, 6th ed., Saunders, Philadelphia, 1954. Adapted from Patten.)

14 weeks (107 mm.)

Proportions of the head and body are approaching the normal, with reduction in head growth and increase in body growth (Fig. 8.71). Hair, sweat glands, and sebaceous glands are appearing in the well-formed epidermis. The cerebral hemispheres overlap the rest of the brain, and the cerebellum is becoming evident (Fig. 8.56G). The sense organs are almost completed; nasal sinuses are forming; and the pituitary continues to develop. The *tonsils* are enlarged, with lymphocytes; the respiratory system is almost completed; and the digestive tract glands are appearing. Cardiac muscle is substantial; almost all the bones are indicated, except in the digits; and spontaneous body movements are frequent. The spleen is active in hematopoiesis. The heart is almost completed (Fig. 8.50F). The metanephros is like the kidney of the newborn, the mesonephros is degenerating, and urogenital structures are well differentiated in both sexes (Fig. 8.8G,J). The mesenteries are well formed.

After 18 weeks (160 mm. on)

Fetal *lanugo* develops. The proportions approach those of the newborn, but the body is thin and wrinkled, and the skin is red (Fig. 8.65H'). The eyes reopen.

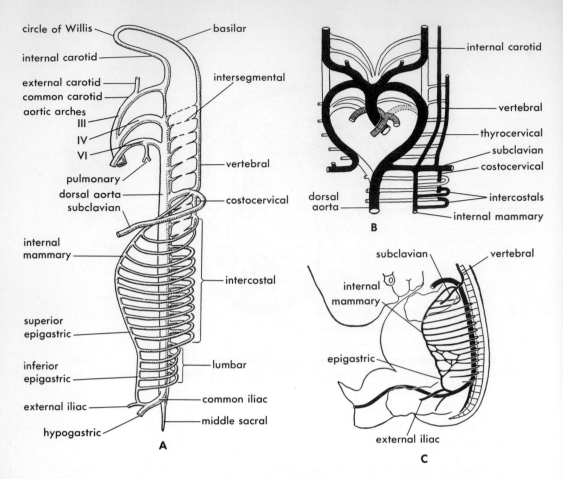

Fig. 8.63 Derivatives of dorsal branches (intersegmental arteries) of human aorta: A, lateral view; B, ventral view, showing origins in vicinity of subclavian artery; C, lateral view, showing origins and relations of internal mammary and epigastric arteries at 16 mm. (From L. B. Arey, *Developmental Anatomy,* 6th ed., Saunders, Philadelphia, 1954. Adapted from Mall.)

The cerebral cortex becomes convoluted and creased; myelination of the cord and then the brain is achieved; the head sense organs acquire skeletal parts (Fig. 8.81); and the retina becomes light-sensitive, although the ear is not yet audiosensitive. Permanent teeth primordia are present, but the milk teeth are not yet exposed; the tonsils are fully formed; lung alveoli are developing but are not completed even at birth; and the large intestine is distinguishable. The digestive tract layers are well developed; the somatic muscles are frequently active; and the perineal muscles are completed. The digital bones are ossifying, and epiphyseal centers appear in a few places. Hematopoiesis is more active in the bone marrow and less active in the liver (Fig. 8.82); and extensive and sudden changes occur in the circulatory system at delivery, with the cut-off of placental circulation, the closure of the ductus arteriosus, and the inflation of the lungs. The kidneys are completed; in the female the vagina, uterus, and accessory glands are completed (Figs. 8.8D,K, 8.14E,F); and in the male the testes descend, usually just before delivery, into the otherwise unexpanded scrotum (Fig. 8.8C,H).

■ Experimental Embryology

Since experimentation with the human embryo is obviously impossible, investigators must rely on studies of rodents and other suitable forms for their knowledge of most human anomalies. However, it has been shown clinically that rubella, radiation, and certain drugs produce some congenital anomalies in the human, and the diagnosis of additional anomalies is possible early in life through examination of the chromosomes.

Genetics, or the study of the mechanisms of heredity, is no longer concentrated chiefly on plants and Drosophila. Data are rapidly accumulating on the inheritance mechanisms in the rodent and in man, and the number of centers for human studies is growing. This progress is due in part to the development of new and reliable methods for the counting and identifying of mammalian chromosomes.

The diploid number of human chromosomes was long thought to be either 47 for the male and 48 for the female or 48 for both. This was believed to include 23 pairs of autosomal chromosomes together with XX for the female and either XO or XY for the male. Then it was shown (Tjio and Levan, 1956) that the normal number for the human is 46, including the sex chromosomes. This total consists of 22 pairs of autosomes and XX or XY sex chromosomes (Fig. 8.82). The word *normal* must be qualified here; it refers only to the usual or majority situation, neither guaranteeing normality nor excluding apparently normal individuals with other chromosome combinations.

One modern technique for studying mammalian chromosomes utilizes tissue culture to obtain adequate numbers of dividing cells in monolayers, colchicine treatment to increase the number of metaphase figures, hypotonic treatment to swell the cells and heighten chromosome visibility, and flatten-

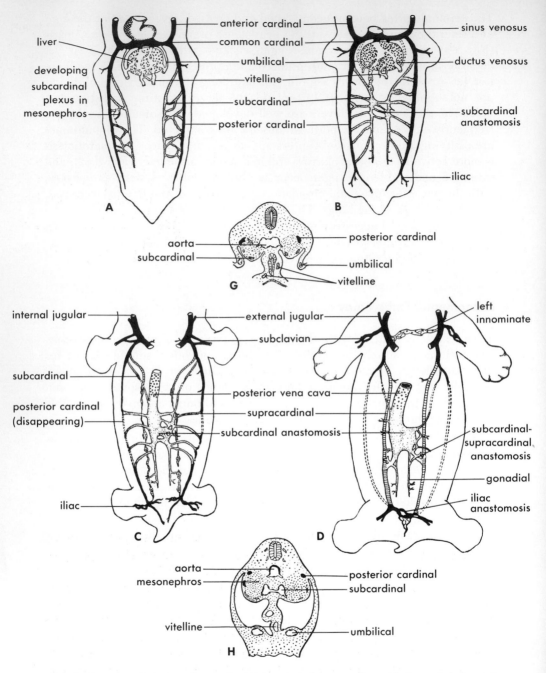

Fig. 8.64   Development of posterior vena cava in human embryo: A–F, ventral views; A, at 4 weeks; B, at 5½ weeks; C, at 6 weeks; D, at 7 weeks; E, at 8 weeks; F, at term; G, transverse section at 4 to 5½ weeks; H, transverse section at 6 to 7 weeks; I, transverse section at 8 weeks to term. (From B. M. Patten, *Human Embryology*, 2nd ed., McGraw-Hill, New York, 1953. Based on work of McClure and Butler.)

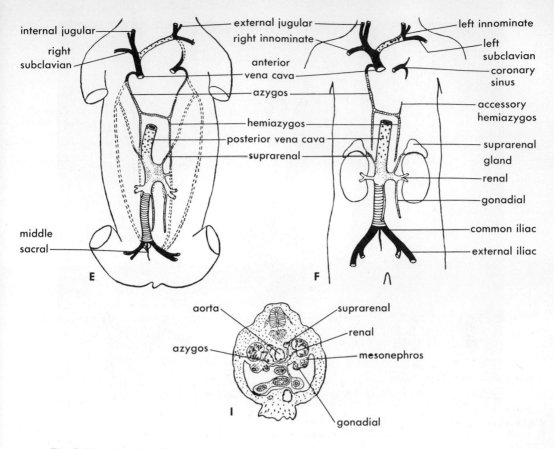

Fig. 8.64　(continued)

ing of the cells onto a single optical plane for photographic analysis. Blood samples are frequent sources of cells for culture. The leucocytes are separated from the erythrocytes and incubated from 3 to 5 days in a tissue culture medium containing one of several mitogenic bean extracts. After this processing a series of 25 to 100 or more metaphase figures is examined; the chromosomes are counted, and photographs are taken of a number of the cells. Karyotype analysis consists of matching the chromosomes in a metaphase figure into pairs according to relative length, position of the centromere (primary constriction), presence or absence of a secondary constriction, and size of the satellites. The satellites may be very minute or relatively large, or they may appear as finely connected pieces of chromatin material. They are integral parts of chromosomes and are the only means of distinguishing certain pairs of human chromosomes.　(continued on page 508)

A

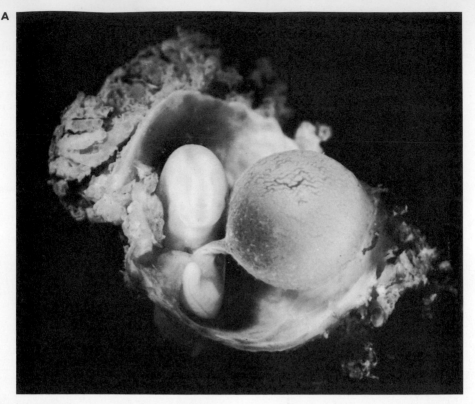

Fig. 8.65 Development of human embryo from 4 weeks: A, at 5.2 mm. (28 days); B, at 6 mm. (32 days); C, at 7 mm. (35 days); D, at 8 mm. (35 days); E, at 10 mm. (39 days); F, at 11 mm. (40 days); G, 11-mm. chorionic vesicle; H, at 12 mm. (42 days); I, 12-mm. embryo in chorionic vesicle; J, at 13 mm. (42 days); K, at 14 mm. (44 days); L, at 15 mm. (45 days); M, at 16 mm. (47 days); N, at 17 mm. (49 days); O, at 18 mm. (49 days); P, at 19 mm. (49 days); Q, at 20 mm. (49 days); R, at 21 mm. (50 days); S, at 22 mm. (51 days); T, at 23 mm. (52 days); U, at 24 mm. (53 days); V, at 25 mm. (54 days); W, at 27 mm. (56 days); X, at 28 mm. (56 days); Y, at 29 mm. (56 days); Z, at 30 mm. (56 days); A', at 31 mm. (57 days); B', at 32 mm. (58 days); C', at 33 mm. (59 days); D', at 34 mm. (60 days); E', at 36 mm. (61 days); F', at 38 mm. (62 days); G', at 40 mm. (63 days); H', at 133 mm. (16 wks.). (A, C from G. L. Streeter, *Carnegie Inst. Wash. Publ.* No. 557, Contribs. *Embryology* No. 199 (1945); B, F, H–G' from E. Ludwig, Anatomical Institute, Univ. of Basel, Switzerland; D from G. L. Streeter, *Carnegie Inst. Wash. Publ.* No. 575, Contribs. *Embryology* No. 211 (1948); H' from R. Grill, Carnegie Institution of Washington.)

B

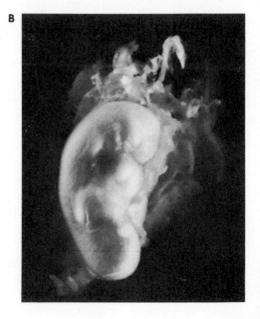

C

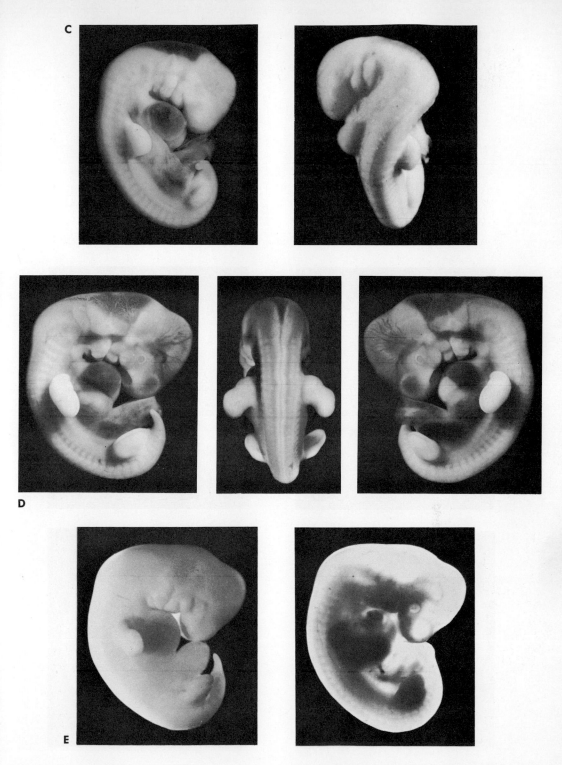

D

E

Fig. 8.65 (continued)

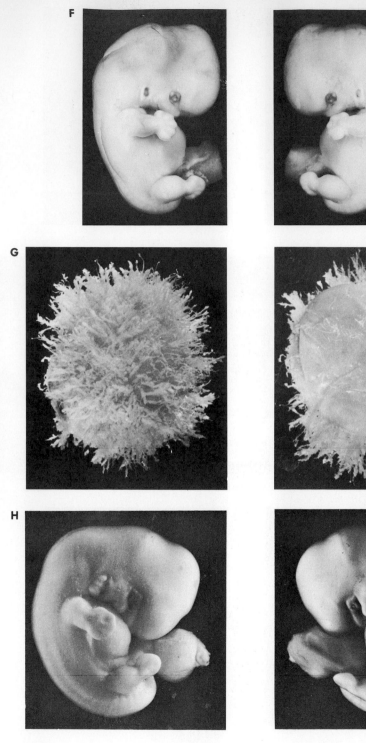

F

G

H

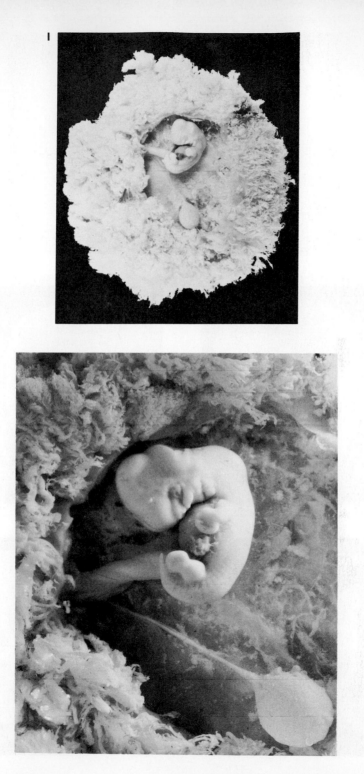

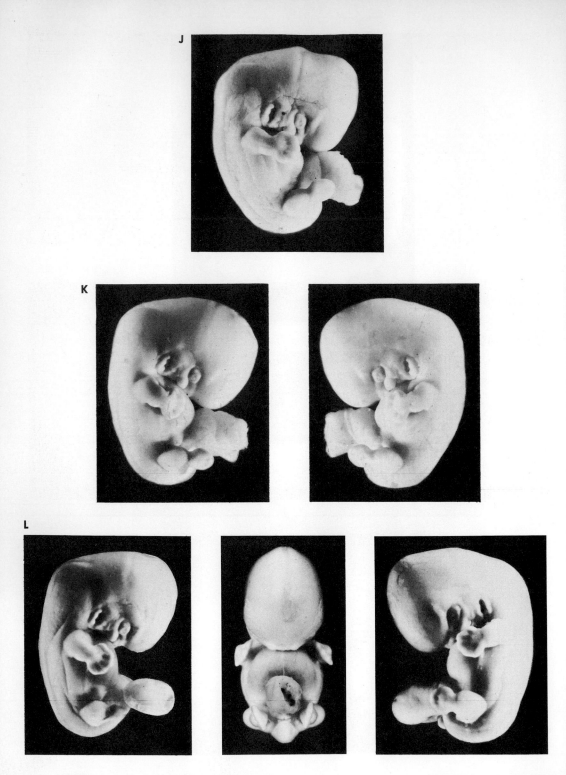

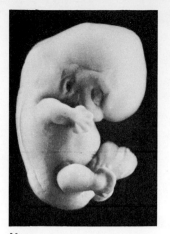

M

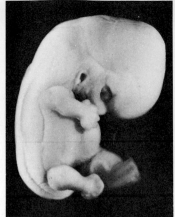

N

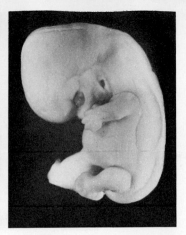

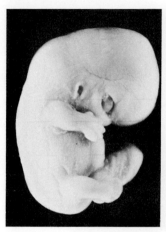

O

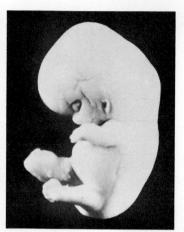

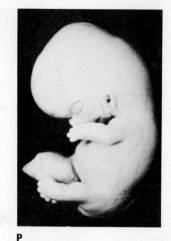

P

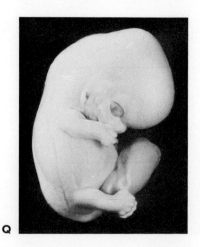

Q

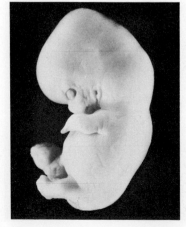

Fig. 8.65 (continued)

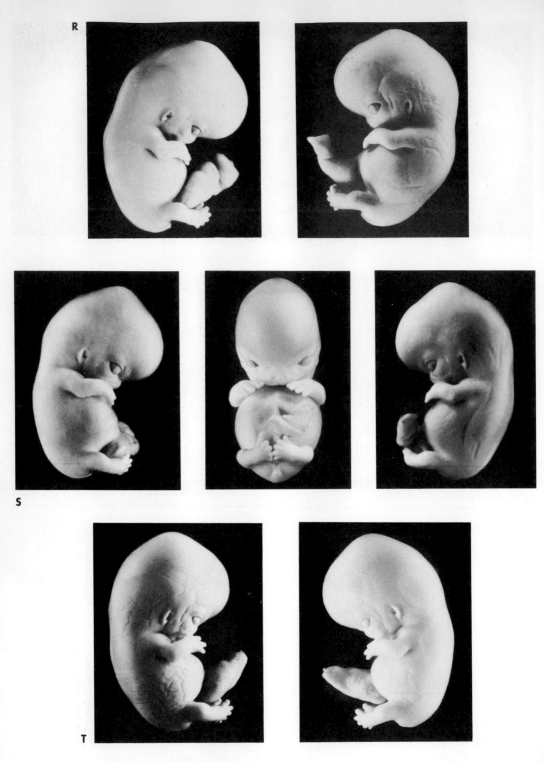

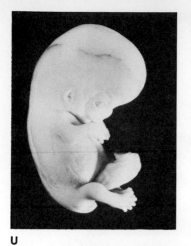
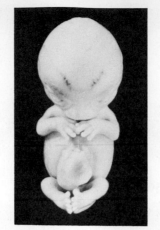
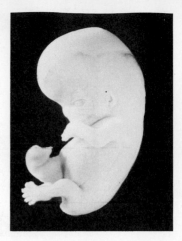

U

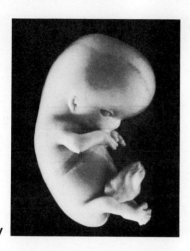

V

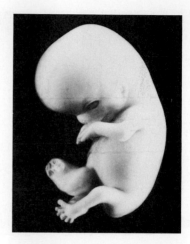

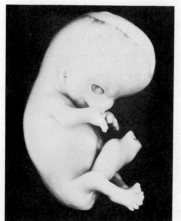

W

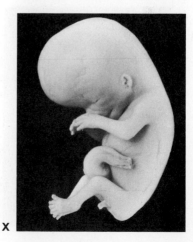

X

Fig. 8.65   (continued)

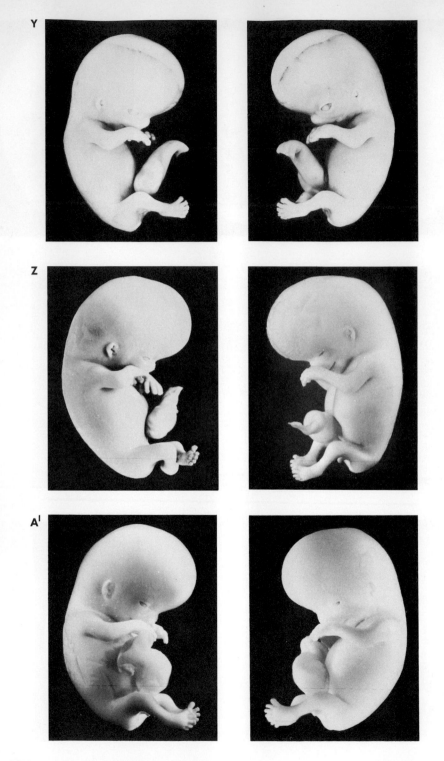

Y

Z

A¹

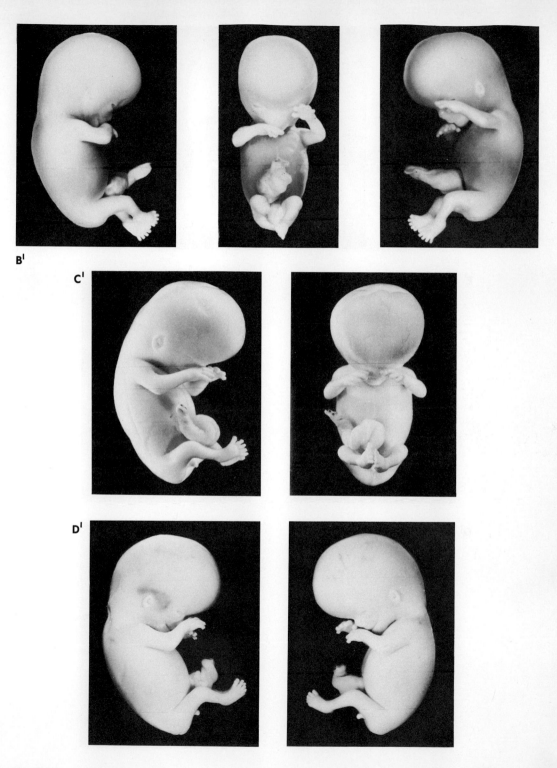

B'

C'

D'

Fig. 8.65　(continued)　　　　*Experimental Embryology*　**487**

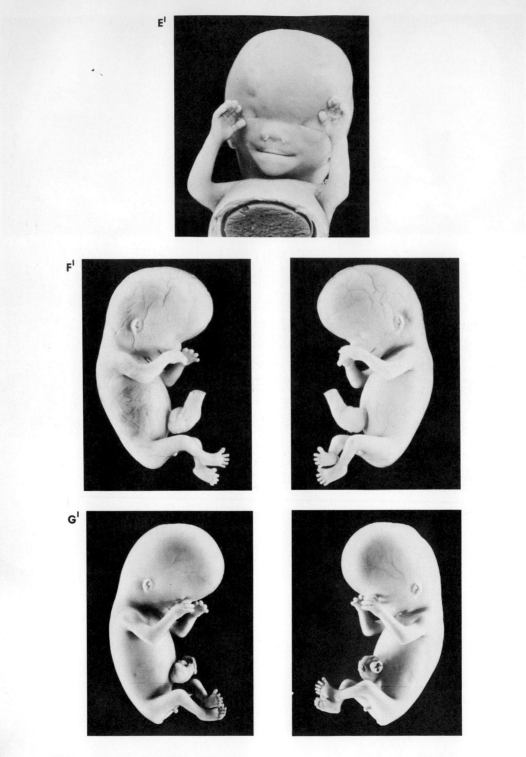

THE HUMAN: *A Discoid Placentate* **Fig. 8.65** (continued)

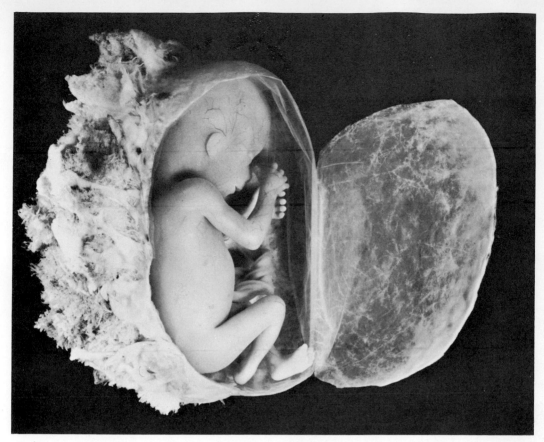

H¹

Fig. 8.65 (continued)

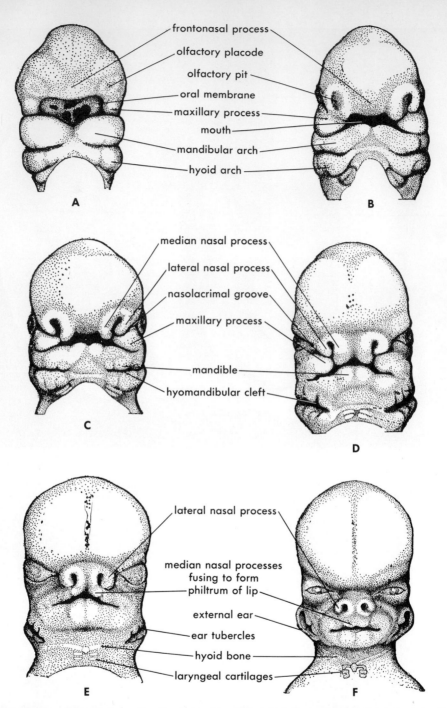

Fig. 8.66 Frontal views showing formation of face in human embryo: A, at 4 weeks; B, at 5 weeks; C, at 5½ weeks; D, at 6 weeks; E, at 7 weeks; F, at 8 weeks. (From B. M. Patten, *Human Embryology*, 2nd ed., McGraw-Hill, New York, 1953.)

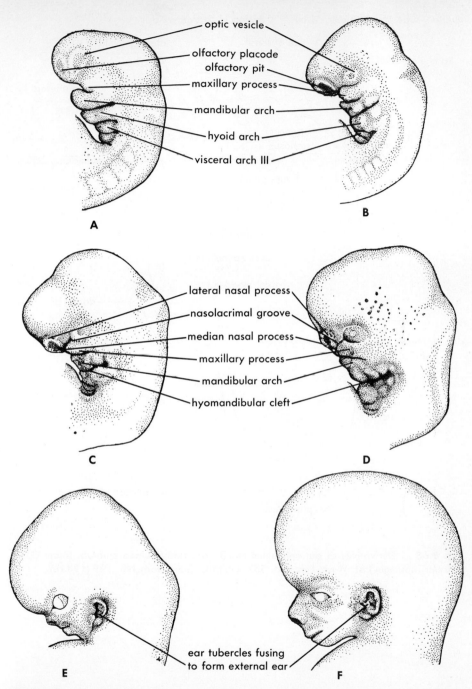

Fig. 8.67   Lateral views showing formation of face in human embryo: A, at 4 weeks; B, at 5 weeks; C, at 5½ weeks; D, at 6 weeks; E, at 7 weeks; F, at 8 weeks. (From B. M. Patten, *Human Embryology*, 2nd ed., McGraw-Hill, New York, 1953. Adapted from W. Patten.)

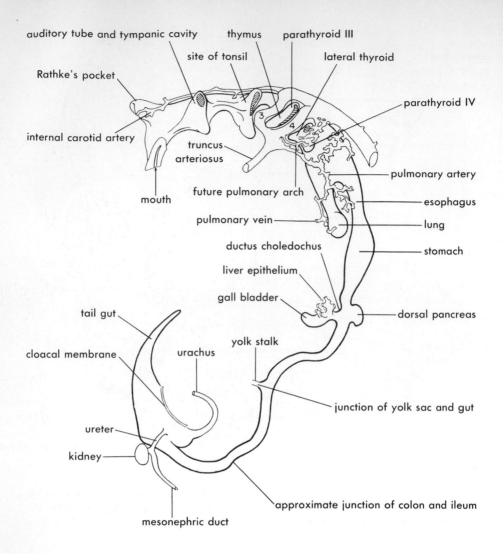

Fig. 8.68   Derivatives of gut epithelium in 28- to 30-day human embryo. (From G. L. Streeter, *Carnegie Inst. Wash. Publ.* No. 557, *Contribs. Embryology* No. 199 (1945).)

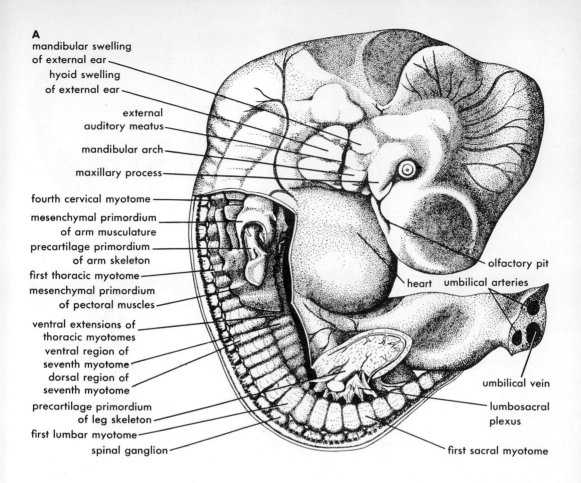

A

mandibular swelling
of external ear

hyoid swelling
of external ear

external
auditory meatus

mandibular arch

maxillary process

fourth cervical myotome

mesenchymal primordium
of arm musculature

precartilage primordium
of arm skeleton

first thoracic myotome

mesenchymal primordium
of pectoral muscles

ventral extensions of
thoracic myotomes

ventral region of
seventh myotome

dorsal region of
seventh myotome

precartilage primordium
of leg skeleton

first lumbar myotome

spinal ganglion

olfactory pit

heart   umbilical arteries

umbilical vein

lumbosacral
plexus

first sacral myotome

Fig. 8.69   Lateral views showing muscle development in human embryo: A, at 9 mm.; B, at 11 mm. (From O. E. Nelsen, *Comparative Embryology of the Vertebrates*, McGraw-Hill, New York, 1953. Adapted from Bardeen and Lewis.)

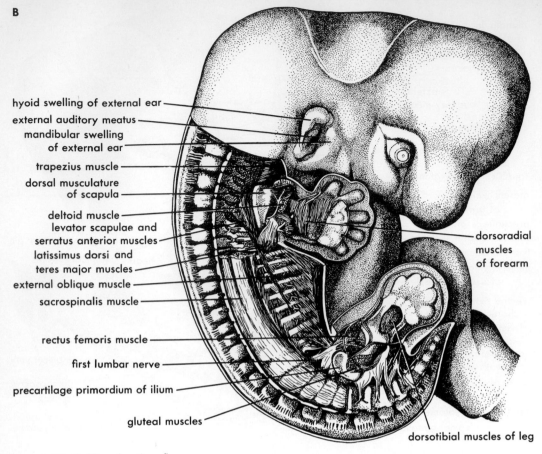

hyoid swelling of external ear

external auditory meatus

mandibular swelling
of external ear

trapezius muscle

dorsal musculature
of scapula

deltoid muscle

levator scapulae and
serratus anterior muscles

latissimus dorsi and
teres major muscles

external oblique muscle

sacrospinalis muscle

rectus femoris muscle

first lumbar nerve

precartilage primordium of ilium

gluteal muscles

dorsoradial
muscles
of forearm

dorsotibial muscles of leg

Fig. 8.69   (continued)

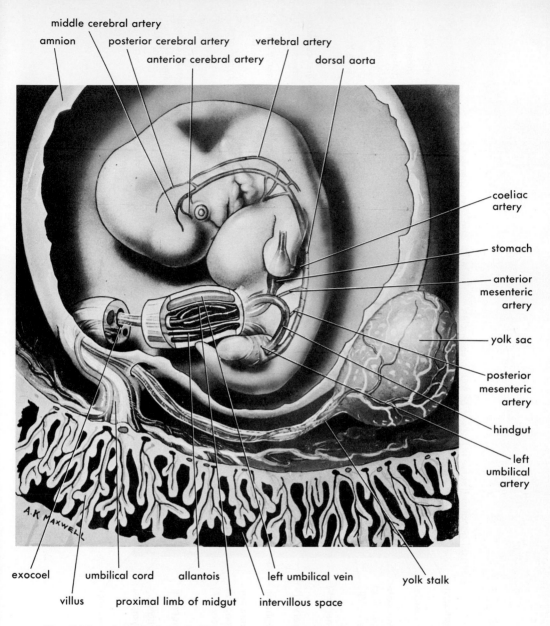

middle cerebral artery

amnion

posterior cerebral artery

anterior cerebral artery

vertebral artery

dorsal aorta

coeliac artery

stomach

anterior mesenteric artery

yolk sac

posterior mesenteric artery

hindgut

left umbilical artery

A.K MAXWELL

exocoel

villus

umbilical cord

proximal limb of midgut

allantois

intervillous space

left umbilical vein

yolk stalk

Fig. 8.70 Lateral view of 10-mm. human embryo in chorionic sac, showing vascular system and contents of umbilical cord. (From W. J. Hamilton, J. D. Boyd, and H. W. Mossman, *Human Embryology*, 2nd ed., Williams & Wilkins, Baltimore, 1952.)

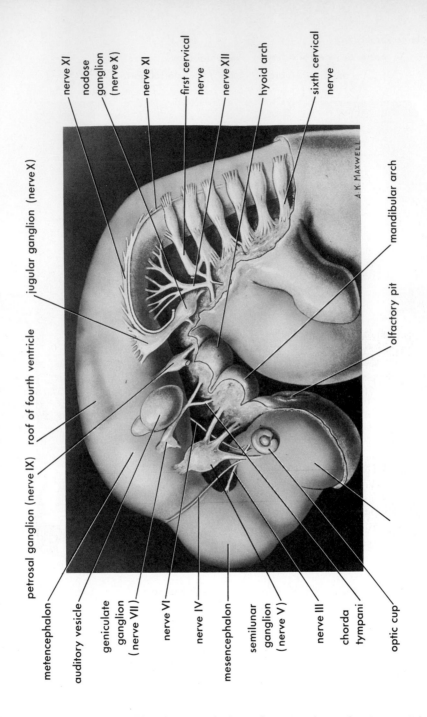

Fig. 8.71 Lateral view of head region of 10-mm. human embryo, showing cranial and upper spinal nerves. (From W. J. Hamilton, J. D. Boyd, and H. W. Mossman, *Human Embryology*, 2nd ed., Williams & Wilkins, Baltimore, 1952.)

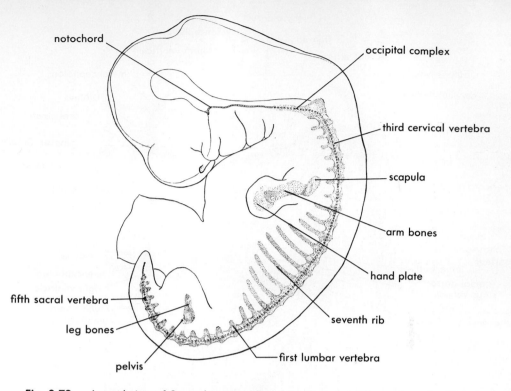

notochord

occipital complex

third cervical vertebra

scapula

arm bones

hand plate

fifth sacral vertebra

leg bones

pelvis

seventh rib

first lumbar vertebra

Fig. 8.72 Lateral view of 9-mm. human embryo, showing precartilage primordia. (From B. M. Patten, *Human Embryology*, 2nd ed., McGraw-Hill, New York, 1953. Adapted from Bardeen *et al.*)

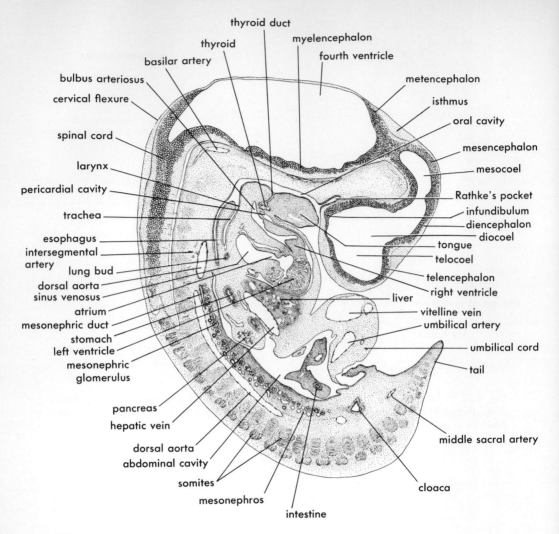

Fig. 8.73 Sagittal section of 10-mm. human embryo.

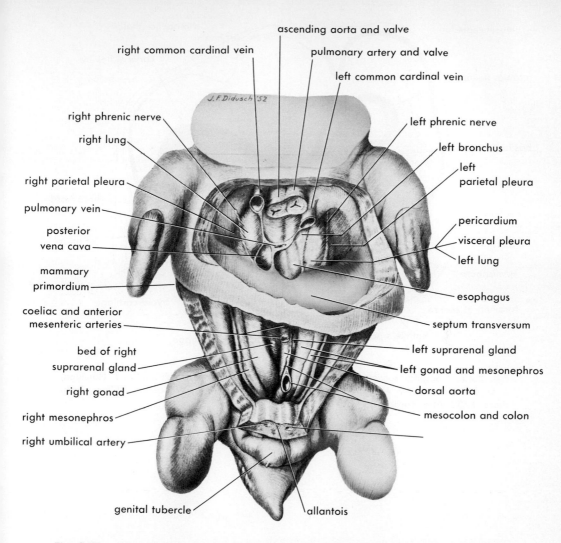

Fig. 8.74 Ventral view showing heart, lung, and urogenital regions of 13-mm. human embryo. (From L. S. Wells, *Carnegie Inst. Wash. Publ.* No. 603, *Contribs. Embryology* No. 236 (1954).)

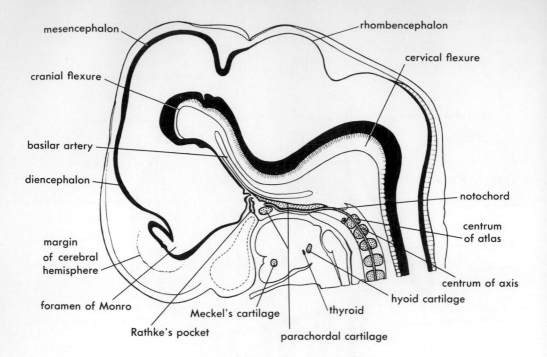

mesencephalon

rhombencephalon

cranial flexure

cervical flexure

basilar artery

diencephalon

notochord

centrum
of atlas

margin
of cerebral
hemisphere

centrum of axis

hyoid cartilage

foramen of Monro

thyroid

Meckel's cartilage

Rathke's pocket

parachordal cartilage

Fig. 8.75   Sagittal section of head of 14-mm. human embryo. (From W. J. Hamilton, J. D. Boyd, and H. W. Mossman, *Human Embryology*, 2nd ed., Williams & Wilkins, Baltimore, 1952. After Bardeen.)

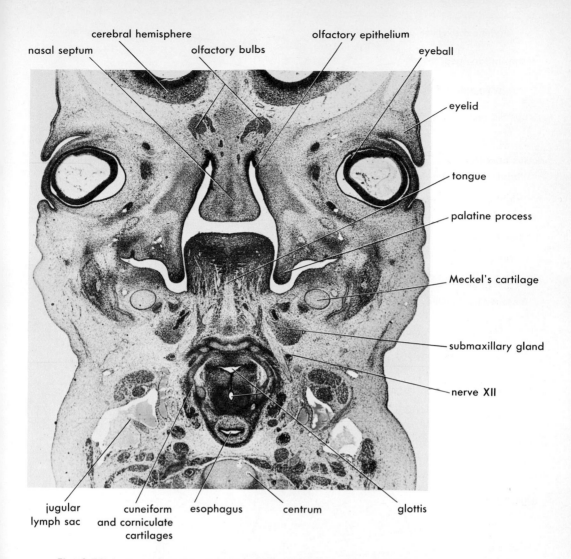

nasal septum

cerebral hemisphere

olfactory bulbs

olfactory epithelium

eyeball

eyelid

tongue

palatine process

Meckel's cartilage

submaxillary gland

nerve XII

jugular
lymph sac

cuneiform
and corniculate
cartilages

esophagus

centrum

glottis

Fig. 8.76 Frontal section through mouth and nasal region of 20-mm. human embryo. (From W. J. Hamilton, J. D. Boyd, and H. W. Mossman, *Human Embryology*, 2nd ed., Williams & Wilkins, Baltimore, 1952.)

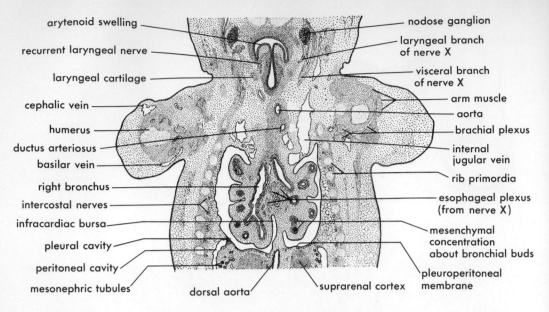

Fig. 8.77 Frontal section of thoracic region of 15-mm. human embryo. (From B. M. Patten, *Human Embryology*, 2nd ed., McGraw-Hill, New York, 1953. Adapted from Univ. of Michigan Coll. EH 227.)

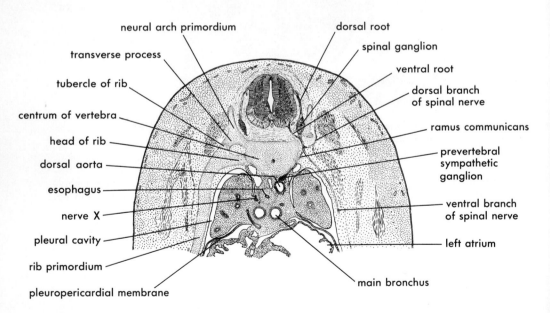

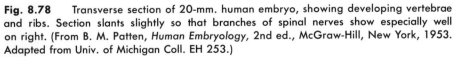

Fig. 8.78 Transverse section of 20-mm. human embryo, showing developing vertebrae and ribs. Section slants slightly so that branches of spinal nerves show especially well on right. (From B. M. Patten, *Human Embryology*, 2nd ed., McGraw-Hill, New York, 1953. Adapted from Univ. of Michigan Coll. EH 253.)

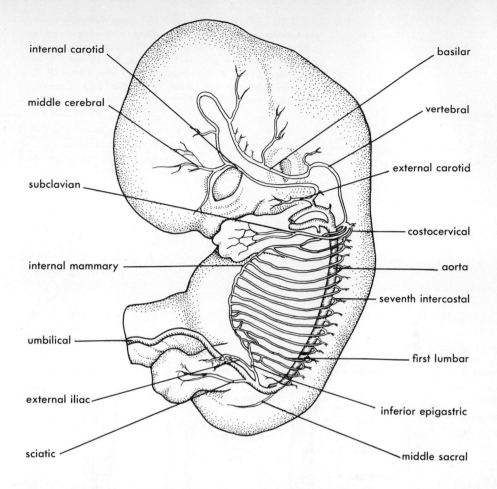

internal carotid

middle cerebral

subclavian

internal mammary

umbilical

external iliac

sciatic

basilar

vertebral

external carotid

costocervical

aorta

seventh intercostal

first lumbar

inferior epigastric

middle sacral

Fig. 8.79 Arteries of body wall in 7-week human embryo. (From B. M. Patten, *Human Embryology*, 2nd ed., McGraw-Hill, New York, 1953. Adapted from Mall.)

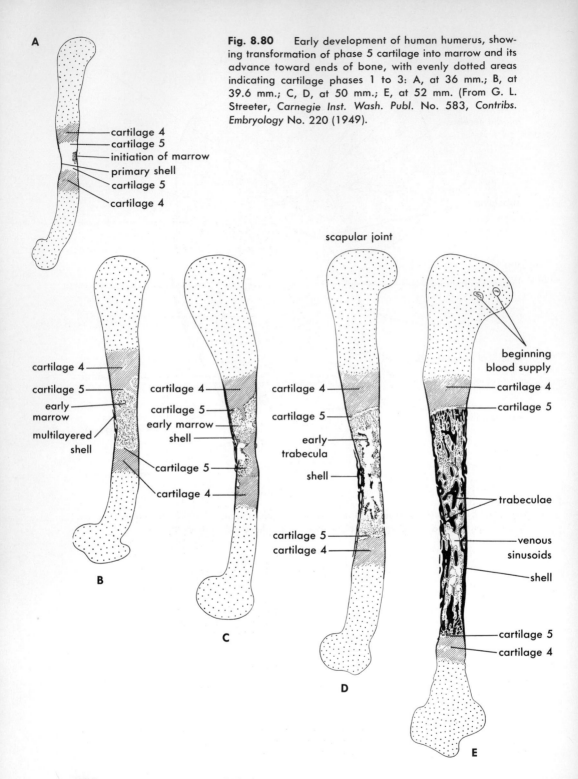

Fig. 8.80 Early development of human humerus, showing transformation of phase 5 cartilage into marrow and its advance toward ends of bone, with evenly dotted areas indicating cartilage phases 1 to 3: A, at 36 mm.; B, at 39.6 mm.; C, D, at 50 mm.; E, at 52 mm. (From G. L. Streeter, *Carnegie Inst. Wash. Publ.* No. 583, *Contribs. Embryology* No. 220 (1949).

A

cartilage 4
cartilage 5
initiation of marrow
primary shell
cartilage 5
cartilage 4

scapular joint

cartilage 4
cartilage 5
early marrow
multilayered shell

cartilage 4
cartilage 5
early marrow
shell

cartilage 5
cartilage 4

B

cartilage 4
cartilage 5
early trabecula
shell

cartilage 5
cartilage 4

C

beginning blood supply

cartilage 4
cartilage 5

trabeculae

venous sinusoids

shell

cartilage 5
cartilage 4

D

E

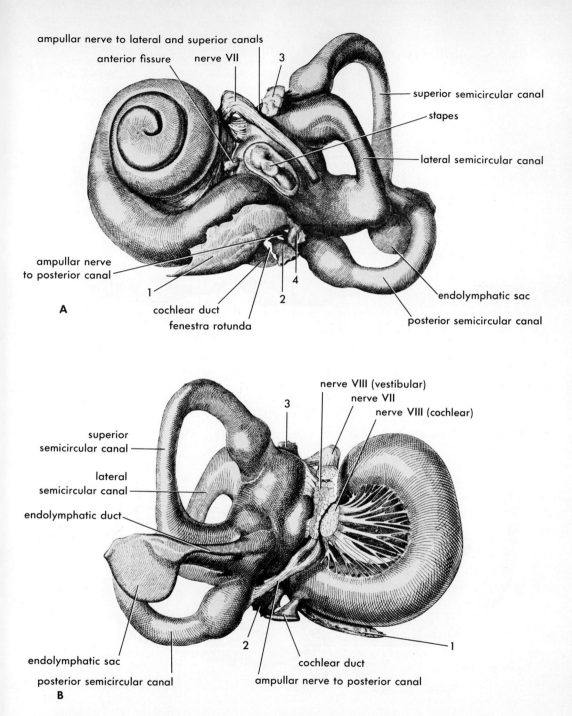

Fig. 8.81 Ossification of auditory capsule in human: A, B, at 126 mm.; C, at 155 mm.; D, E, at 161 mm. Numbers indicate specific regions. (From T. H. Bast, *Carnegie Inst. Wash. Publ.* No. 407, *Contribs. Embryology* No. 121 (1930).)

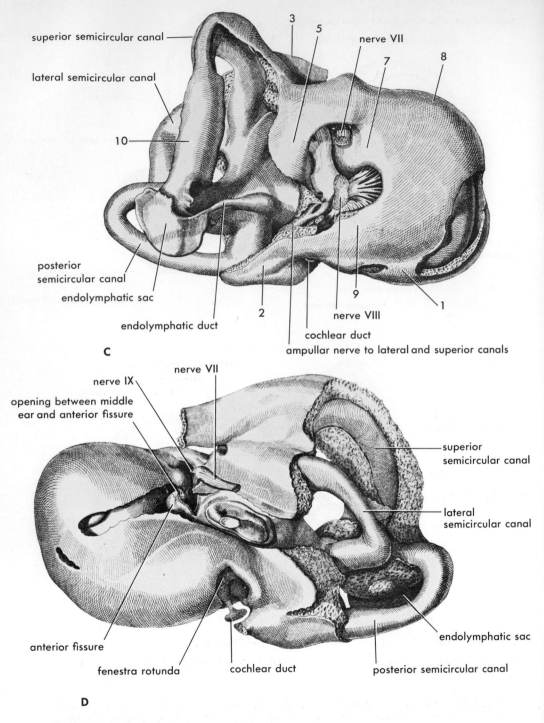

superior semicircular canal

lateral semicircular canal

10

posterior
semicircular canal

endolymphatic sac

endolymphatic duct

2

3

5

nerve VII

7

8

9

nerve VIII

cochlear duct

ampullar nerve to lateral and superior canals

1

C

nerve IX

nerve VII

opening between middle
ear and anterior fissure

superior
semicircular canal

lateral
semicircular canal

endolymphatic sac

anterior fissure

fenestra rotunda

cochlear duct

posterior semicircular canal

D

Fig. 8.81 (continued)

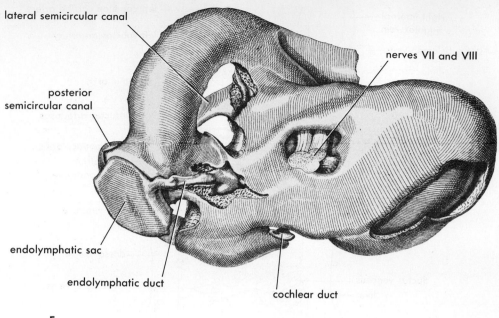

lateral semicircular canal

nerves VII and VIII

posterior
semicircular canal

endolymphatic sac

endolymphatic duct

cochlear duct

E

Fig. 8.81   (continued)

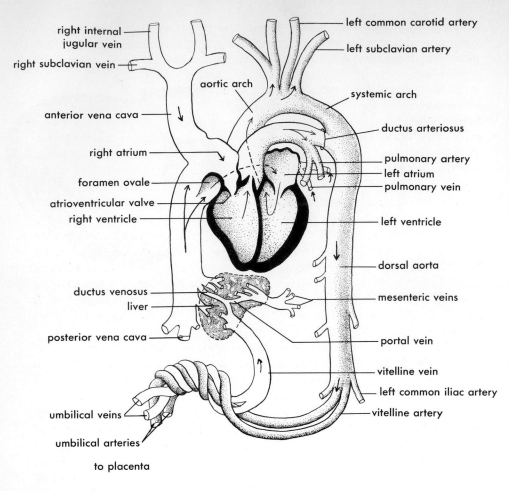

right internal jugular vein

right subclavian vein

anterior vena cava

right atrium

foramen ovale

atrioventricular valve

right ventricle

ductus venosus

liver

posterior vena cava

umbilical veins

umbilical arteries

to placenta

left common carotid artery

left subclavian artery

aortic arch

systemic arch

ductus arteriosus

pulmonary artery

left atrium

pulmonary vein

left ventricle

dorsal aorta

mesenteric veins

portal vein

vitelline vein

left common iliac artery

vitelline artery

Fig. 8.82   Ventral view of human vascular system just before birth.

Because of the lack of controlled experimental material, and the small size of human litters, human genetic data are slow and difficult to obtain. However, mental institutions and hospitals offer increasing opportunities for the study of chromosome configurations of apparently normal as well as obviously abnormal individuals, and correlations are being made. Except for the sex chromosomes, where some 10% crossing over has been found between hemophilia and color blindness, little is yet known about linkages in the autosomes. There is evidence of some linkage between certain blood groups (A-B-O) and the nail patella syndrome, and also between Rh factor and ovalocytosis, and glucose-6-phosphatedehydrogenase enzyme has been provisionally linked with certain eye conditions.

In the original Drosophila literature, a female possessing three X chromosomes was called a superfemale. Such extra X chromosome females have been found among humans, but no evidence exists of any phenotypically correlated superiority. On the contrary, a correlated low-level I.Q., in the range of 60 to 90, often appears. However, such females can have quite normal offspring, and the possibility is that the polar bodies formed during maturation of the ova carry off two X's and leave but a single normal X for the ovum. That a certain three X mother has had 12 normal children supports this thesis.

It must be emphasized that a single individual may present several karyotypes. Accordingly, analysis of several karyofigures from an individual is the usual practice. Buccal epithelium is satisfactory for metaphase figures but not for chromosome counts or identifications. For these, the germ cells, bone marrow, cultured tissues, or, better, peripheral blood (leucocytes) is proving valuable. It may soon be possible to examine a small child, suspect with regard to certain inheritable conditions, to determine the likelihood of his developing an anomaly.

A brief report of one area of recent study follows. Mongolism appears 50 times as often in children born to women over 40 as in children born to women under 25. It is characterized by a typical face, short stature, scoliosis and lordosis, short forearms, short and broad hands, and low I.Q. (30 to 40) and is always associated with a trisomic condition for chromosome pair number 21 of the Denver classification. Investigators (Miller *et al.*, 1961) discovered a single family containing an XXXXY male with Mongolism, two number 21 trisomic females with Mongolism, and a leukemic male. Buccal mucosal smears from the XXXXY male showed that about 14% of the leucocytes had three sex chromatin masses, and peripheral blood cells confirmed that the chromosome count was 49 instead of the normal 46 (Figs. 8.83, 8.84). The individual exhibited severe mental retardation, with an I.Q. of only 21, a cleft palate, strabismus, multiple anomalies of the skeletal system, and eunuchoidism. His voice was unbroken, and he had no facial or axillary hair and only scanty pubic hair. His penis was exceptionally small but otherwise normal. The small scrotum contained a small 1-cm. mass on each side, representing atrophied testes. Mongolism appeared among his aunts and other close relatives. In all of these Mongoloids the extra chromosome was in the number 21 pair of chromosomes. The researchers explain the origin of the XXXXY child by nondisjunction, probably during meiosis.

The association of certain chromosomal aberrations with anomalous conditions in the adult will progress rapidly in the months immediately ahead. It may be some time, however, before the mechanism of genetic effect on development, which results in such anomalies, is clearly understood. This is the field of genetoembryology of the future.

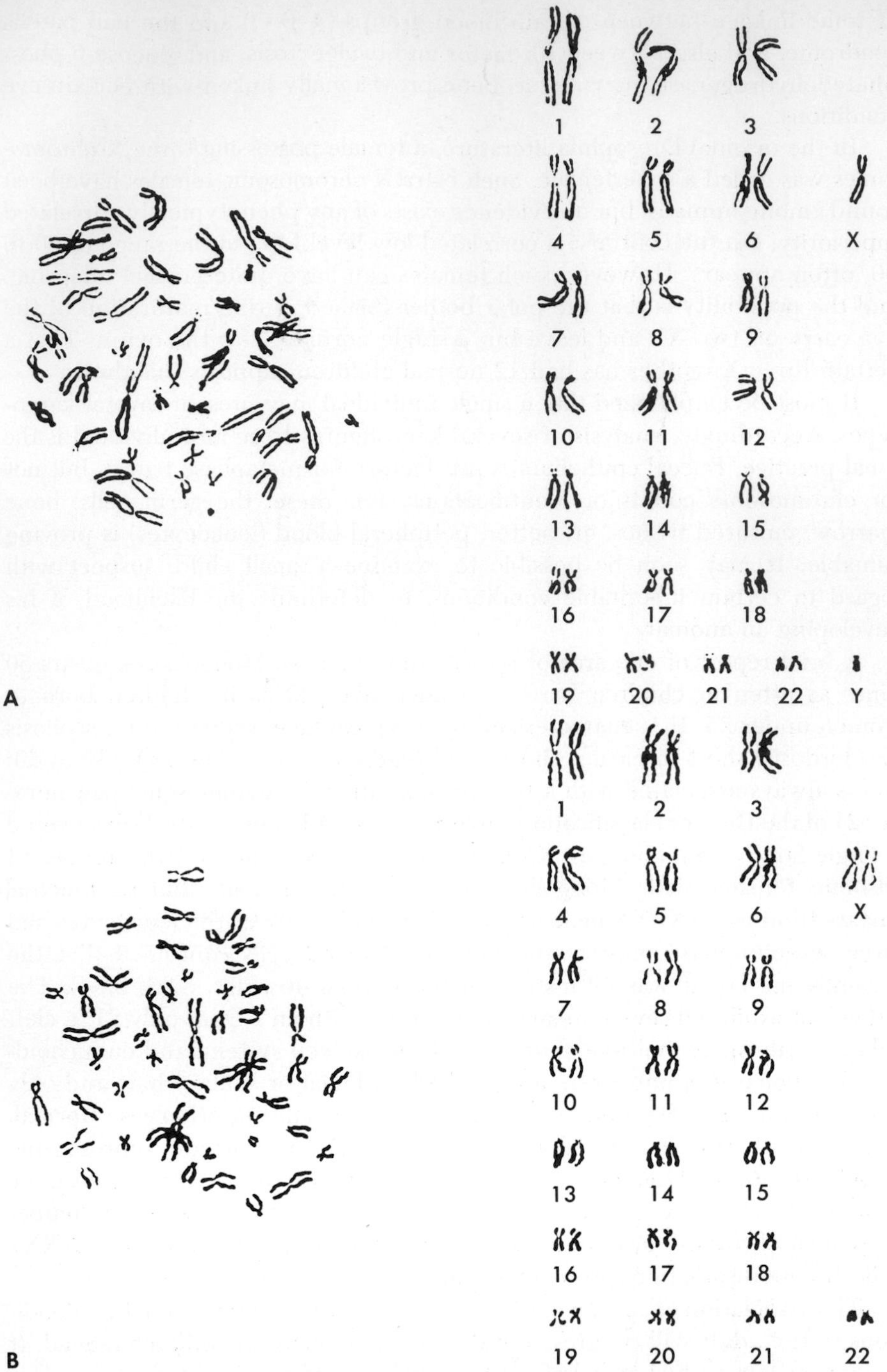

Fig. 8.83 Normal human chromosome configuration, as seen in smear and with chromosomes paired: A, male; B, female. (A from O. J. Miller; B from W. R. Berg.)

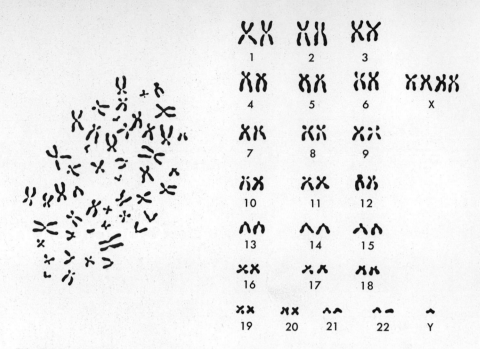

Fig. 8.84 Chromosome configuration of XXXXY male, as seen in smear and chromosomes paired. (From O. J. Miller.)

Conclusion

9

In the Introduction the author attempted to give a perspective, a point of view for approaching the subject of embryology. At that time the student had no basis in knowledge for any over-all generalizations about development. Now, after a study of development in a variety of vertebrate forms, from frog to man, an evaluation of some of the principles that seem to emerge is appropriate.

The author has tried to present here the most likely of a number of interpretations. To that extent he has assumed the role of editor. The purpose has been to clarify the presentation and to avoid confusion for the student. There are and always will be differences of opinion even regarding the same facts and differences in interpretation of the same data. Some erroneous interpretations fall by the wayside quickly, but others persist for years, even decades, before being discarded in the light of further revelations. It seems poor pedagogy for a teacher to confront the student, without proper comment, with various points of view, expecting him to discern for himself what is correct. It seems a better policy for the teacher to give the student the interpretation that is most likely correct and to warn him that further research may make necessary some modifications. For the student who makes advanced investigations in biology or medicine, digressions from this presentation will be the exception and will be of stimulating interest, academically if not in fact. This approach better prepares the student to make his own contributions to the archives of embryology than one in which emphasis is placed upon a superficial array of poorly interpreted observations.

Certain considerations are basic to both biology and embryology. They have been implied in this study of development and are summarized in the following discussion.

■ Cell Division

Virchow's famous concept (1858) stated, *"Omnis cellula e cellula"* ("All cells from cells"). According to Fleming in 1882, every living cell arises from a preexisting cell by a complicated process of division known as *mitosis* (or *karyokinesis*). Amitotic division may occur but has yet to be verified. In fact, as improved optical equipment has become available, cells once presumed to divide without mitosis have been shown to divide mitotically. Certain cells do appear to divide by simple constriction, but some device exists within them to induce this accomplishment.

The term mitosis (*mitos*, thread) refers to the process in which discrete chromatin threads form, contract, split lengthwise, grow, and are shifted into two identical daughter cells by an elaborate mechanism known as the *mitotic spindle.* As a rule, this apparatus is more complex and better seen in animal cells than in plant cells. Since this process is fundamental to all biology, it is generally one of the first objects of study for the beginner. Obviously, it is of primary importance in the embryo because it entails division of the fertilized ovum into two, four, eight, sixteen, and an infinite number of daughter cells in the normal course of growth.

Mitosis proceeds as follows. On completion of a mitotic division, that is, at the beginning of *interphase*, a nuclear membrane even more permeable than the cell membrane bounds the nucleus, and within it are a *nucleolus* containing abundant ribonucleic acid (RNA) and a delicate network of chromatin, a substance rich in deoxyribonucleic acid (DNA) that stains with basic dyes. As interphase progresses, DNA builds up in the nucleus. The first indication of impending mitosis, at *prophase*, is the appearance within the nucleus of dense, discrete filaments of chromatin, the *chromosomes.* Each chromosome consists of a pair of threads or *chromatids*, which coil into spiral structures. The nucleolus vanishes, and the nuclear membrane starts disintegrating, as a fibrous protein spindle arises in the cytoplasm and extends through the long axis of the cell. At *metaphase* the chromosomes assemble along an equatorial plane in the center of the cell, perpendicular to the spindle axis, and each attaches itself to a spindle fiber at a single point, the *centromere*, which usually is at a bend in the chromosome. At *anaphase* each chromosome splits, and the two resultant chromatids move in opposite directions along the spindle fibers toward the respective poles of the spindle, where they become chromosomes again. At *telophase* the chromosomes at each pole uncoil, elongate, swell, and transform into a chromatin network; a new nuclear membrane forms around each chromatin mass, which becomes spherical; and nucleoli appear. Finally actual cytoplasmic division occurs, creating two cells from the original one.

Mitosis is now well understood, but the cause of it is not. Why cells start and, at a certain stage, stop dividing is still one of the unanswered questions in biology.

Meiosis is always associated with mitosis but is basically different from it, since it results in the production of daughter cells that are unequal with respect to their chromosomes. Meiosis involves two successive divisions in which the chromosomal material is duplicated but once. The chromatin network of a cell nucleus resolves into single chromosomes, which consist of pairs of chromatids. These chromosomes pair with homologous chromosomes and coil as the nucleolus and nuclear membrane disappear. The chromosome pairs then assemble on a spindle. At this time the chromatids can and often do exchange places with homologous chromatids, in a process known as *crossing over*. Crossing over and mutation are the only means available to living organisms to vary qualitatively their genetic constitutions. The two members of each chromosome pair separate and move to opposite poles of the spindle, where new nuclei form. New nucleoli arise, and cytoplasmic division follows. Since there is no reduction of the chromatid content of a single chromosome, only a separation of chromosomes, the resultant cells differ from each other and from their progenitor; each contains only half the normal number of chromosomes. The chromosomes in each new cell assemble on a spindle, and the two chromatids in each chromosome separate, move to opposite poles, and form two identical cells by mitosis. From the original cell, therefore, four new cells of two different types arise.

The kinetic mechanism of meiosis may be similar or even identical to that of mitosis, but the resultant cells are different from each other, at least in the reductional division phase. Further, meiosis occurs only in the maturation of germ cells, alternating with mitosis. Somatic, or nongerminal, cells have never been known to undergo meiotic divisions. Another biological enigma is the manner in which certain cells are designated to undergo meiosis rather than mitosis at the correct time and place in order to provide mature germ cells for the propagation of the race.

■ Developmental Process

Development involves far more than a multiplication of cells. There is a tremendous increase in mass from a single cell (the *zygote*) to the numerous cells of greatest variety in structure and in function. The early stages of development appear to consist merely of mitotic division, but shortly each cell increases in size before it divides, the resultant cells grow and divide, and so on.

When growth and multiplication have reached a certain stage, new forces begin to act, producing cells in which the cytoplasm, at least, is different from that of the parent cell. This is the process of *differentiation*. Although it occurs simultaneously with mitosis, it is in no way related to mitosis. Terms used to describe the attendant developmental changes include proliferation, determination, morphogenesis, histogenesis, organogenesis, and organismic integration. Histogenesis brings about variations of tissues. Still later organismic influences mold specialized tissues into specific organ complexes, which become integrated into the whole both structurally and functionally.

An early theory suggested that the ovum of any species represented a fixed and definite system and that the function of the spermatozoon was simply to initiate the development of that system. This was one expression of the *theory of preformation*. Soon there were preformationists with the opposite view, who saw a minute human form (*homunculus*, little man) sitting in the head of the spermatozoon. They assumed that the individual was already formed in the spermatozoon and that the ovum merely supplied the nutrition necessary for the growth of this individual. With the improvement of microscopes, both schools of preformationists (*ovists* and *spermists*) were thrown into disregard, and the pendulum swung to the other extreme, as represented by the *epigeneticists*. Their theory was that nothing was preformed, that development was an unfolding, a process building up step by step from almost nothing to great complexity.

Modern embryology involves an intermediate concept of development. Certainly there is no miniature individual, either in the ovum or the spermatozoon, simply to grow. Nor is either the spermatozoon or the ovum completely unorganized, completely without a fixed direction. The genes determine whether a zygote will become a mouse or giraffe. Thus the issue resolves itself to the method by which these predetermining genes influence the cytoplasm to differentiate along the specific course necessary to produce either a mouse or a giraffe. It is readily agreed that there is genetic predetermination and that there is gradual development from the simple to the complex, but the process that causes a visibly undifferentiated cell to become a recognizably differentiated cell remains the central problem of embryology.

Differentiation is forward development. Every step produces more complexity. Among lower forms (for example, sponges) some rather crudely differentiated cells may become dedifferentiated and later and under certain conditions may redifferentiate along other lines, but such a process is not known among higher forms. Thus in vertebrate embryology differentiation is irreversible. The forces causing a cell to lose its total potency in favor of differentation have so far eluded physiochemical analysis. The most plausible theory is that differentiation occurs when cells are chemically changed by the segregation of certain enzymes inside (or outside) them.

■ Germ Layer Concept

The tendency of the scientific mind to categorize all information probably led originally to the *germ layer* concept (1879–1883, Oskar and Richard Hertwig). (Some confusion arises from the use of the word *germ*, which has other connotations pertaining to the reproductive cells. The term *germ layer*, of course, in no way relates to the reproductive material.) It is a fact that in the development of all higher forms three distinct layers of cells appear at an early stage. (In some lower forms only two layers exist.) These layers are distinct in position, in movement, and soon in texture. The outermost layer is known as *ectoderm;* the innermost layer, as *endoderm;* and, finally, the intermediate mass, at first not so clearly layered, as *mesoderm*.

Under normal conditions the three layers have specific derivatives, and the various tissues and organs that derive from ectoderm, for instance, are morphologically comparable in all higher animals. Ectoderm gives rise to the nervous system and to skin, hair, feathers, scales, sebaceous glands, milk glands, or whatever constitutes the outer covering of the particular animal being studied. Under experimental conditions the three layers may be transplanted or exchanged and will then give rise to other tissues or organs. In other words, nothing is inherently specific or peculiar to ectoderm that limits it and prevents it from forming gut epithelium, muscle, or other non-ectodermal tissue if it is transplanted prior to organogenesis. Ectoderm at first is not a differentiated tissue but simply the outer layer of a three-layered embryo, and it retains its total potentiality until tissue differentiation begins. Until that time it can replace or be replaced by either of the other two germ layers.

Reference to the derivatives of any germ layer may be misleading oversimplification. For example, human ectoderm gives rise to the epidermis, which includes the sweat glands, sebaceous glands, mammary glands, hair, nails, and lens of the eye. Except for the hair, nails, and lens, every one of these structures contains blood vessels and consequently mesoderm. Thus only the outermost layer of tissue (hair, nails, lens) or the functional lining of the glands is ectodermal; the supporting elements of each structure are mesodermal. Furthermore, almost every tissue of the body, of whatever germ layer origin, is eventually permeated by nerve cells or their processes (from ectoderm). Obviously, then, a clear-cut distinction between the primary germ layers is a transient property of the early embryo. Therefore, although the idea of germ layers is a useful part of modern teaching, its importance should not be overemphasized.

■ Embryonic Primordia

The term *primordium* defines a region of the embryo that is a center of activity leading to the development of a specific organ or organ system. Although in early organogenesis the cells of a primordium may not differ in physical appearance from other cells, if they are excised or transplanted elsewhere, they differentiate in the originally destined direction. As the cells differentiate, they form an aggregate, which offers morphological evidence that a particular organ system will eventuate from the region.

In one sense the zygote is the primordium of the embryo since it contains all the materials prerequisite to embryonic development. However, there is no specialization of any parts of the zygote, and the two cells resulting from the first division may even separate and give rise to complete individuals (identical twins). This possibility emphasizes that every early cell is at one time totipotent, containing all the potentialities of every other cell by virtue of its genetic make-up. The zygote or any of the early blastomeres can develop into bone or blood, epithelium or cartilage, neuron or muscle cell. The relatively unlimited potentialities of the early cells gradually give way to specializations, and soon after blastulation and actively during gastrulation, the primordia develop.

One can stain with vital dyes the various surface areas of the early gastrula and follow them up to the organs eventually derived from them, thereby establishing "fate maps," which are in fact "primordium maps." Injury to the surface cells results in deficiencies or actual loss in certain organ systems, depending upon where the injury occurs. The outer ectodermal epithelium of the embryo forms the lens, auditory vesicle lining, hypophysis, lining of the visceral clefts, etc., according to where it lies with respect to structures developing beneath it.

The question of the origin of the primordia is intimately related to that concerning differentiation. The answer, in all probability, lies in an understanding of the mechanism of gene action.

■ Organizers and Inductors

The terms *inductor* and *organizer* have been used to describe a region of the embryo that influences the development of a neighboring area toward a specific end. Actually an inductor is an irritant or stimulant, not necessarily living matter, that elicits from living matter a particular response, inherent in the reacting area. It is like a trigger setting off a chain reaction, the mechanism for which is latent within the cells involved. On the other hand, an organizer is always a group of living cells having the power to direct undifferentiated cells along a specific course, even though it may not be the one for which they were destined originally. For example, in the amphibian embryo the dorsal lip of the blastopore, which invaginates to establish the main axis of the embryo, is the most active organizing center, and it was, for a time, believed that all other regions passively awaited orders from this center. Attempts to analyze an organizer have resulted in the isolation of chemical substances with inductive powers but not as yet in a thorough diagnosis. However, without an organizer an embryo cannot develop, and experiments have shown that extra organizers cause the formation of a multibodied embryo. The organizer is the first real manifestation of integrative development within what appears to be a homogeneous grouping of like cells.

The expression *organism as a whole,* originated by Loeb in 1916, refers to another period of development, later than that of the organizer. Loeb's concept emphasizes that, as development proceeds, forces within the embryo integrate its various parts to the utility of all the other parts. If such forces were not present, an embryo would consist of cell conglomerates with no organization into an integrated whole. The fact that anomalies are the exception supports Loeb's thesis that something (perhaps of endocrine or nervous origin) fits all the parts of the embryo into a general pattern resulting in an efficiently functioning unit. If an area is removed, it is replaced or regenerated, or the remaining cells are reorganized. If foreign or excess tissue is implanted, it is sloughed off or isolated. Some power of "organization of the whole" ensures the integration of the parts.

■ Continuity of Germ Plasm

Weismann's concept (1892) that the *germ* (reproductive) cells and the *somatic* (body) cells are structurally and functionally different obviously has some basis. According to this idea, the fertilized egg cell has the potential of developing the soma but always reserves a bit of unaltered protoplasm from which the next generation derives. This germ plasm forms the link between generations and, in fact, between the first protoplasm and all later living matter. The soma, produced by the germ, surrounds the germ and provides it with nourishment, protection, and the means of eventual perpetuation.

Although Weismann's concept is probably fact, the varying theories as to the origin of the germ plasm indicate that it has not been validated experimentally. Every cell of the soma contains every chromosome (and gene) of both generating cells (spermatozoon and ovum), and this situation points up the basic similarity between germ and somatic cells. Furthermore, even though two germ cells together as a zygote undergo cleavages, all the early blastomeres appear to be equipotential and, if separated, can give rise to whole organisms; every early cell can theoretically provide some germ plasm for the next generation. It is believed that the germinal primordium comes from mesoderm closely associated with the excretory system, but it seems quite clear that the cells arise elsewhere, probably from gut or yolk sac endoderm, and congregate at this region. Thus the exact mechanism by which germ plasm is continuous is not known as yet. Once the continuity is interrupted, however, the line ceases forever.

■ Biogenetic Law or Theory of Recapitulation

It was Haeckel who first drew attention, in 1867, to the possible significance of the fact that all embryos pass through a double-layered stage of development, in which they have an outer ectoderm and an inner endoderm. Thus he conceived the so-called blastula-gastrula theory, using the terms *blastaea* and *gastraea*. He referred to the blastaea as the long-extinct common form of all embryos, basically similar to the surviving blastula. Some colonial Protozoa (for example, Volvox) are permanent blastulae. They are therefore thought to resemble the ancestral blastaea.

Haeckel homologized the permanent form of the Phylum Coelenterata with the transient gastrula stage of all higher forms and called it the gastraea. Pointing to the transition from tubular to two-, three-, and four-chambered hearts in the ascent of the phylogenetic scale; to the temporary circulatory structures associated with an aquatic existence, even in mammals; to the developmental sequence for almost every system; and to vestigial structures of all sorts (for example, tail and pronephros), he had no difficulty in finding support for the theory that all higher forms stemmed from a simple ancestral two-layered prototype much like an adult coelenterate. In fact, one could further homologize the zygote with an amoeba; the blastula with Volvox; the gastrula with Hydra; the cleaving embryo with a worm or clam; the notochord stage with an elasmobranch; and the gill stage with a fish or amphibian. Embryonic man therefore becomes a repository of the residues left by his ancestors. Thus arose the *theory of recapitulation,* which was originally and erroneously interpreted, "Ontogeny recapitulates phylogeny," meaning, "The development of an individual retraces its ancestral history." In other words, a parallel exists between the history of a race, as exemplified by its adults, and the development of an individual member of that race.

Haeckel and his followers (notably Thomas Huxley) carried their homologies further than was acceptable to modern science. They used their theory to explain evolutionary change, declaring that somatic characters acquired during the lifetimes of individuals made impressions upon the germ plasm (a thesis similar to Darwin's *pangenesis*) and that these hereditary traits revealed themselves in ontogeny in the same chronological order in which they were acquired during phylogeny.

Experimental embryology and genetics invalidated this application of the theory of recapitulation. Weismann showed that the germ plasm influences the soma, not the reverse; and Morgan demonstrated that in many instances new characters replace old ones rather than modify them.

The innumerable exceptions to the general law of recapitulation include these: spiral cleavage, characteristic of worms and mollusks, represents no feature of either embryonic or adult life; the cartilaginous skull of the mammalian embryo resembles that of the embryonic and not the adult shark; the visceral clefts of embryonic reptiles, birds, and mammals do not resemble the gill slits of adult fishes; fishes preserve and elaborate their gill slits whereas reptiles, birds, and mammals convert their visceral clefts into structures such as the Eustachian tube and ultimobranchial bodies; the fins of fishes are transposed up and down their bodies in phylogeny, but there is no comparable shifting in ontogeny; in most chordates the neural tube arises as a groove, the sides of which fold over to form a tube, but in Petromyzon, Lepidosteus, Lepidosiren, and the Teleostei in general, it arises as a solid rod, which subsequently hollows out to form a canal; in *Rana esculenta* the formation of the lens is not dependent upon the presence of the optic cup; the chick shows a precocious development of the heart not seen in its presumed ancestor, the frog; in the chick and primitive mammals the amnion and chorion form *after* the embryo, but in man they form *before;* the amnion and allantois of reptiles, birds, and mammals are not present in any adult ancestral form; phylogenetically the respiratory apparatus appears early, but in ontogeny the lung appears as a mass of dense mesenchyme into which endodermal lung buds grow late in embryonic development; in the amphioxus and the frog the liver begins as a simple outpocketing of the gut, but in the mammal it arises as a compact mass of cells permeated by bile canaliculi. The repetition of structures in various embryos indicates, then, the essential natures of the particular structures rather than necessarily a recapitulation of ancestral development. Any attempt to predict future evolutionary change should probably involve embryos rather than adults, but it is impossible to foresee what new structures may emerge and what vestiges may be retained because, along with them and possibly genetically linked with them, are structures of better survival value.

As noted in the Introduction, development of all forms tends to follow a certain basic pattern. Natural selection may eliminate all but those embryos conforming to this fundamental pattern and could thus lead erroneously to the assumption of common origin. However, both natural selection and common origin may be involved. Although the human embryo is never identical to that of a fish, amphibian, or ape, it resembles them in having gills, a pronephros, etc., and during *early* development it is quite possible to confuse them. In 1828 von Baer stated, "I have two small embryos, preserved in alcohol, that I forgot to label. At present I am unable to determine the genus to which they belong. They may be lizards, small birds, or even mammals." He offered the following generalizations that some have taken as support for the theory of recapitulation:

1. In any embryo the more general features of the group to which it belongs arise first.
2. The less general features of the group appear next.
3. The embryo then tends to depart or deviate in its development from too much likeness to other species. It does not pass through any stages representing other species.
4. The embryo of a higher species may be compared with an embryo of a lower species but not with an adult of the lower species.

Modern embryology recognizes the similarities during early development. Whether these are circumstantial evidence of recapitulation or repetition is debatable.

■ Teratology

There is a range of variation for any species within which perfectly normal individuals occur. In fact, one criterion of a species is simply the ability to crossbreed. If a cross fails to produce a new and fertile generation, the two mates are regarded as being from different species (for example, horse × ass = sterile mule). Such a wide variety of normal individuals represents a single species (for example, Drosophila or dogs) that genetic studies are possible.

The material available for investigation is almost limitless—eye color in Drosophila, jaw apparatus in dogs, diabetes in man, etc.

At times, however, individuals are produced exhibiting conditions outside the range of normality. Their malformations or anomalies are either *genetic* or *congenital*, and the distinction may be difficult if the origins are not traceable. A genetic anomaly is assumed to be due to a mutational factor contributed by either parent, and its appearance is to some extent predictable. A congenital anomaly is due to some physical disturbance during development. It is never inherited or inheritable, since it is not caused by mutation.

Congenital anomalies are more probable at certain stages of embryonic development than at others. Nevertheless, all stages are susceptible because differentiating cells are always present and it is these that are most sensitive to changes in the environment. Each organ undergoes one or more periods of extremely active differentiation, such as, for instance, that during which the limb bud or optic cup is forming. If the embryo is subjected to unusual tension or stress, the organs normally differentiating at the time are most likely to exhibit malformations. This situation gave rise to the concept of *critical periods*, meaning periods of development during which an organ is particularly sensitive to disturbances. Unfortunately this concept implied that such periods were limited and that organ systems were not adversely affected at any other times. The truth is that prior to the completion of differentiation the entire organism and every organ are liable to teratologic influences. Long before a primordium appears, the area of the prospective organ can be damaged by a traumatic impact on the embryo. For example, central nervous system anomalies in the mouse can be caused by x-irradiation at the two-cell stage, days before the onset of neurogenesis. After the differentiation of an organ is complete (as, for instance, after the formation of the eye), congenital anomalies cannot be produced in it by any amount of trauma.

Various explanations arise for embryonic malformations resulting from (1) complete *failure* in development of an organ; (2) *interruption* of development of an organ, as a cleft palate; (3) *exaggeration* of development of an organ, excessive body size, number of digits, hirsutism, etc.; (4) *misplacement* of an organ, as a dislocated heart or kidney; and (5) *fusion or splitting* of an organ, as webbed fingers or toes. Most of these anomalies appear in the experimental embryology laboratory as well as in nature, and some are experimentally induced with regularity.

The physician, particularly the obstetrician, encounters congenital anomalies in 5 to 10% of human births. Many of these are tolerable, not seriously deforming or handicapping the individual. Many others can be rectified by minor surgery. All are interesting objects for study in connection with abnormal human development. If deformities, such as the absence of hands or feet, appear to be congenital but upon investigation of family histories are found to be genetic, the practitioner has an obligation to inform those concerned. As indicated earlier, there is not one scintilla of evidence that characters acquired during one's lifetime can in any way affect his germ plasm and hence his offspring. Fortunately, the germ plasm is immune to the severe strains that are often placed upon the soma, and the mutilations of war and the indiscretions of man cannot reach the genetic inheritance levels. Moreover, no amount of training of either parent frees the new generation from the necessity to learn, whether it is to walk, to talk, to play the violin, or whatever. Biologically, potentialities are transmitted just as they are received, with the possibility of a mutation now and then to alter permanently the genetic line in some minor or even major way. It may yet be shown that mutations result from the environment—from penetrating natural ionizing radiations, for instance. In any event, over the centuries many changes occur, and those characters that in the composite organism best fit the environment survive to pass to further generations.

Extensive monsters are comparatively rare, and it is amazing that so many organisms are born normal. Although congenital anomalies represent some pathological response to environmental disturbances, the vast majority of embryos can tolerate considerable, even drastic, environmental changes and arrive at full development without abnormalities. Some species are particularly sensitive to a slight rise or fall in temperature and react by deviating from the normal, but others can be frozen and yet survive. Certain salt water fishes can even adjust to fresh water, a radical change indeed.

Experimental embryology is the study of the embryo as it responds to variations in its environment or to transpositions of its parts. Its objective is the determination of the conditions (temperature, light, oxygen supply, salinity, moisture) necessary for normal development. As a rule, embryos do not encounter such extreme shifts in their environment as are forced upon them by the experimentalist, and it may be presumptuous to draw conclusions as to the reactions in nature from the severe and temporary situations in the laboratory. However, much valuable information regarding the mechanisms of development has resulted from experimental procedures. More still will result from the use of increasingly penetrating optical equipment and other means to investigate the *normal* changes occurring during development. Without a basic knowledge of normal morphological and chemical embryology, no amount of experimental data has any real or compelling meaning in the understanding of embryology.

Although teratology, the study of anomalies, has importance as a curiosity, it throws little if any light on the marvelous normal processes of reproduction and development. The abnormal is the exception and can never be considered a sufficient revelation of the normal. The range of variations within the definition of normality is unquestionably the basis of the most interesting and informative embryology.

Bibliography

Arey, L. B., *Developmental Anatomy*, 6th ed., Saunders, Philadelphia, 1954.

Bacci, G., et al., *Problemi di sviluppo*, Casa Editrice Ambrosiana, Milan, 1954.

Balinsky, B. I., *An Introduction to Embryology*, Saunders, Philadelphia, 1960.

Barth, L. G., *Embryology*, rev. ed., Holt, Rinehart and Winston, New York, 1953.

Barth, L. G., and L. J. Barth, *The Energetics of Development*, Columbia Univ. Press, New York, 1954.

Bertalanffy, L. V., *Modern Theories of Development,* trans. by J. H. Woodger, Harper and Row, New York, 1962.

Bishop, S. C., *Handbook of Salamanders*, Comstock, Ithaca, N.Y., 1943.

Bonner, J. T., *The Evolution of Development*, Cambridge Univ. Press, Cambridge, 1958.

Boyden, E. A., *A Laboratory Atlas of the 13 mm. Pig Embryo*, Wistar Institute, Philadelphia, 1933.

Brachet, J., *The Biochemistry of Development*, Pergamon Press, New York, 1960.

Brambell, F. W., *The Development of Sex in Vertebrates*, 5th ed., Macmillan, New York, 1930.

Carnegie Institute of Washington Publications in Embryology, Washington, D.C.

Child, C. M., *Patterns and Problems of Development*, Univ. of Chicago Press, Chicago, 1941.

Corner, G. W., *The Hormones in Human Reproduction*, rev. ed., Princeton Univ. Press, Princeton, N.J., 1947.

Dalcq, A. M., *Form and Causality in Development*, Cambridge Univ. Press, Cambridge, 1928.

————, *Introduction to General Embryology*, Oxford Univ. Press, London, 1957.

De Beer, G. R., *Embryos and Ancestors*, 3rd ed., Clarendon Press, Oxford, 1958.

————, *Introduction to Experimental Embryology*, 2nd ed., Clarendon Press, Oxford, 1934.

Detwiler, S. R., *Neuroembryology: An Experimental Study*, Macmillan, New York, 1936.

Driesch, H., *Science and Philosophy of the Organism*, Macmillan, New York, 1928.

Durken, B., *Experimental Analysis of Development*, trans. by H. G. and A. M. Newth, Allen, London, 1932.

Duval, M., *Atlas d'embryologie*, Masson, Paris, 1889.

Farris, E. H., *Care and Breeding of Laboratory Animals*, Wiley, New York.

Faure-Fremiet, E., *Cinétique du développement*, Les Presses Universitaire de France, Paris, 1925.

Goette, A., *Atlas zur Entwicklungsgeschichte der Unke*, Voss, Leipzig, 1874.

Goldschmidt, R., *Mechanism and Physiology of Sex Determination*, Methuen, London, 1923.

Gray, J., *Text-book of Experimental Cytology*, Cambridge Univ. Press, Cambridge, 1931.

Hamburger, V. A., *A Manual for Experimental Embryology*, rev. ed., Univ. of Chicago Press, Chicago, 1960.

Hamilton, W. J., J. D. Boyd, and H. W. Mossman, *Human Embryology*, 2nd ed., Williams & Wilkins, Baltimore, 1952.

Harris, D. B., ed., *The Concept of Development*, Univ. of Minnesota Press, Minneapolis, 1957.

Henderson, L. J., *The Fitness of the Environment: An Introduction into Biological Significance of the Properties of Matter*, Smith, Gloucester, Mass., 1959.

Hertwig, O., *Handbuch der vergleichenden und experimentallen Entwicklungslehre der Wirbeltiere*, Fischer, Jena, 1906.

Hörstadius, S. O., *The Neural Crest: Its Properties and Derivatives in the Light of Experimental Research*, Oxford Univ. Press, London, 1950.

Huettner, A. F., *Fundamentals of Comparative Embryology of the Vertebrates*, rev. ed., Macmillan, New York, 1949.

Huxley, J. S. and G. R. de Beer, *The Elements of Experimental Embryology*, Cambridge Univ. Press, Cambridge, 1934.

Jenkinson, J. W., *Vertebrate Embryology*, Clarendon Press, Oxford, 1925.

Jordan, H. E. and J. E. Kindred, *Textbook of Embryology*, 5th ed., Appleton, New York, 1948.

Just, E. E., *Basic Methods for Experiments on Eggs of Marine Animals*, Blakiston, Philadelphia, 1939.

————, *The Biology of the Cell Surface*, Blakiston, Philadelphia, 1930.

Keibel, F., *Normentafeln zur Entwicklungsgeschichte der Wirbeltiere*, Fischer, Jena, 1938.

Keibel, F., and K. Abraham, *Normentafeln zur Entwicklungsgeschichte des Huhnes (Gallus domesticus)*, Fischer, Jena, 1900.

Kellicott, W. E., *Outlines of Chordate Development*, Holt, New York, 1913.

————, *A Textbook of General Embryology*, Holt, New York, 1913.

Kollmann, J., *Handatlas der Entwicklungsgeschichte des Menschen*, 1907.

Korschelt, E., *Regeneration und Transplantation*, Borntraeger, Berlin, 1927.

————, *Vergleichende Entwicklungsgeschichte der Tiere*, Fischer, Jena, 1936.

Kuhn, A., *Vorlesungen über Entwicklungsphysiologie*, Springer, Berlin, 1955.

Lehmann, F. E., *Einführung in die physiologische Embryologie*, Borkhauser, Basel, 1945.

Lillie, F. R., *The Problems of Fertilization*, Univ. of Chicago Press, Chicago, 1919.

Lillie, F. R., and H. L. Hamilton, *Lillie's Development of the Chick: An Introduction to Embryology*, 3rd ed., Holt, Rinehart and Winston, New York, 1952.

Loeb, J., *Artificial Parthenogenesis and Fertilization*, Univ. of Chicago Press, Chicago, 1913.

————, *The Organism as a Whole*, Putnam, New York, 1916.

McBride, E. W., *Text-book of Embryology*, Vols. 1 and 2, Macmillan, New York, 1914.

McElroy, W. and B. Glass, *A Symposium on the Chemical Basis of Development*, Johns Hopkins Press, Baltimore, 1958.

McEwen, R. S., *Vertebrate Embryology*, 4th ed., Holt, Rinehart and Winston, New York, 1957.

Mangold, O., "Das Determinationsproblem," *Ergeb. Biol.*, **3, 5, 7** (1928–31).

————, "Methode für wissenschaftliche Biologie," *Ergeb. Biol.*, **2** (1930).

Marshall, A. M., *The Frog*, Macmillan, New York, 1885.

May, R., *La formation du système nerveux*, Gauthier-Villars, Paris, 1945.

Meyer, A. W., *The Rise of Embryology*, Stanford Univ. Press, Stanford, Calif., 1939.

Morgan, T. H., *The Development of the Frog's Egg*, Macmillan, New York, 1897.

——, *Embryology and Genetics*, Columbia Univ. Press, New York, 1934.

——, *Experimental Embryology*, Columbia Univ. Press, New York, 1927.

Needham, J., *Biochemistry and Morphogenesis*, Cambridge Univ. Press, Cambridge, 1942.

——, *Chemical Embryology*, Vols. 1 and 2, Macmillan, New York, 1930.

——, *The History of Embryology*, 2nd ed., Abelard-Schuman, New York, 1959.

Nelsen, O. E., *Comparative Embryology of the Vertebrates*, McGraw-Hill, New York, 1953.

Nordenskiold, E., *The History of Biology: A Survey*, Tudor, New York, 1960.

Patten, B. M., *The Early Embryology of the Chick*, 4th ed., McGraw-Hill, New York, 1951.

——, *The Embryology of the Pig*, 3rd ed., McGraw-Hill, New York, 1948.

——, *Foundations of Embryology*, McGraw-Hill, New York, 1958.

——, *Human Embryology*, 2nd ed., McGraw-Hill, New York, 1953.

Raven, P., *The Outline of Developmental Physiology*, Pergamon Press, New York, 1960.

Richards, A. N., *Outline of Comparative Embryology*, Wiley, New York, 1931.

Robertson, T. B., *Chemical Basis for Growth and Senescence*, Lippincott, Philadelphia, 1924.

Romanoff, A. L., and A. J. Romanoff, *The Avian Egg*, Wiley, New York, 1949.

Rugh, R., *Experimental Embryology: Techniques and Procedures*, 3rd ed., Burgess, Minneapolis, 1962.

——, *The Frog: Its Reproduction and Development*, McGraw-Hill, New York, 1951.

——, *Laboratory Manual of Vertebrate Embryology*, 5th ed., Burgess, Minneapolis, 1961.

Russell, E. S., *Form and Function*, Murray, London, 1916.

Schliep, W., *Die Determination der Primitiventwicklung*, Akademische Verlag, 1929.

Shumway, W., and F. B. Adamstone, *Introduction to Vertebrate Embryology*, 5th ed., Wiley, New York, 1954.

Spemann, H., *Embryonic Development and Induction*, Yale Univ. Press, New Haven, 1938.

Sussman, M., *Animal Growth and Development*, Prentice-Hall, Englewood Cliffs, N.J., 1960.

Thompson, D'A., *On Growth and Form*, Putnam, New York, 1917.

Tyler, A., "Developmental Processes and Energetics," *Quart. Rev. Biol.*, **17**, 197 (1942).

Velardo, J. T., ed., *The Endocrinology of Reproduction*, Oxford Univ. Press, New York, 1958.

Waddington, C. H., *Organisers and Genes*, Cambridge Univ. Press, Cambridge, 1940.

——, *Principles of Embryology*, Macmillan, New York, 1956.

Waterman, A. J., *A Laboratory Manual of Comparative Vertebrate Embryology*, Holt, New York, 1948.

Weismann, A., *Germplasm*, Scribner, New York, 1893.

Weiss, P., ed., *Developmental Biology Conference Series 1956*, Univ. of Chicago Press, Chicago, 1959.

Weiss, P., *Principles of Development*, Holt, New York, 1939.

Wieman, H. L., *An Introduction to Vertebrate Embryology*, McGraw-Hill, New York, 1930.

Willier, B. H., P. Weiss, and V. Hamburger, *Analysis of Development,* Saunders, Philadelphia, 1955.

Wilson, E. B., *The Cell in Development and Inheritance,* Macmillan, New York, 1925.

Windle, W. F., *Physiology of the Fetus,* Saunders, Philadelphia, 1940.

Witschi, E., *Development of Vertebrates,* Saunders, Philadelphia, 1956.

Wright, A. H., and A. A. Wright, *Handbook of Frogs and Toads of the United States and Canada,* 3rd ed., Comstock, Ithaca, N.Y., 1949.

Wurmbach, H., *Lehrbuch der Zoologie,* Fischer, Stuttgart, 1957.

Zubek, J. P., and P. A. Solberg, *Human Development,* McGraw-Hill, New York, 1954.

Glossary

abortion   Termination of pregnancy before the embryo has reached a viable stage.

achondroplastic   Having abnormally short extremities with normal head and trunk proportions, as in some dwarfs.

acidophil   Staining with acid dyes; often used to designate an entire cell type; oxyphil.

acrosome   Pointed structure on the head of a mature spermatozoon, presumably functional in the penetration of the egg cortex during fertilization; perforatorium.

activation   Process of initiating development in an ovum, normally achieved by a spermatozoon of the same species but also accomplished artificially (parthenogenesis); stimulation of a spermatozoon to accelerated activity by chemical means.

activity, functional   Stimulation or inhibition of development of an organ by environmental variables (e.g., hypertrophy of urodele gills in an oxygen-deficient medium).

adaptation   Functional or structural change resulting in selective elimination.

adnexa   Accessory structures.

affinity   Tendency of cells and tissues of the early embryo to cling together when removed from their normal environment.

afterbirth   Extraembryonic membranes delivered after the emergence of the fetus (mammal).

agenesis   Failure of a primordium to develop (e.g., absence of an arm or kidney).

agglutination   Cluster formation; a spontaneously reversible reaction of spermatozoa to the fluid surrounding an ovum.

aggregation   Coming together of cells (e.g., spermatozoa) without sticking; an irreversible reaction comparable to chemotropism.

agnathia   Congenital absence of the jaw, usually the lower one.

alar plate   Dorsolateral wall of the myelencephalon, separated from the basal plate by the sulcus limitans.

albumen   Protein substance secreted by the walls of the oviducts around the eggs of reptiles and birds.

albumen sac   Two-layered ectodermal sac enclosing the albumen of an egg during early development and separated for a time from the yolk by the vitelline membrane; it later releases some of its contents into the amniotic cavity through the ruptured amniotic raphe.

alecithal   *See* egg.

alimentary castration   Prolonged starvation.

allantoic artery   *See* umbilical artery.

allantoic vein   *See* umbilical vein.

allantoin Nitrogenous portion of allantoic fluid.

allantois Saclike organ of respiration and excretion in embryos of reptiles, birds, and mammals, consisting of splanchnic mesoderm and evaginated hindgut endoderm.

allelomorph One of a pair of homologous Mendelian characters.

allohaploid Androgenetic haploid.

allometry Study of the relative sizes of parts of animals at different absolute sizes, weights, ages, or chemical compositions.

allomorphosis Physical or chemical relation of part of an organism or the whole at some early stage to either the part or the whole at a later stage (e.g., comparison of egg size with adult size).

allophore Cell containing red pigment.

allopolyploid Polyploid species hybrid.

amboceptor Double receptor (e.g., one reacting with both sperm and egg receptors in fertilization; it may also receive blood inhibitors).

ameloblast Cell that secretes the enamel of the tooth (mammal).

amelus Individual without limbs.

amitosis Direct nuclear division without chromosomal rearrangement.

amniocardiac vesicles Paired primordia of the pericardial cavity appearing in the mesoderm lateral to the head fold of the chick embryo and growing beneath the foregut.

amnion Thin, double membrane enclosing the embryos of some invertebrates and of reptiles, birds, and mammals and deriving from the somatopleure in vertebrates.

amniotic bands Fibrous bands from the amnion to the embryo due to local necrosis of embryonic tissues.

amniotic cavity, false Temporary cavity in the dorsal trophoblast of a mammalian embryo, distinct from the true amniotic cavity.

amniotic folds Folds of the amnion extending up over an embryo.

amniotic raphe Knot of tissue at the junction of the anterior, posterior, and lateral amniotic folds over an embryo; seroamniotic connection.

ampherotoky Parthenogenetic production of both males and females; amphitoky.

amphiblastic Characterized by total but unequal segmentation, as in moderately telolecithal eggs.

amphiblastula Morula formed by unequal segmentation.

amphimixis Mixing of germinal substances during fertilization.

amphitene *See* synaptene.

amphitoky *See* ampherotoky.

amplexus Sexual embrace of male and female amphibians, which may (frog, toad) or may not (urodele) occur at the time of oviposition.

analogous Having the same functions but different origins or structures; opposed to homologous.

analogy Similarity in function but not in origin or structure.

anamniote Form never developing an amnion (cyclostome, fish, amphibian).

anaphase Stage in mitosis, between metaphase and telophase, during which the paired chromosomes separate at the equator and begin to move toward the poles of the spindle.

anastomosis Junction to form a network, as of blood vessels or nerves.

androgamone Acidic protein of low molecular weight in spermatozoa, presumably functional in fertilization.

androgenesis Development of an egg with sperm chromosomes only, accomplished by removing or destroying the egg nucleus before syngamy.

andromerogone   Egg fragment developing with the sperm nucleus only, after surgical removal of the egg nucleus and some cytoplasm or after separation of the pronuclei before syngamy by constriction or centrifugation.

anencephaly   Congenital absence of the brain.

anenteron   Formation and constriction of the archenteron by evagination instead of invagination, following the application of heat.

anestrus   Quiescent period following estrus in the reproductive cycle of the female mammal.

aneuploid, multiform   Complex chromosomal mosaic, possibly the result of multipolar mitoses.

aneuploidy   Deviation from normal diploidy involving partial sets of chromosomes.

aneurogenic   Developing without proper components of the central nervous system (e.g., limb buds in an embryo without a spinal cord).

angenesis   Regeneration of tissue.

angioblast   Mesenchyme cell that forms vascular endothelium.

animal hemisphere   Region of an ovum where the polar bodies form; region of a telolecithal ovum containing the nucleus and the bulk of the cytoplasm and giving rise largely to ectodermal structures; animal pole; apical pole.

animalization   Transformation by physical or chemical means of normally endodermal regions to ectoderm; ectodermization; opposed to vegetalization.

anophthalmia   Congenital absence of the eyes.

anormogenesis   Development deviating in a typical manner from the normal.

anterior   Toward the head; cephalic; cranial; rostral.

anterior intestinal portal   Opening from the yolk sac into the foregut.

anuran   Tailless amphibian (frog, toad); salientian.

anus   Posterior opening of the digestive tract.

aortic arch   Blood vessel connecting the dorsal and ventral aortae through a visceral arch.

aprosopia   Congenital absence of facial features.

aqueduct of Sylvius   Ventricle of the mesencephalon (mesocoel), between the third and fourth ventricles; iter.

aqueous humor   Watery fluid filling the anterior chamber of the eye.

archenteron   Primitive gut, appearing in the gastrula and communicating with the outside (amphibian, bird) through the blastopore; gastrocoel.

archoplasm   Protoplasm that gives rise to the centrosomes, asters, and spindle fibers.

arcualia   Small blocks of sclerotome that form the vertebrae.

area   Region of a fate map, generally at the blastula stage or later, consisting of a morphogenetic cell group.

area opaca   Opaque area surrounding the area pellucida; it is opaque because of the underlying adherent yolk.

area pellucida   Central, transparent area of a blastoderm (reptile, bird), originally represented by the central cells; it appears transparent because a cavity separates it from the underlying yolk.

area vasculosa   Three-layered portion of the area opaca in which blood islands develop, appearing first posteriorly to the embryo and progressing forward along the sides of the embryo with the expansion of the mesoderm.

area vitellina   Two-layered peripheral portion of the area opaca, consisting of the area vitellina interna and the area vitellina externa, the latter including the zone of junction.

arrhenokaryotic Having only the haploid set of male chromosomes, owing to a separation of the nuclear components after fertilization.

arrhenotoky Parthenogenetic production of males only.

arthrogryposis Persistent flexure of a joint.

aster Aggregate of lines radiating from a centrosome during animal mitosis.

astomia Congenital absence of a mouth.

astral ray Line of an aster.

astrocyte Star-shaped neuroglial cell.

asyntaxia dorsalis Failure of the neural tube to close.

ateliosis Incomplete development of the skeleton due to nonunion of the epiphyses, as in some dwarfs.

atresia Imperforation.

atrium Thin-walled chamber of the heart that receives blood from the sinus venosus and delivers it to the ventricle.

attachment point Point of chromosome attaching to the spindle fiber and therefore nearest the centrosome in anaphase; centromere; chromocenter; kinetochore.

attraction, nonspecific Attraction of nerve fibers by any structure in the vicinity.

auditory tube Tube connecting the pharynx and the tympanic cavity; Eustachian tube.

auditory vesicle Ectodermal sac that gives rise to the inner ear.

Auflagerung Placing of responsive ectoderm on a dead inductor to test its inductive power.

auricle Earlike appendage on an atrium.

autogamy Self-fertilization.

autoparthenogenesis Parthenogenetic stimulation of an egg by materials from another egg.

autosome Any chromosome except a so-called sex (X or Y) chromosome.

auxesis Growth by cell expansion without cell division.

auxocyte Premeiotic germ cell; primary spermatocyte or oöcyte; meiocyte.

axial filament Central fiber in the tail of a spermatozoon.

axis, of cell Line (imaginary) passing through the nucleus, the centrosome, and, generally, the geometrical center of a cell.

axis, of embryo Line (imaginary) defining anterior and posterior directions in an embryo.

balancers Cylindrical, paired projections of ectoderm with mesenchyme cores, used as tactile and balancing organs in place of suckers (urodele).

Balfour's law The velocity of segmentation in any part of the ovum is, roughly speaking, proportional to the concentration of the protoplasm there; and the size of the segments is inversely proportional to the concentration of the protoplasm.

Barfuth's rule When oblique cuts are made on amphibian tails, the axis of the regenerated tail will be at first perpendicular to the cut surface.

basal plate Ventrolateral wall of the myelencephalon, separated from the alar plate by the sulcus limitans.

basophil Staining with basic dyes; often used to designate an entire cell type.

Bateson's rule The long axes of duplicated structures lie in the same plane. Duplicated limbs are mirror images of each other about a plane that bisects the angle between the long axes of the members and that is at right angles to the plane of these axes.

Bidder's organ. Anterior portion of an anuran gonad, ovarian in character, developing from the cortex of the gonad primordium and indicating failure of the medullary substance to diffuse to the anterior extremity of the gonad primordium.

bioelectric current Electrical potential characteristic of life, associated with the activities of muscles, nerves, etc.

biogenetic law Embryos of higher species resemble the embryos of lower species in certain respects but do not resemble the adults of lower species. Embryonic development proceeds gradually from the more general (phylogenetic) to the more specific (ontogenetic).

biological memory Ontogenetic development of phylogenetically accumulated characters.

biotonus Ratio of assimilation to dissimilation.

blastema Group of cells about to be organized into definite tissue; the new cells covering a cut surface, functional in tissue regeneration.

Blastemfeld Fieldlike structure (or functional state) without a primordium; a primordial field present in the egg stage; a field activated only by induction.

blastocoel Cavity of a blastula; segmentation cavity.

blastocyst Mammalian blastula; blastodermic vesicle.

blastoderm Portion of an egg from which the embryo and its membranes are derived; the cellular blastodisc.

blastodermic vesicle *See* blastocyst.

blastokinesis Reversal of the anteroposterior axis in an egg (e.g., insect), often accomplished by movement during early development; revolution.

blastomere Cell of a blastula; designated as a micromere or macromere, according to size.

blastopore Opening of the archenteron to the outside.

blastopore, dorsal lip of Region of the first involution of cells in an amphibian gastrula; originally the region of the gray crescent.

blastopore, ventral lip of Region of a blastopore opposite the dorsal lip.

blastula Stage in embryonic development between the appearance of distinct blastomeres and the beginning of gastrulation, generally characterized by a blastocoel and invariably monodermic.

blood island Group of mesodermal cells in the splanchnopleure, from which arise a blood vessel and corpuscles.

bottle cell Long-necked, cylindrical cell of the blastopore lips (amphibian), appearing wherever infolding occurs.

Bowman's capsule Double-walled glomerular cup associated with a uriniferous tubule.

brachydactylia Abnormal shortness of the digits.

bradyauxesis Development in which a part grows more slowly than the whole.

bradygenesis Lengthening of certain stages in development.

branchial Pertaining to respiration.

branchial arch Visceral arch associated with respiration; gill arch.

branchial artery Blood vessel passing through the gills (external or internal) of an embryo; gill artery.

branchial chamber *See* opercular chamber.

branchial cleft Visceral cleft associated with respiration.

branchial groove Visceral groove associated with respiration.

branchiomere Metamere in the visceral arches.

bud Undeveloped branch, generally a primordium (e.g., limb or lung bud).

budding Reproductive process in which a small bud develops on an organism, gradually approaches the size of the parent, and finally separates to form a new individual.

bulbourethral glands Paired genital glands at the anterior end of the urethra in a male mammal.

bulbus arteriosus Most anterior division of an embryonic heart, leading from the ventricle to the truncus arteriosus.

cacogenesis Abnormal growth or development.

calcium-release theory Theory that the activating agent in parthenogenesis releases calcium from calcium proteinate in the cell cortex and that the free calcium causes a protoplasmic clotting that initiates development.

canals of Gartner Remnants of mesonephric ducts in the broad ligament close to the uterus and vagina.

carcinogen Chemical substance capable of causing cancer.

caudad Toward the tail.

caval fold Lateral fold of the dorsal mesentery in which the posterior vena cava develops.

cell Protoplasmic territory under the control of a single nucleus, whether or not the territory is bounded by a membrane.

cell chain theory Theory that a peripheral nerve is of multicellular origin; opposed to the outgrowth theory.

cell cone Single cell (other than a zygote) and all the cells derived from it by division.

cell theory Theory that the body of any living organism is composed of structural and functional units called cells.

cellulation Development of cytoplasmic areas around normal nuclei.

cementoblast Cement-forming cell of a tooth.

central canal *See* neurocoel.

central cell Cell in the center of the chick blastoderm, bounded on all sides in surface view but perhaps connected with other cells beneath the surface.

centriole Granular core of a centrosome; the small granule in the cytoplasm of a spermatid that gives rise to its flagellum-like tail.

centromere *See* attachment point.

centrosome Clear zone surrounding a centriole.

centrosome theory, heterodynamic Theory that centrosomes may have different powers, thereby causing unequal cell division, as in many molluscs.

centrosphere Dense zone outside a centrosome, with surrounding rays.

cephalothoracopagus Conjoined twins fused in the head and chest regions.

cerebral peduncles Longitudinal tracts in the floor of the mesencephalon.

cervical cyst Cyst resulting from imperfect closure of a visceral cleft; branchial cyst.

cervical fistula Fistula resulting from incomplete closure of a visceral cleft; branchial fistula.

cervical flexure Extensive transverse flexure of the embryo at the junction of the brain and spinal cord.

cervical sinus Depression between the third and fourth visceral clefts and the body.

chalaza Twisted cord of heavy albumen immediately outside the vitelline membrane of the bird egg, which helps to hold the yolk in position.

chalone Internal secretion with inhibitory effects; opposed to hormone.

chemoneurotropism Chemical attraction of regenerating nerve fibers to a degenerating nerve.

chimera Compound embryo generally produced by grafting major portions of two embryos, usually of different species; also may result from an abnormal chromosomal distribution in cleavage after normal fertilization.

choana Opening of the internal naris into the pharynx.

chondrification Cartilage formation by the secretion of a homogeneous matrix among primitive cells.

chondrocranium Originally cartilaginous portion of a skull.

chorda dorsalis *See* notochord.

chordamesoderm Region of a late amphibian blastula, originating in the gray crescent, that gives rise to the notochord and mesoderm.

chorioallantoic graft Transplantation of part of an embryo to the chorioallantoic membrane.

chorioallantoic membrane Extraembryonic membrane formed by the fusion of the inner wall of the chorion and the outer wall of the allantois (both mesoderm) in a reptile or bird embryo.

chorion Extraembryonic membrane developing from the somatopleure as a corollary of the amnion and enclosing both the amnion and the allantois; it consists of inner mesoderm and outer ectoderm; serosa; false amnion.

chorion frondosum Portion of the mammalian chorion that forms the placenta and adheres to the decidua basalis.

chorion laeve Mammalian chorion exclusive of the chorion frondosum.

choroid Mesenchymal and sometimes pigmented coat inside the sclera and outside the pigmented layer of the retina.

choroid fissure Inverted groove in the optic stalk through which pass the optic nerve and blood vessels to and from the eyeball.

choroid knot Thickened region, near the pupil, of the fused folds of the choroid fissure, from which arise the cells of the iris.

choroid plexus Vascular folds of the thin roof of the brain, projecting into the cavity of the telencephalon (lateral), diencephalon (anterior), and myelencephalon (posterior).

chromaffin tissue Vascular tissue with many nerves in the suprarenal medulla, which exhibits characteristic reactions with chromic acid salts.

chromatid Longitudinal half of a chromosome.

chromatin Dark-staining substance of the nuclear network and the chromosomes; gives a Feulgen reaction.

chromatoblast Potential pigment cell.

chromatophore Pigment-bearing cell found chiefly in the skin, mucous membrane, and choroid of the eye; frequently capable of changing size, shape, and color.

chromidium Cytoplasmic granule that stains like chromatin and may actually be an extruded chromatin granule (protozoan).

chromomere Unit of a chromosome recognized as a chromatin granule.

chromonema Slender chromatin thread that is the core of a chromosome during mitosis.

chromonucleic acid *See* deoxyribonucleic acid.

chromophobe Cell with nonstaining constituents.

chromosin Acidic protein present in a nucleus and considered an essential part of the chromosomes.

chromosome Chromatic, or dark-staining, body in the nucleus, containing a matrix and one or more chromonemata during mitosis.

chromosome, acentric Chromosome without a centromere.

chromosome, dicentric Chromosome with two centromeres.

chromosome, homologous Allelomorphic chromosome.

chromosome, sex X or Y chromosome.

chromosome aberration Irregularity in the constitution or the number of the chromosomes, which may modify the normal course of development.

cicatrix Site of rupture of the thin, nonvascular side of a Graafian follicle to allow the extrusion of the ovum into the body cavity; stigma.

ciliary process Supporting, contractile element of the iris.

circle of Willis Arterial circle formed by anastomoses between the internal carotid arteries and the basilar artery; surrounds the pituitary gland.

circulatory arcs Intraembryonic, vitelline, and allantoic circulatory channels, each involving afferent and efferent vessels and interpolated capillary beds.

cleavage Mitotic division of an egg into blastomeres; segmentation.

cleavage, accessory Cleavage in peripheral or deeper regions of a germinal disc, caused by supernumerary sperm nuclei after normal fertilization.

cleavage, asymmetrical Extremely unequal division of an egg.

cleavage, bilateral Cleavage in which the egg substance is distributed symmetrically with respect to the median plane of the future embryo.

cleavage, determinate Cleavage in which certain parts of a future embryo are isolated in certain blastomeres so that the blastomeres are not qualitatively equipotent; i.e., each blastomere cannot give rise to a complete embryo.

cleavage, discoidal Cleavage affecting only the periphery of an egg; superficial or meroblastic cleavage.

cleavage, equatorial *See* cleavage, horizontal.

cleavage, gastrular Separation of the ectoderm and endoderm by the compressed blastocoel during gastrulation.

cleavage, holoblastic *See* cleavage, total.

cleavage, horizontal Cleavage at right angles to the egg axis; often the typical third cleavage; equatorial or latitudinal cleavage.

cleavage, indeterminate Cleavage resulting in qualitatively equipotent blastomeres; i.e., each blastomere can give rise to a complete embryo.

cleavage, latitudinal *See* cleavage, horizontal.

cleavage, meridional *See* cleavage, vertical.

cleavage, meroblastic *See* cleavage, discoidal.

cleavage, radial Cleavage resulting in tiers of blastomeres.

cleavage, spiral Cleavage at an angle oblique to the egg axis resulting in blastomeres lying in the furrows between earlier blastomeres.

cleavage, superficial Cleavage around the periphery of a centrolecithal egg; peripheral cleavage.

cleavage, total Cleavage resulting in the division of the entire egg into blastomeres, generally equal in size; holoblastic cleavage.

cleavage, vertical Cleavage along the egg axis; generally the first two cleavages of an egg; meridional cleavage.

cleavage nucleus Nucleus controlling cleavage.

clinostat Apparatus providing constant rotation.

clitoris Small conical structure of a female mammal comparable in origin and position to the penis of the male.

cloacal membrane Junction of evaginated hindgut endoderm and the mid-ventral ectoderm of the proctodeum, later perforated to form the anus; anal plate.

coadaptation Correlated variation in two mutually dependent organs.

cochlea Portion of the auditory vesicle associated with hearing (mammal); supplied by nerve VIII; lagena (lower vertebrate).

coelom Body cavity developing from a split in the lateral plate mesoderm; subdivided in higher forms into pericardial, pleural, and peritoneal cavities.

coitus Sexual intercourse; copulation.

collecting tubule Portion of a nephric tubule leading to a nephric duct.

colliculi, inferior Posterior pair of the four thickenings of the dorsolateral walls of the mesencephalon (corpora quadrigemina), containing synaptic centers for auditory reflexes (mammal).

colliculi, superior Anterior pair of the four thickenings of the dorsolateral walls of the mesencephalon (corpora quadrigemina), containing synaptic centers for visual reflexes (mammal).

colloid Finely divided substance containing particles ranging from molecular size to a size just visible to the unaided eye; physical state of protoplasm.

columella Cartilaginous connection between the auditory capsule and the tympanic membrane across the tympanic cavity (amphibian, reptile, bird); plectrum.

commissure, anterior Nerve fibers crossing in the lamina terminalis.

commissure, posterior Nerve fibers crossing in the roof of the diencephalon behind the epiphysis.

commissure, transverse Nerve fibers crossing in the floor of the diencephalon behind the mammillary tubercle.

commissure, trochlear Nerve fibers crossing in the roof of the isthmus, between the mesencephalon and the metencephalon.

common cardinal vein Vein carrying blood to the sinus venosus from the anterior and posterior cardinal veins; duct of Cuvier.

competence Ability of an embryonic region to react to a stimulus.

compression Either an acceleration of development or an extension of certain stages with a concomitant shortening or omission of others, resulting in an unbalanced time schedule.

cone, entrance Temporary depression of the surface of an ovum following the entrance of a spermatozoon.

cone, fertilization Conical projection of the cytoplasm from the surface of an ovum to meet a spermatozoon.

congenital Acquired during embryonic life; opposed to genetic.

convergence, dorsal Movement of material from the marginal zone toward the dorsal mid-line as it involutes and invaginates during gastrulation, resulting in a compensatory ventral divergence; concrescence; confluence.

coprodeum Anterior portion of the cloaca (bird).

cornea Transparent head ectoderm and underlying mesenchyme covering the front of the eyeball.

corona radiata Layer of elongated follicle cells immediately surrounding the ovum at ovulation.

corpora quadrigemina *See* colliculi.

corpus albicans Scar tissue at the site of rupture of a Graafian follicle following absorption of the corpus luteum (mammal).

corpus hemorrhagicum Ruptured Graafian follicle filled with clotted blood (mammal).

corpus luteum Ruptured Graafian follicle filled with a yellow granular substance derived from the membrana granulosa (mammal).

corpus striatum Center of coordination of certain complex muscular activities, formed by the thickening of the ventrolateral wall of the lateral ventricle.

correlation coefficient Relation of growth rates of different parts of an embryo.

Cowper's glands *See* bulbourethral glands.

cranial Pertaining to the head; cephalic; rostral.

cranial flexure Extensive transverse flexure of the embryo at the midbrain level.

craniopagus Conjoined twins united at the crania.

craniorrhachischisis Congenital fissure of the skull and spinal column.

cranioschisis Congenital fissure of the cranium; acrania.

cranium bifidum Congenital cleft of the cranium.

crescent, gray Crescent-shaped region on the surface of an amphibian egg at the margin of the animal pole, gray because of the migration of pigment away from it and toward the sperm entrance point; region of future blastopore and anus.

crescent, mesodermal Crescent-shaped region on the surface of an amphioxus egg at the four-cell stage, which gives rise to the mesoderm.

crescent, yellow Yellow, crescent-shaped region on the surface of an ascidian egg, which gives rise to the mesoderm.

crest segment Segment of a neural crest from which spinal or possibly cranial ganglia develop.

crop Spindle-shaped dilatation of the esophagus of a bird.

cross-fertilization Union of gametes produced by different individuals.

crossing over Exchange of portions of allelomorphic chromosomes during synapsis.

cryptorchism Condition in which the testes do not descend into the scrotum, usually resulting in sterility because of body heat.

cumulus oöphorus Aggregation of cells around the ovum in the Graafian follicle (mammal).

cuticle Outermost and thinnest of the three egg shell layers.

cutis plate *See* dermatome.

cyanosis Bluing of the skin due to insufficient oxygenation of the blood.

cyclopia Congenital failure of the eyes to separate properly.

cyt-, cyte-, cyto- Combining form meaning cell.

cytarme Flattening of previously rounded blastomeres against each other following the completion of cleavage.

cytasters Asters arising apart from the nucleus in the cytoplasm.

cytochorismus Apparent partial separation of the blastomeres at the surface of an egg.

cytochrome Oxidizable pigment present in nearly all cells.

cytoleosis Process by which a cell, already irreversibly differentiated, proceeds to its final specialization.

cytolisthesis Tendency of embryonic cells to aggregate and to fill up the intervening spaces, even in the absence of a common surface membrane, due to surface tension and selective adhesiveness; movement of cells over one another by sliding, rotation, or both.

cytology Branch of biology concerned with cell structure and function.

cytolysis Disintegration of a cell, indicated by a dispersal of its components.

cytoplasm Material of the cell exclusive of the nucleus; i.e., protoplasm apart from nucleoplasm.

cytosome Cell body exclusive of the nucleus.

cytotaxis Attraction (positive cytotaxis) or repulsion (negative cytotaxis) of cells for one another.

cytotrophoblast Thin inner cellular layer of trophoblast of a human embryo.

cytotropism Movement of a cell in response to external forces.

dark-field ring Orange-yellow ring seen under dark-field illumination on the silvery white surface of a sea urchin egg.

decidua Portion of the uterine mucosa cast off at parturition.

decidua basalis Portion of the uterine mucosa to which the placenta is attached; decidua serotina.

decidua capsularis Portion of the uterine mucosa overlying the embryo, which with embroyonic growth approaches and finally contacts the decidua parietalis; decidua reflexa.

decidua parietalis Portion of the uterine mucosa aside from the decidua basalis and the decidua capsularis; decidua vera.

deciduate Characterized by an intimate association of the chorionic villi with the uterine mucosa.

dedifferentiation Process of relinquishing specialized characters and returning to a primitive condition, thereby regaining the original, wide range of potencies; possibly occurring in regenerating tissue.

deflection Movement away from the line of normal development; inability of dedifferentiated cells to redifferentiate.

degrowth Reduction in mass following prolonged growth.

delamination Separation of cell layers, as in mesoderm formation.

dental papilla Mesenchymal portion of a tooth primordium.

dental ridge Cellular plate growing from the mouth lining into the gums of an embryo and giving rise to enamel-forming cells.

dentine Main portion of a tooth, derived from mesoderm.

deoxyribonucleic acid Nucleic acid present in the nucleus and active in chromosome duplication; DNA; chromonucleic acid.

dermal bone Bone deriving from the dermis.

dermatome Outer portion of a somite, which gives rise to the dermis; cutis plate.

dermis Deep layer of the skin, derived from mesoderm (dermatome).

determinant Corpuscular unit determining the qualities and actions of the cells containing it.

determination Development of a tissue, whether isolated or transplanted, in the normal manner.

Determinationsgeschehen All the invisible processes in the morphogenesis of a primordium.

deuterotoky Parthenogenetic production of both sexes.

deutoplasm *See* yolk.

diakinesis Stage in meiotic prophase following diplotene, during which the homologous chromosomes fuse, generally in curious shapes, to form the haploid number.

diapause Dormant state in the normal development of some animals (e.g., insects), independent of environmental factors.

dicentric Having two centromeres.

dicephalus Two-headed monster.

dicephalus tetrabrachinus Coincidence of the first cleavage furrow of the amphibian egg with the sagittal plane; the constriction is exaggerated and results in duplication of the notochord, auditory vesicles, and forelimbs.

diencephalon Portion of the prosencephalon posterior to the telencephalon.

differentiating center Area responsible for the determination and localization of a region of the embryo; organization center.

differentiation Progressive diversification leading to morphogenesis and histogenesis; the process by which a fertilized egg becomes a complex organism.

differentiation, axial Variations in the densities of chemical substances in the direction of one diameter of the egg, called the egg axis.

differentiation, corporative Differentiation resulting from the functioning of parts of an organism.

differentiation, dependent Differentiation of parts of an organism under mutual influences, such as activating, limiting, or inhibiting influences; the inability of parts of an organism to develop independently of other parts.

differentiation, functional Differentiation resulting from forces (stresses and strains) associated with the functioning of parts of an organism.

differentiation, individuative Differentiation resulting from the action of morphogenetic fields rather than the functioning of parts of an organism.

differentiation, regional Differentiation of different organs by different parts of an organizer; formation of organ districts within a morphogenetic field.

differentiation, self- Adherence to a definite course of development by a part of an organism, regardless of environmental changes.

differentiation potency Scope of specializations, cytological and histological, available to a given cell.

dikinetic *See* dicentric.

diocoel Cavity of the diencephalon.

diplochromosome Chromosome with four chromatids, formed by the pairing of homologous chromosomes without subsequent separation.

diploid Having the number of chromosomes normal to a somatic or primordial germ cell, twice the (haploid) number characteristic of a mature gamete.

diplomyelia Presence of a lengthwise fissure in the spinal cord.

diplotene Stage in meiotic prophase, between pachytene and diakinesis, during which the homologous chromosomes uncoil.

dipygus Conjoined twins with a single head and thorax and duplicated pelvis and lower extremities; duplicitas posterior.

discoblastula Disc-shaped blastula resulting from the discoidal cleavage of an ovum.

discus proligerus *See* cumulus oöphorus.

dissogeny Reproduction in which an individual has two periods of sexual maturity, one as a larva and one as an adult.

distal Farthest from any point of reference in the main body mass.

district Region in which activities show field character although none of them can be identified with a particular component of a field.

diverticulum Blind outpocketing.

dominant Gene inherited from one parent and masking a contrasted gene from the other parent in a hybrid; opposed to recessive.

dopa 3,4-Dihydroxyphenylalanine; an intermediate oxidation product of tyrosine that appears as a precursor of melanin in mammals.

dorsal Pertaining to the back; opposed to ventral.

dorsal root Aggregation of nerve cells derived from the neural crest and sending processes into the dorsolateral wall of the neural tube.

double assurance Working together of two processes, either one of which is sufficient to accomplish the end result.

duct, cochlear Connection between the lagena (cochlea) and the utricle.

duct, of Cuvier *See* common cardinal vein.

duct, ejaculatory Short duct between the seminal vesicle and the urethra (mammal).

duct, endolymphatic Tube extending from the auditory vesicle toward the surface.

duct, Gartner's Remnant of the mesonephric duct in a female mammal.

duct, hepatocystic Connection between the liver and the gall bladder in a bird embryo.

duct, hepatoenteric   Connection between the liver and the ductus choledochus in a bird embryo.

ductus arteriosus   Portion of the sixth aortic arch between the dorsal aorta and the pulmonary artery, normally occluded; ductus Botalli.

ductus choledochus   Common chamber between the duodenum and the ducts from the liver, the gall bladder, and the pancreas.

ductus venosus   Major channel through the liver, which carries blood from the left and right portal veins through a junction of the left and right hepatic veins and on into the posterior vena cava.

duodenum   Portion of the gut between the stomach and the small intestine from which the liver and the pancreas arise.

duplicitas cruciata   Conjoined twins resulting from grafting or the inversion of a two-cell embryo.

dyad   Single chromosome, consisting of two chromatids.

dysplastic treatment   Introduction of a transplant from an organism of a different phylum.

ecdysis   Molting.

ectobronchus   One of six evaginations from the dorsal wall of the middle portion of the main bronchus (bird); classed as a secondary bronchus.

ectocardia   Congenital misplacement of the heart; ectopia cordis.

ectoderm   Outermost layer of the gastrula, which gives rise to the epidermis, the nervous system, and the sense organs; ectoblast; epiblast.

ectopic   Out of the normal position.

ectoplasm   Outer layer of protoplasm of a cell, just inside the cell membrane; cortex.

ectrodactylia   Congenital absence of one or more digits.

egg, alecithal   Egg with little or no yolk.

egg, centrolecithal   Egg with the yolk concentrated in the center.

egg, cleidoic   Egg covered by a protective shell.

egg, ectolecithal   Egg with the yolk outside the cytoplasm.

egg, giant   Abnormal polyploid egg, developing into giant cells and embryo.

egg, homolecithal   *See* egg, isolecithal.

egg, isolecithal   Egg with a small amount of yolk distributed homogeneously throughout the cytoplasm.

egg, macrolecithal   Egg with a large amount of yolk; megolecithal egg.

egg, microlecithal   Egg with a small amount of yolk; oligolecithal egg.

egg, telolecithal   Egg with a large amount of yolk concentrated at one pole.

egg envelope   Material around the egg but not necessarily a part of it (e.g., vitelline membrane, jelly, albumen).

egg jelly   Mucin deposited on an amphibian egg as it passes through the oviduct.

egg membranes   All the membranes covering an egg (e.g., vitelline membrane, chorion, shell membranes).

egg tooth   Hard structure with a pointed tip, in the upper jaw of the bird embryo at the time of hatching, with the sole function of breaking the shell.

egg water   Extract diffusing from a living egg.

Einsteckung   Testing the power of induction by implanting living or dead tissue, or a chemical substance, into the blastocoel of a living gastrula.

ejaculation   Forcible emission of mature spermatozoa from the body of the male.

electrodynamic theory   Theory that mitosis produces a potential that directs a growing nerve root toward the brain.

emancipation   Establishment of local autonomy within an embryonic region.

emboitement theory   Preformationist theory that the ovary of the first female contained miniatures of all subsequent human beings; encasement theory.

embryo   Developmental stage between fertilization of an ovum and hatching or birth.

embryoma   *See* teratoma.

embryonic disc   Portion of the early mammalian embryo deriving from the inner cell mass and giving rise to the embryonic structures; blastoderm; embryonic shield.

embryonic field   Region of an embryo in which a certain organ develops.

embryonic knob   *See* inner cell mass.

embryonic membranes   Amnion, chorion, allantois, and yolk sac.

embryonic shield   *See* embryonic disc.

embryotroph   Nutritive material resulting from the destruction of maternal tissue prior to the establishment of the placental circulation (mammal); histotroph.

embryotrophy   Nourishment of an embryo.

enamel organ   Ectodermal portion of the tooth primordium.

endocardial cushion   Partition dividing the atrioventricular canal into right and left channels.

endocardium   Endothelial lining of the heart.

endochondral bone   Bone formed from cartilage; cartilage bone.

endoderm   Innermost layer of the gastrula, which gives rise to the lining membranes of the gut and its derivatives; entoderm; endoblast; hypoblast.

endolymphatic sac   Sac formed by the closing of the outer end of the endolymphatic duct.

endometrium   *See* uterine mucosa.

endoplasm   Inner medullary protoplasm of a cell, generally granular, soft, watery, and less refractive than ectoplasm.

endysis   Development of a new cuticular layer.

entelechy   Intangible agent controlling development, according to one theory; élan vital; vital force; psychism; perfecting principle.

enteron   Gut.

entobronchus   One of four evaginations from the median wall of the anterior portion of the main bronchus (bird); classed as a secondary bronchus.

entopic   In the normal position.

Entwicklungsmechanik   Morphogenetic forces apparently responsible for embryonic segregation.

Entwicklungspotenzen   Potentials of a primordium, experimentally determined.

entypy   Amnion formation in which the trophoblast over the embryonic disc is never interrupted (mammal); gastrulation in which the endoderm comes to lie outside the ectoderm (rodent).

ependyma   Thin layer of ciliated, non-nervous cells around the neurocoel, from the outer ends of which branching processes extend to the periphery of the spinal cord, forming a framework for other cellular elements.

epiboly   Growing around; process by which the rapidly dividing animal hemisphere cells flow over the vegetal hemisphere.

epicardium   Thin membrane covering the myocardium; originally part of the epimyocardium.

epidermis   Ectodermal portion of the skin, including the cutaneous glands, hair, feathers, nails, hoofs, and some types of horns and scales.

epididymis Tube between the testis and the vas deferens.

epigamic Tending to attract the opposite sex.

epigenesis Theory that an individual is created as a result of the union of a spermatozoon and an ovum and develops from the simple fertilized egg into a complex organism; opposed to preformation.

epimere *See* somite.

epimorphosis Regeneration by extensive cell proliferation.

epiphysis Evagination of the anterior wall of the diencephalon, which becomes separated from the brain as an endocrine gland; pineal body.

epiploic foramen Opening between the peritoneal cavity and the omental bursa; foramen of Winslow.

epithelioid bodies Endodermal masses arising from the third and fourth visceral pouches (amphibian); postbranchial bodies.

epithelium Thin covering layer of cells; ectodermal, endodermal, or mesodermal.

epoöphoron Anterior portion of the mesonephros, vestigial in the female.

equational division Maturation division in which there is no reduction in chromosome number; opposed to reductional division.

ergastoplasm Basophilic portion of the cytoplasm, containing ribonucleic acid.

Errera's law A cellular membrane tends to assume the form that would be assumed under the same conditions by an elastic membrane destitute of weight.

esophagus Tubular portion of the foregut between the pharynx and the stomach region.

estivation Reduced activity during summer; opposed to hibernation.

estrous cycle Reproductive cycle of a mammal, characterized by changes in endocrine, ovarian, and uterine function relating to ovulation, repair, and the preparation of the uterus for implantation of the ovum.

estrus Stage in the estrous cycle during which the uterus is prepared for implantation of the ovum; the period of sexual receptivity in most mammals.

euchromatin Weakly staining portion of the chromatin, consisting of genes.

euploidy Deviation from the normal diploid condition involving complete sets of chromosomes.

evagination Outward growth; outpocketing.

evocation Calling forth the potentialities of an embryonic region through contact; nonassimilative induction.

evocator Substance capable of calling forth the potentialities of an embryonic region; a morphogenetic stimulus.

evolution Theory that all living forms are derived, by gradual modification, from simpler forms.

exclusivity Discreteness of the differentiation process.

exencephalia Congenital exposure of the brain due to a defective skull.

exocoel Portion of the coelom outside the embryo proper; extraembryonic coelom; seroamniotic cavity.

exogastrula Embryo in which gastrulation is modified experimentally by environmental conditions so that invagination is partially or totally hindered and some mesoderm and endoderm is not enclosed by ectoderm.

exogenous Originating outside.

experimental method Analysis of the causes and effects in any system.

experimentum crucis Concluding experiment, in which a control is no longer needed; presumably a final, successful demonstration.

explantation   Culturing of an isolated primordium or tissue in vitro.

expressivity   Degree in which a group of organisms is affected by the presence of a particular gene; penetrance.

extension   Elongation of cells at the dorsal lip of the blastopore during gastrulation.

extraembryonic   Outside or apart from the embryo proper (e.g., the membranes).

extraovate   Portion of egg substance extruded from the cell (e.g., in hypotonic solution); exovate.

falciform ligament   Crescent-shaped fold of peritoneum extending between the liver and the ventral body wall and supporting the liver.

Fallopian tube   Oviduct of a mammal.

fate map   Map of a blastula or early gastrula indicating the prospective significance of various surface areas, based on previous studies of normal development as shown by vital dye markings.

feeding, maximal   Procedure in which the organism is provided with all the food that it can possibly consume.

fertilization   Activation of an ovum by a spermatozoon and syngamy of the pronuclei; union of male and female gamete nuclei.

fertilization, dry   Placing the concentrated spermatozoa of an aquatic form directly over practically dry eggs before flooding with water.

fertilization, fractional   Fertilization following the removal of part of a spermatozoon by centrifugation, after partial penetration of an ovum.

fertilization, partial   Fertilization in which cleavage begins before the sperm nucleus reaches the egg nucleus, although the sperm aster may have reached the egg nucleus and given rise to a spindle.

fertilization, selective   Fertilization in which a physiological block prevents some combinations of spermatozoon and ovum, perhaps indicating differential fertilizing powers of spermatozoa even from a common source.

fertilization membrane   Elevated vitelline membrane, apparent immediately after activation of an egg by fertilization or artificial stimulation.

fertilizin   Chemical substance in the cortex of a mature ovum, apparently necessary for normal fertilization.

fetus   Mammalian embryo in the later stages of development, when it has a recognizable form.

Feulgen reaction   Purple coloration exhibited by deoxyribonucleic acid in cell nuclei after hydrolysis with dilute hydrochloric acid and treatment with Schiff reagent.

fibrillation   Formation of (collagenous) fibers by the aggregation of ultramicrons with nearly parallel axes.

field   Region exhibiting specific space and time relationships within a developing organism.

field, heteroaxial   Region in which structures develop along three coordinates.

field, heteropolar   Region in which activities are opposed along the same axis.

field, morphogenetic   Region in which a specific structure develops.

field, organ   Region in which a specific organ develops.

field, tactic   Region governing the displacement of cells.

field, vegetative   Presumptive endoderm.

field laws   (1) When material separates from a field-bearing system, the material remaining contains the field in its typical structure. (2) When unorganized but labile material enters a field, it is included within the field; the field spreads over the whole of the material at its disposal, preserving its initial structure even though somewhat enlarged. (3) A field has the tendency to take up and include an equivalent, adjacent field.

fontanelle Area on top of an embryonic and newborn infant skull that is not covered by bone.

foramen ovale Opening in the septum secundum of an embryonic heart (mammal).

freemartin Masculinized, usually sterile female calf born as the twin of a male calf.

frontal At right angles to both the transverse and the sagittal, dividing the dorsal from the ventral.

function, homologous Synchronous behavior.

foramen of Monro Opening from a lateral ventricle of the brain into the third ventricle.

frontonasal process Median projection over the mouth and between the olfactory pits.

gamete Mature germ cell, capable of functioning in fertilization.

gametogenesis Development of germ cells.

ganglion Aggregation of neurons, generally derived from a neural crest.

ganglion, acoustic Ganglion giving rise to nerve VIII, purely sensory.

ganglion, acousticofacial Early, undifferentiated association of the acoustic and geniculate ganglia.

ganglion, geniculate Ganglion giving rise to nerve VII, both sensory and motor.

ganglion, jugular One of two ganglia giving rise to nerve X, both sensory and motor; mesial to the nodose ganglion.

ganglion, nodose One of two ganglia giving rise to nerve X, both sensory and motor; distal to the jugular ganglion.

ganglion, petrosal One of two ganglia giving rise to nerve IX, largely sensory; distal to the superior ganglion.

ganglion, semilunar Ganglion giving rise to nerve V, both sensory and motor; Gasserian ganglion; trigeminal ganglion.

ganglion, superior One of two ganglia giving rise to nerve IX, largely sensory; mesial to the petrosal ganglion.

gastraea theory Theory that since all higher animals exhibit gastrula stages a common ancestor in the form of a permanent gastrula, like a coelenterate, may have existed.

gastral mesoderm Mesoderm derived from the dorsal lip of the blastopore.

gastrocoel *See* archenteron.

gastroschisis Congenital opening in the abdominal wall.

gastrula Stage in which a monodermic blastula develops an archenteron and second and third germ layers.

gastrulation Developmental process involving cell movements that change the embryo from a monodermic blastula to a tridermic gastrula.

gel Solid or semisolid phase of a colloidal solution.

gene Factor transmitted by a chromosome that determines the development of a particular character of an individual.

genetic limitation Theory that each cell reacts in accord with the standards of the species in which it occurs.

genital Pertaining to the reproductive organs or processes.

genital duct Duct conveying gametes from their point of origin to the region of insemination (e.g., vasa efferentia, epididymis, vas deferens, seminal vesicle, oviduct or Fallopian tube); gonoduct.

genitalia   External and/or internal reproductive organs.

genital folds   Folds on either side of the genital tubercle, which form the penile urethra of the male and the labia minora of the female.

genital ridge   Gonad primordium, a mesodermal thickening between the mesonephros and the dorsal mesentery.

genital swellings   Moundlike protuberances on either side of the genital tubercle, which give rise to the scrotum of the male and the labia minora of the female.

genital tubercle   Primordium of the penis or clitoris (mammal).

genome   Haploid gene complex; minimum (haploid) number of chromosomes with their genes, derived from a gamete.

genotype   Actual genetic make-up of an individual, regardless of its appearance.

germ bands   Distinguishable bands in a mollusc egg that give rise to ectoderm and mesoderm.

germ cell   Spermatozoon or ovum; gamete.

germinal disc   Small protoplasmic disc on the surface of the yolk of a telolecithal egg.

germinal epithelium   Epithelium from which the reproductive cells develop.

germinal localization   Theory that every region of a blastoderm (or of an unfertilized ovum) corresponds to some future organ and that unequal growth results in the differentiation of parts.

germinal spot   Nucleolus of an ovum.

germinal vesicle   Nucleus of an ovum.

germ layer   Group of cells occupying a particular position in the gastrula; ectoderm, endoderm, or mesoderm.

germ plasm   Hereditary material, capable of producing new individuals; opposed to somatoplasm.

germ ring   Ring of cells exhibiting accelerated mitosis, generally at the blastopore lips.

germ wall   Outer marginal cells between the blastoderm and the periblast of a reptile or bird embryo.

Gestalt   System of configurations consisting of a ladder of levels—electron, atom, molecule, cell, tissue, organ, and organism—each one of which exhibits specifically new modes of action that cannot be understood as mere additive phenomena of the previous levels. With each higher level new concepts become necessary. The parts of a cell cannot exist independently. Hence the cell is more than a mere aggregation of its parts; it is a patterned whole.

gestation   Period during which an embryo is situated within the uterus (mammal).

gill   Respiratory organ of a fish or an embryonic amphibian.

gill, external   Outgrowth of a visceral arch, which functions as a temporary (anuran) or permanent (urodele) respiratory organ.

gill, internal   Gill functioning in a tadpole after the degeneration of the external gills.

gill plate   Ectodermal thickening behind the sense plate of an amphibian embryo, in which the visceral grooves develop.

gill rakers   Fingerlike, ectodermal projections that sift the water passing from the pharynx into the opercular chamber of a tadpole.

glia cell   *See* neuroglia.

glomerulus   Aggregation of capillaries within a mesonephros or metanephros, from which nitrogenous wastes drain into a tubule.

glomus   Vascular tissue mass within a pronephros, possibly representing a primitive glomerulus.

glottis   Opening between the pharynx and the larynx.

Golgi apparatus Internal reticular apparatus of a cell.

gonad Organ within which germ cells mature; ovary or testis.

gonium Primitive germ cell (e.g., spermatogonium, oögonium).

gonochorism Normal differentiation of gonads, appropriate to the sex.

gonocoel Cavity within a gonad, generally the ovary, in which the ova may rupture (amphioxus and some fish).

Graafian follicle Ovarian follicle, consisting of the theca folliculi; the membrana propria, the cumulus oöphorus, and the liquor folliculi.

gradient Gradual variation in a particular direction.

graft Cell, tissue, or organ transplanted from one region or organism to another.

graft, hybrid Organism formed from a host and a transplant, showing characteristics of both stocks.

growth, accretionary Growth involving an increase in rigid structural material; appositional growth.

growth, auxetic Growth involving an increase in cell size alone; differential growth.

growth, disharmonic Growth in which relative growth rates are extremely unbalanced.

growth, multiplicative Growth involving an increase in the number of nuclei and cells.

growth circumstantials Factors responsible for growth but not for characters.

growth coefficient Ratio of the growth rate of a part to the growth rate of the whole organism.

growth equilibrium Condition in which growth of a part is regulated with respect to the whole organism.

growth partition coefficients Inherent growth rates (e.g, in limb primordia) involving changes in proportions.

growth regulator Substance present in the circulating medium of an organism, and distinct from nutritional factors, which controls growth.

guanophore Cell containing yellow guanine crystals, which give it a highly refractive metallic luster.

gubernaculum testis Fibrous cord that draws a testis down into the scrotum of a male mammal just before birth.

gynandromorphy Condition in which an individual is part male and part female; not to be confused with hermaphroditism.

gynogenesis Development of an egg without activation by a spermatozoon.

haploid Having a single set (half the diploid number) of chromosomes, as in a mature gamete; opposed to diploid.

Harrison's rules of minor symmetry (1) If the anteroposterior axis of a limb bud is reversed in a graft, the resulting limb will have the asymmetry proper to the opposite side of the body from that on which it is placed (i.e., it becomes disharmonic, whether originally taken from the same or the opposite side). (2) If the anteroposterior axis is not reversed in a graft, the resulting limb will have the asymmetry proper to the side on which it is placed (i.e., it becomes disharmonic, whether originally taken from the same or the opposite side). (3) If double limbs arise, the original member (i.e., the first to begin development) will have its asymmetry fixed by rule 1 or rule 2, depending upon the orientation of the graft, whereas the secondary member will be the mirror image of the first.

hatching Beginning of the larval life of a fish or amphibian or the emergence of a reptile or bird embryo from its shell.

head fold Anteriorly projecting semicircular fold of the neural plate, involving both ectoderm and endoderm.

head process Faint line of cells anterior to Hensen's node and continuous with the primitive streak.

heat *See* estrus.

hemiblastula Half-blastula derived by cauterizing one blastomere of the two-cell stage.

hemikaryotic Haploid.

hemiplacenta Chorion, yolk sac, and generally allantois, which together serve as an organ of nutrition for an embryonic marsupial.

hemivertebra Defect of one-half of a vertebra.

hemizygote Diploid organism in which one chromosome is present only once, as in the case of the sex (X) chromosome in the male of many species.

hemophilia Hereditary disease characterized by an abnormal tendency to bleeding, resulting from a deficiency of clotting substances in the blood; sex-linked recessive character.

hemotroph Nutritive material supplied to the embryo by the maternal blood stream.

Hensen's node Anterior end of the primitive streak; primitive knot.

Hensen's theory Theory that nerve fibers develop from protoplasmic bridges existing throughout the embryonic body; protoplasmic bridge theory.

hepatic vein Vein formed by the junction of the vitelline veins between the liver and the heart.

hermaphroditism Condition in which an individual is capable of producing both spermatozoa and ova.

hermaphroditism, protandrous Hermaphroditism in which male elements mature before female elements.

hermaphroditism, protogynous Hermaphroditism in which female elements mature before male elements.

Hertwig's law The nucleus tends to center itself in its sphere of activity; the longitudinal axis of the mitotic spindle tends to lie along the longitudinal axis of the yolk-free cytoplasm of the cell.

heteroagglutinin Fertilizin of an ovum, which agglutinates a foreign spermatozoon.

heterochromatin Densely staining portion of the chromatin, apparently active in the formation of the nucleolus.

heterochronia Development of organs out of the normal sequence.

heteromorphosis Development of one kind of tissue from one of a different kind.

heteroplasia Development of a tissue or organ in an abnormal site.

heteroplasty Grafting from one individual to another of a different species.

heteroploidy Any deviation from the normal diploid number of chromosomes.

heterotaxia Abnormal arrangement of parts in relation to each other.

heterotopia Presence of a tissue or organ in an abnormal site.

heterotrophia Abnormal acquisition of nourishment.

heterozygote Zygote produced by the union of two gametes of different genetic constitutions.

heterozygous Hybrid; produced by unlike gametes (bearing allelomorphic genes); opposed to homozygous.

hibernation Reduced activity during the winter.

hindgut Portion of the gut giving rise to the rectum, cloaca, tail gut, allantois, and caudal portions of the urogenital system.

histogenesis Origin and development of tissues.

histolysis Destruction of tissues.

histomere theory   Theory that ontogenetic division of a histological system results in an organ.

histoteleosis   Process by which a cell line, already irreversibly differentiated, proceeds to its final histological specialization.

histotroph   *See* embryotroph.

Hoffman's nucleus   Group of neuroblasts at the external margin of the white matter, just above the ventral roots, in the spinal cord of a bird.

homoiothermic   Warm-blooded; having a relatively uniform body temperature; opposed to poikilothermic.

homology   Similarity in origin or structure but not in function.

homomorphosis   Regeneration in which the new part is similar to the lost part.

homozygote   Zygote produced by the union of two gametes of identical genetic constitutions; zygote containing only one of a pair of allelomorphic genes.

homozygous   Produced by gametes having identical genes.

homunculus   Minute human form believed by performationists to exist within the spermatozoon or ovum.

hormone   Secretion of one part of the body that is carried in the blood to another part, where it stimulates or inhibits activity.

hormone, morphogenetic   Inductor producing distant (not local) effects.

humor   Body fluid, circulating through vessels (blood or lymph) or diffusing freely into body cavities or tissue spaces (vitreous humor, aqueous humor).

hyaloplasm   Liquid matrix of protoplasm.

hybrid   Cross between two different species or two different varieties of the same species.

hybridization   Mating of a male and female of two different species or two different varieties of the same species.

hydramnios   Excess of amniotic fluid.

hydronephrosis   Abnormal distention of the renal pelvis and calyces with fluid.

hydroureter   Abnormal distention of the ureter with fluid.

hymen   Membrane partially closing the vaginal orifice in a virgin.

hyoid arch   Mesodermal mass between the visceral pouches or clefts I and II; visceral arch II.

hyomandibular   Between the mandibular and hyoid arches (visceral arches I and II).

hyperinnervation   Supplying an organ with more than the single, normal nerve fiber.

hyperplasia   Overgrowth; an increase in the bulk of a part due to an increase in the number of tissue elements in the part, excluding tumor formation; not related to a demand for increased functional activity.

hypertrophy   Overgrowth; an increase in the bulk of a part due to an increase in the size (not number) of tissue elements in the part, excluding tumor formation; related to a demand for increased functional activity.

hypertrophy, compensation   Increase in the bulk of a part due to the loss or removal of some of the part (or of the other member of a pair of parts).

hypochord   *See* subnotochordal rod.

hypomere   *See* lateral plate mesoderm.

hypophysis   Invagination of the ectoderm anterior to the stomodeum, which grows up toward the infundibulum to give rise to the anterior lobe of the pituitary gland (amphibian); Rathke's pocket.

hypoplasia   Undergrowth; deficiency in a part due to the destruction of some of its elements.

hypothalamus   Ventral portion of the lateral thickening of the diencephalon.

hypothesis   Supposition; a conclusion based on probable, but not conclusive, evidence.

hypothesis, working   Tentative theory based on known facts and used to guide further investigation.

idioplasm   Germ plasm.

implant   Graft; transplant.

implantation   Grafting without removing any part of the host; the attachment of the mammalian embryo to the uterine wall.

incompatibility   Tendency of cells or cell groups to repel each other when removed from their normal environment.

incubation   Maintenance of an egg in an environment favorable for hatching.

induction   Stimulation resulting in morphogenetic changes within an embryo.

induction, assimilative   Stimulation resulting in a change in the "fate" of a region.

induction, autonomous   Failure of an implant and its host to stimulate each other; opposed to complementary induction.

induction, complementary   Reciprocal stimulation by an implant and its host, resulting in the completion of differentiation; opposed to autonomous induction.

induction, direct   Stimulation of ventral ectoderm by a chemical resulting directly in the formation of a new neural axis.

induction, heterogenetic   Stimulation by an inductor of unlike tissue.

induction, homogenetic   Stimulation by an inductor of like tissue.

induction, indirect   Stimulation of ventral ectoderm by a chemical resulting in the liberation of a secondary inductor in the reacting tissue, which causes the formation of a new neural axis.

induction, palisade   Stimulation of neural tissue without neural tube formation; the cells are arranged in a palisade around the inductor.

induction capacity   Organizational ability, which increases with age up to a point and is then lost.

inductor   Stimulant that elicits from living matter a particular response, inherent in the reacting area.

inductor, nuclear   Stimulating substance derived from the nucleus and therefore bearing hereditary influences.

infection   Acquisition of inductive power by a group of cells not normally possessing it by diffusion from temporarily contiguous organizer material; Weckung.

infundibulum   Evagination of the floor of the diencephalon, which grows down toward the hypophysis (Rathke's pocket) to give rise to the posterior lobe of the pituitary gland; ostium tubae.

ingression   Inward movement of the yolk endoderm of the amphibian blastula.

inguinal canal   Passage between the abdominal cavity and the scrotum of a male mammal, through which the testes may descend just before birth.

inhibition   Restraint or nullification of a tendency to differentiate.

inhibition, differential   Restraint of regeneration by toxic agents.

inner cell mass   Aggregation of spherical cells on one side of the blastocoel in a blastocyst.

insemination   Introduction of semen into the vagina.

instinct   Tendency to action natural to the species.

interatrial foramen   Opening in the interatrial septum.

interatrial septum   Partition dividing the atrium into right and left chambers.

interkinesis   Resting stage between meiotic divisions.

interphase   Resting stage between mitotic divisions.

intersex   Individual with a blending of maleness and femaleness.

interstitial cell   Hormone-producing cell in the interstitial tissue of the testis.

interstitial tissue   Connective tissue separating and supporting the seminiferous tubules and secreting male sex hormones.

interventricular foramen   *See* foramen of Monro.

interventricular septum   Partition dividing the ventricle into right and left chambers.

intervertebral fissure   Cleft between two adjacent vertebrae.

interzonal fiber   Spindle fiber between chromosome groups in anaphase and telophase.

intestinal portal   Opening from the midgut into the foregut or hindgut.

invagination   Folding of a cell layer into an existing cavity.

involution   Rolling or turning in of cells over a rim.

iris   Membrane bounding the pupil of the eye in which the pigmented and sensory layers of the retina combine to produce a particular color.

ischiopagus   Conjoined twins widely separated except at their tails.

isoelectric point   Point at which the tendency of protein to release hydrogen ions just balances its tendency to release hydroxyl ions.

isogamy   Union of two similar gametes.

isolation   Removal of a part of a developing organism and its maintenance in the living condition (e.g., tissue culture); interposition of a mass of inert material between two regions.

isometry   Study of relative sizes of parts of organisms of the same age.

isotrophy   Absence of predetermined axes in an egg; equivalence of all parts of the egg protoplasm.

isthmus   Depression in the roof of the brain between the mesencephalon and the metencephalon; short, posterior portion of the oviduct (bird), where the two shell membranes are secreted over the albumen of an egg.

iter   *See* aqueduct of Sylvius.

janiceps   Conjoined twins united at the backs of their heads so that they face in opposite directions; Janus monster.

jugular vein   Vein carrying blood from the head to the heart.

karyolysis   Dissociation or destruction of the nucleus.

karyorrhexis   Fragmentation of the nucleus.

Kern-plasma relation   Ratio of the amount of nuclear material to that of cytoplasmic material in the cell.

kinetochore   *See* attachment point.

labia   Lateral epithelial folds at the vaginal orifice, homologous to the scrotum.

lacuna   Gap in the tissue at an implantation site in which maternal blood collects when the uterine vessels are destroyed.

lagena   *See* cochlea.

lamina terminalis   Thickening at the anterior limit of the telencephalon, between the optic recess and the velum transversum.

lampbrush effect   Appearance of side branches and loops on a chromosome (e.g., in an oöcyte).

lanugo   Fine hairy covering of an embryonic mammal.

larva   Stage in development after an organism emerges from its membranes but before it completes its metamorphosis.

laryngotracheal groove   Depression in the floor of the gut between the pharynx and the lung primordia.

larynx   Tube deriving from the anterior portion of the laryngotracheal groove and opening into the pharynx through the glottis.

latebra   Stalk of white yolk extending from the center of an ovum (bird) to its nucleus.

lateral line organs   System of sensory structures along the sides of the body (fish, amphibian), innervated by a branch of nerve X (vagus) and presumably functioning in the detection of vibrations in water.

lateral nasal process   Lateral portion of the elevation around an olfactory pit.

lateral plate mesoderm   Most lateral mesoderm, in which the body cavity (coelom and exocoel) arises; hypomere.

lateral rotation   Twisting that begins at the anterior end of a reptile or bird embryo and proceeds posteriorly until the embryo is lying on its left side.

lateral ventricles   Paired, thick-walled cavities of the cerebral hemispheres, which open into the third ventricle by way of the foramina of Monro; first and second ventricles.

lecithin   Organismic fat in the form of a phospholipid.

lens   Biconvex structure between the iris and the vitreous humor of the eye, which focuses light rays on the retina.

lens placode   Thickened ectodermal primordium of the lens.

lenticular zone   Region of the optic cup adjacent to the pupil, separated from the retinal zone by the ora serrata.

leptotene   First stage in meiotic prophase, during which the chromatin appears as tangled threads (spireme).

lesser omentum   Mesentery between the stomach and the liver.

lethal defect   Suppression of a vital organ or a vital function by a local defect.

Liesegang's figures   Strata, as of formative substances in an egg.

limicola cell type   Isolated embryonic cell moving like *Amoeba limicola*, which has balloonlike pseudopoda.

limiting sulcus   Undercutting groove separating the embryonic and extraembryonic regions in an embryo developing from a telolecithal egg.

lingual glands   Solid ingrowths of the oral mucosa under the sides of the tongue and along the lingual cartilage.

linkage   Association of two genes in a single chromosome.

lipids   Water-insoluble fats and fatty substances (e.g., lecithin, cholesterol, ergosterol).

lipogenesis   Production of fat; breakdown of food into fat.

lipophore   Cell in the dermis and epidermis derived from the neural crests and containing diffuse yellow pigment (lipochrome).

liquor folliculi   Fluid in a mammalian Graafian follicle.

lithopedion   Mummified or calcified fetus; "stone child."

lobster claw   Condition, probably inherited, in which fingers or toes are missing or a hand or foot is split.

lumbosacral flexure   Most posterior of the four flexures of a mammalian embryo.

lunar periodicity   Maturation and oviposition according to a lunar or monthly cycle.

lutein   Yellow material in the cells that fill an empty mammalian Graafian follicle.

maceration   Softening by soaking.

macrencephalia   Abnormal largeness of the head; often the brain is swollen with cerebrospinal fluid (hydrocephalus).

macromere   Large, yolk-laden cell in the vegetal hemisphere of a blastula.

macrosomia   Gigantism.

mammary glands   Milk glands, typical of a mammal.

mammillary layer   Inner of the three layers of the bird egg shell, consisting of fused calcareous particles.

mandibular arch   First visceral arch, the rudiment of the lower jaw or mandible.

mandibular glands   Solid ingrowths of the oral mucosa along both sides of the base of the tongue.

mantle layer of the spinal cord   Thick layer of the spinal cord, between the ependymal layer and the marginal layer, which contains closely packed cells and nuclei.

marginal layer of the spinal cord   Vacuolated outer layer of the spinal cord, which is practically devoid of nuclei.

margin of overgrowth   Cells at the edge of a bird blastoderm that are lifted off the yolk as the blastoderm enlarges.

massa intermedia   Bridge formed by the union of the two thalami across the third ventricle.

maternal placenta   Uterine mucosal portions of a placenta.

matrix   Ground substance of a cell; fundamental cytoplasm.

maturation   Process by which a primitive germ cell (spermatogonium or oögonium) becomes functionally mature, involving mitotic and meiotic divisions.

Mauthner's fibers   Two highly differentiated, giant neurons in the medulla (teleost fish, amphibian), with axons extending from the acoustic ganglion through the spinal cord and extensive dendritic connections; the fibers maintain the sense of equilibrium and are necessary for sustained rhythmic motor reflexes.

meatus venosus   Junction of the vitelline veins posterior to the sinus venosus, around which the substance of the liver develops.

mechanism   Theory that biological processes are mechanical and can be explained by physical and chemical laws; opposed to organicism.

Meckel's cartilage   Cartilaginous core of the mandible.

meconium   Viscous green mixture of necrotic cells, mucus, and bile in the embryonic gut.

median nasal process   Median portion of the elevation around an olfactory pit.

medulla oblongata   Most posterior portion of the brain, adjacent to the spinal cord.

medullary   Pertaining to the medulla.

medullary cords   Central cords of the suprarenal glands or of the gonads.

megasphere   Yolk mass cut off from the floor of the archenteron in a bird gastrula and lying in the cavity.

meiosis   Maturation division in a germ cell, involving a separation of members of chromosome pairs so that the resulting cells contain the haploid number of chromosomes.

melanophore   Cell containing black or brown (melanin) pigment, derived from a neural crest.

melanophore, adepidermal   Dermal melanophore.

melanophore, dependent   Dermal melanophore that develops pigment only under the influence of overlying transplanted pigmented epidermis.

membrana granulosa   Layer of yellow follicle cells surrounding an ovum (bird, mammal), so called because of its granular appearance.

membranous bone   Bone developing from connective tissue, not cartilage.

membranous labyrinth   Inner ear, lined with ectoderm and filled with endolymphatic fluid.

meningocele   Hernia of the membranes of the brain or spinal cord.

menstruation   Periodic loss (generally once a month) of uterine mucosa and blood in Primates, caused by a decreased secretion of estrogenic hormones.

merogony   Incomplete development of a partially or wholly enucleated fragment of a fertilized egg.

merogony, andro-   Incomplete development of a fragment of a fertilized egg containing a sperm nucleus only.

merogony, diploid   Incomplete development of a fragment of a fertilized egg containing a normal diploid nucleus.

merogony, double   Incomplete development of two fragments of a fertilized egg, one containing a normal diploid nucleus and the other containing a sperm nucleus only.

merogony, gyno-   Development of a fragment of a fertilized egg containing an egg nucleus only.

merogony, parthenogenetic   Development of a fragment of an egg activated by artificial means and containing an egg nucleus only.

mesencephalon   Middle portion of the brain, between the prosencephalon and the rhombencephalon, which gives rise to the optic lobes, crura cerebri, and aqueduct of Sylvius; midbrain.

mesenchyme   Loosely distributed mesoderm.

mesendoderm   Inner layer of a gastrula before the separation of endoderm and mesoderm.

mesentery   Mesodermal sheet supporting an organ.

mesobronchus   Portion of a main bronchus within a lung.

mesocardium   Mesentery supporting the heart.

mesocolon   Mesentery supporting the colon.

mesoderm   Third primary germ layer, developing between the ectoderm and endoderm and deriving from ectoderm in some forms and from endoderm in others.

mesoderm, axial   *See* somite.

mesoderm, gastral   *See* gastral mesoderm.

mesoderm, lateral plate   *See* lateral plate mesoderm.

mesoderm, paraxial   *See* somite.

mesoderm, peristomial   *See* peristomial mesoderm.

mesoderm, somatic   *See* somatic mesoderm.

mesoderm, splanchnic   *See* splanchnic mesoderm.

mesogastrium   Mesentery supporting the stomach and duodenum.

mesomere   *See* nephrotome.

mesometrium   Mesentery attaching the uterus to the dorsal body wall (mammal); broad ligament of the uterus.

mesonephric duct   Tube carrying body wastes posteriorly from the mesonephric tubules to the cloaca; Wolffian duct.

mesonephric tubules   Small tubes in the mesonephros, which receive body wastes and empty them into the mesonephric duct.

mesonephros Intermediate kidney, functional in the adult fish and amphibian and in the embryonic reptile, bird, and mammal; Wolffian body.

mesorchium Mesentery attaching a testis to a kidney (amphibian) or to the dorsal body wall.

mesothelium Membranous mesoderm.

mesovarium Mesentery attaching an ovary to the dorsal body wall.

metabolism Sum of the chemical changes concerned with the nutrition of an organism.

metabolism, animal Metabolism associated with differentiation in an animal (ectodermal) direction and characterized by increased oxygen consumption; can be checked by lithium.

metabolism, vegetal Metabolism associated with differentiation in a vegetal (endodermal) direction and characterized by protein breakdown; checked by an absence of sulfate ions.

metamerism Serial segmentation.

metamorphosis Change in form, structure, or function (e.g., change in structure related to a change from an aquatic habitat to a terrestrial one).

metamorphosis, anuran Loss of larval tail, mouth, and gills; reduction of the gut; development of limbs.

metamorphosis, urodele Reduction of gills; shedding of skin; development of eyelids.

metanephros Permanent kidney of the reptile, bird, and mammal.

metaphase Stage in mitosis, between prophase and anaphase, during which the paired chromosomes are lined up on the equator.

metaplasia Permanent and irreversible change in cell type and character; differentiation of embryonic tissue in several directions (some differentiated tissue may become undifferentiated and then undergo a new differentiation in a different direction).

metatela Tela chorioidea of the fourth ventricle.

metathetely Appearance of embryonic structures at a stage later than normal (e.g., larval organs in pupae); opposed to prothetely.

metencephalon Anterior protion of the rhombencephalon, which gives rise to the cerebellum and the pons.

metestrus Short period of regressive changes in the uterine mucosa during which the evidences of fruitless preparation for pregnancy disappear; postestrus.

microcephalia Abnormal smallness of the head.

micrognathia Abnormal smallness of the jaws, especially the lower one.

micromelia Abnormal smallness of the limbs.

micromere Small cell in the animal hemisphere of a blastula.

micrometry Measurement of an object with a micrometer and a microscope.

microphthalmia Abnormal smallness of the eyeballs.

micropyle Aperture in the covering of an ovum through which spermatozoa may enter (the only possible sperm entrance point in many fish eggs).

microsomia Dwarfishness.

microsurgery Operative procedures in which steel and glass instruments of microscopic dimensions are used.

midbrain *See* mesencephalon.

midgut Portion of the gut that gives rise to the intestine.

milieu All the physicochemical and biological factors surrounding a living system.

milk line Lateral ridge of tissue ventral to the somites, which gives rise to the mammary glands.

mitochondria Small cytoplasmic granules.

mitogenetic ray   Ray of short wavelength emanating from a growing point and exciting cell division in tissues capable of proliferation.

mitosis   Process of division in a somatic cell, in which each daughter cell has the same number of chromosomes as the parent cell; equational division.

mitotic index   Proportion of dividing cells in any tissue at any specified time.

modulation   Physiological fluctuation of a cell in response to environmental conditions, indicating a latitude of adaptation; reversible cellular change; temporary reaction of a cell to new environmental conditions without a loss of its original potential.

modulator   Substance that induces a specific kind of tissue characteristic of a definite region.

molting   Shedding of cornified epidermis, hair, or feathers.

monospermy   Fertilization by only one spermatozoon; opposed to polyspermy.

monster, autosite-parasite   Conjoined twins of such great size discrepancy that the smaller one has a parasitic relationship with the larger, better-developed one.

morphogenesis   Differentiation leading to the formation of characteristic structures in an organ or in an organism compounded of organs.

morphogenetic movements   Cell or area movements concerned with the formation of a germ layer (e.g., during gastrulation) or organ primordia; Gestaltungsbewegungen.

morphogenetic potential   Product of a reaction between the egg cortex and yolk just sufficient to bring about response in a competent area; threshold value.

morula   Spherical mass of cells (16 or more), as yet without a blastocoel.

mosaic   Pertaining to development in which the fates of all parts of the egg are fixed at an early stage, possibly even at fertilization, so that local injury or excision causes the loss of a specific organ; opposed to regulative.

movement, formative   Localized changes in cell areas resulting in the formation of specific, recognizable embryonic regions.

movement, homologous   Synchronous contraction of homologous muscles in transplanted limbs.

Müllerian duct   Duct along the tract of, and perhaps a vestige of, a pronephric duct, which becomes the oviduct or Fallopian tube in the female and degenerates in the male.

muscle plate   *See* myotome.

mutation   Sudden variation in one or more heritable characters, due to changes in genes or chromosomes.

myelencephalon   Posterior portion of the rhombencephalon, which has a thin roof that gives rise to the choroid plexus of the fourth ventricle and thick ventral and ventrolateral walls that give rise to the medulla oblongata.

myeloblast   Immature cell in the bone marrow.

myelocoel   Cavity of the myelencephalon; fourth ventricle.

myeloschisis   Congenital cleft of the spinal cord.

myoblast   Muscle-forming cell.

myocardium   Muscular layer of the heart, between the endocardium and the epicardium.

myocoel   Cavity in a myotome.

myoma   Benign tumor, derived from muscle fibers.

myotome   Thickened muscle primordium in a somite; muscle plate.

naris, external   External opening of a nasal tube.

naris, internal   Opening from the choanal canal into the pharynx.

nasal pit   *See* olfactory pit.

nasolacrimal groove Depression at the junction of a lateral nasal process and a maxillary process, which gives rise to the lacrimal duct; nasooptic furrow.

necrohormone Chemical produced by degenerating nuclei, which causes premature and incomplete divisions of oöcytes in sexually mature mammals and the formation of oligopyrene spermatozoa in molluscs.

necrosis Pathological death of a cell or group of cells, due to nuclear damage.

neighborwise Developing (as a transplant) in a manner appropriate to its new environment, indicating its plasticity, pluripotency, or lack of determination; artgemäss.

neomorph New structure with no or only slight similarity to any in lower orders; sometimes resembles a structure from another part of the same body.

neoplasm Atypical new growth, generally a tumor.

neotony Retention of a larval form (e.g., axolotl, necturus).

nephrocoel Cavity in the nephrotome, which joins the myocoel and the coelom temporarily.

nephrogenic cord *See* nephrotome.

nephrogenic tissue *See* nephrotome.

nephrostome Ciliated, funnel-shaped opening from a pronephric tubule (amphibian) or an anterior mesonephric tubule (reptile, bird, mammal) into the coelom.

nephrotome Continuous cord of mesoderm between the somites and the lateral plate mesoderm, which gives rise to the excretory system; intermediate cell mass; mesomere.

nerve, abducens Cranial nerve VI, motor, arising from the floor plate of the myelencephalon and supplying the lateral rectus eye muscle.

nerve, accessory Cranial nerve XI, motor, arising from the posterior portion of the myelencephalon and the cervical portion of the spinal cord and supplying the smooth muscles of the viscera and the striated muscles of the pharynx, larynx, and neck region.

nerve, acoustic Cranial nerve VIII, sensory, arising from the acoustic ganglion and supplying the semicircular canals and cochlea.

nerve, facial Cranial nerve VII, sensory and motor, arising from the facial ganglion and supplying the facial muscles and taste organs.

nerve, glossopharyngeal Cranial nerve IX, sensory and motor, arising from the superior and petrosal ganglia and supplying the ear, tongue, and pharynx.

nerve, hypoglossal Cranial nerve XII, motor, arising from the posterior portion of the myelencephalon and supplying the tongue muscles.

nerve, oculomotor Cranial nerve III, motor, arising from the floor plate of the mesencephalon and supplying the eye muscles.

nerve, olfactory Cranial nerve I, sensory, arising from the telencephalon and supplying the olfactory organ.

nerve, optic Cranial nerve II, sensory, arising from the diencephalon and supplying the retina.

nerve, trigeminal Cranial nerve V, sensory and motor, arising from the semilunar ganglion and supplying the ophthalmic, maxillary, and mandibular regions.

nerve, trochlear Cranial nerve IV, motor, arising from the dorsal wall of the mesencephalon and supplying the superior oblique eye muscle.

nerve, vagus Cranial nerve X, sensory and motor, arising from the jugular and nodose ganglia and supplying the pharynx and midgut and derivatives.

nervous layer Inner of two layers in the roof of a blastocoel (amphibian), which gives rise to most of the central nervous system.

neural arch   Ossified cartilage extending dorsally from a centrum around the spinal cord; vertebral arch; spinous process.

neural canal   *See* neurocoel.

neural crest   Continuous cord of ectodermally derived cells between the neural tube and the body ectoderm, separated from the ectoderm at the time of closure of the neural tube, which gives rise to the spinal, and possibly some of the cranial, ganglia.

neural folds   Elevations of ectoderm on either side of the neural groove, which meet dorsally to form the neural tube; medullary folds.

neural groove   Longitudinal groove in the center of the neural plate, which is incorporated in the neural tube; medullary groove.

neural plate   Thickened strip of ectoderm along the dorsal side of the body, which gives rise to the central nervous system; medullary plate.

neural tube   Tube formed by the dorsal fusion of the neural folds, the primordium of the spinal cord.

neurenteric canal   Connection between the posterior neurocoel and the hindgut (amphibian).

neurobiotaxis   Concentration of nerve cells in the region of greatest stimulation.

neuroblast   Primitive nerve cell.

neurocoel   Central cavity of the neural tube; neural canal; central canal.

neurocranium   Dorsal portion of the skull, covering the brain and sense organs.

neurogen   Evocator causing the formation of neurons.

neurogenesis, mechanical hypothesis of   Mechanical tension of plasma in any definite direction orients and aggregates fibrin micellae in a corresponding direction.

neuroglia   Small, round supporting cells of the spinal cord; glia cells.

neurohumor   Hormone-like chemical produced by nervous tissue, particularly the ends of developing nerves, which consequently act as stimulants.

neuromere   Metamere of the embryonic brain; three are in the prosencephalon, two in the mesencephalon, and six in the rhombencephalon.

neuropore, anterior   Opening from the anterior end of the normal tube to the surface, the final point of fusion of the neural folds.

neuropore, posterior   Opening from the posterior end of the neural tube to the surface; sinus rhomboidalis.

neurula   Stage in embryonic development following gastrulation, during which the neural tube forms.

neutral medium   Environmental medium free of chemical or physical inductors and physiologically isotonic.

normalizing   Associated with development as an integral part of the organism; integrating and balancing.

notochord   Rod of vacuolated cells dorsal to the gut and beneath the forming neural tube, which represents the primary supporting axis of a vertebrate; chorda dorsalis.

notochordal canal   Elongated extension of the primitive pit into the notochord.

notochordal sheath   Double mesodermal sheath around the notochord, consisting of an outer elastic layer and an inner fibrous layer.

nucleal reaction   *See* Feulgen reaction.

nuclear medium   Calcium-free but otherwise balanced and isotonic salt medium in which an isolated nucleus can survive for some time.

nucleofugal   Growing outward in two or more directions from the nuclear region (e.g., the formation of myelin around a nerve fiber, starting at the sheath cell nucleus and proceeding in two directions).

nucleolus Body in a nucleus that has no affinity for chromatin dyes but that stains with acid or cytoplasmic dyes; plasmosome.

nucleoplasm Protoplasm in the nucleus; karyoplasm.

nucleus of Pander Plate of white yolk beneath the nucleus of an egg (bird); Pander's island.

Nussbaum's law The course of a nerve within a muscle may be taken as an index of the direction in which the particular muscle has grown.

odontoblast Columnar, dentine-forming cell of the dental papilla.

olfactory capsule Cartilaginous covering of the olfactory organ.

olfactory lobe Anterior extremity of a cerebral hemisphere, partially constricted and associated with cranial nerve I.

olfactory pit Depression in the olfactory placode.

olfactory placode Ectodermal thickening lateral to the stomodeum, which gives rise to the olfactory organ.

oligodactylia Congenital absence of digits.

omental bursa Pouch between the dorsal mesogastrium and the stomach.

omentum *See* mesogastrium; lesser omentum.

omnipotent Capable, as a cell, of differentiating in every direction possible in a species; capable of giving rise by division to cells differentiating in such varied directions.

omphalocele Hernia of the umbilicus.

omphalomesenteric artery *See* vitelline artery.

omphalomesenteric vein *See* vitelline vein.

ontogeny Developmental history of an individual, from the fertilization of an egg to hatching or birth.

oöcyte Presumptive ovum after the completion of growth in the oögonium stage; ovocyte.

oögenesis Maturation of an ovum; development of an oögonium into a mature ovum; ovogenesis.

oögonium Presumptive ovum before the attainment of maximum size and the beginning of meiosis.

oöplasm Cytoplasm involved in building rather than maintaining a reserve during the development of an ovum.

opercular chamber Chamber enclosing the gills (amphibian).

operculum Posterior growth of visceral arch II, which covers the gills (amphibian).

optic chiasma Thickening in the prosencephalon ventral to the infundibulum, which eventually consists of crossing optic nerve fibers.

optic cup Cup formed by the invagination of the outer wall of the optic vesicle and consisting of two layers, a thick internal retinal layer and a thin external pigmented layer.

optic lobe Evagination of the dorsolateral wall of the mesencephalon.

optico-ocular apparatus All the structures related to vision (e.g., optic vesicles, optic stalks, optic chiasma).

optic recess Depression in the prosencephalon anterior to the optic chiasma, which leads to the optic stalks.

optic stalk Connection between an optic vesicle and the diencephalon, tubular at first but becoming solid.

optic vesicle Evagination of the dorsolateral wall of the diencephalon, which gives rise to an eye.

oral membrane   Fusion of stomodeal ectoderm and pharyngeal endoderm, which breaks to form the mouth; oral plate; pharyngeal membrane; stomodeal plate.

oral plate   *See* oral membrane.

oral sucker   *See* sucker.

ora serrata   Wavy boundary line between the retinal and lenticular zones of the eye.

organ-forming substance   Substance that, through chemodifferentiation and segregation, becomes localized in certain blastomeres to initiate the development of an organ.

organicism   Theory that biological processes depend on the autonomous organization of a system and not on its components; the idea of the organism as a whole; opposed to mechanism.

organic points theory   Discarded theory that preformed determinants are unequally distributed among blastomeres.

organization   Differentiation or specialization according to a definite pattern.

organizer   Region capable of directing undifferentiated cells along a specific course; dominating center of integrative development.

organizer, nucleolar   Region in a set of chromosomes where the nucleolus forms.

organogenesis   Development of organs; morphological differentiation.

organ of Jacobson   Horizontal groove in the median wall of the olfactory pit, which has a sensory function in amphibia and reptiles; vomeronasal organ.

organ, rudimentary   Incompletely developed structure with no detectable function.

orthotopic   Transplanted in a homologous region.

osmotic pressure   Pressure developing when two solutions of different concentrations are separated by a semipermeable membrane (one permeable to solvent but not to solute).

ossein fiber   Organic constituent of bone, which gives it strength and resiliency.

ossification   Bone formation.

osteoblast   Bone-forming cell.

osteoclast   Bone-destroying cell.

ostium tubae   Anterior, fimbriated end of a Fallopian tube; infundibulum.

otic vesicle   *See* auditory vesicle.

otocephaly   Congenital lack of a lower jaw, with a union of the ears below the face.

otocleisis   Closure of the auditory tube.

otocyst   *See* auditory vesicle.

otolith   Cluster of cells in an auditory vesicle.

outgrowth neuron theory   Nerve fiber develops as a protoplasmic extension from a single ganglion cell.

ovary   Female sex gland, in which ova are produced.

oviducal membranes   Membranes applied to an egg as it passes through the oviduct (amphibian, reptile, bird).

oviduct   Duct conveying ova from the ovary to the uterus; Fallopian tube (mammal).

ovigerous cords   Secondary sexual cords in the ovarian cortex, which become follicles; tubes of Pfluger; egg tubes.

oviparity   Production of eggs that hatch after laying; opposed to viviparity.

oviposition   Laying of an egg.

ovocyte   *See* oöcyte.

ovogenesis   *See* oögenesis.

ovogonium   *See* oögonium.

ovoviviparity   Production of eggs with well-developed shells that hatch within the maternal body.

ovulation   Release of an ovum from the ovary.

ovum   Egg.

ovum, Peter's   Human embryo about 13 days old, which furnished much information on early embryonic development.

pachytene   Stage in meiotic prophase, between synaptene and diplotene, during which the homologous chromosomes are coiled about each other.

palatine glands   Oral glands near the choanae in a bird embryo.

palatoquadrate bone   Bone developing from the proximal portions of the first three visceral arches, a portion of which gives rise to the tympanic ring.

palingenesis   Repetition or recapitulation of stages reflecting the developmental history of a race.

pallium   Thickened lateral wall of the telencephalon, which gives rise to a cerebral hemisphere.

pancreas   Endocrine digestive gland arising as a single dorsal diverticulum and paired ventral diverticuli from the gut in the liver region.

papillary muscle   One of the trabeculae carneae that controls the heart valves.

parabiosis   Union of two organisms in several or all vital processes but not necessarily in such a way that they are dependent on each other.

parabronchus   Branches of the secondary bronchi; tertiary bronchi.

paradidymis   Remnant of posterior mesonephric tubules in a male.

paraphysis   Pouchlike evagination in the roof of the telencephalon dorsal to the velum transversum.

parasynapsis   Lateral fusion of chromosomes during maturation.

parathyroids   Endocrine glands arising from visceral pouches III and IV and controlling calcium and phosphorus metabolism.

parencephalon   Anterior portion of the diencephalon (bird), separated from the synencephalon by the epiphysis.

parthenogenesis   Development of an egg without fertilization by a spermatozoon.

parthenogenesis, artificial   Development of an unfertilized egg activated by artificial means.

parthenogenesis, facultative   Development of an egg before fertilization by a spermatozoon.

parthenogenesis, natural   Development of an unfertilized egg activated by natural means (typical of some forms).

parthenogenetic cleavage   Fragmentation of the protoplasm of an old, unfertilized egg, sometimes mistaken for true cleavage.

partition coefficient   Factor determining the size of a part, based on its nutrition.

parturition   Act of giving birth.

path, copulation   Second portion of the sperm path through the egg toward the egg nucleus, when the sperm deviates from the penetration path.

pathfinder   Nerve fiber growing into previously uninvaded peripheral tissue.

path, penetration   Sperm entrance path in an egg.

pedogenesis   Parthenogenetic reproduction during the larval stage; precocious sex development.

pedomorphism   Retention of childlike characteristics in an adult.

penetrance   *See* expressivity.

penis   Organ of copulation in a male, through which spermatozoa are transmitted to the vagina of a female.

perforatorium   *See* acrosome.

periaxial cords   Primordia of the semilunar and acousticofacial ganglia (chick).

periblast   Layer of free protoplasm adjoining the white yolk in a reptile or bird egg.

periblast, central   Syncytial layer in the floor of the blastocoel (reptile, bird).

periblast, marginal   Syncytial layer bounding the marginal cells of the blastoderm (reptile, bird).

pericardial cavity   Portion of the coelom surrounding the heart and enclosed by the pericardium.

pericardium   Membrane enclosing the pericardial cavity and the heart.

perichondrium   Bone deposits around cartilage.

perichordal sheath   Thin mesodermal layer around the notochord.

perilymph   Fluid between the bony and membranous labyrinths.

periosteum   Mesenchymal layer, often originally perichondrium, around forming bone.

peristomial mesoderm   Mesoderm derived from the ventral lip of the blastopore; prostomial mesoderm.

peritoneal cavity   Portion of the coelom surrounding the abdominal organs.

peritoneum   Membrane enclosing the peritoneal cavity and the abdominal organs.

perivitelline membrane   *See* vitelline membrane.

perivitelline space   Space between the fertilization (elevated vitelline) membrane and the egg, generally filled with fluid.

permeability   Susceptibility to penetration by a liquid, depending on mass, area, time, and concentration as well as the environment.

Pfluger, tubes of   *See* ovigerous cords.

pH   Logarithm of the reciprocal of the hydrogen-ion concentration (a neutral solution has a pH of 7, an acid a pH below 7, and a base a pH above 7).

phallus   Indeterminate external sex organ, arising from the genital tubercle, which becomes the penis in a male or the clitoris in a female.

phenocopy   Individual with a phenotype imitating that of another genotype.

phenocritical period   Period in the development of an organism when a particular gene effect is most easily influenced by environmental factors.

phenotype   Physical make-up of an individual, resulting from the action of the environment on its genetic constitution; opposed to genotype.

philtrum   Groove at the mid-line of the upper lip where the lateral halves fuse.

phocomelus   Individual in which the proximal portions of appendages have not developed, although the distal portions may be normal.

phylogeny   Developmental history of a race.

pigmented layer of retina   Thin outer layer of the optic cup, posterior to the sensory layer.

pineal body   *See* epiphysis.

pituitary   Endocrine gland at the base of the brain arising from the union of the infundibulum and the hypophysis (Rathke's pocket); hypophysis.

placenta   Extraembryonic vascular structure (mammal) that invades the uterine mucosa and serves as the organ of nutrition, respiration, and excretion for an embryo.

placenta, cotyledonary   Placenta with villi clustered in rosettes.

placenta, deciduate   Placenta with villi securely embedded in the maternal tissue.

placenta, diffuse   Placenta with villi covering the entire surface of the chorion.

placenta, discoid   Placenta with villi concentrated in one or two disc-shaped areas of the chorion.

placenta, nondeciduate Diffuse placenta, with scattered chorionic villi that do not deeply penetrate the maternal tissue.

placenta, semideciduate Placenta in which villi are not intimately associated with the maternal tissue but are more firmly implanted than those in a nondeciduate placenta.

placenta, true *See* placenta, deciduate.

placenta, zonary Placenta with villi forming a band around the middle of the chorion and embryo.

placode Platelike ectodermal thickening, which gives rise to sensory or nervous structures.

plasm Distinguishable region of a mosaic egg, which gives rise to a specific organ.

plasmalemma Thin, viscous outer layer of ectoplasm in a fertilized egg, which does not change during centrifugation.

plasmal reaction Test with Schiff reagent for fats and aldehydes in cytoplasm; also positive for certain aliphatic ketones, unsaturated compounds (e.g., oleic acid), alkalis, weak salts of strong bases (e.g., acetates, phosphates), amino oxides, and catalytic oxidizing systems.

plasmodesmata Protoplasmic bridges between adjacent cells.

plasmosome *See* nucleolus.

plasmoditrophoblast *See* cytotrophoblast.

plasticity Ability of cell areas to respond to environmental influences, up to the end of gastrulation; pluripotency.

plectrum *See* columella.

pleiotropia Over-all effect of a single gene on an organism.

pleura Membrane enclosing the pleural cavity.

pleural cavity Portion of the coelom surrounding the lungs.

pleuroperitoneal membrane Outgrowth from accessory membranes associated with the esophagus and septum transversum, which separates the pleural and peritoneal cavities.

poikilothermic Cold-blooded; having a body temperature that varies with the environmental temperature, owing to the absence of an internal regulating mechanism; opposed to homoiothermic.

polar Pertaining to a pole.

polar body Nucleus discarded from an oöcyte after a meiotic division; polocyte.

polarity Axial distribution, to animal and vegetal poles.

polar plasm Vegetal pole protoplasm, identifiable in some eggs (e.g., annelid, mollusc) by its consistency.

pole, animal Region of the egg where the nucleus is located and the polar bodies are eliminated; ectoderm-forming region; apical or animal hemisphere.

pole, vegetal Region of the egg opposite the animal pole, with the lowest metabolic rate and the most yolk; endoderm-forming region; vegetal hemisphere.

polydactylia Presence of extra digits.

polyembryony Production of several individuals from one egg by an early separation of blastomeres.

polyhydramnios Excess in the amount of amniotic fluid.

polyinvagination theory Theory that individual cells migrate beneath the surface of the chick blastodisc and spread out to form the endoderm.

polyploid Having a multiple of the normal haploid number of chromosomes.

polyspermy Invasion of an ovum by many spermatozoa.

pons varoli   Thickened floor of the metencephalon.

pontine flexure   Flexure in the floor of the myelencephalon in a reptile or bird embryo and in the roof between the metencephalon and the myelencephalon in a mammalian embryo.

portal vein   Vein formed by the union of the vitelline veins posteriorly to the liver.

posterior intestinal portal   Opening from the yolk sac into the hindgut.

postgeneration   Regeneration from new rather than already differentiated tissue; restoration of a part by the utilization of material from an injured blastomere.

postreduction   Maturation in which the equational division precedes the reductional division.

potency   Ability to differentiate.

potency, active   Ability to differentiate in isolation, without inductive forces.

potency, passive   Ability to differentiate only with inductive forces.

potency, prospective   Sum total of developmental possibilities for a region.

potential, morphogenetic   Ability to develop into a specific structure.

pouch, marsupial   Maternal abdominal pouch in which a newborn marsupial is carried and provided with nourishment until independent.

preformation, theory of   Theory that an ovum or spermatozoon contains a fully formed miniature individual and that development consists merely of enlargement.

prefunctional period   Period of morphological and histological differentiation, preparing an organ for functioning.

pregnancy   Condition in which an embryo is present in the uterus; gestation; gravidity.

premigratory germ cell   Yolk-laden splanchnopleuric cell destined to migrate by way of blood vessels to a gonad primordium and become a germ cell.

prenatal   Before birth.

prereduction   Maturation in which the reductional division precedes the equational division.

primary oöcyte   Presumptive ovum after the completion of oögonial growth and before any maturation division.

primary spermatocyte   Presumptive spermatozoon after the completion of spermatogonial growth and before any maturation division.

primitive folds   Elevations on either side of a primitive groove.

primitive groove   Elongated groove in a primitive streak, bounded by the primitive folds and ending anteriorly at the primitive pit and posteriorly at the primitive plate.

primitive knot   *See* Hensen's node.

primitive pit   Depression at the anterior end of the primitive groove, surrounded by or just posterior to Hensen's node.

primitive plate   Expanded posterior end of a primitive streak.

primitive streak   Linear thickening of ectoderm, which is the first sign of an embryonic axis and which gives rise to the notochord and the mesoderm.

primordial germ cell   Diploid cell destined to become an ovum or spermatozoon; an oögonium or spermatogonium.

primordium   Cell mass constituting the first trace of a part or an organ; rudiment; anlage.

proamnion   Region of the area pellucida just anterior and lateral to the head process (bird), which is devoid of mesoderm for some time.

processus vaginalis   Peritoneal diverticulum through the abdominal wall into the scrotum.

proctodeum   Invagination of ectoderm at the posterior end of the gut, which gives rise to the anus.

proestrus   Period of active preparation of the uterine mucosa leading to estrus.

progesterone   Hormone from the corpus luteum, which causes a thickening of the uterine mucosa.

pronephric capsule   Connective tissue covering of a pronephros.

pronephric chamber   Portion of the coelom surrounding the pronephroi (amphibian), open anteriorly and posteriorly but closed ventrally by the lungs.

pronephric duct   Elongated tube directed posteriorly from a pronephros; segmental duct.

pronephric tubule   Tube connecting the coelom with a pronephric duct.

pronephros   Most primitive embryonic kidney; head kidney.

pronucleus   Nucleus of an ovum or a spermatozoon after entrance of the spermatozoon into the ovum.

prophase   First stage in mitosis, before metaphase, during which the chromosomes become apparent.

prosocoel   Cavity of the prosencephalon.

prospective significance   Normal fate of any embryonic region at the beginning of development; prospective Bedeutung; potentialité réelle.

prostate gland   Male sex gland (mammal) surrounding the urethra near the neck of the bladder and secreting fluid for the activation and transport of spermatozoa.

protandry   Hermaphroditism in which the male organs or products mature before the female organs or products.

prothetely   Appearance of a structure earlier than normal (e.g., pupal organs in a larva); opposed to metathetely.

protogyny   Hermaphroditism in which the female organs or products mature before the male organs or products.

protoplasmic bridge theory   *See* plasmodesmata.

proventriculus   Anterior portion of a bird's stomach, between the crop and the gizzard.

proximal   Nearest to any point of reference in the main body mass.

pseudencephalus   Embryo with an open cranium containing a mass of poorly developed nervous and connective tissue.

pupil   Circular opening into the vitreous chamber, partly occluded by the lens and regulated in diameter by the ciliary muscles of the iris, through which light enters the eye.

pycnosis   Increase in density of a cell or its nucleus.

pygopagus   Conjoined twins united at the buttocks.

pygostyle   Fused last four vertebrae of a bird.

rachischisis   Cleft spine.

ramus communicans   Connection between a spinal nerve and a sympathetic ganglion.

rate-gene   Gene leading to different rates of formation of specific materials.

Rathke's pocket   *See* hypophysis.

Rauber's layer   Trophoblast cells covering the inner cell mass (mammal).

recapitulation theory   Theory that the development of an organism retraces its ancestral history.

recessive   Gene that can be masked in a phenotype by its allelomorph; opposed to dominant.

reconstitution   Formation of a new organ within old tissue rather than by regeneration from a cut surface; rearrangement of parts into a new form.

rectum   Posterior portion of the hindgut, which opens into the cloaca.

recuperation   Reappearance of competence; restoration of the normal state.

redifferentiation   Return to a condition of increased specialization.

reductional division   Maturation division in which members of chromosome pairs separate so that the resulting cells are haploid; opposed to equational division.

reduplication   Formation of double (or even treble) structures (e.g., limbs) joined at some point, the reduplicated member usually being a mirror image of the original.

regeneration   Repair or replacement of a damaged or lost part.

regeneration, biaxial   Regeneration leading to two apical or basal regions (e.g., crotch head in Planaria, formed when the head is cut off and the body split from the posterior end anteriorly).

regeneration, physiological   Restorative processes occurring as a part of the life cycle of an organism.

regeneration, restorative   Repair or replacement of a damaged or lost part in a regular manner after an accident.

regenerative capacity   Ability to repair or replace a damaged or lost part, which generally varies inversely with the level of development.

region, presumptive   Region of the blastula that has been shown to develop in a specific direction under normal ontogenetic influences.

regulation   Reorganization toward the whole; utilization of material remaining in a pregastrula embryo after partial excision to bring about normal conditions.

renal corpuscle   Part of a mesonephric tubule consisting of a glomerulus and a Bowman's capsule; Malpighian body.

renal portal system   Veins carrying blood to the kidneys.

reproduction, asexual   Reproduction without a union of gametes.

resonance theory of reflex activity   Theory that the central nervous system emits different types of excitation and that a specific muscle responds only to the excitation appropriate to it.

response, homologous   Reaction of an extra (transplanted) muscle along with a normally present homologous muscle.

rete cords   Solid epithelial strands in a gonad, which give rise to the rete testis.

retina   Portion of an optic cup consisting of a thick inner sensory layer and a thin outer pigmented layer.

reunition   Reassembling of component parts of an organism into a functional whole after their separation.

rhinencephalon   Portion of the telencephalon concerned with the olfactory sense; olfactory lobe.

rhombencephalon   Hindmost of the three primitive brain divisions.

rut   Seasonal period of sexual desire in the males of some mammals, during which spermatogenesis and mating occur.

saccule   Outer, ventral portion of the inner ear, which is connected with the cochlear duct.

Sach's law   All cells tend to divide into equal parts, and each new plane of division tends to intersect the preceding one at right angles.

sclera   Tough connective tissue layer outside the choroid.

sclerotome   Mesenchyme proliferating from the median ventral surface of a myotome and migrating toward the notochord to give rise to a vertebra.

scrotum   Sac, outside the body proper, containing the testes (mammal, except elephant).

secondary oöcyte   Presumptive ovum after the separation of the first polar body.

secondary spermatocyte   Cell resulting from division of a primary spermatocyte.

section, frontal   Section parallel to the longitudinal axis and separating the dorsal and ventral regions; horizontal section.

section, sagittal   Section parallel to the longitudinal axis and separating the right and left regions.

section, transverse   Section perpendicular to the longitudinal axis; cross section.

sections, serial   Thin slices mounted on slides in the order of their removal from a specimen.

Seessel's pocket   Portion of the pharynx anterior to the mouth; preoral gut.

segmentation   Division of a structure into segments; metamerism; cleavage.

segmentation cavity   *See* blastocoel.

segregation   Separation of differentiating regions; organization.

segregation, precocious   Separation of differentiating regions even before cleavage (mosaic egg), with a minimum modification in response to internal environmental factors during subsequent development.

self-differentiating capacity   Ability of a region to develop along a specific course, determined by its intrinsic properties.

selfwise   According to the normal prospective significance (e.g., behavior of a transplant in a manner expected in its original environment).

semen   Fluid containing spermatozoa and secretions from the seminal vesicles, the prostate gland, and the bulbourethral glands.

semicircular canals   Tubes of the inner ear, which are accessory balancing organs.

semilunar valves   Cuplike pockets in the walls of the aorta and the arteries, which prevent the backflow of blood.

seminal vesicle   Dilation of (amphibian) or diverticulum from the distal end of a vas deferens, in which spermatozoa are stored before ejaculation.

seminiferous tubule   Tube of the testis, which contains developing spermatozoa and Sertoli cells.

senescence   Beginning old age; progressive loss of the ability to grow.

sense plate   Transverse neural fold formed by the fusion of the anterior limits of the neural folds (amphibian), which gives rise to the lenses of the eyes, the olfactory placodes, and the oral suckers.

sensitization theory   Theory that calcium is the true activating agent in artificial parthenogenesis and that other substances simply increase the permeability of the egg cortex to calcium.

septum   Partition.

septum spurium   Temporary partition in the right atrium, remnants of which become the valve of the posterior vena cava and the valve of the coronary sinus; false septum.

septum transversum   Membranous partition between the peritoneal and pericardial cavities.

serosa   *See* chorion.

Sertoli cell   Supporting and nursing cell for spermatozoa in a seminiferous tubule.

sex, heterogametic   Sex producing two types of gametes with respect to sex-influencing chromosomes (e.g., human male).

sex-linked   Carried by a gene on a sex chromosome and therefore determined by the hereditary distribution of the sex chromosomes.

sexual cords   Ingrowths of germinal epithelium in a gonad, which contain primitive germ cells and become seminiferous tubules in a male and ovigerous cords in a female.

sexual cycle   *See* estrous cycle.

sheath, myelin   Covering of an axon in the white matter of the brain and spinal cord.

shell   Covering of an egg, in a bird consisting of carbonates and phosphates of calcium and magnesium and having three layers: an inner mammillary layer of calcareous particles; an intermediate spongy layer of matted calcareous strands; and an outer, surface cuticle, which is porous but otherwise structureless.

shell gland   Glandular portion of a bird uterus, which provides material for a shell.

shell membrane   Double membrane just inside an egg shell, consisting of a thick outer layer and a thin inner layer of matted organic fibers that cross each other in every direction, the two layers being separated only by the air space at the blunt end of the egg.

sinus rhomboidalis   *See* posterior neuropore.

sinus terminalis   Vein encircling the area vasculosa (bird, marsupial); vena terminalis.

sinus venosus   Most posterior division of an embryonic heart, leading from the vitelline veins to the atrium.

situs inversus   Transposition of the viscera.

skeletogenous sheath   Sclerotome around the notochord and neural tube.

skin   Integument.

somatic   Pertaining to the body or the wall of the body cavity; physical; parietal.

somatic doubling   Doubling of the number of chromosomes initially present in a fertilized egg, which probably occurs during the early cleavages.

somatic mesoderm   Mesoderm adjacent to ectoderm.

somatopleure   Layer of somatic mesoderm and adjacent ectoderm, which gives rise to the amnion and chorion.

somite   Condensation of mesoderm lateral to the notochord, which gives rise to the dermatome, myotome, and sclerotome; epimere.

Spaltung   Conjoined twins united at the posterior ends of their spinal cords.

spawning   Act of emitting eggs from the uterus of an anamniote.

specificity   Summation of the cytochemical characteristics of a particular protoplasm.

spermatid   Cell resulting from the division of a secondary spermatocyte, which becomes a mature spermatozoon.

spermatocyte   Presumptive spermatozoon after the completion of growth in the spermatogonium stage.

spermatogenesis   Formation of spermatozoa.

spermatogonium   Presumptive spermatozoon before the attainment of maximum size and the beginning of meiosis; spermatospore; spermatophore.

spermatogonium, intermediate type   Spermatogonium arising from a Type A cell and gradually progressing to a Type B cell; the nucleus darkens and becomes rounded, its membrane thickens, and a few chromatin flakes appear close to the membrane.

spermatogonium, Type A   Spermatogonium having a pale, oval nucleus with a thin membrane, many fine chromatin granules, and one large chromatin granule.

spermatogonium, Type B   Spermatogonium having a dark, spherical nucleus with coarse chromatin granules attached to its membrane, and giving rise to a primary spermatocyte.

spermatophore   Sperm-bearing bundle emitted by the male of some species.

spermatozoon   Functionally mature male gamete; sperm.

spermophile group   Portion of fertilizin into which sperm receptors fit in fertilization.

sperm receptor   Chemical group associated with the spermatozoa and reacting with fertilizin in fertilization.

spina bifida   Congenital cleft of the vertebral column with protrusion of the meninges.

thyroid Evagination in the floor of the pharynx between visceral arches II, which separates to become an endocrine gland.

tissue culture Maintenance of an isolated tissue or organ in an artificial medium.

tongue Solid mesodermal mass, covered with endoderm, in the floor of the mouth.

tonsils Paired lymphatic structures derived from visceral pouches II.

torus transversus Thickening in the wall of the telencephalon, just anterior to the optic recess, which gives rise to the anterior commissure.

totipotency Ability (of an isolated blastomere) to produce a complete embryo.

trachea Portion of the respiratory tract between the larynx and the lungs.

tracheal groove *See* laryngotracheal groove.

transplant Graft of a cell, tissue, or organ from one region or organism to another.

transplant, autoplastic Graft from one region to another of the same organism.

transplant, heteroplastic Graft from one organism to another of a different species but the same genus.

transplant, heterotopic Graft from one region to another.

transplant, homoplastic Graft from one organism to another of the same species; homoioplastic transplant; homograft.

transplant, homotopic Graft from one region to the same or a homologous region; orthotopic transplant.

transplant, xenoplastic Graft between organisms of different genera or those even farther apart phylogenetically.

transverse neural fold *See* sense plate.

triaster Abnormal mitotic figure of three asters, which generally causes irregular distribution of the chromosomes and abnormal cleavages.

trigger reaction Response that is in no way related to the stimulant.

trophectoderm Thin layer of ectoderm bounding the yolk cavity except in the region of the egg cylinder (mouse); ectoderm that gives rise to trophoblast.

trophoblast Thin outermost layer of cells of a blastocyst.

trophochromatin Nutritive chromatin of the nucleus.

trophoderm Trophoblast and the adjacent somatic mesoderm; extraembryonic somatopleure; chorion; serosa.

true knot Looped umbilical cord; distinguished from a false knot, which consists of a looped blood vessel and causes an external bulging.

truncus arteriosus Anterior extension of the bulbus arteriosus.

tubal fissure Longitudinal slit in the roof of the pharynx, which connects the auditory tubes with the oral cavity (chick).

tubal ridge Strip of peritoneum on the dorsolateral surface of a mesonephros, which gives rise to an oviduct (bird).

tuberculum impar Median thickening in the floor of the pharynx, which gives rise to part of the tongue.

tuberculum posterius Invagination in the floor of the brain at the boundary between the diencephalon and the mesencephalon and near the anterior end of the notochord.

tubotympanic cavity Remnant of visceral pouch I, which becomes the auditory tube.

tunica albuginea Fibrous connective tissue covering of a testis or an ovary.

twins, identical Twins of the same sex produced from a single fertilized egg and having common embryonic membranes; monovular twins.

twins, fraternal Twins produced from separate fertilized eggs and having separate embryonic membranes; diovular twins.

tympanic cavity Cavity of the middle ear.

tympanic membrane   Membrane between the tympanic cavity and the outer ear; tympanum; ear drum.

ultimobranchial bodies   Paired glands derived from visceral pouches VI in an amphibian, V in a bird, and IV or V in a mammal.

umbilical artery   Branch of the dorsal aorta carrying blood to the allantois.

umbilical cord   Tubular connection between a mammalian embryo and its extraembryonic structures, which contains the body stalk, the allantoic stalk with its arteries and veins, and the yolk stalk with its arteries and veins.

umbilical vein   Vein carrying blood from the allantois to a common cardinal vein.

Umhüllung   Process of wrapping an inductor in sheets of competent ectoderm to test its inductive power.

unipotency   Ability to differentiate in only one direction.

urachus   Portion of the allantoic stalk between the umbilical cord and the bladder (mammal).

ureter   Duct carrying urine from a kidney to the cloaca (reptile, bird) or the bladder (amphibian, mammal).

urethra   Duct discharging urine from the bladder and seminal fluid from the genital tract (mammal).

urinary bladder   Vesicle into which the mesonephric ducts (male amphibian) or the ureters (female amphibian, mammal) empty.

uriniferous tubule   Nephric tubule secreting urine; secreting tubule.

urodeum   Intermediate portion of the cloaca (bird), which receives the urinary and genital ducts.

urogenital duct   Duct carrying both urinary and genital products (e.g., mesonephric duct of a male amphibian).

urogenital ridge   Ridge on the ventral surface of a mesonephros, which gives rise to a gonad.

urogenital system   Excretory and reproductive organs.

urostyle   Skeletal element derived from the two last somites (anuran).

uterine glands   Glands of the uterine mucosa, which secrete uterine milk.

uterine milk   Nutritive fluid secreted by the uterine mucosa and absorbed by the trophoblast.

uterine mucosa   Lining of the uterus; endometrium.

uterus   Thick-walled chamber through which an egg passes (amphibian, reptile, bird) or in which an embryo develops (mammal); womb.

utricle   Superior portion of the auditory vesicle, into which the semicircular canals open.

vagina   Thin-walled passage from the uterus to the cloaca (bird) or the vestibule (mammal).

vasa efferentia   Ducts conveying spermatozoa from the seminiferous tubules to the Bowman's capsules (amphibian) or the epididymis (reptile, bird, mammal).

vas deferens   Duct conveying spermatozoa from the epididymis to the cloaca (reptile, bird) or the urethra (mammal).

vegetalization   Transformation by physical or chemical means of normally ectodermal regions to endoderm; endodermization; opposed to animalization.

velar plate   Fold of the pharyngeal wall separating the pharynx from the gill rakers and the gills (amphibian).

velum transversum Thickening in the roof of the prosencephalon, which marks the dorsal boundary between the telencephalon and the diencephalon.

vena cava, anterior Large vein between the right innominate vein and the heart, formed by the junction of the right anterior cardinal vein and the right common cardinal vein; superior vena cava.

vena cava, posterior Single median ventral vein proceeding from the liver to the sinus venosus; inferior vena cava.

ventral Pertaining to the belly or abdomen; opposed to dorsal.

ventral mesentery Membrane attaching the gut to the ventral body wall.

ventricle, third Cavity of the diencephalon, which opens into the paired lateral ventricles through the foramina of Monro.

ventricle, fourth Cavity of the metencepholon and myelencephalon, joining the aqueduct of Sylvius anteriorly and the spinal cord posteriorly.

ventricle of the heart Muscular chamber of the heart that receives blood from an atrium and delivers it to the bulbus arteriosus (paired in mammal).

vernix caseosa Cheeselike substance of dead epithelial cells and fat, which covers an embryo.

vertebra Segment of the spinal column.

vertebral arch *See* neural arch.

vertebral plate *See* somite.

vestibule Area between the labia into which the vagina and the urethra open.

villi, chorionic Fingerlike projections of trophoblast and the underlying somatic mesoderm, which invade the uterine mucosa in implantation.

villus Fingerlike projection.

visceral Pertaining to the viscera.

visceral arch Mesodermal mass between consecutive visceral pouches and lateral to the pharynx; pharyngeal (gill, branchial) arch.

visceral cleft Slit between consecutive visceral arches, which connects the pharynx to the outside; pharyngeal (gill, branchial) cleft.

visceral groove Invagination of ectoderm between consecutive visceral arches; pharyngeal (gill, branchial) groove.

visceral mesoderm *See* splanchnic mesoderm.

visceral plexus Aggregation of sympathetic neurons controlling the viscera.

visceral pouch Evagination of pharyngeal endoderm between consecutive visceral arches; pharyngeal (gill, branchial) pouch.

viscosity Inner molecular friction.

vitalism Theory that biological processes are directed by forces that are neither physical and chemical nor organic but supernatural.

vital stain Nontoxic dye for the localized staining of living tissue.

vitelline Pertaining to yolk.

vitelline artery Branch of the dorsal aorta carrying blood to the yolk sac.

vitelline membrane Thin membrane covering an ovum.

vitelline vein Vessel carrying blood from the yolk sac to the sinus venosus.

vitreous humor Viscous fluid filling the posterior chamber of the eye.

viviparity Production of living young (rather than eggs) from within the maternal body; opposed to oviparity.

Weber's law   The degree of sensitivity to a stimulus in any reacting system depends not only on the nature of the stimulus but also on the life span and the strength of an already existing stimulus.

Wolffian body   *See* mesonephros.

Wolffian duct   *See* mesonephric duct.

wolf snout   Projection of the premaxilla from the face accompanied by a harelip and sometimes a cleft palate.

xanthophore   Cell containing yellow pigment.

X chromosome   Sex chromosome associated with femaleness.

xiphopagus   Conjoined twins with xiphoid fusion.

Y chromosome   Sex chromosome associated with maleness.

yolk   Highly nutritious substance consisting of globules of fat; deutoplasm.

yolk nucleus   Concentrated mass of protoplasm at one side of an oögonium (bird), around which the yolk accumulates during the growth phase of oögenesis.

yolk plug   Plug formed by yolk cells too large to be incorporated immediately in the archenteron during gastrulation (amphibian) and therefore protruding slightly from the blastopore.

yolk sac   Extraembryonic structure consisting of splanchnopleure, which surrounds the yolk mass except for the region of the yolk stalk.

yolk sac endoderm   Endoderm of the splanchnopleure surrounding the yolk.

yolk sac septa   Projections into the yolk of the splanchnopleure around it, which contain glands that secrete yolk-digesting enzymes.

yolk sac splanchnopleure   Splanchnopleure surrounding the yolk.

yolk sac umbilicus   Region in which the yolk stalk joins an embryo.

yolk stalk   Tubular stalk connecting the midgut and the yolk sac.

zona pellucida   Clear area outside a vitelline membrane.

zona radiata   Radiating striations in the zona pellucida.

zone, lenticular   *See* lenticular zone.

zone, marginal   Presumptive chordamesodermal-endodermal complex at the junction of the roof and the floor of an early gastrula; germ ring.

zone of junction   Portion of the marginal periblast beneath the margin of overgrowth and adjoining the yolk (bird).

zygote   Diploid cell formed by the union of two gametes; fertilized egg.

zygotene   *See* synaptene.

Index

574

457, 458, 498
  in mouse, 270, 274, 296
  in pig, 324, 357
bursa, omental, *see* omental bursa

cilia, sensory, in frog, 83, 99
ciliary process, 468
    in chick, 191
    human, 471
ciliary zonule, 468
circle of Willis, human, 474
    in pig, 352, 354
circulation, embryonic, human, 430
    fetal, human, 429
    maternal, human, 429, 430
cleavage, 15–16
    in chick, 105, 113, 115, 117, 118, 119, 121,
        122
    in frog, 31, 35–36, 37
    human, 401, 407–08, 439
    in mouse, 247–48
    in pig, 312
cleavage furrow, in chick, 117, 121, 122, 123
    in frog, 35
clitoral gland, in mouse, 241, 244
clitoris, human, 387, 388, 389, 394, 397, 398
    in mouse, 241, 244
    in pig, 311
cloaca, in chick, 192, 200, 206, 220
    in frog, 22, 25, 27, 52, 63, 64, 89
    human, 383, 385, 447, 448, 452, 453, 454,
        471, 498
    in mouse, 270, 283, 284, 286, 292, 297
    in pig, 332, 348, 361, 376
    in rooster, 107
cloacal membrane, in chick, 159, 206
    human, 385, 386, 420, 454, 459, 492
    in mouse, 270
    in pig, 323, 371
coagulating gland, in mouse, 240, 241, 242
cochlea, in frog, 81, 82
    in mouse, 286
    in pig, 344 (table)
    See also lagena
cochlear duct, in chick, 195, 196, 197
    human, 505, 506, 507
cochlear nerve, human, 505
coeliac artery, in chick, 192, 204, 209
    in frog, 93
    human, 495, 499
    in pig, 334, 355, 356, 357, 374
coeliacomesenteric artery, in frog, 95
coelom, in chick, 139, 142, 153, 154, 160, 161,
        175, 204, 205, 206, 215, 217, 218, 219
    in frog, 53, 83, 91
    human, 419, 431, 438, 439, 446, 452, 456
    in mouse, 259, 262, 272, 273, 280, 281, 282,
        290, 291, 293
    in pig, 316, 319, 323, 324, 332, 345, 368
coelomic spaces, in frog, 48, 64
coitus, see copulation
colliculi, mesencephalic, see mesencephalic
    colliculi
colliculus, superior, human, 445
colon, human, 448, 492, 499

in pig, 347, 367, 369, 372
color blindness, 508
columella, in frog, 79
commissural artery, in frog, 94
commissure, anterior, in chick, 185, 189
commissure, posterior, see posterior commissure
commissure, transverse, in chick, 189
common bile duct, see ductus choledochus
common cardinal vein, in chick, 152, 165, 166,
        176, 178, 179, 182, 193, 201, 202, 206,
        208, 213
    in frog, 92, 93, 96, 97
    human, 450, 451, 455, 457, 458, 473, 476,
        499
    in mouse, 283, 284, 289, 293
    in pig, 324, 325, 334, 353, 355, 356, 358,
        373
comparison of mouse and human embryos,
        266, 267, 269 (table)
cones of retina, 470
conjunctiva, 468
coprodeum, in chick, 200
copulation, in frog, 30, 31, 34, 35
    human, 402
    in mouse, 237
    in pig, 305
cornea, 468
    in chick, 193, 194, 469
    human, 437
    in mouse, 295
    in pig, 470
corneal ectoderm, in frog, 81
corniculate cartilage, human, 501
corona radiata, human, 391, 400, 401
    in pig, 311
coronary sinus, human, 451, 477
    in pig, 358
corpora quadrigemina, in pig, 370
corpus albicans, human, 400, 401
    in pig, 310
corpus cavernosum, human, 382
corpus hemorrhagicum, human, 400
    in pig, 310
corpus luteum, human, 400, 401, 402, 410, 421
    in mouse, 242
    in pig, 310
corpus striatum, in chick, 181
    in pig, 342, 367, 369
corpus of uterus, human, 395, 396, 397, 398,
        399
cortex, cerebral, human, 475
cortex, suprarenal, human, 502
cortex of ovum, 15
cortical substance, in frog, 98
costocervical artery, human, 474, 503
cotyledonary placentae, 234, 235 (table)
cranial flexure, in chick, 106, 143, 155, 164,
        165, 166, 167, 182
    in human, 462, 463, 500
    in mouse, 286

in pig, 321, 330, 331
cranial ganglia, human, 459
  in pig, 322
cranial nerves, in chick, 167, 188
  in frog, 77–78
  human, 452
  in pig, 342, 344 (table), 365
crop, in chick, 199
crossing over, 515
crown-rump length, human, 433 (table)
  in mouse, 270 (table), 302
crura cerebri, in frog, 73, 75
cryptobranchus, 62
cumulus oöphorus, human, 391, 392, 393
  in pig, 309, 311
cuneiform cartilage, human, 501
cutaneous artery, in frog, 93, 94, 95
cystic duct, in chick, 204
  human, 386, 456
  in pig, 348, 371
  See also bile duct
cytolysis, defined, 15
cytoplasm, in maturation, 10
cytotrophoblast, human, 411, 416, 423, 427

d

Darwin, Charles, 5, 520
decidua, 233
  human, 410, 417, 427
  in mouse, 248, 254, 257, 265
deltoid muscle, human, 494
dendrites, in chick, 187
  in pig, 362
dental papillae, human, 471
  in mouse, 299
deoxyribonucleic acid, 514
dermatome, in chick, 174
  in frog, 89
  in mouse, 274, 275, 279
  in pig, 319, 345
dermomyotomic plate, in chick, 174
determination, embryological, 515
deutoplasm, see yolk
diaphragm, human, 448, 471
  in mouse, 297
  in pig, 366, 367, 368, 369, 372
diaphragmatic ligament of human meso-
    nephros, 390
diencephalon, in chick, 143, 164, 165, 166,
    167, 168, 169, 182, 183, 185, 188, 193,
    198, 468, 469
  in frog, 49, 71, 76, 77 (table), 78
  human, 459, 463, 498, 500
  in mouse, 271, 283, 286, 287, 293, 294, 301
  in pig, 321, 322, 330, 331, 333, 335, 337,
    342, 344 (table), 367, 370
diestrus, in mouse, 237, 239, 245

differentiation, 3, 16, 515, 516, 518
  in frog, 42
diffuse placentae, 233–34, 235 (table)
digestive tract development, in human em-
    bryo, 447–48, 473, 475
diocoel, in frog, 52, 61, 62, 73, 74, 75, 76, 78,
    80, 88
  human, 498
  in mouse, 271, 276, 294
  in pig, 367, 368
discoid placentae, 234, 235 (table)
distal endoderm, in mouse, 248, 250, 251, 252,
    255, 256, 257
diverticulum, urethral, in mouse, 242
DNA, 514
dorsal aorta, in chick, 146, 148, 153, 156, 158,
    160, 161, 166, 168, 169, 175, 178, 179,
    182, 188, 191, 192, 193, 201, 202, 204,
    205, 206, 210, 214–20 pass.
  in frog, 63, 74, 76, 77, 86, 91, 93, 94, 95
  human, 387, 425, 427, 443, 445, 455, 458,
    473, 474, 495, 498, 499, 502, 508
  in mouse, 262, 272, 273, 278, 280, 281, 283,
    288, 292, 296, 297
  in pig, 323, 324, 325, 332, 334, 335, 339,
    341, 345, 350, 354, 356, 357, 359, 360,
    367, 368, 369, 374, 375
dorsal blastopore lip, in chick, 121, 124
  in frog, 39, 40, 42, 43, 44, 45
dorsal flexure, in chick, 182
dorsal mesentery, in chick, 171, 172, 204, 207,
    215, 220
  in frog, 91
  human, 448, 459
  in mouse, 296, 297
  in pig, 323, 334, 335, 351, 360, 371
dorsal root, in chick, 188, 191
  in frog, 77
  human, 502
  in mouse, 295, 296, 297
  in pig, 345
dorsoradial muscles of forearm, 494
dorsotibial muscles of human leg, 494
Drosophila, 521, 522
  chromosomes in, 509
ductus arteriosus, in chick, 177, 203, 297
  in frog, 93, 96
  human, 475, 502, 508
  in pig, 352, 354, 374, 375
ductus choledochus, in chick, 173, 203, 204
  human, 385, 386, 456, 492
  in mouse, 280, 282
  in pig, 322, 347, 367, 371
ductus venosus, in chick, 169, 173, 182, 188,
    208, 211, 212, 213, 214
  human, 459, 476, 508
  in mouse, 280, 283, 290
  in pig, 332, 355, 356, 358, 373, 374
duodenum, in chick, 199, 203, 204, 219
  human, 385, 386, 459

duodenum (*cont.*)

  in mouse, 282

  in pig, 334, 339, 347, 348, 367, 369, 371

e

ear, in chick, 136, 193–95, 196

  in frog, 44, 45, 62, 77, 79, 81, 82

  human, 459, 475, 490, 491, 493, 505–07

  in mouse, 278, 285, 297, 301

  in pig, 344 (table)

ectoderm, 16, 17, 516, 517, 519

  derivatives in chick, 135–37, 149, 162–71, 181–95

  derivatives in frog, 69–83, 84 (table)

  derivatives in human, 437

  derivatives in pig, 321–22, 335, 362, 365–70

  in gastrulation of chick, 121, 124

  in gastrulation of frog, 39, 40, 43, 44, 45

  in gastrulation of mouse, 248, 249, 254, 258

  in gastrulation of pig, 316, 317

  in incubation of chick embryo, 130, 131, 132, 133, 138, 139, 140, 141, 144, 153, 154, 156, 175, 186, 187, 196, 205, 206

  in organogenesis of mouse, 258, 260, 261, 264

ectoplacenta, in mouse, 259, 261, 262

ectoplacental cavity, in mouse, 254, 256, 257, 260, 261

ectoplacental cone, in mouse, 249, 251, 253, 254, 255, 256, 258, 260, 261

efferent neurons, 362

egg cylinder, in mouse, 248, 249, 250, 254

egg tooth, in chick, 181, 195

ejaculatory duct, human, 382, 390

  in pig, 306, 307

embryonic axes, in frog, 29, 31, 32, 35, 40

embryonic disc, human, 409, 410, 412, 413, 415, 416, 417, 425

  in pig, 313, 315, 317

  See also blastoderm

embryonic ectoderm, in mouse, 248, 250, 251, 252, 253, 255, 256, 257, 258, 261, 272

embryonic membranes, in chick, 181

  human, 424–32

  in mouse, 301

  in pig, 326–29

embryonic tissue, in mouse, 275, 284

embryos, comparison of mouse and human, 266, 267, 269 (table)

enamel organs, human, 471

endocardial cushion, in chick, 207

  in pig, 325, 352, 353

endocardial septum, in chick, 153

endocardium, in chick, 148, 149, 153, 154, 160, 161, 168

  in frog, 53, 64, 86

  human, 426, 441, 445, 446, 452

  in mouse, 261, 263

  in pig, 324

endochondral bones, in chick, 221

endocrine factors, in experimental embryology, 102

endoderm, 16, 17, 516, 519

  derivatives in chick, 137, 149, 171–73, 195–205

  derivatives in frog, 83–89

  derivatives in human, 437–38

  derivatives in pig, 322–23, 347–48, 370–71

  in gastrulation of chick, 121, 124

  in gastrulation of frog, 39, 40, 43, 44, 45

  in gastrulation of mouse, 248, 249, 255, 258

  in gastrulation of pig, 316

  in incubation of chick embryo, 130, 131, 132, 133, 138, 139, 140, 141, 144, 147, 153, 154, 156, 186, 187

endolymphatic duct, in chick, 171, 195, 196, 197

  in frog, 78, 79, 81

  human, 456, 505, 506, 507

  in mouse, 278, 282, 283, 285, 294, 295

  in pig, 336, 345, 346

endolymphatic sac, human, 505, 506, 507

  in mouse, 295

endometrium, *see* uterine mucosa

endothelial cells, human, 449

endothelium, in chick, 147

ependyma, in cat, 466

  in chick, 188, 191, 466

  in frog, 73

  in opossum, 467

  in pig, 466, 467

epiboly, in frog, 40, 41

epicardium, in mouse, 263

  in pig, 324, 353

epidermis, in frog, 44, 45

  human, 424, 437, 471, 472, 473, 517

epididymis, human, 382, 384, 390

  in mouse, 240, 241, 242, 297

  in pig, 305, 306, 307

  in rooster, 107, 215

epigastric arteries, human, 474, 503

epigeneticists, 516

epiglottis, human, 448

  in pig, 347, 367, 369

epimere, *see* somites

epimyocardium, human, 445

  in mouse, 261

epiphysis, in chick, 143, 166, 167, 182, 183, 185, 188, 189, 198

  in frog, 49, 52, 62, 63, 74, 75, 78

  human, 459, 463, 464

  in mouse, 283, 286

  in pig, 319, 338, 368, 369, 370

epiploic foramen, in pig, 371

epithelial tag, human, 388, 389

epithelioid bodies, in frog, 86

epithelium, germinal, *see* germinal epithelium

epoöphoron, in chicken, 220

in mouse, 240, 241, 283, 284, 297
  in pig, 306, 367, 368, 369
Graafian follicle, in chicken, 109, 111
  human, 391, 394, 399, 400
  in mouse, 242, 245
  in pig, 310
gravid uterus, human, 410
  in mouse, 267
  See also pregnancy
gray crescent, in frog, 29, 30, 31, 34, 35, 38,
    39, 47
gray matter, in chick, 188, 191
  in frog, 72, 73
  in pig, 333, 342, 365, 466
great cardiac vein, human, 451
growth, of human embryo, 432–38
growth-promoting hormone, human, 403
gubernaculum testis, human, 390
gut, in chick, 175, 200, 206, 211
  in frog, 72, 74, 76, 78, 94
  human, 385, 387, 424, 425, 431, 437, 438,
    447, 452, 459, 470, 471, 472, 492, 498
  in mouse, 283, 289, 290, 291, 293, 296, 297,
    301
  in pig, 322, 323, 332, 348, 351, 358, 361,
    374
  See also foregut; hindgut; midgut
gyri, 365

h

habenular commissure, in frog, 75
Haeckel, Ernst, 4, 519, 520
hair, human, 473
hair follicles, human, 471
  in mouse, 286, 292
hand plate, human, 497
hatching, of frog larva, 62
head, in frog, 52
  human, 387, 447, 452, 459, 471, 472, 473,
    496, 500
  in pig, 319, 327, 334, 362
head ectoderm, in chick, 129, 158
  in frog, 95
  in mouse, 277, 287
  in pig, 345
head fold, in chick, 128, 132, 133, 135, 138,
    144, 155, 168
  human, 447
  in mouse, 259, 260
head mesenchyme, in chick, 153, 165, 173
  in frog, 78, 81, 82
head mesoderm, in chick, 136, 145, 146
  in frog, 78
head process, in chick, 126, 130, 132, 140,
    160
  in human, 413, 439
  in mouse, 255, 256, 258
head vein, primary, in pig, 356
heart, in chick, 146, 148–53 *pass.*, 156, 158,

168, 175, 177, 183, 206, 207, 208, 214,
    520
  in frog, 52, 53, 62, 68, 86, 90, 91, 92, 97
  human, 387, 439, 444, 448, 450–51, 452,
    453, 456, 457, 459, 473, 493, 499
  in mouse, 259, 263, 264, 270, 271, 278, 284,
    288, 289, 292
  in pig, 319–31 *pass.*, 351, 353, 358, 372, 375
heart mesenchyme, in frog, 51, 61
heart mesoderm, in frog, 74
  in mouse, 260
heart primordium, in chick, 106, 151
Hegar's sign of pregnancy, 436
hematopoiesis, human, 472, 473, 475
hemiazygos vein, human, 477
hemocytoblasts, mesenchymal differentiation
    into, 17, 449
hemophilia, 508
hemorrhoidal artery, in frog, 95
Hensen's node, in chick, 106, 126, 127, 128,
    129, 132, 133
  human, 413, 419, 420, 421, 423, 426, 440,
    441, 447
  in pig, 316, 317, 319
hepatic artery, in frog, 95
hepatic duct, human, 385, 386, 456
  in mouse, 282
  in pig, 322, 371
hepatic plexus, human, 457, 458
hepatic vein, in chick, 178, 211, 212, 213
  in frog, 93, 96, 97, 98
  human, 498
  in mouse, 283, 284, 290, 292
  in pig, 355, 358, 373, 374
hepatocardiac vessels, human, 457
hepatocystic duct, in chick, 204
hepatoenteric duct, in chick, 204
heredity, study of, 475, 477
Hertwig, Oskar, 516
Hertwig, Richard, 35, 516
hindbrain, *see* rhombencephalon
hindgut, in chick, 139, 141, 155, 171, 205
  in frog, 44, 45, 51, 52, 53, 64, 89
  human, 387, 427, 443, 444, 447, 460
  in mouse, 259, 260, 261, 297
  in pig, 316, 319, 322, 324, 328
hindlimb, in frog, 62
  in mouse, 282, 297
  in pig, 321, 330, 331, 335, 341, 361
histiocyte, human, 449
histogenesis, 515
holoblastic cleavage, 35
horn, uterine, *see* uterine horn
humerus, human, 502, 504
Huxley, Thomas, 520
hyaloid artery, in chick, 469
  in pig, 470
hyaloid canal, 468
  human, 471
hyaloid vein, in chick, 469

Hydra, 520
hymen, human, 389, 396, 397
hyoid arch, in frog, 52, 64, 85
   human, 490, 491, 496
   in mouse, 270
   in pig, 320, 347
hyoid cartilage, human, 500
hyomandibular cleft, human, 490, 491
hyomandibular groove, in pig, 321, 331
hypogastric artery, human, 474
   in pig, 374
hypoglossal ganglion, in mouse, 296
hypoglossal nerve, in chick, 190
   in pig, 344
hypomere, *see* lateral plate mesoderm
hypophysis, in frog, 48, 52, 61, 62, 63, 64, 71,
   73, 74, 75, 76, 80, 88
   See also pituitary gland; Rathke's pocket
hypothalamus, in frog, 75
   human, 464

i

ileocaecal valve, in pig, 370
ileum, human, 492
iliac artery, in frog, 95
   human, 398, 474, 503, 508
   in pig, 356, 372, 374
iliac vein, in chick, 213
   human, 398, 476, 477
ilium, in chick, 220
   human, 494
implantation of embryo, human, 399, 400,
   401, 414, 415, 418, 421, 422, 423, 429,
   436, 439
incubation of chicken egg, 106
   laying to 33 hours, 126–54
   33 to 72 hours, 155–80
   after 72 hours, 180–220
inductor, defined, 518
infracardiac bursa, human, 502
infundibulum, in chick, 166, 167, 168, 169,
   182, 185, 188, 189, 194
   in frog, 49, 52, 61, 62, 71, 73, 74, 75, 76, 88
   human, 454, 456, 459, 464, 498
   in mouse, 284, 286, 287, 293, 294, 295
   in pig, 322, 342, 347, 368, 370
   See also pituitary gland
inguinal canal, human, 390
   in pig, 307
inguinal ligament, human, 390, 399
   in pig, 306, 307, 308
inner cell mass, human, 409, 410
   in mouse, 248
   in pig, 313, 315
inner nuclear layer of retina, 470
innominate artery, in pig, 352, 354, 374
innominate vein, human, 476, 477
   in pig, 372, 374
insemination, 402

insular region, human, 464, 465
integument ectoderm, in mouse, 274, 275, 279
interatrial foramen, in chick, 214
interatrial septum, in chick, 207
   in frog, 97
   in pig, 325
intercostal artery, human, 474, 503
intercostal nerve, human, 502
interembryonic graft, in experimental embryology, 222
internal gills, in frog, 85, 86, 87, 95
interphase, 9, 514
interruption of development of organ, 522
intersegmental artery, in chick, 149, 175, 176
   in frog, 95
   human, 455, 473, 474, 498
   in mouse, 288
   in pig, 324, 325, 334, 354, 356, 357, 359,
   367
intersegmental vein, in chick, 177
   in pig, 324, 355, 373
interstitial tissue, human, 381, 382, 406
   in mouse, 243
   in rooster, 107
interventricular foramen (foramen of Monro),
   in chick, 185, 207
   in frog, 73
   human, 500
   in mouse, 286
   in pig, 342, 367, 370
interventricular septum, in chick, 207
   in pig, 325, 334, 338, 353
interventricular sulcus, human, 450, 451
intervertebral disc, in pig, 368
intervillous space, human, 417, 427, 429, 495
intestinal artery, in frog, 95
intestinal portal, anterior, *see* anterior intestinal portal
   posterior, *see* posterior intestinal portal
intestine, large, *see* large intestine
   small, *see* small intestine
   See also gut
intraembryonic mesoderm, human, 412
involution of egg surface, in frog, 39, 40
iris, 468
   in chick, 191, 194, 469
   in frog, 79, 80
   human, 437, 471
   in mouse, 297
   in pig, 470
islands of Langerhans, human, 472
isolecithal cleavage, 312

j

jaw, human, 459
jelly layers, in frog's egg, 28, 30
jugular ganglion, in chick, 170, 182
   human, 496
   in mouse, 283, 295

liver diverticulum (*cont.*)
  in mouse, 280
liver primordium, in chick, 171
  human, 445
Loeb, Jacques, 518
LTH, 400, 406
lumbar artery, human, 474, 503
lumbar nerve, human, 494
lumbar vertebra, human, 497
lumbosacral plexus, human, 493
lumen, of seminiferous tubules, 13
  uterine, in mouse, 243, 244, 250, 252, 265
lungs, in chick, 106, 182, 193, 196, 199, 203,
    206, 207, 214
  in frog, 69, 74, 87
  human, 385, 437, 444, 447, 448, 452, 458,
    459, 470, 472, 475, 492, 498, 499
  in mouse, 270, 273, 282, 283, 284, 289, 293,
    296, 301
  in pig, 322, 323, 332, 338, 347, 351, 357,
    366, 367, 368, 372, 375
luteinizing hormone, human, 112, 400, 403,
    406
lymph sac, jugular, human, 501
lymphatic system, in frog, 98
  human, 438
lymphoblast, human, 449
lymphocyte, human, 449, 473

m

macromeres, in frog, 36
macrophages, mesenchymal differentiation
    into, 17, 449
macula lutea, 468
Malpighi, M., 105
mammary artery, human, 474, 503
  in pig, 354, 355
mammary gland, human, 403
mammary primordium, human, 499
mammillary recess, in frog, 75
mammillary tubercle, in chick, 185, 189
mandible, human, 448, 490
  in mouse, 293, 301
  in pig, 329
mandibular arch, in chick, 170
  in frog, 52, 64, 85
  human, 490, 491, 493, 496
  in mouse, 270
  in pig, 320, 347
mandibular nerve, in mouse, 283
  in pig, 333, 343, 365, 366
mandibular vein, in pig, 373
mantle layer of spinal cord, in opossum, 467
  in pig, 342, 466, 467
marrow, in chick, 221
  human, 504
mast cell, human, 449

maternal blood, in mouse, 251, 253, 255, 256,
    257, 265
maternal tissue, human, 410, 411, 430
  in mouse, 275, 284
  in pig, 328
maturation, 9–14
  in chicken, 115, 122
  human, 379
  See also meiosis
maturation division, first, *see* first maturation
    division
  second, *see* second maturation division
maxillary artery, in pig, 354
maxillary nerve, in mouse, 283
  in pig, 333, 343, 365, 366
maxillary process, in chick, 170, 198, 201
  in frog, 68
  human, 452, 490, 491, 493
  in mouse, 270
  in pig, 320, 321, 330, 331, 333, 337, 349
maxillary vein, in pig, 373
meatus venosus, in chick, 204, 211, 212
Meckel's cartilage, human, 500, 501
medulla oblongata, in chick, 185
  in frog, 78
  human, 464
  in pig, 370
medullary substance, in frog, 98
megakaryocyte, human, 449
meiosis, 9, 379, 405, 514–15
  See also maturation
membrane granulosa, human, 391, 392, 393,
    400
  in pig, 311
membranous labyrinth, in frog, 79
menstrual cycle, human, 420–21
menstruation, 397, 399, 400, 420, 421, 422
meroblastic cleavage, 35
mesencephalic colliculi, human, 454
  in mouse, 301
mesencephalon, in chick, 126, 136, 143, 146,
    155, 156, 158, 164, 165, 166, 167, 168,
    169, 170, 181, 182, 183, 185, 188, 189
  in frog, 49, 62, 63, 71, 73, 74, 77 (table), 78
  human, 426, 440, 445, 460, 462, 463, 464,
    465, 496, 498, 500
  in mouse, 271, 283, 287, 293, 301
  in pig, 321, 323, 330, 331, 332, 333, 336,
    344 (table), 366, 367, 368, 369, 370
mesenchyme, 17
  in chick, 121, 126, 137, 141, 167, 195, 197,
    201, 203, 216, 221, 468
  in frog, 40, 44, 51, 52, 61, 62, 63, 64, 85,
    89, 90
  human, 449, 459, 502
  in mouse, 250, 258, 259, 264, 271, 277, 281,
    285, 287, 296
  in pig, 315, 316, 325, 345, 346
mesenteric artery, anterior, *see* anterior mes-
    enteric artery

posterior, *see* posterior mesenteric artery
mesenteric vein, in chick, 211, 212, 213
  human, 508
  in mouse, 296
  in pig, 335
mesentery, caval, *see* caval mesentery
  dorsal, *see* dorsal mesentery
  ventral, *see* ventral mesentery
mesocardia, in chick, 148
  in frog, 91
  human, 445, 450
  in pig, 324
mesocardial vesicles, human, 454
mesocoel, in chick, 153, 168
  in frog, 52, 61, 72, 74, 75
  human, 498
  in mouse, 271, 274, 287, 293
mesocolon, human, 389, 499
mesoderm, 16, 17, 516, 517
  derivatives in chick, 137, 142–43, 149, 173–
    80, 206–21
  derivatives in frog, 79, 84 (table), 89–101
  derivatives in human, 438
  derivatives in pig, 323–26, 352–62, 372–77
  in gastrulation of chick, 121, 125
  in gastrulation of frog, 39, 40, 42, 43, 44, 45
  in gastrulation of mouse, 253, 254, 255, 256
  in gastrulation of pig, 315, 316, 317
  in incubation of chick embryo, 130, 131,
    132, 133, 139, 141, 144, 151, 153, 186,
    187, 206
mesodiencephalic constriction, in chick, 182
mesogastrium, in chick, 207
  in pig, 371
  See also dorsal mesentery; ventral mesentery
mesomere, *see* nephrotome
mesometrium, in mouse, 251
mesonephric arteries, in chick, 209
mesonephric duct, in chick, 166, 180, 205,
    214, 215, 216, 217, 218, 220
  in frog, 21, 98, 99
  human, 383, 384, 385, 386, 388, 389, 390,
    395, 396, 399, 447, 448, 458, 492, 498
  in mouse, 283, 297
  in pig, 306, 308, 323, 326, 334, 335, 341,
    347, 357, 359, 360, 367, 369, 371, 375,
    376
mesonephric glomerulus, in chick, 180, 215,
    218
  in frog, 23, 98
  human, 383, 385, 386, 498
  in pig, 335, 357, 359, 360, 361, 377
mesonephric tubules, in chick, 180, 204, 214,
    215, 216; 217
  human, 382, 384, 385, 458, 502
  in mouse, 289, 291
  in pig, 306, 357, 359, 360, 375, 376
mesonephric vein, in pig, 373
mesonephric vesicles, in frog, 98
mesonephrogenic cord, human, 385

mesonephros, in chick, 180, 212, 213, 215,
    217, 219, 220
  in frog, 21, 22, 23, 25, 69, 98, 99, 100
  human, 382, 383, 384, 387, 389, 390, 395,
    396, 453, 456, 459, 470, 473, 476, 477,
    498, 499
  in mouse, 283, 284, 293, 297
  in pig, 305, 307, 323, 326, 329, 334, 335,
    339, 340, 341, 345, 351, 355, 356, 357,
    359, 361, 366, 368, 375, 376
  See also kidney
mesorchium, in frog, 21, 22
  human, 384
  in rooster, 107
mesosalpinx, human, 397
mesothelium, in chick, 137
  in pig, 311
mesovarium, in chicken, 109, 110
  in frog, 25
  human, 397, 401
  in pig, 310
metamorphosis, in frog, 69, 70–71, 91, 102
metamyelocyte, human, 449
metanephric diverticulum, human, 447, 448
metanephric glomerulus, 377
metanephric duct, human, 383, 384, 388
  in mouse, 283, 297
  in pig, 335, 360, 361, 362, 371, 373, 375
  See also ureter
metanephros, in chicken, 213, 215, 220
  human, 382, 383, 453, 459, 470, 473
  in mouse, 283, 284, 297
  in pig, 347, 366, 367, 368, 369, 376, 377
  See also kidney
metaphase, 9, 475, 477, 509, 514
metatarsals, in mouse, 300
metencephalon, in chick, 143, 164, 165, 167,
    168, 169, 170, 182, 183, 185, 188
  human, 463, 496, 498
  in mouse, 283, 287, 293, 294
  in pig, 321, 322, 330, 331, 332, 333, 335,
    336, 370
metestrus, in mouse, 237, 238, 239, 245
metocoel, in mouse, 294
microglia, human, 437
micromeres, in frog, 36
midbrain, *see* mesencephalon
middle cardiac vein, human, 451
middle plexus (nerves VII and VIII), human,
    458
midgut, in chick, 132, 138, 141, 155, 161, 171,
    173
  in frog, 44, 52, 54, 64, 88, 89
  human, 447, 460, 495
  in mouse, 259, 262
  in pig, 316, 319, 322, 323, 326, 327, 344
    (table)
milk line, human, 459
  in pig, 321, 330, 331
Miller, O. J., 509

misplacement of organ, 522
mitochondria, human, 379, 381
mitosis, 9, 12, 513, 514, 515
    human, 381, 405
mitotic spindle, 9, 15, 514
    in chicken, 115
    in frog, 35
    human, 407
Mongolism, 509
monocytes, in chick, 207
    human, 449
Monro, foramen of, *see* interventricular fora-
    men
morphogenesis, 515
morula, human, 401, 408, 409, 422
    in mouse, 249
    in pig, 312
mouth, in chick, 198, 201
    in frog, 52, 74
    human, 448, 490, 492, 501
    in mouse, 274, 278, 287, 301
    in pig, 322, 323, 333, 347, 348, 349
    See also oral cavity
mucosa, uterine, *see* uterine mucosa
Müllerian duct, in chick, 215, 218, 220
    in frog, 22, 99
    human, 384, 386, 387, 388, 389, 390, 395,
        396, 459, 471
    in pig, 307, 311, 376
Müllerian tubercle, human, 396, 397
muscles, human, 470, 471, 475, 493, 494
mutation, 515
myelencephalon, in chick, 143, 157, 164, 165,
        166, 167, 168, 169, 170, 182, 185, 188,
        195
    human, 463, 498
    in mouse, 270, 278, 283, 285, 287, 295
    in pig, 321, 322, 330, 331, 332, 333, 335,
        336, 344 (table), 346, 367, 368, 369, 370
myelin, in frog, 73
myeloblasts, in chick, 207
    human, 449
myelocoel, in mouse, 274
myelocyte, human, 449
myoblasts, mesenchymal differentiation into,
        17, 18, 449
myocardium, in chick, 145, 148, 149, 153, 154,
        160, 161, 168, 176
    in frog, 53, 64, 86
    human, 426, 441, 445, 446, 452, 454
    in mouse, 263
    in pig, 324, 353
myocoel, in chick, 142, 175
    in frog, 89
    in mouse, 279
    in pig, 319
myoendocardial cavity, human, 454
myometrium, human, 398
myotome, in chick, 174, 176, 191

in frog, 48, 76, 78
human, 444, 459, 493
in mouse, 274, 275, 279
in pig, 319, 345

n

naris, in frog, 78, 82–83
    human, 470, 471
    in mouse, 301
nasal processes, human, 490, 491
nasal septum, human, 501
nasal sinus, human, 473
    in mouse, 301
nasolacrimal groove, in chick, 198
    human, 490, 491
nasomaxillary fissure, in mouse, 284
natural selection, 5, 6, 521
neck, in pig, 362
necturus, 62
nephrocoel, in chick, 142
    in frog, 98
nephrogenic cord, human, 458
    in pig, 326
nephrogenic tissue, in chick, 215
nephrostome, in chick, 180, 217
    in frog, 98, 99
    human, 383
    in mouse, 281, 284
    in pig, 326, 376
nephrotome (mesomere), in chick, 142, 153,
        154, 161, 173, 180, 217
    in frog, 52–53, 54, 98
    human, 419
    in mouse, 259, 272, 273, 281
    in pig, 319, 326
nervous system, in chick, 162–70, 181, 185,
        188–90, 192
    in frog, 69, 71–73, 76
    human, 437, 460–61
    in pig, 335, 362
neural arch, in chick, 175, 220
    human, 502
neural crest, in chick, 135, 161, 167, 185
    in frog, 54, 76
    human, 424, 444, 445
    in mouse, 268, 273, 322
    in pig, 343, 377
neural fold, in chick, 106, 128, 129, 133, 135,
        138, 140, 144, 145, 151
    in frog, 44, 45, 48, 49, 50, 51
    in mouse, 264
    in pig, 317, 318, 319
neural groove, in chick, 128, 129, 135, 138,
        139, 140, 141, 144, 161
    in frog, 48, 50
    human, 415, 425, 440, 444
    in mouse, 258, 262, 264
    in pig, 317, 318, 319

P

pacemaker of heart, in chick, 149
palate, human, 448, 472
  in mouse, 300
  in pig, 369
palatine process, human, 501
  in mouse, 299
palatoquadrate bone, in frog, 79
pancreas, in chick, 173, 199, 204
  in frog, 87
  human, 385, 386, 438, 447, 448, 452, 458,
    471, 492, 498
  in mouse, 270, 280, 282, 293, 297, 301
  in pig, 322, 323, 332, 334, 339, 347, 357,
    367, 369, 370, 371
pancreas primordium, in mouse, 280
  in pig, 348
pancreatic duct, in frog, 87
  in mouse, 282
  in pig, 348
Pander, nucleus of, in chick, 111, 113, 120
pangenesis, 520
papillae, dental, *see* dental papillae
parabronchi, in chick, 203
parachordal cartilage, human, 500
paradidymis, human, 390
  in pig, 306, 307
  in rooster, 215
paraphysis, in chick, 185, 189
parathyroid gland, in chick, 200
  human, 437, 459, 492
  in mouse, 284, 286, 292
  in pig, 347, 348
parencephalon, in chick, 169, 188, 189
parenchyma, renal, 386
paroöphoron, in chicken, 220
  human, 397, 399
  in pig, 308
pars basilaris, in frog, 81, 82
pars caeca, in chick, 191
pars optica, in chick, 191
parthenogenesis, defined, 15
parturition, 431–32, 434–35
pecten, in chick, 193, 469
pectoral vein, in chick, 213
peduncle, cerebral, in pig, 369, 370
pelvic girdle, in chick, 175
pelvis, bony, human, 497
  renal, *see* renal pelvis
penetration path, 15
  in frog, 30, 31, 34, 35
penis, human, 387
  in mouse, 240, 241, 242
  in pig, 305, 306, 309
  See also phallus
perforatorium, 14
  in rooster, 109
periblast, in chick, 120, 121, 148
pericardial cavity, in chick, 148, 153, 154, 168,
  193, 202, 203, 206, 207
  in frog, 53, 62, 64, 68, 86, 88

human, 419, 426, 441, 452, 454, 456, 471,
  498
  in mouse, 261, 263, 274, 293, 296
  in pig, 316, 324, 332, 334, 338, 339, 351
pericardium, in chick, 143, 168, 206
  in frog, 53, 64, 86
  human, 426, 438, 445, 499
  in pig, 334
perichondrium, in chick, 221
perilymphatic fluid, in chick, 194
perineal muscles, human, 471
peritoneal cavity, in chick, 172, 203, 206, 220,
  296
  human, 456, 502
  in mouse, 297
  in pig, 334, 335, 340, 351, 352, 360, 361
peritoneum, in frog, 25
  human, 438
  in pig, 306
perivitelline space, in chicken, 115
  in frog, 27, 30
  in mouse, 247
  in pig, 309
petrosal ganglion, in chick, 170
  human, 496
  in mouse, 283, 295
  in pig, 333, 343, 365, 366
petrosal nerve, 365
Pfluger, E., 35
phagocytes, in chick, 207
phallus, human, 387, 388
  in pig, 309, 311, 362, 367, 368
  See also penis; clitoris
pharyngeal nerve, in pig, 365
pharynx, in chick, 137, 165, 169, 172, 182,
  188, 199, 200, 201
  in frog, 52, 53, 54, 61, 62, 63, 64, 74, 76, 81,
    82, 84 (table), 86, 88, 90
  human, 437, 444, 446, 447, 472
  in mouse, 270, 283, 301
  in pig, 322, 323, 344 (table), 348, 350, 370
phrenic nerve, human, 499
phylogeny, and ontogeny, 520
pia mater primordium, in pig, 466
pigmented layer of retina, in chick, 171, 193,
  469
  in frog, 79, 80, 81
  in mouse, 276, 277, 292
  in pig, 342, 344, 346, 470
pineal body, *see* epiphysis
pinna, in mouse, 292, 295, 297, 301
pituitary gland, in chicken, 112, 185
  in frog, 73, 75, 102
  human, 399–400, 403, 406, 437, 459, 473
  in mouse, 301
  in pig, 354, 369, 370
  See also hypophysis; infundibulum; Rathke's
    pocket
placentae, of human embryo, 428, 430, 431
  of mouse embryo, 284, 299, 301
  of pig embryo, 375

placentae (*cont.*)
types of mammalian, 233–35
placentation, human, 402, 420
placode ganglion, in frog, 78
placodes, in chick, 171
in frog, 78, 81
plasmosome (nucleolus), 14, 514, 515
plectrum, in frog, 79
pleura, human, 438, 499
pleural cavity, in chick, 198, 202, 203, 207
human, 456, 502
in mouse, 293, 296
in pig, 351, 352, 368, 372
pleuropericardial folds, in pig, 372
pleuropericardial membrane, in chick, 206
human, 448, 502
pleuroperitoneal canals, in mouse, 297
in pig, 352
pleuroperitoneal membrane, in chick, 203, 207, 296
human, 448, 502
in mouse, 286
poikilothermism, defined, 35
polar body, first, *see* first polar body
second, *see* second polar body
polyinvagination, in chicken, 125
polyspermy, in chicken, 115
pons, in chick, 185
in pig, 370
pontine arteries, in pig, 354
pontine flexure, in chick, 106, 157, 165,
human, 463
portal vein, in chick, 211, 212, 213
human, 508
in mouse, 293, 296
in pig, 332, 351, 355, 356, 357, 360, 373, 374, 375
posterior amniotic fold, in chick, 159, 179
in mouse, 250, 253, 255, 258
in pig, 316
posterior cardinal vein, in chick, 166, 178, 179, 180, 182, 193, 204, 208, 210, 212, 213, 215, 216, 217, 218
in frog, 63, 92, 93, 96, 97
human, 457, 458, 473, 476
in mouse, 283, 291, 292, 293, 296, 297
in pig, 324, 325, 334, 335, 356, 359, 361, 373
posterior choroid plexus, in frog, 73, 75
in mouse, 286, 293, 301
in pig, 332, 367, 368, 369
posterior commissure, in chick, 185, 189
in frog, 75
posterior intestinal portal, in chick, 155, 166, 179, 206
human, 447
in mouse, 259
in pig, 316, 322
posterior limiting sulcus, in chick, 155
posterior medullary velum, in chick, 189
posterior mesenteric artery, in chick, 209

in frog, 95
human, 495
in pig, 372, 374
posterior neuropore, in chick, 136, 145, 156
human, 444, 453, 454, 455
in mouse, 136, 145, 156
in pig, 318, 319, 321
posterior vena cava, in chick, 204, 211, 212, 213, 214, 220
in frog, 22, 25, 93, 96, 97
human, 450, 451, 459, 476–77, 499, 508
in mouse, 292, 296
in pig, 332, 334, 335, 355, 356, 358, 359, 360, 369, 373, 374, 375
posterior vitelline vein, in frog, 96
postotic bulge, human, 425, 426
precaval vein, in chick, 211, 213
in frog, 97
prechordal mesoderm, in chick, 168
prechordal plate, human, 411
preformation, theory of, 10, 516
pregnancy, human, 422, 430–32
See also gravid uterus
preotic bulge, human, 425, 426
prevertebral sympathetic ganglion, human, 502
primary head vein, human, 445, 458
in pig, 356
primary spermatocyte, 13
in frog, 24
human, 379, 381, 405, 406
in mouse, 243
in pig, 305
in rooster, 107, 108
primitive ectoderm, human, 410
primitive endoderm, human, 410, 412, 413, 415
primitive folds, in chick, 126, 127, 128, 130, 131, 132, 133
primitive groove, in chick, 126, 127, 130, 131, 132, 133, 139, 141, 142
human, 413, 419, 420, 421, 423, 425
in pig, 315
primitive pit, in chick, 126, 127, 132, 133, 141
human, 413, 419, 420, 421
primitive plate, in chick, 126, 127, 128, 131, 139
primitive streak, in chick, 106, 126, 127, 128, 129, 132, 142, 145, 146, 151, 156, 157, 158, 165
human, 412, 415, 423, 436, 439
in mouse, 250, 253, 255, 256, 258, 259, 260, 261
in pig, 315, 316, 317, 318
primordium, defined, 517
proamnion, in chick, 128, 129, 132, 138, 144, 145, 146, 153, 157, 158, 168
proamniotic cavity, in mouse, 248, 251, 252, 253, 255
processus vaginalis, human, 390
proctodeum, in chick, 106, 200

in frog, 51, 52, 61, 62, 63, 64
human, 387, 447, 448, 459
in pig, 307, 322, 323, 332
proestrus, in mouse, 237, 238, 239, 245
progesterone, 112, 403, 421
prolactin, 112
proliferation, 515
proliferative phase, of menstrual cycle, 403, 420
promyelocyte, human, 449
pronephric duct, in chick, 180, 217
in frog, 63, 64, 98, 99
human, 383, 384
in mouse, 270, 282, 291
in pig, 307, 326, 376
pronephric protuberances, in frog, 48
pronephric tubules, in chick, 180
in frog, 64, 85, 98
in mouse, 270, 281, 282
in pig, 326, 376
pronephros, in chick, 180
in frog, 53, 62
human, 382, 383, 384, 444, 453
in mouse, 282
in pig, 326, 376
proneurons, in pig, 362
pronuclei, 15
in chicken, 115, 123
human, 407
in pig, 312
prophase, 9, 514
prosencephalon, in chick, 136, 140, 143, 155, 156, 160, 164, 165, 167, 468
in frog, 49, 71
human, 426, 437, 460, 462
in pig, 321, 323, 324
prosocoel, in chick, 140, 160, 168
prostate gland, human, 382, 384, 388, 390
in mouse, 240, 241, 242
in pig, 305, 306, 307
prostatic sinus, human, 390
in pig, 307
proventriculus, in chick, 199
proximal endoderm, in mouse, 248, 250, 251, 252, 253, 255, 256, 258
proximal limb of midgut, human, 495
pubic hairs, 390–91
pubis, human, 382, 397
in mouse, 242
in pig, 306
pulmocutaneous artery, in frog, 93, 94, 95, 96
pulmonary artery, in chick, 177, 178, 207, 214
in frog, 93, 94, 95
human, 450, 451, 474, 492, 499, 508
in mouse, 292
in pig, 334, 352, 353, 356, 357, 367, 368, 369, 373, 374
pulmonary vein, in chick, 203, 207, 214
in frog, 93, 96, 97
human, 451, 492, 499, 508
in pig, 355, 374, 375

puntum saliens, in chick, 149
pygostyle, in chick, 175
pylorus, human, 385, 386

r

radial filaments, in pig, 466
radiations, and anomalies in human embryo, 475
mouse exposed to, 302–03
radix aorta, in frog, 94
ramus communicans, in chick, 190
in frog, 76, 77
human, 502
in pig, 344
ramus, dorsal, in pig, 344
ventral, in pig, 344
Rathke's pocket, in chick, 163, 166, 169, 172, 182, 185, 188, 189, 194, 199
human, 426, 437, 447, 448, 452, 454, 456, 459, 464, 470, 492, 498, 500
in mouse, 284, 286, 287, 293, 295
in pig, 322, 323, 332, 333, 342, 347, 352, 368, 370
See also hypophysis; pituitary gland
recapitulation, theory of, 4, 520
rectum, in chick, 200, 204
in frog, 52, 89
human, 382, 385, 386, 388, 389, 395, 398, 448
in mouse, 292
in pig, 308, 332, 335, 347, 348, 361, 367, 369, 371
rectus fermoris muscle, human, 494
reductional division, defined, 12
reflex arcs, 362
reflexes, 362
Reichert's membrane, in mouse, 253, 254, 257, 261, 262, 265, 275
Remak's ganglion, in chick, 192
renal artery, in chick, 209
in mouse, 293
in pig, 355, 359, 372, 374, 377
renal calyces, 386
renal corpuscle, in chick, 214, 218
renal parenchyma, 386
renal pelvis, human, 385, 386
in pig, 362
renal portal vein, in chick, 213
in frog, 96, 98
renal vein, in chick, 211, 213, 216, 217
in frog, 97, 98
human, 477
in mouse, 292
in pig, 374
repair phase, of menstrual cycle, 420
reproductive system, in chick, 106–15
in frog, 21–26
human, 379–99
in mouse, 240–46

in frog, 79, 81, 344
in mouse, 276, 277, 292
in pig, 342, 346, 470
septum, endocardial, in chick, 153
interatrial, *see* interatrial septum
septum primum, in pig, 325, 353, 374
septum secundum, in pig, 352, 374
septum transversum, in chick, 206
in frog, 91
human, 447, 448, 452, 499
in pig, 352
serosa, in pig, 319, 326, 327, 328
See also chorion
serratus anterior muscle, human, 494
Sertoli cells, 13
in frog, 24
human, 379, 381, 382, 406
in mouse, 240, 243
sex cell ridge, in frog, 99
sex determination, in human, 472
sexual cords, in chick, 218
sheath cells, in chick, 167
shell of chicken egg, 112, 187, 209
in experimental embryology, 222
sinoatrial canal, in mouse, 289
sinoatrial septum, in mouse, 293
sinus, coronary, in pig, 358
nasal, *see* nasal sinus
superior, in frog, 81, 373
terminalis, in chick, 147
transverse, in pig, 373
urogenital, *see* urogenital sinus
venarum, human, 451
venosus, in chick, 148, 149, 152, 162, 163,
166, 168, 169, 175, 178, 182, 188, 202,
208, 212, 214
in frog, 63, 64, 91, 92, 93, 94, 178
human, 446, 450, 452, 453, 454, 455, 457,
458, 470, 476, 498
in mouse, 270, 280, 283, 289, 293, 296, 301
in pig, 324, 334, 352, 353, 355, 358, 373
sinusoids of implantation site, in human, 412,
413, 415, 417
skeletal development, in frog, 101
human, 438, 470, 471
in mouse, 288, 300
small cardiac vein, human, 451
small intestine, in chick, 200
human, 385, 386, 448
in pig, 347, 348, 357, 367, 368, 369, 370
snout, in mouse, 297
in pig, 362
somatic cells, number of chromosomes in, 11,
405
somatic mesoderm, in chick, 153, 154, 156,
161
in frog, 51, 61, 64
in mouse, 261
in pig, 316, 323
somatopleure, 233

in chick, 142, 148, 153, 154, 157, 159, 160,
175
in frog, 53, 83
human, 387, 411, 418, 424, 429, 438
in mouse, 259
in pig, 316, 319, 326, 327
somites, in chick, 128, 129, 137, 141–46 *pass.*,
151, 152, 155, 158, 161, 163, 165, 166,
170, 173, 174, 175, 182, 205, 224–31
in frog, 44, 45, 52, 54, 61, 62, 83, 88, 89, 98,
101
human, 419, 424, 425, 437, 438, 444, 446,
452, 457, 458, 498
in mouse, 259, 263, 270 (table), 271, 272,
273, 279, 281, 282, 288
in pig, 318, 319, 320, 321, 322, 323, 324,
329, 330, 331, 341
sperm entrance path, *see* penetration path
spermatids, 13
in frog, 24
human, 379, 381, 405, 406
in mouse, 243
in pig, 305
in rooster, 107, 108
spermatocyte, primary, *see* primary spermatocyte
secondary, *see* secondary spermatocyte
spermatogenesis, 13–14
in frog, 21–24
human, 379–82
in mouse, 240–41
in pig, 305
in rooster, 107, 108
spermatogonium, 13, 14
in frog, 21, 24, 29
human, 379, 381, 405, 406
in mouse, 240, 243
in pig, 305
in rooster, 107
spermatozoon, 515, 516, 519
compared with ovum, 14 (table)
in frog, 21, 23, 27, 32
human, 380, 381, 390, 400, 401, 402, 404,
405, 407
and mitosis, 9, 14
in mouse, 240, 243, 246
in pig, 305, 306, 311, 312
in rooster, 105, 107, 108, 113, 115
spermiogenesis, human, 379
spinal cord, in chick, 135, 136, 154, 156, 158,
163, 166, 176, 182, 187, 191, 192, 206,
219
in frog, 54, 71, 73, 74, 75, 76, 78
human, 426, 445, 460, 471, 498
in mouse, 274, 283, 286, 293, 295, 296, 297,
301
in pig, 323, 333, 334, 335, 338, 342, 344
(table), 345, 362, 368, 369
spinal ganglion, in chick, 191, 192
in frog, 76, 77

turbinate, in pig, 369
tympanic cavity, in chick, 194
  in frog, 79
  in mouse, 301
  in pig, 347
tympanic membrane, in frog, 79
  human, 437
tympanic nerve, in pig, 365
tympanic ring, in frog, 79
  in mouse, 300

u

ultimobranchial body, in chick, 172, 200
  in frog, 87
  human, 458, 459, 471
  in mouse, 284, 292
  in pig, 347, 348
umbilical arterial plexus, human, 440
umbilical artery, in chick, 159, 192, 209
  human, 425, 427, 431, 443, 446, 455, 458,
    473, 493, 495, 498, 499, 503, 508
  in mouse, 283, 296
  in pig, 324, 325, 335, 355, 356, 357, 360,
    368, 373, 374
umbilical cord, 233
  human, 387, 428, 431, 438, 456, 459, 471,
    495, 498
  in mouse, 263, 283, 296, 299, 301
  in pig, 320, 321, 322, 324, 326, 327, 329,
    330, 331, 335, 361, 362, 366, 368, 374
umbilical hernia, 284, 292, 301
umbilical stalk, in chick, 157, 186
umbilical vein, in chick, 159, 182, 209, 210,
    211, 212, 213
  human, 425, 427, 431, 442, 443, 444, 445,
    446, 450, 453, 457, 458, 459, 473, 476,
    493, 495, 508
  in mouse, 283, 284, 292, 293, 296
  in pig, 324, 325, 334, 335, 340, 351, 355,
    356, 357, 358, 373, 374, 375
umbilical venous plexus, human, 440
  in pig, 324, 325
umbilicus, human, 431
urachus, human, 386, 388, 395, 453, 492
ureter, in chick, 215
  in frog, 21, 25, 99
  human, 382, 384, 385, 386, 388, 390, 395,
    398, 399, 456, 492
  in mouse, 241, 242, 244, 283, 286, 297
  in pig, 306, 307, 308, 335, 347, 360, 362,
    367, 369, 371, 376
urethra, human, 382, 384, 387, 388, 390, 398,
    438
  in mouse, 240, 241, 244
  in pig, 305, 306, 307, 308, 309, 311, 347,
    369, 371
urethral diverticulum, in mouse, 242
urethral groove, human, 388
urethral opening, human, 389

urinary bladder, in frog, 22, 25, 89
  human, 382, 383, 384, 388, 390, 396, 398,
    399, 438, 448, 471
  in mouse, 241, 242, 244
  in pig, 306, 307, 308, 347, 367, 369, 371
uriniferous tubule, in chick, 214
  human, 383
urodeum, in chick, 200, 204
urogenital artery, in frog, 95
urogenital ridge, human, 382
urogenital sinus, human, 385, 386, 387, 388,
    395, 396, 397
  in mouse, 292, 297
  in pig, 306, 311, 335, 341, 347, 348, 361,
    367, 369, 371
urogenital system, in frog, 22, 25
urorectal septum, human, 385, 386, 388
urostyle, in frog, 101
uterine gland, human, 412, 413, 417, 421, 427
uterine horn, human, 397, 399
  in mouse, 243, 244
  in pig, 308, 309
uterine lumen, human, 421
  in mouse, 243, 244, 250, 252, 265
uterine mucosa, 398, 400, 403, 411, 412, 413,
    415, 417, 420, 424
  in mouse, 275
  in pig, 310, 328
uterovaginal rudiment, human, 388
uterus, in chicken, 105, 109, 112, 221
  in frog, 22, 25
  human, 384, 388, 389, 394, 395, 396, 397,
    398, 399, 400, 401, 404, 410, 418, 431,
    432, 475
  in mouse, 241, 243, 245, 267, 299, 301
  in pig, 308, 309, 311, 328
utricle, in chick, 194, 195, 197
  in frog, 81, 82
  human, 387
  in mouse, 282, 285

v

vagina, in chicken, 109, 112
  human, 388, 394, 397, 398, 399, 438, 471,
    475
  in mouse, 238, 241, 244, 245
  in pig, 305, 308, 309, 311
vagina primordium, human, 396
vaginal orifice, human, 398
vaginal plug, in mouse, 237, 238
vaginalis, processus, human, 390
vagus ganglion, in frog, 78
vagus nerve, in chick, 170, 190
  in frog, 77 (table), 78, 83
  in pig, 344 (table)
vas deferens, in frog, 21, 99
  human, 382, 384, 388, 389
  in mouse, 240, 241, 242
  in pig, 305, 306, 307

B 6
C 7
D 8
E 9
F 0
G 1
H 2
I 3
J